NASA SP-368

Biomedical Results of APOLLO

Managing Editors

Richard S. Johnston, Lawrence F. Dietlein, M.D., and
Charles A. Berry, M.D.

Lyndon B. Johnson Space Center

Scientific and Technical Information Office   1975
NATIONAL AERONAUTICS AND SPACE ADMINISTRATION
Washington, D.C.

Compiled by

BioTechnology, Inc.

under the direction of

James F. Parker, Jr., Ph.D.
Vita West

NASA Headquarters Contract NASW-2630

Walton L. Jones, M.D., Scientific Officer

Editorial Board

The material submitted for "Biomedical Results of Apollo" was reviewed by a NASA Editorial Review Board consisting of:

For sale by the Superintendent of Documents,
U.S. Government Printing Office, Washington, D.C.   20402
Price $13.15
Library of Congress Catalog Card Number 75–600030
Stock Number 003–000–00628–4

FOREWORD

The accolades bestowed on the Apollo Program and those who participated in it are uncountable and are richly deserved. It was a tremendously successful effort — achieving virtually every goal set for it and turning every setback into a temporary misstep toward superior achievement. The excitement which built as Apollo 11 brought man toward his first step on the moon was felt in all parts of the world. Indeed, television viewers in many lands watched in real time as the first lunar exploration took place. It was a bringing together of mankind.

The success of the Apollo Program reflects its utilization of the talents of many teams, disciplines, and individuals. A particular contribution was made by the life scientists — the physicians, engineers, scientists, and technicians who provided the life support for Apollo. These persons were directly responsible for ensuring that the astronauts remained in good health and physically fit to perform these perilous missions. The life scientists also collected critical data concerning the response of man to the stresses of extended space flight; data that continue to allow meaningful plans to be made for future space voyages.

The performance of the life scientists in the Apollo Program was exceptional. This book documents the efforts of this team and presents the results of the principal medical experiments conducted during Apollo. I extend my sincere thanks to the many life scientists who worked so hard and contributed so much to the Apollo Program.

Dr. Christopher C. Kraft, Jr.
Director
Lyndon B. Johnson Space Center

iii

PREFACE

Biomedical research is difficult under the best of laboratory conditions. Biomedical research, imbedded in the complex matrix of manned space flight, is very, very difficult. This volume summarizes the Life Science studies carried out during the Apollo Program. That such research was possible at all is a tribute to the ingenuity and hard work of the many investigators associated with the program. It represents both a learning experience for those involved and a solid scientific basis on which to build for future manned flight.

David L. Winter, M.D.
NASA Director for Life Sciences

TABLE OF CONTENTS

Page

Section I.   **Introductory** 1

    Chapter 1.   Introduction 3

    Chapter 2.   Apollo Missions 9

Section II.   **Crew Health and Inflight Monitoring** 41

    Chapter 1.   Clinical Aspects of Crew Health 43

    Chapter 2.   Microbiological Investigations 83

    Chapter 3.   Radiation Protection and Instrumentation 105

    Chapter 4.   Metabolism and Heat Dissipation During
                  Apollo EVA Periods 115

    Chapter 5.   Environmental Factors 129

    Chapter 6.   Flight Crew Health Stabilization Program 141

    Chapter 7.   The Role of Toxicology in the Apollo Space Program . . . 151

Section III.   **Preflight and Postflight Medical Testing** 161

    Chapter 1.   Endocrine, Electrolyte, and Fluid Volume Changes
                  Associated with Apollo Missions 163

    Chapter 2.   Clinical Biochemistry 185

    Chapter 3.   Hematology and Immunology Studies 197

    Chapter 4.   Apollo Flight Crew Cardiovascular Evaluations 227

    Chapter 5.   Exercise Response 265

    Chapter 6.   Nutritional Studies 277

    Chapter 7.   Skeletal Response 303

    Chapter 8.   Apollo Flight Crew Vestibular Assessment 323

Section IV.   Inflight Experiments 341

    Chapter 1.   BIOSTACK – A Study of the Biological Effects
              of HZE Galactic Cosmic Radiation 343

    Chapter 2.   Apollo Light Flash Investigations 355

    Chapter 3.   The Apollo 16 Microbial Response to Space
              Environment Experiment 367

    Chapter 4.   The Apollo 17 Pocket Mouse Experiment (BIOCORE) 381

Section V.   Quarantine 405

    Chapter 1.   The Lunar Quarantine Program 407

    Chapter 2.   Quarantine Testing and Biocharacterization
              of Lunar Materials 425

Section VI.   Systems 435

    Chapter 1.   Apollo Food Technology 437

    Chapter 2.   Waste Management System 469

    Chapter 3.   Bioinstrumentation 485

    Chapter 4.   Potable Water Supply 495

    Chapter 5.   Apollo Command and Service Module and Lunar
              Module Environmental Control Systems 517

    Chapter 6.   Extravehicular Mobility Unit 545

Section VII.   A Summing Up 571

    Chapter 1.   Summary and Conclusions 573

    Chapter 2.   Perspectives on Apollo 581

SECTION I

Introductory

CHAPTER 1
INTRODUCTION

by

Richard S. Johnston
Director of Life Sciences
Lyndon B. Johnson Space Center

The Apollo Program has been acclaimed as one of the greatest feats of exploration and engineering development ever accomplished. Landing men on the moon and returning them safely to Earth was considered impossible only a few decades earlier. No doubt the vigor and determination which characterized the Apollo Program were largely attributable to the challenge of President John F. Kennedy in 1961 that it be accomplished "before this decade is out." It is also evident, however, that the events which culminated in sending men to the moon were not brought forth *de novo*, to implement President Kennedy's proclamation. These events were in large measure an extension of technology which made possible an achievement whose time had come.

There were three principal technology requirements imposed by the Apollo mission. First, because the United States was committed to manned lunar exploration, it became necessary to identify the means to ensure man's health and functional capability in a hostile environment. Here, the program drew on the tremendous developmental advances in full pressure suit and oxygen system technologies made during and immediately following World War II. Second, because habitable vehicles sufficiently large to accommodate several men and their necessities would be used, a very complex and powerful launch and transportation system was required. The technology of chemical rocket propulsion, begun earlier in this century by Tsiolkovsky, Goddard, Oberth, and others, with significant advances in World War II, was available. Third, because man would participate, the mission would require the highest probability that the vehicle would reach the moon and return safely. This requirement drew on the substantial advances in rocket guidance and navigation technology begun in World War II and extended during the Mercury and Gemini Programs.

Project Apollo, owing much to existing technology, repaid the debt many times with dramatic technological and scientific progress in many fields, including medicine. The contribution of Apollo to the biomedical sciences was twofold. First, there was opportunity to study man performing useful work in the space environment. In dealing with the health issues of a lunar exploration mission, the practice of *space medicine* became a reality. Second, significant advances were made in life support systems, biotelemetry techniques, and inflight monitoring methodology. The biomedical hardware necessary to support space flight developed appreciably in functional capability, in reliability, and in acceptability to the crewman.

The purpose of this book is to describe the biomedical program developed for Apollo, to list the findings of those investigations which were conducted to assess the effects of space flight on man's physiological and functional capacities, and to document significant medical events in Apollo.

Biomedical Objectives

There were three principal objectives of the Apollo biomedical program. These three distinct and rather separate goals, listed below, served in large measure as a basis for the functional organization of the biomedical effort.

1. *Ensure the Safety and Health of Crewmembers.* The Mercury flights showed that man could safely withstand the stresses of space flight for limited periods. In the Gemini 7 flight, the period of exposure was increased to 14 days with no major adverse findings. Therefore, it was well established prior to the first Apollo flight that man could be kept safe and healthy for the mission durations under consideration. However, there remained a number of health issues to be assessed. Principal among these was that of inflight illness. During the orbital flights of Mercury and Gemini, it was always possible to abort the mission and recover the astronaut within a reasonable time should an inflight medical emergency occur. This alternative was greatly reduced during Apollo. A serious illness occurring during circumlunar flight could not receive direct medical attention for at least several days. For this reason, it was necessary to develop a program which would keep the possibility of inflight illness at an absolute minimum and which would make provision for emergency treatment during the course of the mission.

2. *Prevent Contamination of Earth by Extraterrestrial Organisms.* Prior to the first lunar mission, there was great concern over possible contamination either of the moon by Earth-borne microorganisms or the Earth by unknown or strange microorganisms carried from the lunar surface by the crew or in lunar samples.

The prevention of the contamination of Earth by microorganisms returned from the moon was considered especially important since the nature of the microorganisms would be unknown. For these reasons, Apollo biomedical personnel were given the responsibility for developing techniques to minimize the contamination of the moon and to preclude the introduction of any lunar organisms into the Earth's ecology.

3. *Study Specific Effects of Exposure to Space.* The Gemini missions amply demonstrated that man could survive in space for as long as 14 days with minimal physiological changes. There were some findings, however, which caused concern as to their possible significance on much longer flights. For example, red blood cell mass losses in the order of 20 percent were noted after the eight-day Gemini flight. Obviously, a finding such as this meant that additional study was required both for verification and to assess the real meaning of the observed changes.

A number of investigations were conducted during the Apollo Program to determine the effects of the space environment on specific body systems and functional performance. Subsequent chapters describe these investigations in detail.

Mercury and Gemini Background

The foundations of the Apollo biomedical program can be found in earlier Mercury and Gemini efforts. The basic organizational structure for medical support was developed during Mercury. Many of the Apollo personnel had worked through both the Mercury and Gemini flights.

The first biomedical issue to be confronted in Project Mercury was the need to establish selection criteria for astronauts. This assignment was given to members of the newly-formed Space Task Group, a unit established at Langley Field, Virginia, in October 1958. This group, under the direction of Dr. Robert R. Gilruth, was responsible for establishing the nation's first manned spacecraft project, later to be known as "Project Mercury."

General physical requirements for Mercury astronauts were established by the NASA Life Sciences Committee, an advisory group of prominent physicians and life scientists chaired by Dr. W. Randolph Lovelace. Aeromedical personnel and facilities of the Department of Defense were used to conduct psychological and stress testing of candidates. Final selection was based on a review of the medical findings and technical experience of the candidates. The basic and extensive screening and testing procedures defined for the selection of Mercury astronauts were used for the later selection of Gemini and Apollo astronauts.

The success of Project Mercury demonstrated that man could indeed exist in the space environment. While the Mercury missions, one of which lasted for 34 hours, were primarily demonstration flights, some quite meaningful medical information was obtained. The principal conclusions were:

1. There was no evidence of loss in pilot performance capability.

2. All measured physiological functions remained within normal tolerances.

3. There was no evidence of abnormal sensory or psychological response.

4. The radiation dose received was considered medically insignificant.

5. An orthostatic rise in heart rate and fall in blood pressure was noted postflight and it persisted for between seven and nineteen hours after landing.

The biomedical information obtained during the Mercury flights had a positive reinforcing effect in terms of expanding the manned space flight program. Plans for Project Gemini were pressed with increased confidence.

With the launch of the first manned Gemini flight in 1965, the United States space program entered a new phase. With Project Gemini, the broad objective was to gain operational proficiency in manned space flight. The three major goals of the program were (1) to acomplish rendezvous and docking of two space vehicles, a necessary step toward the lunar landing program; (2) to perform extravehicular activity and to validate personal life support systems and astronaut performance capabilities under those conditions; and (3) to develop a better understanding of how man adapts to extended weightless flight, that is, whether stability was achieved for all physiological measures, or whether significant changes occurred.

As a result of the change of emphasis of Project Gemini, there was an improved opportunity to study the effects of space on man. There also was a requirement to develop systems which would maintain man in space over much longer periods than flown in Project Mercury. In the 14-day Gemini 7 flight, extensive observations were made of the physiological and psychological response of astronauts to the stresses of space.

At the conclusion of the Gemini Program, approximately 2000 man-hours of weightless experience had been logged by U.S. astronauts. The principal biomedical conclusions were:

1. Extension of the Project Mercury finding that man could tolerate exposure to the space environment quite well. No significant performance decrement was noted.

2. Postflight orthostatic hypotension, persisting for some 50 hours, was observed during tilt table tests.

3. A decrease in red cell mass of the order of five to twenty percent was noted.

4. Bone demineralization, noted as percent change in radiographic density in the *os calcis*, was observed.

5. No adverse psychological reactions were observed, even during fourteen days' confinement in a restrictive cabin environment.

6. No vestibular disturbances were reported.

The techniques used for the study of man in the Gemini Program, and the life support systems which were used, established the plan-of-action to be followed in Apollo.

Development of Apollo Biomedical Effort

The formal structuring of the Apollo Program had its genesis in 1961. It actually began, however, several years earlier with the award of three study contracts to industry and with an in-house study program conducted by the Langley Space Task Group. The initial objective of these efforts was to develop specifications for circumlunar flight. Then, in 1961, President Kennedy changed the goal to one of lunar landing.

It was also in 1961 that the National Aeronautics and Space Administration announced it would build, on a site near Houston, Texas, a 60 million dollar research and command center for the Project Apollo Program of manned flight to the moon and for later space flight programs. This center, with Dr. Robert R. Gilruth as its Director, was to be used to train space flight crews; to design, develop, and test spacecraft; and to conduct manned space flight operations. The life scientists associated with the Langley Space Task Group soon moved to temporary quarters in Houston to await the completion of the Manned Spacecraft Center at Clear Lake.

New and unique requirements were placed on the Life Sciences Team by the Apollo Program. Medical personnel were required to develop requirements, to make projections of physiological functions and to conduct their daily activities as part of an engineering-oriented team effort. The space program also emphasized the study of healthy individuals and an understanding of normal physiological responses as opposed to the conventional medical concerns of diagnosis and care of the ill. Life scientists concerned with manned space flight programs continually demonstrated an ability to adapt to a new working environment and, throughout the various flight programs, maintained a dedication to the health and safety of space flight crewmen.

And so, although the principal objectives of Apollo were manned lunar landing and subsequent lunar exploration, a considerable body of useful biomedical information was derived from the program. These findings are documented in this volume and, in part, served as a basis for asking more incisive, more penetrating biomedical questions of the forthcoming and very ambitious Skylab Program. This volume then may be regarded as "a prelude to Skylab."

CHAPTER 2
APOLLO MISSIONS

by

Richard S. Johnston
Wayland E. Hull

Lyndon B. Johnson Space Center

Introduction

The manned Lunar Landing Program was the most complex and largest single scientific exploration undertaken in the history of mankind. On the 20th of July, 1969, Neil A. Armstrong and Edwin E. Aldrin, Jr. set foot on the moon. For two hours and 21 minutes, the two men, first cautiously and then boldly, negotiated their way about the lunar terrain. They demonstrated to themselves and to the 500 million people viewing their triumph throughout the world that movement on the lunar surface was a relatively easy and even enjoyable thing. They set up scientific experiments and collected rock and soil samples for return to Earth for subsequent analysis.

The Apollo Program ultimately placed twelve men on the lunar surface. It was a major national event. During peak activity, more than 400 000 people and 20 000 companies were involved. Table 1 summarizes the manned Apollo flights, listing the crews, landing sites, launch dates, and mission durations. This chapter precedes the discussion of the biomedical results of the Apollo missions in order to give the reader some historical perspective from which to view the Apollo findings. The Apollo systems and highlights of each mission are presented.

The Apollo Spacecraft

The Apollo spacecraft launch and lunar landing configurations are pictured in figure 1. The launch configuration of the assembly was 15 meters (48 feet) long and consisted of five major segments: Launch Escape System, Command Module, Service Module, Lunar Module Adapter, and Lunar Module.

The Launch Escape System

The Launch Escape System consisted of the 10-meter (33-foot) tower weighing 3629 kg (8000 lb) and a solid rocket motor 4.72 m (15.5 ft) providing 66 675 kg (147 000 lb) of thrust. The Launch Escape System provided a means for escape during

Table 1
Summary of Apollo Manned Flights

Apollo Missions	Crewmen	Lunar Landing Site	Mission Description	Launch Date	Mission Duration (hrs)	
					Total Time	Lunar Surface
7	Schirra, Cunningham, Eisele	—	Earth orbit test of Command Module	9-11-68	260.1	—
8	Borman, Lovell, Anders	—	First manned circumlunar flight	12-21-68	147	—
9	McDivitt, Scott, Schweickart	—	Earth orbit test of Lunar Module First time spacecraft separated inflight	3-3-69	241	—
10	Stafford, Cernan, Young	—	Circumlunar mission Lunar Module separation and descent engine firing	5-18-69	192	—
11	Armstrong, Collins, Aldrin	Sea of Tranquility	First manned lunar landing First returned lunar samples	7-16-69	194	22.2
12	Conrad, Gordon, Bean	Ocean of Storms	Second lunar landing First Apollo Lunar Surface Experiment Package (ALSEP)	11-14-69	244.5	31.5
13	Lovell, Swigert, Haise	—	Aborted lunar landing mission due to oxygen tank failure	4-11-70	142.9	—
14	Shepard, Roosa, Mitchell	Fra Mauro	Third lunar landing Explored lunar highlands	1-31-71	216	33.5
15	Scott, Worden, Irwin	Hadley Rille	First lunar rover used Geological sampling of the Apennine Mountain base	7-26-71	295	67
16	Young, Mattingly, Duke	Descartes	Geological sampling from volcanic areas of moon	4-16-72	265.8	71
17	Cernan, Evans, Schmitt	Taurus-Littrow	Exploration of area to provide information about formation and history of moon	12-7-72	301.8	75
					2,500.1	300.2

countdown or in the first 100 seconds of the lift-off sequence, should a fire or other abort situation develop. Upon activation, the escape tower would lift the spacecraft about 1.6 km (1 mile) clear of the launch pad and rocket. Descent would be provided by the main parachute system.

Figure 1. Apollo spacecraft at launch (left);
perspective drawing (right).

Command Module

The basic structure of the Command Module (CM) was a pressure vessel encased in a heat shield. The Module was conical shaped, measuring 3.48 m long (11.5 ft), with a base diameter of 3.91 m (12 ft, 10 in.). The Command Module consisted of a forward compartment containing two reaction control engines and parachutes used for the Earth landing system. The crew compartment or inner pressure vessel contained crew accommodations, controls and displays, and other spacecraft systems. The aft compartment housed ten reaction control engines, propellant tanks, helium tanks, water tanks, and the Command Service Module umbilical cable. The habitable volume of the crew compartment was 5.95 m^3 (210 ft^3).

Within the Command Module the Commander, who operated the flight controls, was positioned at the left; the Command Module Pilot, who was responsible for guidance and navigation, was couched in the center; and the Lunar Module Pilot, responsible for management of subsystems, was on the right. The couches faced the display console.

The atmosphere of the Command Module was planned to be 100 percent oxygen at 34 x 10^{3}N/m^2 (5 psia) and was altered as a result of a spacecraft fire in 1967 to a 60/40 oxygen/nitrogen mixture at 103 x 10^{3}N/m^2 (15 psia) at lift-off. The cabin pressure was allowed to equilibrate at 5 psia as altitude was reached. The atmosphere was enriched with oxygen until the breathing gas approached 100 percent oxygen. Oxygen was used in flight to furnish breathing gas as well as to make up for spacecraft leakage, resulting in an oxygen-rich atmosphere. The thermal control portion of the environmental control system maintained the cabin temperature of the spacecraft in a comfortable range of 294.15° to 297.15°K (21° to 24°C). The Command Module contained two hatches, one at the side for entry and one at the top for use when the spacecraft was docked with the Lunar Module. Five observation windows permitted extensive outside viewing and photography during the missions.

Service Module

The Service Module (SM) was a cylindrical structure, 3.91 m in diameter (12 ft, 10 in.) by 7.49 m long (24 ft, 7 in.). This part of the spacecraft contained the main propulsion system and provided stowage for most of the consumable supplies.

The Service Module remained attached to the Command Module on the flight to the moon. During the return flight, separation occurred just before Earth atmosphere reentry. The service propulsion system was used for midcourse maneuvers and to reduce the velocity of the spacecraft to enter lunar orbit.

A Scientific Instrument Module (SIM) was carried in the Service Module for the first time on the Apollo 15 mission. The SIM accommodated eight experiments utilizing spectrometers, panoramic and mapping cameras, a laser altimeter, and a subsatellite for injection into lunar orbit. Figure 2 shows schematics and cutaway diagrams of the Command and Service Modules.

Lunar Module Adapter

This segment of the spacecraft served as a smooth aerodynamic enclosure for the Lunar Module and provided the attachment for the Command Module to the launch vehicle. The Lunar Module was extracted from the Adapter shortly after the spacecraft left Earth orbit.

The Lunar Module

The Lunar Module (LM) was a two-stage vehicle with a vertical dimension of 6.985 m (22 ft, 11 in.). The diagonal width between landing gear was 9.45 m (31 ft). The Lunar Module transported astronauts from the lunar orbiting Command Module to the lunar surface, provided living quarters and a base of operations on the moon, and returned the crew to the Command Module in lunar orbit. The Lunar Module ascent and descent stages are shown in figure 3. The two stages were joined by four explosive bolts and umbilicals. The ascent stage functioned as a single spacecraft for rendezvous and docking with the Command Service Module at the conclusion of lunar surface missions. Because it was designed to fly only in the vacuum of space, the LM was incapable of reentering Earth's atmosphere.

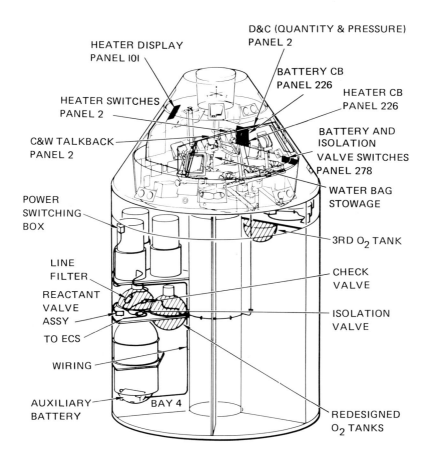

Figure 2. Diagram of Apollo Command and Service Modules.

The ascent stage was made up of three main sections: the crew compartment, the midsection, and the aft equipment bay. The crew compartment and midsection were pressurized. The habitable cabin volume was 6.7 m³ (235 ft³). The ascent stage was 3.76 m long by 4.29 m in diameter (12 ft, 4 in. x 14 ft, 1 in.). Figure 4 (A and B) shows the interior of the Lunar Module cabin.

The descent stage was the unmanned portion of the Lunar Module. It supported the ascent stage for the landing on the lunar surface, and contained the propulsion system

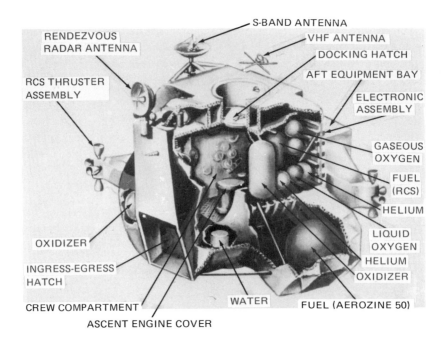

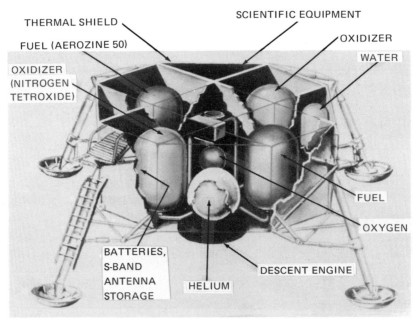

Figure 3. Lunar Module ascent and descent stages.

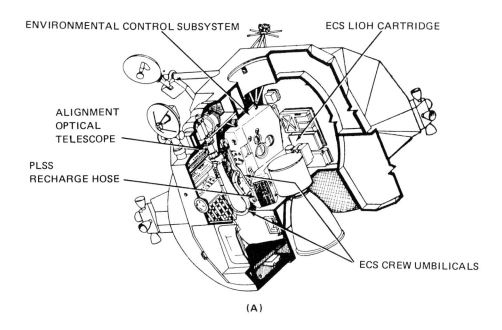

(A)

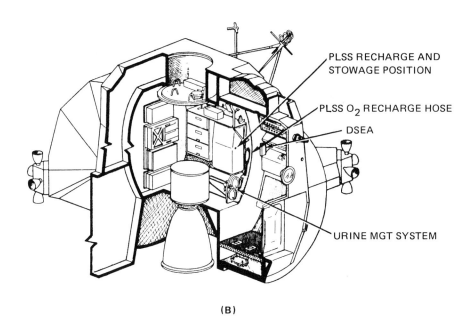

(B)

Figure 4. Lunar Module cabin interior.

used to slow the spacecraft for a safe landing on the moon. During descent, four landing gear struts were released from a folded stowage position to form the landing gear for the vehicle. Each of the struts was filled with crushable aluminum honeycomb to absorb the landing impact. Foot pads at the ends of the legs contained sensing probes which signaled the crew to shut down the descent engine upon contact with the lunar surface. The landing radar provided information pertaining to the altitude and velocity of the Lunar Module relative to the lunar surface. Four bays surrounded the descent engine and contained the propellant tanks, the Modularized Equipment Stowage Assembly (TV equipment, lunar sample containers, and portable life support systems), the Lunar Roving Vehicle (LRV), and the Apollo Lunar Surface Experiment Package (ALSEP).

Lunar Roving Vehicle. The Lunar Roving Vehicle was used for the first time with great success on the Apollo 15 mission. Figure 5 shows the vehicle beside the Lunar Module. The lunar payload capacity was several times the vehicle's Earth weight. The vehicle propulsion system was battery operated, each wheel of the vehicle being individually driven by a one-quarter horsepower electric motor. The operational life was 72 hours during the lunar day, enough to easily provide a 9.65 km (6 mile) exploration radius. It was transported to the moon folded tightly into a storage quadrant of the Lunar Module and was deployed by pulling two nylon operating tapes and removing release pins. The Rover was then unfolded for use.

Figure 5. Apollo 16 Lunar Module and Lunar Roving Vehicle.

Figure 6 is a diagram of the LRV. The T-shaped hand controller permitted the vehicle to be operated by either of the two astronaut passengers. The LRV could climb and descend slopes of 25 degrees inclination. It was equipped with a dead-reckoning navigation system which the crew used to find their way back to the Lunar Module from long explorations when out of sight of the home base.

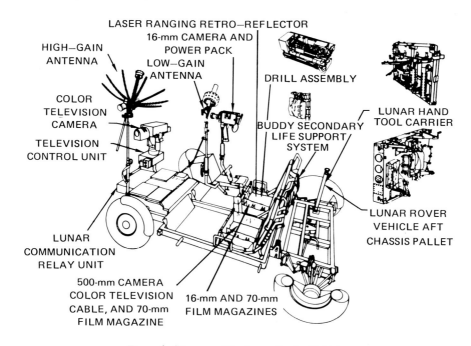

LASER RANGING RETRO—REFLECTOR
16-mm CAMERA AND
POWER PACK
HIGH—GAIN
ANTENNA
LOW—GAIN
ANTENNA
DRILL ASSEMBLY
COLOR
TELEVISION
CAMERA
BUDDY SECONDARY
LIFE SUPPORT
SYSTEM
LUNAR HAND
TOOL CARRIER
TELEVISION
CONTROL UNIT
LUNAR
COMMUNICATION
RELAY UNIT
LUNAR ROVER
VEHICLE AFT
CHASSIS PALLET
500-mm CAMERA
COLOR TELEVISION
CABLE, AND 70-mm
FILM MAGAZINE
16-mm AND 70-mm
FILM MAGAZINES

Figure 6. Diagram of the Lunar Roving Vehicle.

The LRV doubled traverse distance during lunar expeditions. A remotely controlled television camera mounted on the vehicle enabled Mission Control and the public to observe activities carried out during its use. The Lunar Communications Relay Unit was carried on the LRV to provide for voice communications and transmission of portable life support system data and biomedical data. In addition, the system provided color television transmission which was observed by the mission controllers and, at certain times, by the public. The Communications Relay Unit was a self-contained, battery powered system, stowed in the Lunar Module descent stage at launch and placed on the LRV for lunar surface operations. The television camera was mounted on a motor driven gimbal system, controlled from the Earth to direct the camera at points of interest and at the crew during exploration. At the conclusion of lunar surface missions, the television system provided pictures of the breakaway of the ascent stage from the descent stage and the rising of the ascent stage toward lunar orbit.

Apollo Lunar Surface Experiment Package. The Apollo Lunar Surface Experiment Package (ALSEP) was a system of scientific instruments carried to the moon in the Lunar Module and set up on the lunar surface by Apollo crews. Using a self-contained power supply and communications equipment, each ALSEP collected and transmitted to Earth scientific and engineering data for several years following astronaut departure from the lunar surface.

Because of power and weight limitations, no single flight could carry all the ALSEP experiments. Certain elements of the total program were assigned to Apollo flights 12 through 17. On the Apollo 15 and 17 missions the experiment package included a particles and fields subsatellite. The subsatellite was a 76.2 cm (30 in.) tall, 47.6 kg (106 lb), solar-cell—powered spacecraft which was inserted into lunar orbit from the Service Module. It carried a magnetometer, particle detector instruments, and a transmitter, all of which were operated from Earth to collect and relay data on the extralunar environment.

Apollo Space Suits and Portable Life Support System

The space suit used by the crew in the lunar exploration program had its roots in concepts reaching as far back as the late 19th Century. Jules Verne was probably the first to conceive of pressure suits for protection against reduced barometric pressures of higher altitudes. In 1872, he described closed circuit, extravehicular pressure suit operation for flight around the moon. In August 1934, Wiley Post made the first aircraft flight in a pressure suit. The suit was constructed of two layers, an inner rubber bag designed to contain gas under pressure and an outer cloth fabric to maintain the desired suit shape. Following World War II, both the Air Force and Navy continued development of space suits.

The space suit worn by Mercury astronauts was similar to pressure suits used in high altitude military jet aircraft flight. The Project Mercury suit consisted of an inner layer of neoprene-coated nylon fabric and a strain-resistant layer of aluminized nylon fabric. The aluminized coating was used to reject increased cabin heat during reentry. Biomedical sensors were contained inside the suit to monitor body temperature, electrocardiogram, blood pressure, and respiration rate. Urine was collected in a special bag within the suit. The breathing gas, oxygen, was supplied to a fitting at the front of the torso and was then distributed throughout the interior of the suit to be discharged into the helmet in such a way as to sweep exhaled moisture from the visor portion of the helmet. The suit weighed approximately 9.1 kg (20 lb). The Mercury suit was to be used as an emergency backup to the spacecraft pressurization system in case of cabin system failure. A high degree of mobility was not a requirement because of the restrictive volume of the Mercury space capsule.

Because Project Gemini was to involve extravehicular activity, the structural requirements for the space suit changed. Additional layers were added to afford the needed protection in free space operations. The Gemini suit consisted of an outer layer of temperature resistant nylon, a layer of "link-net" to provide pressurized mobility and to control ballooning of the suit, a pressure-tight layer of neoprene-coated nylon, and an inner aluminized layer of nylon for thermal and micrometeoroid protection. A removable visor was added to the helmet to protect the inner visor from impact damage and to provide additional protection from the increased levels of ultraviolet radiation encountered outside the Earth's atmosphere. As before, the breathing gas was 100 percent oxygen and the suit was worn for the entire duration of the mission.

The Gemini flights gave mission planners confidence in spacecraft integrity. Micrometeoroids proved less of a menace to spacecraft integrity than some individuals had feared. As a consequence, Apollo astronauts did not wear pressure suits through all of the mission, donning them only for critical spacecraft operations such as launch, rendezvous, and docking. The Apollo suit was similar to the Gemini suit, with a multilayered construction. The outer suit layer of Teflon-coated fabric was woven of Beta glass. Beneath this layer was a restraint layer of Nomex and convoluted joints to restrain internal pressure and maintain the shape of the suit. The next layer below was a neoprene-coated nylon pressure bladder; and the final layer was a high-temperature resistant nylon liner which replaced an earlier simple comfort layer. As in earlier suits, 100 percent oxygen was supplied through a fitting in the front of the torso. Communications and biomedical data lines passed through the suit by a multiple circuit electrical connection on the front of the suit. The Apollo suit assembly weighed about 16.15 kg (35.6 lb).

Apollo astronauts who performed EVA were provided with a self-contained Portable Life Support System (PLSS) carried in a backpack unit. This permitted operation at great distances from the spacecraft. The system supplied oxygen for pressurization and metabolic consumption, and cooling water for operation of a liquid cooling under-garment. The portable life support system also contained communications and telemetry equipment, and a transmitter power supply. Mounted atop the PLSS was an oxygen purge system which provided a contingency supply of gaseous oxygen lasting 40 minutes when activated. The PLSS was a part of the Extravehicular Mobility Unit (EMU), which consisted also of an extravehicular space suit, a liquid cooling garment, an oxygen purge system, a lunar extravehicular visor assembly, and a special lunar overshoe.

The Apollo Extravehicular Mobility Unit gave man a completely self-contained mode for moving about on the moon for a fixed period of time. The system worked extremely well. There were no failures experienced with the suit on the lunar surface. The prospect, however slim, of suit failure was extremely unnerving because it was not possible to build the same degree of redundancy into certain parts of the space suit as could be built into the spacecraft. Only one pressure bladder layer could be provided because redundant layers would tend to make the space suit excessively stiff and hard. The total success of the Apollo space suit system must be credited both to excellence in design and meticulous testing.

Unmanned Missions

The way was paved for the manned Apollo Program by a series of unmanned flights. The early flights were made by Surveyor spacecraft that were launched on Atlas-Centaur launch vehicles. The first Surveyor flight was launched on May 30, 1966, from Cape Canaveral, Florida, on a direct-ascent lunar trajectory. The Surveyor flights validated several critical aspects of advanced soft landing techniques for later use by Apollo. They provided essential data on the compatibility of the Apollo design with conditions encountered on the lunar surface, and yielded information about the topography of the lunar surface and its thermal environment. In addition to the Surveyor flights, three

Lunar Orbiter flights produced medium and high resolution photographs over broad areas of the moon to aid in site selection for the Apollo manned landing program (see figure 7).

Figure 7. First photograph of Earth from the vicinity of the moon; taken by Lunar Orbiter I, 25 August 1966.

Apollo/Saturn 201

The first Apollo/Saturn mission employed an unmanned Apollo spacecraft on a suborbital flight that gathered data for qualifying the Apollo Command Module heat shield, the Service Module prime propulsion system, and the first flight of the Saturn I-B launch vehicle. The spacecraft was flown 8047 km (5000 miles) in a suborbital flight on February 26, 1966. The engines of the upper stage of the launch vehicle, the Saturn IV-B, were fired in flight for seven minutes to demonstrate the J-2 liquid hydrogen/liquid oxygen engine. The service propulsion system engine also was fired twice to demonstrate engine restart capability. These two engine firings were used to propel the spacecraft to a reentry velocity of 8071 meters/second (26 481 feet/second) which is 299 meters per second (981 feet/second) above orbital velocity. By achieving this velocity, the capability of the Command Module heat shield to withstand Earth reentry heating was demonstrated. Recovery of the spacecraft was normal, and all mission objectives were accomplished.

Apollo/Saturn 203

Apollo/Saturn 203 served as an unmanned flight test of the uprated Saturn I launch vehicle. An Apollo spacecraft was not carried in this mission; instead, the upper stage of the launch vehicle was mounted with a nose cone. This large assembly was 28.04 m (92 ft) long and weighed 26 535 kg (58 500 lb). It was placed into Earth orbit on July 5, 1966. During the first four orbits, liquid hydrogen studies were conducted to determine the behavior of cryogenic liquids in the absence of gravity. Again, all mission objectives were accomplished.

Apollo/Saturn 202

This unmanned suborbital mission was used to qualify the Command and Service Modules and the uprated Saturn I launch vehicle for manned flight. The spacecraft was launched on August 25, 1966, from the Kennedy Space Center and traveled approximately 27 350 km (17 000 miles) to land in the Pacific Ocean. The Service Module propulsion system was fired for 215 seconds to place the spacecraft into a trajectory to provide a steep angle/high heating reentry. For the first time, the Apollo guidance and navigation system provided the onboard control of spacecraft attitudes and trajectory. This system automatically controlled the propulsion system burns and guided the spacecraft through entry and landing.

Apollo 4

On November 9, 1967, an unmanned Earth-orbital flight test of the Saturn V launch vehicle and Apollo Command Module was undertaken. The three stages of the Saturn V placed into orbit a record payload of over 127 066 kg (280 000 lb). Flawless performance of the launch vehicle on its first unmanned flight provided the U.S. with a major operational capability for orbiting large payloads. The Saturn IV-B engine was fired twice to place the Command and Service Modules into a 18 092 km (9769 nautical miles) apogee at the end of the second orbit. The Saturn IV-B was separated and the service propulsion system engine was burned twice to accelerate the Command Module to a lunar return velocity of 10 973 meters/second (36 000 feet/second). The mission qualified the Command Module ablative heat shield to withstand Earth reentry from lunar return speeds. Apollo 4 was the first man-made object to withstand reentry into the Earth's atmosphere at such an extreme velocity.

Apollo 5

Apollo 5 was an unmanned flight and the first flight test of the Lunar Module. The launch date was January 22, 1968. The primary objective of the flight was to test the Lunar Module propulsion systems and the abort staging function for manned flight. The test for both the descent and ascent stage propulsion systems was successful, except for one descent engine shutdown during the first firing. The abort sequencing was successfully demonstrated during the second and third descent engine firings. This flight test qualified the Lunar Module for manned Earth-orbital flights.

Apollo 6

The last of the unmanned Apollo missions was a test of the Saturn V launch vehicle. On April 4, 1968, the Apollo Command and Service Modules and the Saturn IV-B were placed into an Earth orbit. Approximately two minutes after lift-off and during the first stage boost, a major structural anomaly occurred in the spacecraft/launch vehicle adapter. Oscillations induced by the launch vehicle in excess of spacecraft design criteria were apparently the cause of the abrupt changes manifested in strain, vibration, and acceleration measurements in the spacecraft and adapter. The S-II second stage engines shut off early and the Saturn IV-B stage engines were required to place the spacecraft into orbit. Upon investigation, improper installation of signal wires was found to be the cause of the premature engine shutdown. The Service Module propulsion system was fired for seven minutes to place the spacecraft into a trajectory with a 19 312 km (12 000 mile) apogee and a high speed Earth reentry. The reentry velocity was 10 006 meters/second (32 830 feet/second) which was approximately 1219 meters/second (4000 feet/second) less than planned. The test provided additional qualification data for the Command Module heat shield. Based on the results of the unmanned flight program, Apollo moved to the manned space flight phase.

Manned Missions

Apollo 1 (Apollo 204)

The first manned Apollo flight was scheduled for late February 1967, but because of an unanticipated tragedy, was delayed until October 1968. The tragedy occurred on January 27th when the three-man crew for Flight 204* died instantly after a flash fire swept through the Apollo spacecraft. Killed in the accident on Cape Canaveral's Pad 34 (then, Cape Kennedy) were Virgil I. Grissom, Commander; Edward H. White, Command Module Pilot; and Roger B. Chaffee, Lunar Module Pilot. Virgil Grissom was one of the seven original Mercury astronauts, Edward White was the first American to "walk" in space during the Gemini Program, and Roger Chaffee was preparing for his first space flight. The accident occurred at 6:31 p.m. Eastern Standard Time during the first major rehearsal for the mission.

The cause of the Apollo 204 fire has never been positively identified. For a detailed description of the accident and its investigation, the reader is referred to the *Report of the Apollo 204 Review Board* to the Administrator, National Aeronautics and Space Administration, 5 April 1967, available from the Superintendent of Documents, U.S. Government Printing Office, Washington, D.C. 20402.

As a result of the 204 fire, alterations were made in the spacecraft systems, in the cabin atmosphere, and in materials used within the spacecraft to maximize the resistance to fire.

The impact of the fire on the medical program *per se* was threefold. After the addition of nitrogen gas to the cabin atmosphere, careful observations had to be made to determine if there might be some physiological effects as a result of the small amount of

---

*In commemoration of the crew, the mission was redesignated Apollo 1.

nitrogen remaining. However, no clear-cut effect could be identified. As an added safety precaution after the fire, vital signs of all crewmen were monitored during the launch period, whereas only one had been followed previously. Finally, the inflight medical experiments program planned for earlier Apollo flights was eliminated. Program energies and resources had to be directed exclusively toward the task of getting man to the moon safely and safely returning him to Earth. The accident brought a renewed dedication and purposefulness to the goal of landing an American on the moon before the end of the decade of the '60s.

Apollo 7

Apollo 7 was the first manned orbital flight test of the Apollo spacecraft. On October 11, 1968, a Saturn I-B launch vehicle placed the Command Module and Service Module into a near-Earth orbit of eleven days duration. The crewmembers were Walter M. Schirra, Jr., Commander; Donn F. Eisele, Command Module Pilot; and R. Walter Cunningham, Lunar Module Pilot. The primary goal of Apollo 7 was to demonstrate crew and spacecraft performance. The mission, unlike manned orbital flights in previous programs, involved little scientific experimentation.

Prior to separation of the Command and Service Modules from the Saturn IV-B launch stage, the crew manually flew the spacecraft/Saturn IV-B combination. The spacecraft was then separated from the Saturn IV-B and a simulated transposition and docking maneuver was completed. This maneuver simulated the spacecraft operation required during a lunar mission to couple the Command Module with the Lunar Module, and to separate the Lunar Module from the Saturn IV-B. Later, the Apollo 7 crew successfully maneuvered the spacecraft for a re-rendezvous with the Saturn IV-B. Eight planned maneuvers were successfully completed using the Service Module propulsion system.

In general, all spacecraft subsystem performance was excellent. Real-time television images were transmitted by the crewmen to Earth. These showed spacecraft interior activities and views of the Earth. The crew suffered head colds during the mission which hampered some spacecraft operations. For the first time, U.S. astronauts did not wear space suit helmets during entry into the Earth's atmosphere.

All mission and scientific objectives were met by the flight of Apollo 7, qualifying the Command and Service Modules for eleven-day manned missions. One of the most significant findings of this flight was that the volume of the Command Module proved to be quite adequate for a three-man crew operating in weightlessness. The crew enjoyed relative comfort compared with the conditions prevailing in the Gemini spacecraft.

The flight of Apollo 7 ended with a splashdown in the Atlantic Ocean 260 hours and 9 minutes after launch from Kennedy Space Center (figure 8). The crew was retrieved by helicopter and the spacecraft was later taken aboard the USS *Essex*. The successful flight of Apollo 7 represented a major milestone in the U.S. manned space flight program.

The Apollo 7 mission and all subsequent manned missions are described in detail, including biomedically significant findings, in the Apollo Mission Report series. These documents are available through the Scientific and Technical Library, Lyndon B. Johnson Space Center, Houston, Texas.

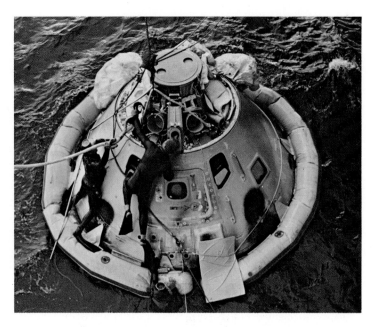

Figure 8. Apollo 7 spacecraft following splashdown.

Apollo 8

Man's first lunar orbital flight began on December 21, 1968, when a Saturn V launch vehicle placed the Apollo 8 Command and Service Modules in Earth orbit. Frank Borman was the Commander; James A. Lovell, Jr., the Command Module Pilot; and William A. Anders, the Lunar Module Pilot. The Apollo 8 crew was the first to be launched by the 2722 metric ton (3000 ton) Saturn V. The crew checked out the spacecraft, and, after approximately three hours in Earth orbit, the Saturn IV-B stage was fired for approximately five minutes to accelerate the spacecraft to an Earth-gravity escape velocity of 40 233 km/hr (25 000 mph) to begin its 370 149 km (230 000 mile) coast to the moon. Following the translunar injection maneuver, the Apollo spacecraft was separated from the Saturn IV-B stage.

During the transearth period, the crew transmitted live television pictures of the spacecraft interior and of the Earth. The spacecraft velocity decreased during the coast period due to the Earth's gravitational force. As the spacecraft neared the moon, it was accelerated by the pull of lunar gravity, and the Service Module propulsion system was fired to slow the vehicle to 6035 km/hr (3750 mph) and place it in lunar orbit.

Apollo 8 achieved lunar orbit on Christmas Eve. Lunar operations lasted for ten orbits, at an altitude of 96.56 km (60 miles) above the lunar surface. The crew transmitted television pictures of the lunar surface, studied potential Apollo landing sites, and took excellent photographs, including those shown in figure 9 (A & B). They filmed and photographed the far side of the moon, which had never before been seen by man.

Figure 9. Photographs of the lunar landscape
taken by the crew of Apollo 8.

After approximately twenty hours of lunar orbital operations, the Service Module propulsion system engines were fired for three minutes to accelerate the spacecraft to a velocity sufficient to escape from the moon's gravitational force. The transearth coast period lasted for approximately 63 hours. The spacecraft landed in the Pacific Ocean, where the crew and spacecraft were recovered by the USS *Yorktown*, just eleven seconds earlier than the time computed in the flight plan months before the mission. The Apollo 8 mission had lasted six days.

With only minor discrepancies, the spacecraft and systems functioned with precision throughout the mission. The accuracy of the onboard guidance and navigation control system demonstrated that astronauts could return safely from the moon without the aid of Earth-based tracking systems. Crew performance was excellent, despite some minor illness early in the mission. All mission objectives were met. Apollo 8 qualified the launch vehicle and spacecraft for lunar flight. The crew provided valuable information on the lunar surface, and demonstrated the ability to recognize surface features needed in lunar landing navigation. The Apollo 8 crew received this Nation's highest recognition, including an appearance before a joint session of the United States Congress. The flight of Apollo 8 was heralded as an odyssey without precedent in man's history.

Apollo 9

Apollo 9 was the first manned flight with the Lunar Module and the first mission employing two manned spacecraft. The flight lasted ten days. The crewmen were James A. McDivitt, Commander; David R. Scott, Command Module Pilot; and Russell L. Schweickart, Lunar Module Pilot. The objectives of this mission were to evaluate the Lunar Module under space flight conditions, perform an extravehicular contingency transfer from the Lunar Module to the Command Module, and demonstrate the capability to fly the two spacecraft on lunar landing type trajectories to achieve rendezvous and docking.

The spacecraft was launched into Earth orbit by a Saturn V launch vehicle on March 3, 1969. The Command and Service Modules were separated from the Saturn IV-B stage which contained the Lunar Module (figure 10). The Command and Service Modules were turned around to face the Lunar Module and docked with it. The two spacecraft then separated from the Saturn IV-B stage. For the next several days, combined spacecraft operations were conducted, and Russell Schweickart carried out an abbreviated extravehicular mission on the fourth day. The space walk was delayed because Schweickart suffered nausea and vomiting early in the flight. He, along with the other two crewmen, suffered from colds during the mission. In place of the space walk, he climbed out of the Lunar Module and stood on its porch for approximately 47 minutes. On the fifth day of the mission, McDivitt and Schweickart separated the Lunar Module from the Command Module and, using both the descent and ascent propulsion systems, flew a simulated lunar landing and ascent trajectory while Scott remained in the Command Module. The vehicles were separated for about four hours at distances up to 351.9 km (190 nautical miles). When the two craft were 182 km (113 miles) apart, Schweickart and McDivitt jettisoned the descent stage to simulate takeoff from the lunar surface. They fired the ascent engine and the two spacecraft rendezvoused and docked as planned. For the remainder of the ten-day mission, the crew performed landmark tracking and photographic tasks.

Figure 10. Artist's conception of Command/Service Module
and Lunar Module separating from the Saturn IV-B third-stage rocket.

The spacecraft splashed down in the Atlantic Ocean only 4.8 km (three miles) from the recovery aircraft carrier, the USS *Guadalcanal*. The recovery went extremely well.

The performance of both the spacecraft and its subsystems was nearly flawless, and all mission objectives were met. The Apollo 9 mission qualified the launch vehicle, the lunar landing spacecraft, the portable life support system (PLSS) backpack, and the flight control techniques designed for manned lunar landing flights.

Apollo 10

Apollo 10 was the last planned manned lunar orbital flight. The Apollo 10 mission lasted eight days and was, in effect, a dress rehearsal for the manned lunar landing. The flight successfully demonstrated the complete Apollo spacecraft system, including Lunar Module descent to within 14.4 km (47 400 ft) of the lunar surface. The crewmembers were Thomas P. Stafford, Commander; John W. Young, Command Module Pilot; and Eugene A. Cernan, Lunar Module Pilot. The launch date was May 18, 1969. After two and one-half hours in Earth orbit following launch by the Saturn V vehicle, the Saturn IV-B second stage was injected to place the spacecraft on a translunar trajectory.

The mission plan closely followed the Apollo 11 lunar landing flight plan. The crewmen separated the Command Module from the Saturn IV-B stage, rotating the craft 180 degrees and docking it with the Lunar Module which was extracted from the Saturn IV-B. The docking operations were viewed via color television that was transmitted to Earth. The docked spacecraft were placed in lunar orbit and thirty-two revolutions were made around the moon by the Command and Service Modules at a distance of 97 km (60 miles) from the lunar surface.

On the fourth day of the mission, with Astronaut Young in control of the Command Module, Stafford and Cernan undocked the Lunar Module and made a simulated landing in the LM by descending to within 14 km (9 miles) of the lunar surface. The descent stage propulsion system was used to slow the Lunar Module to begin the descent toward the moon. The ascent engine was fired to place the Lunar Module into a trajectory to rendezvous and dock with the lunar orbiting Command Module. After eight hours of separation, the two spacecraft docked successfully, and the Lunar Module crew reentered the Command Module for the return trip to Earth.

The Apollo 10 mission accomplished its primary aim of providing quantitative operational data on the spacecraft and the experience in lunar landmark tracking needed to ensure a high probability of success for the lunar landing mission. The Apollo 10 mission completed final qualification of the Lunar Landing Module by means of a rigorous duplication of all aspects of the Apollo 11 mission profile, with the exception of an actual landing.

Apollo 11

On July 16, 1969, Apollo 11, the first lunar landing flight, was launched from Kennedy Space Center, Florida, before an onsite audience of over one million people. The mission Commander was Neil A. Armstrong, the Command Module Pilot was Michael Collins, and the Lunar Module Pilot was Edwin E. Aldrin, Jr.

The lunar landing was achieved by a method established in July of 1962. The method ultimately chosen, demonstrated as feasible by the Apollo 10 mission, was a lunar orbit rendezvous. This technique met the constraints of time, funds, safety, and technology. The scheme was recommended to NASA management by John C. Houbolt, an aeronautical engineer at the NASA Langley Research Center. In Houbolt's scheme, a Saturn V rocket would launch the Apollo craft, a three-man crew, and a lunar landing craft on a lunar orbital course. Once in orbit, two men would transfer to the lunar landing spacecraft, undock from the mother ship, and descend to the lunar surface. After the lunar visit, the crew would launch and rendezvous with the Command ship in lunar orbit, leave the landing vehicle in orbit, and return to Earth. The selection of the method for accomplishing the lunar landing was of great importance for the design of the spacecraft and the launch vehicle. Lunar orbit rendezvous was ultimately selected based on a tradeoff which considered launch weights and other operational considerations.

Three days after the launch to the moon, the Apollo 11 spacecraft was slowed by the Service Module propulsion system from a velocity of 10 139 km/hr (6300 mph) to 6437 km/hr (4000 mph). On Saturday, July 19, 1969, the spacecraft achieved lunar orbital insertion. The orbit ranged from 86.6 by 105.7 km (53.8 by 65.7 miles) from the lunar surface. On Sunday, July 20th, with Michael Collins remaining behind in the Command Module, *Columbia*, Astronauts Armstrong and Aldrin entered the Lunar Module, *Eagle*. On the 13th lunar orbit, the spacecraft separated and the Lunar Module descent engine was fired. Astronaut Armstrong used the manual control mode to land the craft. He had realized that the Sea of Tranquility was strewn with boulders, and he wished to place the spacecraft down in a safe attitude. Over 500 million people heard the first words from the moon, "Contact light. Okay, engine stopped...Houston, Tranquility Base here. The *Eagle* has landed." Six hours after the successful landing, Astronaut Armstrong set foot on the lunar surface. Twenty minutes later, he was followed by Astronaut Aldrin (figure 11).

Figure 11. Astronaut Edwin E. Aldrin, Jr., Apollo 11 Lunar Module Pilot, stepping onto the lunar surface.

The astronauts quickly adapted to movement in lunar gravity, adopting a loping gait, a kind of kangaroo hop, as the most efficient for negotiating the lunar surface. They collected approximately 21 kg (46 lb) of rock and soil samples and set up the Apollo Early Surface Experiment Package (ESEP). The scientific payload consisted of a passive seismometer, a direct Earth-moon communications link, a solar wind experiment designed to isolate exotic gases in the solar wind, such as argon and krypton, for return to Earth for analysis; and an array of optical reflectors serving as targets for laser pointing systems on Earth, with the objective of more precisely measuring the distance between the Earth and the moon. After two and one-half hours of work on the lunar surface, the astronauts returned to the Lunar Module. Several hours later, the Lunar Module ascent stage was launched; it docked about three and one-half hours afterwards with the Command Module. During the return flight to Earth, the crew vacuum cleaned their clothing and equipment and took numerous precautions as part of a quarantine program to avoid carrying back to Earth any possible contamination from the moon. On Thursday,

July 24, after an eight-day mission, the crew splashed down in the Pacific Ocean. They donned biological isolation garments and were recovered by helicopter and transferred to the recovery ship USS *Hornet* where they were placed in a Mobile Quarantine Facility, a trailer modified for the purpose. They traveled in the MQF to the Lunar Receiving Laboratory in Houston, where they were kept in isolation for 21 days after lift-off from the lunar surface to preclude the possibility of contaminating the Earth with lunar organisms or material. Extensive medical and biological tests determined that no harmful organisms were present in any of the materials returned from the moon, and quarantine was terminated.

The materials returned from the 1 533 225 km (952 700 mile) journey to the moon and back were distributed to 144 scientists throughout the world. Figure 12 illustrates material from lunar rock. Among the scientific findings reported was the fact that the moon is approximately 4.6 billion years old.[*] The presence of minute deposits of gold, silver, and rubies in the lunar rilles was established, and evidence was found indicating that there were lava flows on the moon at one time. Additionally, three new mineral elements were discovered in the Apollo 11 samples analysis.

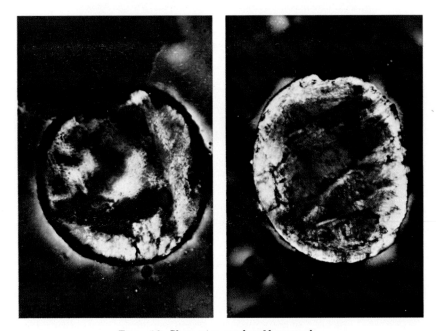

Figure 12. Photomicrographs of lunar rock.

---

[*]For further information concerning lunar scientific discoveries, the reader is referred to the Apollo 11 Lunar Science, Conference, Volumes 1-3 (Pergamon Press, 1970); the Proceedings of the Second Lunar Science Conference, Volumes 1-3 (The MIT Press, 1971); and the Proceedings of the Third Through Fifth Lunar Science Conferences (Pergamon Press, 1972-1974).

During the transearth trajectory, the Apollo 11 crew reported seeing streaks, points, and flashes of light. These visual phenomena were observed with the eyes both open and closed. It is believed that the effect was generated by extremely high energy particles of cosmic origin. These phenomena were reported by all subsequent Apollo crews.

Apollo 12

On November 14, 1969, Apollo 12 began its 244.5-hour (10-day) mission. The second lunar landing mission was crewed by Charles Conrad, Jr., Commander; Richard F. Gordon, Jr., Command Module Pilot; and Alan L. Bean, Lunar Module Pilot. During the launch, the spacecraft was struck twice by lightning, causing some interruption in electrical power. Contact with Mission Control was lost briefly. This was the first instance where any situation occurred that could have resulted in mission abort during launch. After about two hours of electrical system checkout in Earth orbit, all systems were pronounced in good working order.

The prime engineering objective of the Apollo 12 mission was to accomplish a point landing of the Lunar Module. On the Apollo 11 mission, the objective was simply to land in a safe general area, and the vehicle had touched down 6.5 km (4 miles) beyond the planned target point. The landing site selected for the Apollo 12 mission was a point 305 m (1000 ft) east and 152 m (500 ft) north of the site where Surveyor 3 had softlanded on the moon in 1967. Lunar orbit was achieved three days after launch. On November 19, Astronauts Conrad and Bean piloted the Lunar Module to the target lunar site. The Lunar Module, *Intrepid,* succeeded in touching down only 163 m (535 ft) from the Surveyor 3 spacecraft in the Ocean of Storms (figure 13).

Despite some loss of visibility due to dust created by the descent engine, the Apollo 12 Lunar Module landed with a reserve of propellants that was equivalent to 58 seconds of hover time. The Apollo 12 lunar surface crew made two extravehicular excursions, remaining on the moon for 31 hours, seven and three-quarters of which were spent exploring and working on the lunar surface. The first EVA was devoted to the emplacement of an Apollo Lunar Surface Experiment Package (ALSEP) (figure 14) and the collection of lunar rock samples. The ALSEP experiments included a passive seismometer to measure seismic events; a lunar atmosphere detector to determine the density of any atmosphere the moon might have had; a lunar ionosphere detector to provide information on the energy and mass spectra of the positive ions close to the lunar surface, among other objectives; and a device to measure the amount of lunar dust which accumulated on the ALSEP station.

The second lunar EVA, which lasted for three hours and 49 minutes, was devoted to collecting additional lunar samples, taking photographs, and inspecting the Surveyor 3 spacecraft. The Surveyor had made a major contribution to the Apollo 12 flight by sending back more than 6000 photographs of the Apollo 12 landing area. The Apollo 12 astronauts retrieved a television camera from the Surveyor, as well as sections of aluminum tubing and bits of glass insulation and cables. The astronauts probed the lunar surface to a depth of 81.3 cm (32 in.), bringing back rock samples from this layer of the lunar crust. In all, 34 kg (75 lb) of rock and soil samples were collected.

After ascent from the lunar surface and docking with the Command Module, the Lunar Module ascent stage was intentionally jettisoned and allowed to crash into the

Figure 13. Surveyor 3 spacecraft (foreground)
and Apollo 12 Lunar Module on the lunar surface.

Figure 14. Deployment of the Apollo Lunar Surface Experiment Package (ALSEP)
during the Apollo 12 mission.

lunar surface in order to calibrate the seismometer. The *Intrepid* impacted the moon 64.4 km (40 miles) from the Apollo 12 landing site and the seismometer installation, setting off vibrations which continued for almost an hour. This occurrence suggested that the moon was an unstable structure and that the impact had initiated a series of "avalanches." Before leaving lunar orbit, the crew obtained extensive photographic mapping data used for training future crews.

After a safe landing in the Pacific Ocean, the Apollo 12 crew, like the Apollo 11 crew, were quarantined while medical and biological studies were performed. Again, no life forms were found in lunar materials. Another unqualified success in the space program, the Apollo 12 mission provided data through the ALSEP experiments and lunar sample collection that added greatly to man's knowledge of the moon.

Apollo 13

The harrowing odyssey of Apollo 13 ended in the South Pacific Ocean on April 17, 1970. The mission was launched from the Kennedy Space Center on April 11 with a crew comprised of James A. Lovell, Jr., Commander; John L. Swigert, Jr., Command Module Pilot (replacing Thomas K. Mattingly who was relieved of duty after exposure to German measles); and Fred W. Haise, Jr., Lunar Module Pilot.

Apollo 13 would have been the first lunar mission to be dedicated almost entirely to geological research. The Lunar Module was to have landed on one of the roughest areas of the moon yet to be explored. The lunar surface crew would have traversed greater distances on the moon than any previous crews, with the distance being left to their own discretion. They were scheduled to climb one of the ridges of Fra Mauro and descend into a crater to check communications degradation, carrying a three-meter (10-ft) long drill to withdraw a core sample from beneath the lunar surface.

Approximately four hours after launch, the Command Module was docked with the Lunar Module. The hatches were opened between the spacecraft and the lunar surface crew entered the Lunar Module to perform checkout operations. About 56 hours into the mission, the crew reported that emergency alarms had sounded in the Command Module and that they had heard a muffled explosion. "Okay, Houston. Hey, we've got a problem here," the spacecraft transmitted. In rapid order, the spacecraft reported problems with two of the three fuel cells in the Service Module. These cells supplied electrical power for the spacecraft and produced oxygen and water as byproducts. They also reported venting of gases from the Service Module. The existence of an extreme emergency was clearly indicated.

An electrical short circuit occurring in oxygen tank number 2 caused combustion within the tank. This combustion created a pressure and temperature rise and, within seconds, rupture of the tank. This set off a pressure rise inside Service Module bay No. 4, and the panel covering the compartment blew out. Oxygen required for breathing and for the electricity-producing fuel cells was rapidly depleted. This was the most serious failure ever experienced in manned space flight, particularly since the crew was on a lunar trajectory and could not return to Earth for approximately four days.

Emergency procedures were rapidly developed by the crew and by ground control teams. The plan adopted was for the crew to man the Lunar Module, which had not been affected by the accident, and use the vehicle as a "life boat." The Lunar Module life support system was used to pressurize both spacecraft. Batteries in the Lunar Module supplied power for essential communications and for operation of navigational equipment. The Lunar Module descent stage propulsion system was to be used for required maneuvers.

At first, the dearth of vital supplies was of great concern. Only about 38 hours of power, water, and oxygen were available, and this was about half as much time as would be needed to bring the craft home. However, ground-based personnel devised techniques for powering down the systems to conserve supplies. This created a hardship on the crew because the Lunar Module became uncomfortably cold, but it did provide an ample safety margin for the return trip. One significant problem was that the Lunar Module equipment could not extract sufficient amounts of carbon dioxide to make the atmosphere safe to breathe. Improvised carbon dioxide removal systems conceived by ground personnel were assembled by the crew, and these successfully resolved the problem.

On April 17, the Lunar Module was jettisoned one hour before entry into the Earth's atmosphere. The crew splashed down in the Pacific Ocean within 6 km (4 miles) of the recovery ship and were onboard the carrier within 45 minutes of touchdown. Apart from a urinary tract infection developed by one of the crewmen, the crew was in reasonably good health. Six days and 1 001 933 585 km (541 000 856 nautical miles) after its launch, the hazardous journey of Apollo 13 had come to an end.[*]

Apollo 14

The third successful lunar expedition was commanded by America's first man in space, Alan B. Shepard, Jr., and lasted nine days. The mission's Command Module Pilot was Stuart A. Roosa, and the Lunar Module Pilot was Edgar D. Mitchell. The mission, launched on January 31, 1971, stressed geological studies and the emplacement of experimental packages. The launch was the first in the Apollo series to be delayed, this because the experience of Apollo 12 engendered caution when rain clouds were noted in the Cape Canaveral vicinity. After insertion into the translunar trajectory, approximately six attempts were required before successfully docking the Command Module with the Lunar Module.

The docked spacecraft were placed in very low lunar orbit, about 97 km (60 miles) at the high point and 15 250 m (50 000 ft) at the low point. This was the lowest lunar orbit executed in the docked configuration and another fuel saving maneuver for the lunar landing. Following separation, the Command and Service Module was inserted into a 97-km (60-mile) circular orbit. Some problems were experienced with the abort system in the Lunar Module landing radar after separation from the Command Module, but the spacecraft was nonetheless brought to a safe touchdown on February 5. The first lunar EVA lasted four hours and 44 minutes, during which an ALSEP package was deployed in

[*]Anon: The Apollo 13 Accident. Hearings before the Committee on Science and Astronautics, U.S. House of Representatives. U.S. Government Printing Office (Washington, D.C.), June 16, 1970.

Anon: The Apollo 13 Mission Review. Hearings before the Committee on Aeronautical and Space Sciences, U.S. Senate, 91st Congress, 2nd Session. U.S. Government Printing Office (Washington, D.C.), June 30, 1970.

the vicinity of Doublet Craters in the Fra Mauro region of the moon. During this EVA, the astronauts took photographs of large boulders and collected geological samples. On the next day, the lunar surface crew loaded hand tools onto a Modularized Equipment Transporter (MET). With the two-wheeled, two-legged, rickshaw type device, the astronauts set out for Cone Crater, 1.3 km (one mile) away. They were to bring the device up the crater, 122 m (400 ft) to the rim, and roll stones down its inner side. After two hours and ten minutes, 50 minutes behind schedule, the task had to be abandoned because the crew was tiring seriously and their heart rates were elevated, to 150 beats per minute in Shepard's case, and 128 in Mitchell's.

On February 6, the Lunar Module, *Antares,* lifted off from the moon to rendezvous with the Command Module for return to Earth. Fortunately, no further docking problems occurred. A record amount of lunar surface material, 43 kg (95 lb), was returned for study on Earth.

The Apollo 14 crew was the last to be quarantined after space flight. Their quarantine program, because of rigorous preflight procedures, was the most stringent observed. After the exposure of the Apollo 13 crewman to a communicable disease, a special program was designed to curtail the number of contacts with other individuals prior to flight. Only wives and a group of about 150 people considered essential to the mission had any direct contact with the prime and backup crews. Also, special air filtration equipment was installed in buildings they used. Three weeks from the time they took off from the lunar surface, the U.S. postlanding lunar quarantine program ended.

Apollo 15

The Apollo 15 mission was the fourth successful manned lunar landing mission, and the first in a series of three lunar missions designed to maximally utilize man's capability for scientific exploration of the lunar surface. Mission Commander, David R. Scott, a veteran of the Apollo 9 and Gemini 8 missions; Lunar Module Pilot, James B. Irwin; and Command Module Pilot/Lunar Orbital Science Experimenter, Alfred M. Worden, began their twelve-day mission on July 26, 1971. The mission included extensive lunar extravehicular activity and was the first to use the Lunar Roving Vehicle (figure 15). Changes in extravehicular life support equipment extended EVA time from four to five hours to seven to eight hours without recharging. Further, the Lunar Module was modified to permit lunar surface stays of double the length of the previous 37-hour maximum. The crew accomplished detailed orbital mapping of the lunar surface from orbit using a three camera system and a laser altimeter, and placed a subsatellite in lunar orbit designed to transmit data on the moon's environment for a period of one year.

The Apollo 15 Lunar Module, *Falcon,* landed on the moon approximately 549 m (1800 ft) from its target, along the base of the Apennine Mountains, some of the highest on the near side of the moon, whose peaks rise to 3658 m (12 000 ft) above the plains. The landing site was selected to allow collection of lunar samples from a mare basin, mountains, and a rille in one mission.

Astronaut Scott described the lunar features as very smooth. He reported that the tops of the mountains were rounded, and that there were no sharp peaks or large boulders. Scott and Astronaut Irwin made three lunar excursions, two for seven hours duration and one for six. During the first excursion, the crew deployed the Lunar Roving

Vehicle, set up the third lunar surface experiment package, and obtained lunar samples. A color television camera was mounted on the Lunar Rover and remotely controlled by Mission Control in Houston to permit engineers and scientists on Earth to follow the crew's activities. The crew exceeded the planned 8 km (5 mile) excursion radius and drove nearly 10.3 km (6.4 miles) on their first EVA. In all, the astronauts spent 19½ hours exploring over a distance of 27.9 km (17½ miles) on the moon. They collected an astounding 77.6 kg (171 lb) of lunar material.

Figure 15. Apollo 15 Lunar Roving Vehicle.

The Apollo 15 crew was the first to experience any serious physiological difficulty. The crew's reactions differed radically from those of other crews, and stand out as an anomaly in the Apollo Program. Irregular heart beats were noted on the lunar surface and, again, on the return flight to Earth. Bigeminies and premature auricular and ventricular contractions were seen. In one instance, an arrhythmia recorded during a sleep period was accompanied by a very low heart rate, 28 beats per minute. These arrhythmias are believed to have been linked to potassium deficits and excessive workloads. There may also have been a relationship between preexisting, undetected coronary artery disease in one crewmember and the arrhythmias noted during the mission. The crew also recovered more slowly upon their return to Earth than did any prior or future crew.

Sixty-seven hours after their lunar landing, Astronauts Scott and Irwin fired the ascent stage engine and left the lunar surface to rendezvous with the Command Module, *Endeavor.* After a successful docking, the Lunar Module was jettisoned and impacted the moon at a previously determined target point to test the seismic equipment left behind.

The Command Module remained in lunar orbit for two days to continue and complete scientific experiments. The subsatellite was successfully ejected from the Scientific Instrument Module Bay (SIMBAY) at this time. Spectrometric measurements were obtained of gamma ray, X-ray, and alpha particles to provide a geochemical compositional map of the moon's surface. Astronaut Worden made a "space walk" during translunar coast, spending some 90 minutes retrieving two film cassettes from the SIMBAY. The tethered EVA was the first ever made for a practical working purpose during a space mission. The crew splashed down in the Pacific Ocean on August 7.

Apollo 16

On April 16, 1972, after a delay of one month for technical problems, Apollo 16 was launched. It was the fourth mission for John W. Young, Commander. Charles M. Duke, Jr., served as Lunar Module Pilot, and Thomas K. Mattingly, II, was the Command Module Pilot. Descartes Crater, the lunar landing site selected for Apollo 16, was chosen because it afforded the opportunity to bring back samples representing the oldest and youngest periods of the moon. Topographical features of this site indicated it to be an area of lunar volcanic and chemical evolution.

Minor problems were encountered on the outward flight which caused the crew to spend a significant amount of time troubleshooting. The first major crisis occurred after undocking of the two spacecraft on the 12th lunar orbit. With just minutes to go before starting their final descent to the lunar surface, Astronauts Young and Duke were ordered to continue orbiting and to reduce the gap between themselves and the Command Module for possible redocking because of an oscillation problem in the Service Module propulsion system. Tests showed that the system was usable and safe, but the investigation of the problem delayed the lunar landing about six hours.

The crew landed 270 m (886 ft) northwest of the planned landing site on a hilly and furrowed edge of the Kent Plateau in the Central Lunar Highlands, among the highest mountains on the lunar surface. With the aid of the Lunar Rover, Young and Duke performed three excursions. The first lasted seven hours and 11 minutes. With an improved drill, they were able to obtain three-meter (10-ft) deep core samples during this EVA without the difficulty which had exhausted the Apollo 15 crew. On the second extravehicular expedition, excellent television coverage permitted scientists on Earth to observe the nature of the landing site. To their surprise, there was no evidence of volcanic activity.

During the second EVA, the astronauts collected lunar samples at Stone Mountain and several craters. On the third excursion, the crew drove the Lunar Rover to the rim of North Ray Crater, photographing and obtaining samples. After a total of 71 hours on the moon, including 20¼ hours of extravehicular time, a journey of about 27 km (17 miles), and the collection of 94 kg (207 lb) of lunar samples, Young and Duke ascended from the lunar surface in the *Orion*. Ascent and docking went perfectly, but an incorrectly positioned switch caused the Lunar Module to tumble immediately after jettisoning. An evasive maneuver by the Command Module left the Lunar Module in lunar orbit, and it did not impact the lunar surface until much later than planned. A second particles and fields subsatellite, like that launched by Apollo 15, was successfully ejected from the SIMBAY and placed in lunar orbit.

During the return to Earth, the crewmen participated in a light flash observation session and took photographs for use in a Skylab Program study on the behavior and effects of particles emanating from the spacecraft. The Command Module Pilot carried out an extravehicular activity which included the retrieval of film cassettes from the scientific instrument module cameras, inspection of the equipment, and activation of an experiment designed to provide data on microbial response to the space environment.

As a result of improved work/rest schedules and other factors, the Apollo 16 crew did not experience any of the physiological problems which characterized the Apollo 15 mission. No irregular heart beats were recorded, and the crew recovered their preflight baseline physiological status in the normal period of time postflight. On March 28, one day earlier than planned, Apollo 16 splashed down in the Pacific Ocean. The mission had lasted eleven days.

Apollo 17

On December 7, 1972, the last lunar landing mission was launched from the Kennedy Space Center. The 14-day mission was manned by Eugene A. Cernan, Commander; Ronald E. Evans, Command Module Pilot; and Dr. Harrison H. Schmitt, Lunar Module Pilot who was also a geologist. The launch, illustrated in figure 16, was the first night launch. Taurus-Littrow was Apollo 17's lunar objective. The site was chosen in the hope that samples found there would answer two key questions left unanswered by previous mission samples. The first was whether the moon had been thermally inactive for the last 3.2 billion years. Secondly, it was hoped that the Taurus-Littrow landing site would contain materials to bridge the critical gap left by previous samples, between 3.7 and 4.5 billion years.

After three hours in Earth orbit, the spacecraft were propelled by the Saturn IV-B on their path to the moon. Eighty-six hours after launch, the spacecraft went into lunar orbit. As on the four previous missions, the Saturn IV-B was maneuvered into position to impact the lunar surface after separation from the docked spacecraft. Impact occurred about 135 km (84 miles) from the planned site and was recorded by the passive seismometers deployed by Apollo 12, 14, 15, and 16. After 21½ hours in lunar orbit, the Lunar Module was undocked, and about three and one-half hours after that, Astronauts Cernan and Schmitt set their craft down on the southeastern rim of the Sea of Serenity at the Taurus-Littrow site.

The crew remained on the lunar surface for about 75 hours, and made three explorations, totaling 22 hours. Again, with the help of the Lunar Rover, large areas of the moon were traversed. At the end of the mission, the astronauts had covered 34 km (21 miles) of lunar surface. The crew's first task was to deploy the Lunar Surface Experiment Package. This time, the ALSEP contained a heat flow experiment to replace a comparable experiment which had suffered a failure on Apollo 16. The objective was to measure heat flow from the interior of the moon to the surface to provide an understanding of the moon's core temperature and, perhaps, the processes involved in its formation and activity. Other experiments in the package included a lunar surface gravity experiment, an atmosphere composition experiment, instruments to detect micrometeorites, and seismic profile equipment for the measurement of moonquake activity, magnetic fields, solar wind, and other parameters.

Figure 16. Night launch of Apollo 17.

The scientific yield of Apollo 17 was perhaps the richest of any Apollo lunar landing mission. The crew collected samples of a greater variety than any previously collected. They discovered significant materials indicating lunar volcanic activity. On their second EVA, the astronauts discovered a unique, orange colored surface material never before observed on the moon. Postflight analysis indicated this material contained magnetite. The site had a very large landslide that was also sampled by the crew. By the end of their 75-hour stay, the crew had collected 110 kg (243 lb) of lunar materials. This was a record in the lunar exploration program.

On previous missions, the Command Module Pilot had taken photographs of the moon with the panoramic and mapping cameras and had utilized the laser altimeter while in lunar orbit during the period of lunar surface exploration. Three new experiments were included in the Service Module of Apollo 17 and were the responsibility of the Command Module Pilot. He conducted lunar atmospheric composition and density measurements with an ultraviolet spectrometer, used an infrared radiometer to map lunar thermal characteristics, and a lunar sounder for the acquisition of subsurface structural data.

The Lunar Module successfully mated with the Command Module and, as had been done on previous missions, the former was jettisoned as part of the seismic experiment after transfer of the crew. The Command Module remained in lunar orbit for two days to complete the experiments begun by the Command Module Pilot. On December 20, the Command Module, *Endeavor,* landed in the Pacific Ocean west of Hawaii. With this event, the Apollo Program was brought to a conclusion.

Concluding Remarks

The Apollo Lunar Landing Program spanned a seven-year period and included seventeen missions. The 29 astronauts who flew in the Program spent a total of 7506 hours in flight. Twelve of them were placed on the moon for a total of more than four man-weeks and all were returned safely to Earth. The Apollo Program is viewed as one of the greatest scientific and engineering successes of man, a national event which held the attention of millions of people in this country and the world, and required the development of new and complex equipment ranging from the spacecraft itself to the tools and clothing used by the crewmen. The Program made it possible to gather lunar material that has begun to disclose clues about the origin of our solar system. And, at last, we were certain that no life exists on the moon. The Apollo Program established that the psychological and physiological effects of the space environment on man were not at all as severe as had been predicted by some scientists. But, perhaps the greatest significance of the Apollo Program lies in the fact that it provided information which will assist scientists and engineers in developing the biomedical and technical support necessary for man to venture still further into the solar system.

Crew Health and

Inflight Monitoring

The health of Apollo crewmembers was a matter of genuine concern. An inflight illness, particularly should it occur during a critical mission phase, could have had serious consequences. To minimize the chance of illness, an extensive health maintenance program was conducted to ensure the highest of health standards. This section describes the clinical practices which were followed and certain special projects conducted to obtain information bearing on the health of astronauts.

CHAPTER 1
CLINICAL ASPECTS OF CREW HEALTH

by

W. Royce Hawkins, M.D.
John F. Zieglschmid, M.D.

Lyndon B. Johnson Space Center

Introduction

While the primary goal of the Apollo Program was to land men on the moon and return them safely to Earth, there were other very important medical objectives. The earlier Mercury and Gemini programs had raised some concerns about the health and safety of future crews. For example, the high metabolic energy expenditure of extravehicular activity during the Gemini missions was unexpected. Before Apollo astronauts could safely explore the lunar surface, reliable predictors of energy cost and real-time monitoring techniques had to be developed. Physiological changes were noted in individual crewmen, some more consistently than others. The most important of these changes was in cardiopulmonary status demonstrated by decreased exercise capacity, loss of red blood cell mass, and cardiovascular deconditioning demonstrated by a decrease in the effectiveness of antigravity cardiovascular responses during postflight stress testing.

At the end of the Gemini program, with 2000 man-hours logged in space, it was clear that man could engage in relatively long space flight without any serious threat to health. However, clarification was still required in many areas. First of all, because of the small number of individuals who flew in space and because of the variability of their responses, it was impossible to distinguish between space-related physiological changes and individual physiological variations. Secondly, for those changes which were directly related to space flight, the relatively short mission durations precluded the identification of trends.

In view of the foregoing considerations, four medical objectives were specified for the Apollo Program:

1. Ensuring crew safety from a medical standpoint. This objective required that every effort be made to identify, eliminate, or minimize anything which posed a potential health hazard to the crew.

43

2. Improving the probability of mission success by ensuring that sufficient medical information was available for management decisions.

3. Preventing back-contamination from the lunar surface.

4. Continuing to further the understanding of the biomedical changes incident to space flight. This objective was formulated to detect, document, and understand changes occurring during space flight.

The program to ensure crew safety commenced long before the Apollo Program itself with the development and implementation of the medical selection and screening program for astronauts. Apollo astronauts were drawn from a pool of individuals who were thoroughly screened to preclude any physical or physiological problems which would jeopardize either the mission or the astronaut candidate. Later, special measures were taken to further protect the health and enhance the safety of those astronauts chosen for specific Apollo missions. These included preflight medical examinations, a health stabilization program, drug sensitivity testing of astronauts for all medications aboard the spacecraft, and other measures.

The preflight medical program was designed to preclude, as far as possible, the development of any clinical medical problems during space flight. Since no preventive medicine program, however carefully conceived, can ever guarantee the absence of illness or disease, medications were carried onboard the Apollo spacecraft. The contents of the medical kit were revised as need indicated throughout the Apollo Program. Onboard bioinstrumentation was provided to monitor vital signs for rapid diagnosis of any physiological difficulty in a crewmember and to provide medical information required for mission management. Additional information was transmitted via voice communication between the crew and the ground-based flight surgeons. During extravehicular activity, methods were added to provide metabolic rate assessment. In addition to heart rate, oxygen consumption was monitored along with inlet/outlet temperature of the liquid cooled garment worn by the crewmen.

Opportunities for inflight medical investigations were severely restricted on the Apollo missions because of conflict with the principal operational objectives. Furtherance of the understanding of the effects of space flight on human physiological functioning had to rely almost exclusively on comparison of preflight and postflight observations. These were carefully selected to focus attention on the areas which appeared most likely to be affected, for example, cardiovascular function. Other areas were also investigated for unforeseen changes and corroborative information.

The sections which follow describe medical procedures and findings for Apollo astronauts in the preflight, inflight, and postflight phases of the Apollo missions.

Preflight Procedures and Findings

The procedures implemented in the preflight period for Apollo missions had five major objectives. These were:

1. The discovery of latent illnesses during the process of selection of astronauts and preparation for missions.

2. The implementation of the health stabilization program and other preventive measures.

3. Determination of individual drug sensitivity to the contents of the Apollo medical kits.

4. Providing baseline data against which to compare postflight data for determination of space flight effects.

5. Prevention of any situations which might delay or otherwise interfere with operational aspects of the missions.

The procedures performed in the preflight period ensured improved performance of flight tasks and, with rare exceptions, prevented the outbreak of illness inflight. This outcome was, in part, the result of medical screening and selection programs designed to provide physically competent crews. Observation and semi-isolation programs also helped to detect latent ailments which might have produced frank symptoms during flight. Finally, a training course was presented to astronauts to acquaint them with stresses of space flight and their effects upon the human organism.

Medical Screening/Examinations

Preventive health care in a population which has been chosen for a particular job begins with the medical selection of that population. Rigorous astronaut selection standards were established to identify:

1. Individuals who were physically capable of performing astronaut duties; specifically those possessing the necessary physical and psychomotor capabilities and not subject to incapacitating physiological disturbances when exposed to the various stresses of space flight.

2. Individuals who were free of underlying physical defects or disease processes which could shorten their useful flight careers.

Apollo astronauts were initially medically screened by techniques which varied only in minor degree from those applied to the first seven Mercury astronauts. The standards used closely approximated U. S. Air Force Flying Class I Standards, except in the selection of scientist-astronauts where visual standards were relaxed to qualify a sufficient number of candidates. These examinations were performed at the U. S. Air Force School of Aerospace Medicine, with final review and medical acceptance of candidates by the NASA Lyndon B. Johnson Space Center medical staff. Listed below are the components of the examination used for medical selection.

1. Medical history and review of systems.

2. Physical examination.

3. Electrocardiographic examinations, including routine electrocardiographic studies at rest, during hyperventilation, carotid massage, and breath holding, a double Master exercise tolerance test, a cold pressor test, and a precordial map.

4. Treadmill exercise tolerance test.

5. Vectorcardiographic study.

6. Phonocardiographic study.

7. Tilt table studies.

8. Pulmonary function studies.

9. Radiographic studies, including cholecystograms, upper GI series, lumbosacral spine, chest, cervical spine, and skull films.

10. Body composition study, using tritium dilution.

11. Laboratory examinations, including complete hematology workup, urinalysis, serologic test, glucose tolerance test, acid alkaline phosphatase, BUN, sodium, potassium, bicarbonate, chloride, calcium, phosphorus, magnesium, uric acid, bilirubin (direct and indirect), thymol turbidity, cephalin flocculation, SGOT, SGPT, total protein with albumin and globulin, separate determinations of Alpha 1 and Alpha 2, Beta and Gamma globulins, protein bound iodine, creatinine, cholesterol, total lipids and phospholipids, hydroxyproline, and RBC intracellular sodium and potassium. Stool specimens were examined for occult blood, and microscopically for ova and parasites. A urine culture for bacterial growth was done, and a 24-hour specimen analyzed for 17-ketosteroids and 17-hydroxycorticosteroids.

12. Detailed examination of the sinuses, larynx, and Eustachian tubes.

13. Vestibular studies.

14. Diagnostic hearing tests.

15. Visual fields and special eye examinations.

16. General surgical evaluation.

17. Procto-sigmoidoscopy.

18. Dental examination.

19. Neurological examination.

20. Psychologic summary, including Wechsler Adult Intelligence Test, Bender Visual-Motor Gestalt Test, Rorschach Test, Thematic Apperception Test, Draw-A-Person Test, Gordon Personal Profile, Edwards' Personal Preference Schedule, Miller Analogies Test, and Performance Testing.

22. Electroencephalographic studies.

23. Centrifuge testing.

The preflight medical examinations for Apollo crewmembers included detailed physical examinations and special studies. The physical examinations commenced 30 days prior to launch and ended on the day of lift-off. The special studies involved collection of baseline data for comparison with postflight findings. The areas of particular interest were microbiology, immuno-hematology, clinical chemistry, and cardiopulmonary function. Baseline data collection in each of these areas, of course, had bearing on crew health, but was additionally obtained in order to answer the following critical questions:

1. Did a change take place in a particular dependent variable?

2. Was the change significantly different from that occurring in a control group?

3. What was the extent of the change?

4. What was the time course of the observed change?

5. Was it possible to provide causal interpretations?

The following sections provide details concerning the preflight physical examinations and special baseline studies.

Physical Examinations. The physical examinations of Apollo crewmembers were intended to document the crewmenbers' physical qualifications for the mission, to detect any medical problems which might require remedial or preventive intervention, and to provide baseline data for postflight comparison. Physical examinations were conducted in the following manner:

1. *Preliminary examination at F-30 days.* At this time, interval history, vital signs, and a general physical examination were conducted.

2. *Interim examination at F-15 days.* General physical examination, dental examination, and monitoring of vital signs were accomplished.

The preliminary and interim examinations included the following procedures:

- An interval history and detailed review of systems, vital signs — to include oral temperature, blood pressure, and pulse rate.

- ENT examination to include visual inspection of the external ears, auditory canals, and tympanic membranes, the nose and nasal passages, transillumination of the frontal and maxillary sinuses, and visual inspection of the anterior and posterior middle pharynx.

- Examination of the eyes to include visual inspection and palpation of the lids and lacrimal apparatus, visual inspection of the conjunctiva, sclera, and cornea, and ophthalmoscopic examination of the lens, media, and fundus.

- Examination of the heart to include palpation, percussion, and auscultation.

- Examination of the lungs to include palpation, percussion, and auscultation.

- Examination of the abdomen to include palpation, percussion, and auscultation.

- Examination of the genitalia and anal regions.

- Examination of the extremities for recent trauma or limitation of function.

- Neurological examination to include a brief examination of the cranial nerves and motor, sensory and proprioceptive modalities.

- Skin, visual inspection.

- Lymph nodes, by palpation.

- Dental examination (interim examination only).

3. *Comprehensive examination at F-5 days.* The comprehensive examination consisted of the procedures on the following page.

- Interval history, vital signs, including height, weight, oral temperature, pulse rate, and blood pressure.
- ENT Examination:

    a. Ears: Visual inspection of external ears, auditory canals and tympanic membranes, screening Rudmose audiometry.

    b. Nose: Visual inspection, sinus transillumination, if indicated by recent history.

    c. Throat: Direct examination of middle pharynx.

    d. Eyes: Same as for preliminary examination, plus distant and near visual acuity, near-point of accommodation, phorias, and visual fields.

- Heart: Palpation, percussion, and auscultation, plus standard twelve-lead EKG.
- Lungs: Palpation, percussion, and auscultation, plus PA chest film.
- Abdomen: Palpation, percussion, and auscultation, plus abdominal scout film.
- Genitalia and anus: Inspection, plus digital rectal examination.
- Extremities: Examination for recent trauma, range of function.
- Neurological examination: Detailed examination of cranial nerves, motor, sensory, and proprioceptive modalities.
- Skin: Visual inspection, plus photographs of any areas of significant interest.

4. *Cursory examination – F-4 to F-0 days.* Brief physical examinations and histories were conducted in the last four days before flight. These included recording of vital signs, oral temperature, pulse, blood pressure, weight, plus a brief examination of the ears, nose, throat, heart, and lungs. Other signs and systems were examined as indicated by the medical history.

The scheduled physical examinations varied slightly with mission requirements. However, these had to commence not earlier than 30 and not later than 21 days prior to lift-off in order to provide sufficient time to diagnose and treat any illnesses of recent onset. Some of the significant medical findings that occurred during the 30-day preflight period are listed in table 1. The comprehensive examination performed five days prior to launch was intended to accurately document the physical status of each crewmember at the outset of the mission. The final examination prior to flight involved last minute recordings of critical parameters to provide the most reliable basis that could be obtained for postflight comparisons.

The following paragraphs provide some detail on various aspects of the physical examination.

Dental Examinations. Dental care was provided as a regular part of the ongoing health care program of astronauts. However, special measures were taken prior to missions to preclude, wherever possible, dental problems during flight. All crewmen were evaluated at or about F-15. Because of the relatively short duration of the Apollo flights, emphasis was placed on general observation rather than definitive quantitative research.

Table 1

Preflight Medical Findings in Apollo Mission Crews

Diagnosis	Number of Occurrences
Pressure suit abrasions	2
Blister, left toe	1
Pressure suit callouses, scapulae and iliac crests	1
Carious lesion, mesial	1
Cellulitis of the hand secondary to laceration	1
Conjunctival injection	3
Dermatitis	3
Dermatophytosis, feet	2
Folliculitis, abdomen	1
Furunculosis	2
Gastroenteritis	7
Gingival burn	1
Hematomas, secondary to trauma	3
Inflammation, medial canthus, right eye	1
Influenza syndrome	3
Keratosic plaque	1
Traumatic lesion of the right buccal mucosa	1
Viral lesion of the buccal mucosa	1
Viral lymphoid hyperplasia of the postpharynx	3
Pyuria	4
Papules/pustules	5
Paronychia	1
Viral pharyngitis	3
Pulpitis, tooth No. 31	1
Prostatitis	1
Tinea crura	1
pedis	1
Viral tympanic membrane infection	1
Seborrhea	2
Viral rhinitis	3
Ringworm, arm	1
Beta-hemolytic pharyngitis	1
Sunburn, face and torso	2
Ulcer, aphthous	2
Urinary tract infection	8

Again, because mission duration was short, no special inflight dental treatment capability was provided for Apollo. It was felt that the risk of a problem occurring was slight and, when weighed against limitations of weight, space, and training time, providing an inflight treatment capability was not indicated. Analgesic and antibiotic drugs were provided for symptomatic treatment of any dental problems. As a further precaution, restorative dental treatment was avoided in the three-month period prior to launch. The object of this measure was to minimize the possibility of barodontalgia, a sudden, severe toothache which can occur when barometric pressure is reduced as a result of expansion of air entrapped in a dental restoration. When a dental problem arose in the three-month period prior to flight and a restoration became necessary, the astronaut in question was subjected to reduced barometric pressure to ascertain the condition of the tooth.

Dental problems that occurred among crewmembers during the Apollo Program resulted in no appreciable mission impact. During the 90-day preflight period, five of the thirty-three Apollo crewmen had dental problems requiring treatment. One preflight and one postflight occurrence of pulpitis could have caused significant crewmember impairment if the pulpitis had occurred during a flight. Pulpitis, an inflammation of the dental pulp, causes severe pain that usually can be stopped only by root-canal therapy, performed by a skilled dentist in a fully equipped dental suite, or by extraction. Prediction of such occurrences is virtually impossible, although the preventive treatment of known causative factors can lower the risk of occurrence. The only other preflight problems were minor fractures of previously placed restorations or minor fractures of part of a crown of a tooth. Inflight, no problems were experienced. No case of barodontalgia ever occurred, although some astronauts had experienced this discomfort during their flying careers.

Experience with Apollo astronauts in an intensive preventive dentistry program led to the conclusion that the probability of a disabling dental emergency in the astronaut population is one occurrence in 9000 man-days. The probability of dental problems of lesser severity, but associated with significant discomfort, is one in 1500 man-days. These figures are comparable to those recorded for Navy personnel on long submarine patrols. From these estimations, it is obvious that a provision for emergency inflight dental care must be made only for very long-duration missions.

Visual Function Testing. Visual function testing was a part of the pre- and postflight physical examination of Apollo astronauts. Ten visual parameters were tested during the Apollo Program:

- Unaided visual acuity, 7 m (20 ft)
- Amplitude of accommodation
- Near point of convergence
- Fusional amplitudes, base-in and base-out
- Horizontal phorias, 7 m and 33 cm (20 ft and 13 in.)
- Refraction
- Intraocular tension
- Color perception
- Depth perception
- Visual fields

One of the major considerations in flight was the amount of harmful ultraviolet (UV) radiation to which the crewmen would be subjected during extravehicular activity. Prior to Apollo missions, the UV threshold of the eye was unknown. Over a three-year period, NASA-sponsored research determined these levels. The problem was, however, subsequently resolved with the development and use of Lexan in the extravehicular visor assembly, since Lexan was opaque to UV radiation. A minimum of 2000 hours of exposure would be required to produce a corneal "burn" through this plastic.

Table 2 gives the data ascertained for ocular thresholds to UV radiation.

Table 2

Ocular Thresholds for Ultaviolet Radiation

Waveband (nm)	Solar Flux $(J/cm^2/sec \times 10^{-4})$	Relative Effectivity	Effective Flux $(J/cm^2/sec \times 10^{-4})$
215 – 225	0.2644	0.40	0.1058
225 – 235	0.5288	0.31	0.1639
235 – 245	0.5288	0.53	0.2803
245 – 255	0.6610	0.50	0.3305
255 – 265	1.4542	0.53	0.7707
265 – 275	2.1152	1.00	2.1152
275 – 285	2.5118	0.68	1.7080
285 – 295	4.7592	0.57	2.7127
295 – 305	5.9490	0.57	3.3909
305 – 315	7.1388	0.29	2.0703

Total ultraviolet effective flux   : $13.6483 \times 10^{-4} \, J/cm^2/sec$
Ocular burn threshold for ultraviolet : $40 \times 10^{-4} W/cm^2$
Ultraviolet band threshold time   :   2.93 seconds

The harmful effects of UV radiation extend over an area slightly greater than the 215 to 315 nanometer range noted above; however, the relative effectivity outside these extremes is very low. Summating these slight effects into the flux listed above could possibly lower the total UV band threshold time to about two and one-half seconds in a Zero Air Mass environment.

Special Studies. A number of special preflight examinations were conducted and measurements made to provide a baseline against which to compare postflight findings in the areas of microbiology, immuno-hematology and clinical chemistry, and cardiopulmonary function. Details of each of these studies are provided in the related chapters in Section III of this book. The preflight examination procedures required for each are discussed only briefly here.

In order to study any microflora alterations which could have occurred in space flight, preflight samples were taken to catalog the microorganisms found on the crewmembers and their clothing, and on spacecraft surfaces. Samples collected for culture included swabs of various parts of the body, throat gargle, and urine and fecal samples. These were collected on four occasions in the month prior to flight. Blood samples were also collected on three occasions in this same time frame.

Baseline data were obtained on the cellular elements of the blood, the chemical constituents of the blood and urine, and the humoral and cellular factors involved in immunity. The hematological and chemical measurements of various blood constituents were one portion of comprehensive examinations designed to disclose the state of well-being or the presence of occult disease in the crews. Blood analyses furnished data which, when integrated with facts obtained from histories and physical examinations, permitted an objective assessment of the physical status of the astronauts and allowed for remedial action if required. However, no values outside of the normal range were observed.

Biochemical and hematological baseline information was obtained, in part to quantitate the effect of the stresses inherent in space flight, and in part to aid medical personnel in medical management of crews in the postflight period.

Cardiopulmonary evaluations and findings are discussed at length in Section III, Chapter 4 *Apollo Flight Crew, Cardiovascular Evaluations*, and Chapter 5, *Exercise Response*. Preflight orthostatic tolerance tests and exercise response tests were performed to provide baseline information to facilitate assessment of space flight effects.

Cardiopulmonary data were obtained to develop heart rate versus metabolic rate calibration curves that would be used for estimating real-time work output during extravehicular activity. Utilization of Douglas bags, a Tissot spirometer, and an oxygen consumption computer or metabolic rate meter also made determination of cardiopulmonary efficiency possible. Evaluation of cardiopulmonary data was accomplished by observing how the dependent variables – workload, oxygen consumption, blood pressure response, respiratory response, and EKG – changed in response to the independent variable, heart rate.

The extent of cardiovascular system "deconditioning" was assessed also by comparison with preflight baseline responses to the application of negative pressure to the lower half of the body by means of the lower body negative pressure (LBNP) device. Preflight evaluations were made at least three times in the month preceding flight. The test procedures involved five minutes with the subject at supine rest in the LBNP device, a total of fifteen minutes at negative pressures ranging from $-40 \times 10^2 N/m^2$ to $-67 \times 10^2 N/m^2$ (-30 to -50mm Hg), and five minutes of recovery. Because missions involving postflight quarantine could not accommodate the size of the LBNP device in the Mobile Quarantine Facility, a static stand-type of orthostatic tolerance testing was substituted. This involved obtaining five minutes of electrocardiographic data while the crewman was standing still with his back to the wall and his feet apart. Test conditions were controlled and standardized to exclude unnecessary variables such as environmental temperature, time of day, food intake, physical exertion, or venipuncture.

Health Stabilization

The problem of communicable disease exposure prior to flight, with subsequent development of symptoms in flight, was recognized as a potential hazard from the beginning of the United States space program. Total isolation of flight crews for a period of time prior to launch offered indisputable advantages but was initially thought to be infeasible because of the operational difficulties involved. Flight crews were required to be in contact with large numbers of people and to move from place to place during the last few weeks of their training in preparation for a space flight.

When clinical illnesses impacted preflight mission operations during Apollo 9 and 13, it became apparent that some type of preflight health stabilization program was imperative. Prior to Apollo 14, 57 percent of the Apollo crewmembers experienced some illness of varying degrees of severity at some time during the 21 days before launch. Based on observations of the first several flights and on the observation of crewmember activities during earlier manned Mercury and Gemini missions, the Flight Crew Health Stabilization Program was developed and implemented for the Apollo 14 mission and subsequent missions. Such a program, rigorously enforced, can result in a significant reduction of infectious disease hazard, although the hazard cannot be eliminated completely.

Table 3 lists the illness events in Apollo crewmen and shows the dramatic reduction in illness following the implementation of the health stabilization program.

Table 3

Effect of Flight Crew Health Stabilization Program (FCHSP)
on the Occurrence of Illness in Prime Apollo Crewmen

Mission	Illness	Number of Crewmen Involved	Mission Phase
Before Implementation of FCHSP			
Apollo 7	Upper respiratory infection	3	Preflight, inflight
8	Viral gastroenteritis	3	Preflight, inflight
9	Upper respiratory infection	3	Preflight
10	Upper respiratory infection	2	Preflgiht
11	None	—	—
12	Skin infection	2	Inflight
13	Rubella infection	1	Preflight
After Implementation of FCHSP			
Apollo 14	—	—	—
15	—	—	—
16	—	—	—
17	Skin infection	1	Preflight

Drug Sensitivity Testing

Drug sensitivity testing was performed to determine the response of flight crewmembers to each item in the medical kit to preclude allergic reactions and other undesirable side effects in flight. Each Apollo crewmember was tested under controlled conditions to determine his response to medical kit items carried onboard the spacecraft. (The medical kit is described later in this chapter in the section concerning Inflight Procedures and Findings.) After a medical history was obtained by a physician regarding the experience of each crewmember with each medication under test, and it had been determined that (1) no adverse reaction had been experienced, and (2) there was no evidence of impaired health at the time of testing, the medication was administered to the astronaut. The crewmember was observed by the physician for an appropriate period of time following administration of the medication and was queried about subjective responses. If positive subjective findings were reported, the test was either repeated with a double-blind placebo method, or an appropriate drug was substituted for which no undesirable side effects had been reported. Individuals were additionally tested for any allergic reaction to the electrode paste.

Table 4 indicates the drug administration and observation constraints applied. All medications used were treated in a similar fashion.

Medical Training

To perform their inflight tasks optimally, Apollo crewmen required an understanding of the interaction of space flight stresses and their effects on the human organism, including the manner in which the body adapts to space flight factors. Further, these crewmen had to recognize any abnormalities in their health status and understand the therapeutic measures which might have been prescribed for inflight problems. Medical training began shortly after astronaut selection with a series of lectures concerned with space flight physiology and therapeutics. The curriculum encompassed about 16 hours of didactic instruction provided by experts in each area. The principal elements were as follows:

Cardiovascular System. Brief outline of anatomy and physiology, methods of observing and monitoring cardiac activity, system response to acceleration, weightlessness, work and other stresses, functional testing, such as tilt table, lower body negative pressure, bicycle and treadmill systems.

Pulmonary System. Brief outline of anatomy and physiology, pulmonary function, gas exchange, problems related to hypo- and hyperbaric environments, physiologic limits of spacecraft atmospheres, contemplated atmospheres for future vehicles, respiratory response to acceleration, weightlessness and work, physical conditioning and testing, respiratory capacity.

Hematology and Laboratory Medicine. Review of Mercury and Gemini findings involving blood elements and chemistries, review of programs scheduled for Apollo and Skylab Programs, illustration of the need to establish good baseline data, controls, and possible expansion of the present program.

The Role of Psychiatry in Crew Selection. Crew and dependents support, personal considerations of long term confinement, group dynamics, and responses to various stresses encountered in flight and on the ground.

Table 4

Typical Pharmacological Agent
Administration and Observation Constraints

Item	Route of Administration	Frequency of Observation by Physician	Constraints
Meperidine HCl (Demerol)	I.M. 1/4 dose (25 mg)	0-15 min; 2nd hour; 4th hour	No flying, driving, or other hazardous pursuit for 8 hours
Hyoscine and D-amphetamine sulfate (Dexedrine)	0.3 mg (Hyoscine) and Oral 5.0 mg (Dexedrine)	1 hour and 4 hours or immediately on development of any reaction	Not within 4-6 hours of planned sleep
Propoxyphene HCl (Darvon)	Oral (65 mg)	One time within 4 hours or immediately on development of any reaction	No flying or driving within 6 hours
Acetylsalicylic acid (ASA)	Oral (300 mg)	One time within 4 hours or immediately on development of any reaction	None
Tetracycline	Oral (250 mg)	Within 4 hours or immediately on development of any reaction	Not within 24 hours of stool collection for microbiology
Diphenoxylate HCl with atropine sulfate (Lomotil)	Oral (0.025 mg)	One time within 4-8 hours or immediately on development of any reaction	None
D-amphetamine sulfate (Dexedrine)	Oral (5 mg)	2nd hour, 4th hour or immediately on development of any reaction	Not within 4 to 6 hours of planned sleep. Heart rate to be recorded
Skin cream	Topical	Within 4-6 hours or immediately on development of any reaction	None
Methylcellulose eye drops	Topical	On application	None
Polymycin B-bacitracin-neomycin sulfate (Neosporin) ointment)	Topical	On application	None

Table 4 (Continued)

Typical Pharmacological Agent
Administration and Observation Constraints

Item	Route of Administration	Frequency of Observation by Physician	Constraints
N-benzhydryl-N-methylpiperazine monoHCl or lactate (Marezine)	Oral (50 mg)	Within 4 hours or immediately on development of any reaction	No flying, driving, etc. for 8 hours
Proparacaine HCl (Opthaine)	Topical	On application	None
Simethicone (Mylicon)	Oral	Within 4 hours	None
Oxymetazoline HCl (Afrin)	Topical	(1) On application (2) 8-12 hours or immediately on development of any reaction	None
Electrode paste	Topical	At 48 and 72 hours following application	None
Ampicillin	Oral (250 mg)	0-15 min; within 4 hours or immediately on development of any reaction	Not within 24 hours of stool collection for microbiology
Triprolidine HCl and pseudo-ephedrine HCl (Actifed)	Oral (60 mg)	One time within 4 hours or immediately on development of any reaction	No flying driving, etc. for 8 hours

Description of Vestibular System. Its function and equilibrium, and testing thereof, response of the vestibular system to acceleration, weightlessness, flight experiments in Gemini, and planning for Apollo and Skylab Programs.

Visual System. Brief description of anatomy and physiology, relationships to other sensory organs, effects of acceleration and weightlessness on eye and visual system, problems in space, such as light, ultraviolet trauma, high closing speeds, and depth perception without reference points.

Refresher courses were required of each astronaut every three years in the technical and practical aspects of altitude physiology and the medical aspects of survival.

Before each mission, a detailed medical briefing was provided by staff members of the Johnson Space Center approximately one month before launch. The purpose of the briefing was as follows:

1. To acquaint the crewmembers with the pre- and postflight medical procedures planned for their mission.
2. To discuss with the crew preventive medicine measures (related to diet, potential sources of infection, and physical conditioning) recommended for their health and comfort.
3. To acquaint the crew with the Apollo medical kit and its uses.
4. To review with the crew the flight food and hygienic supplies selected for their flight.
5. To demonstrate the configuration and operation of the biomedical harness.
6. To achieve final coordination of procedures for logging or communicating medical data during flight.
7. To familiarize the crew with toxicological considerations.

The Astronaut Health Care Program

Once selected, retention of space crewmen on flying status assumes great importance for a number of reasons, not the least of which is the cost of training such individuals. Consequently, comprehensive health care is provided all astronauts and their families through a preventive, diagnostic, and therapeutic program managed by the National Aeronautics and Space Administration, with aid from many civilian and military consultants. Care of families by the same physicians rendering care to the astronauts provides an understanding of the total milieu in which the astronaut lives and functions.

Astronauts must report any and all illnesses and injuries for evaluation and treatment. Once yearly, during the month of their birth, a thorough physical examination is performed, whether or not an astronaut remains on active duty status. Preventive dental care is also rendered. All patients are seen by a dentist at least once every six months and their conditions evaluated at that time. Emphasis is placed on a home care program. During these periodic examinations, care is taken to minimize ionizing radiation exposure during the use of diagnostic X-rays. Astronauts represent a unique population. They have been exposed to some environmental factors never before experienced by man and to others to which men have been exposed, but not in the same combination or sequence. As such, the astronaut population represents the opportunity for a unique longitudinal study which should yield invaluable information for selection of future space flight crews.

Listed in tables 5 through 11 are examples of significant medical problems detected during the annual physical examination. These tables serve to highlight the types of medical findings contained in the past histories of the astronaut crews. The findings are invaluable to the mission flight surgeon as background information in the real-time assessment of inflight medical problems and in pinpointing potential problems that may arise. It is vital that all inflight signs and symptoms be evaluated in the context of past medical findings such as are enumerated in these tables.

Inflight Procedures and Findings

During the inflight phase of Apollo missions, medical care was limited to long-distance biotelemetry monitoring, diagnosis, and treatment with the appropriate onboard drugs. This treatment was carried out by the space crewmen themselves under the direction of ground-based flight surgeons. The weightless flight phase of Apollo missions was characterized by certain transient adaptational difficulties, by a few clinical illnesses, and by a limited number of physiological phenomena apparently related largely to space flight factors. The following sections describe the clinical and medical aspects of the inflight portion of Apollo missions.

Table 5

Infectious Diseases

Infection	Number of Cases
Upper respiratory	133
Influenza	33
Pneumonia	7
Sinusitis	19
Otitis media	1
Otitis externa	6
Gastroenteritis	29
Genitourinary	30
Bacterial dermatitis	9
Superficial fungal dermatitis	20
Conjunctivitis	3
Blepharitis	1
Chalazion	3
Herpes zoster	1
Herpes hominis, recurrent	1
Cellulitis and lymphangitis	1
Rubella	1
Tuberculin skin test conversion	2
Total	301

Table 6

Neoplasms

Neoplasm	Number of Cases
Basal cell carcinoma	2
Epithelioma	2
Polyp, colon	1
Adenoma, thyroid	1
Fibroma	1
Squamous papilloma, eyelid	1
Total	8

Table 7

Hereditary and Metabolic Diseases

Disease	Number of Cases
Plasma thromboplastin antecedent deficiency	1
Gout	1
Abnormal glucose tolerance	2
Hypercholesterolemia	1
Hyperlipemia	1
Idiopathic hyperbilirubinemia	1
Total	7

Table 8

Degenerative Disorders

Disorder	Number of Cases
Hearing loss	6
Presbyopia	6
Lenticular opacities	3
Vertebral degenerative changes	4
Cervical spondylosis - Brown-Sequard syndrome *	1
Degenerative disc disease, early	1
Total	21

* Not detected during annual physical examination.

Table 9

Allergic Problems

Allergic Response	Number of Cases
Angioneurotic edema	1
Urticaria	7
Asthma secondary to aspirin hypersensitivity	1
Skin hypersensitivity, ant bite	1
Allergic vasculitis and synovitis	1
Contact dermatitis	3
Drug rash	2
Total	16

Table 10
Traumatic Injuries

Trauma	Number of Cases
Muscle strain	9
Sprains	9
Torn meniscus (knee)	2
Fractures	11
Dislocation - shoulder and phalanges	2
Lacerations	10
Bursitis or synovitis (elbow)	2
Burns	3
Contusions	3
Eye injuries	9
Dog bite	1
Peripheral compression neuropathy	1
Concussive labyrinthitis	1
Laryngitis (excessive speaking)	1
Total	64

Table 11
Miscellaneous Problems of Medical Significance

	Number of Cases
Cholecystitis or cholelithiasis	2
Hernia	2
Sperm granuloma	1
Hemorrhoids, symptomatic	5
Renal calculus	1
Ménière's syndrome	1
Thrombophlebitis	1
Migraine equivalent	1
Congestive prostatitis	2
Rectal fissure	1
Abdominal pain, unknown etiology, severe	1
Atrial fibrillation	1
Dysbarism, bends	1
Barotitis media	5
Total	25

Monitoring

When the United States space program first began, the concept of obtaining continuous physiological data by instrumenting the human operator was a new one. No sufficiently reliable off-the-shelf hardware was available. Since that time, sophisticated and highly reliable biotelemetry devices have been developed.

Each Apollo crewman wore a biosensor harness which provided a means of transmitting critical physiological data to the ground. Through this system, medical personnel were able to evaluate physiological status during such critical phases as launch and docking, extravehicular activity, and lunar explorations. This real-time telemetry of vital biomedical information was also available for monitoring Apollo crewmen in the event of inflight illness.

The operational bioinstrumentation system was designed as an individually adjustable unit worn under the flight clothing. The biobelt assembly was an electronic system that included sensors, signal conditioners, and telemetry interfaces. The system returned electrocardiogram, heart rate, and respiratory pattern and rate data. A two-lead EKG with synchronous phonocardiography provided an index of cardiac activity. Cardiotachometer equipment made monitoring of instantaneous and average heart rate information possible. Voice communications and real-time television observations, coupled with monitoring of the vital signs, provided the medical basis for an inflight clinical profile of the Apollo astronauts.

Data from the biotelemetry of the spacecraft were displayed at consoles at the launch and mission control centers. The consoles were manned continuously by medical personnel during the course of each mission. Heart and respiration rates were displayed in digital form; electrocardiogram and impedance pneumogram data were presented on a cathode ray oscilloscope.

In general, the equipment worked well, although some minor losses of data were experienced throughout the program. Problems with breakage of bioharness leads and pin connectors encountered on the Apollo 7 mission were corrected for subsequent flights. Some degradation of physiological data was caused by loose biosensors, but restoration of good data was usually obtained by reapplication of the sensors. Sponge pellet electrodes were used in the biosensor harness for the first time on the Apollo 15 mission. This modification reduced skin irritation that had earlier resulted from continuous wearing of the electrodes.

The quality of the data obtained with the new electrodes was excellent. Some data loss resulted because air became trapped under the electrodes during the Apollo 15 mission, but this was easily corrected by modifying the electrodes with small vents.

Additional data were telemetered during lunar surface extravehicular activity to permit assessment of the portable life support system and, additionally, the determination of the metabolic activity during lunar excursions. Metabolic rate was approximated by monitoring the inlet and the outlet temperatures of the liquid cooled garment. Heart rate and oxygen usage were also monitored as metabolic rate indices. Of the three methods, the thermal data and oxygen use methods proved to be reasonably accurate and significantly more reliable as a means for determining metabolic rate than did heart rate data.

Further documentation of the Apollo bioinstrumentation system is reported in Section VI, Chapter 3, *Bioinstrumentation.* Additional information concerning monitoring during extravehicular activity is contained in Section II, Chapter 4, *Metabolism and Heat Dissipation During Apollo Extravehicular Activity Periods.*

Inflight Medications

The initial philosophy regarding use of medication precluded usage except in a medical emergency. Additional experience and the confidence gained thereby permitted some alteration of this philosophy to the extent that certain drugs were prescribed during Apollo missions when indicated. For example, hypnotics were prescribed when adequate rest could not be obtained, particularly when sound sleep was important prior to critical mission phases.

Medical Kit. The contents of the Apollo medical kit (figure 1) were selected based on experience gained during earlier missions. The drugs were intended to treat the contingency situations most likely to arise. As noted previously, crewmembers were tested for sensitivity to all drugs in the medical kit and substitutions were made when necessary.

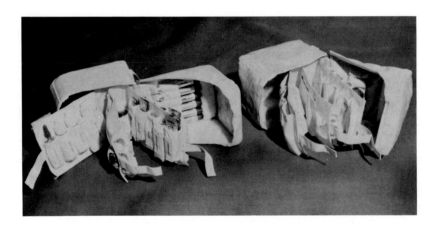

Figure 1. Typical Apollo medical kit.

Table 12 lists drugs and drug stowage and usage aboard the Apollo Command Module. The contents of the medical kits were changed as more effective medications were identified. For example, the combination scopolamine/Dexedrine was substituted after Apollo 11 for the previously stowed Marezine after ground-based tests indicated it was more effective for the treatment of motion sickness. Likewise, a short-acting barbiturate, Seconal, was added after reports of sleep difficulties by the Apollo 7 crew. The cardiac arrhythmias experienced during the Apollo 15 mission dictated the addition of Pronestyl, Lidocaine, atropine, and Demerol in missions subsequent to Apollo 15. Each Apollo vehicle also carried a medical accessory kit in a compartment behind the Lunar Module Pilot's couch. Its contents are listed in table 13. An abbreviated version of the Command

Table 12

Command Module Medical Kit

	Stowed/Used										
	7	8	9	10	11	12	13	14	15	16	17
Methylcellulose eye drops (1/4%)	2/1	2/2	2/0	2/0	2/0	2/0	2/0	2/0	1/0	2/10	1/0
Tetrahydrozoline HCl (Visine)	–	–	–	–	–	–	–	–	–	–	1/1
Compress - bandage	2/0	2/0	2/0	2/0	2/0	2/0	2/0	2/0	2/0	2/0	2/0
Bandaids	12/2	12/0	12/0	12/0	12/0	12/0	12/0	12/0	12/0	12/0	12/0
Antibiotic ointment	1/1	1/0	1/0	1/0	1/0	1/0	1/0	1/0	1/0	2/1	2/1
Skin cream	1/0	1/1	1/1	1/0	1/0	1/0	1/0	1/0	1/0	1/1	1/0
Demerol injectors (90 mg)	3/0	3/0	3/0	3/0	3/0	3/0	3/0	3/0	3/0	–	–
Marezine injectors	3/0	3/0	3/0	3/0	3/0	3/0	3/0	3/0	3/0	–	–
Marezine tablets (50 mg)	24/3	24/1	24/4	12/0	–	–	–	–	–	–	–
Dexedrine tablets (5 mg)	12/1	12/0	12/0	12/0	12/0	12/0	12/1	12/0	12/0	12/0	12/0
Darvon compound capsules (60 mg)	12/2	18/0	18/0	18/0	18/0	18/0	18/0	18/0	18/0	18/0	18/0
Actifed tablets (60 mg)	24/24	60/0	60/12	60/2	60/0	60/18	60/0	60/0	60/0	24/0	60/1
Lomotil tablets	24/8	24/3	24/1	24/13	24/2	24/0	24/1	24/0	24/0	24/0	48/5
Nasal emollient	1/0	2/1	2/1	1/0	1/0	1/0	1/0	1/0	1/0	1/0	1/0
Aspirin tablets (5 gr)	72/48	72/8	72/2	72/16	72/Unk	72/6	72/30	72/0	72/0	72/0	72/0
Tetracycline (250 mg)	24/0	24/0	24/0	15/0	–	–	–	–	–	60/0	60/0
Ampicillin	–	60/0	60/0	45/0	60/0	60/0	60/0	60/0	60/0	60/0	60/0
Seconal capsules (100 mg)	–	21/1	21/10	21/0	21/0	21/6	21/0	–	21/0	21/3	21/16
Seconal capsules (50 mg)	–	12/7	–	–	–	–	–	–	–	–	–
Nose drops (Afrin)	–	3/0	3/1	3/0	3/0	3/1	3/1	3/1	3/0	3/0	3/3
Benadryl (50 mg)	–	8/0	–	–	–	–	–	–	–	–	–
Tylenol (325 mg)	–	14/7	–	–	–	–	–	–	–	–	–
Bacitracin eye ointment	–	–	1/0	–	–	–	–	–	–	–	–
Scopolamine (.3 mg) - Dexedrine (5 mg) capsules	–	–	–	–	12/6	12/0	12/2	12/0	12/0	12/0	12/1
Mylicon tablets	–	–	–	–	40/0	40/0	40/0	40/0	40/0	40/0	40/0
Opthaine	–	–	–	–	–	–	1/0	1/0	1/0	1/0	1/0
Multi-Vitamins	–	–	–	–	–	–	–	20/0	–	–	–
Auxiliary Medications for Apollo 16 & 17											
Pronestyl	–	–	–	–	–	–	–	–	–	80/0	80/0
Lidocaine	–	–	–	–	–	–	–	–	–	12/0	12/0
Atropine	–	–	–	–	–	–	–	–	–	12/0	12/0
Demerol	–	–	–	–	–	–	–	–	–	6/0	6/0

Table 13

Apollo Medical Accessories Kit Contents

Item	Apollo Mission										
	7	8	9	10	11	12	13	14	15	16	17
Constant wear garment harness plug	—	—	—	—	—	—	—	—	3	3	3
ECG sponge packages	—	—	—	—	—	—	—	—	14	14	14
Electrode bag	1	1	1	1	1	1	1	1	1	1	1
Electrode attachment assembly	12	12	12	12	20	20	20	20	100	100	100
Micropore disc	12	12	12	12	20	20	20	20	50	50	50
Sternal harness	1	1	1	1	3	3	3	3	3	3	3
Axillary harness	1	1	1	1	1	1	1	1	1	1	1
Electrode paste	1	1	1	1	1	1	1	1	1	1	1
Oral thermometer	1	1	1	1	1	1	1	1	1	1	1
pH paper	1	1	1	1	1	1	1	1	1	None	None
Urine collection and transfer assembly roll-on cuffs	3	3	6	6	6	6	6	6	6	6	6

Module medical kit was carried in the Lunar Module (table 14). The adequacy of the kits was reviewed after each flight, and appropriate modifications were made for the next flight. The basic contents of the medical kits remained the same for each mission, but there was no "standard" kit.

Table 14

Lunar Module Medical Kit

Medical Package Assembly	Quantity
Rucksack	1
Stimulant pills (Dexedrine)	4
Pain pills (Darvon)	4
Decongestant pills (Actifed)	8
Diarrhea pills (Lomotil)	12
Aspirin	12
Bandaids	6
Compress bandages	2
Eye Drops (methylcellulose)	1
Antibiotic ointment (Neosporin)	1
Sleeping pills (Seconal)	6
Anesthetic eye drops	1
Nose drops (Afrin)	1
Urine collection and transfer assembly roll-on cuffs	6
Pronestyl	12
Injectable Drug Kit	**Quantity**
Injectable drug kit rucksack	1
Lidocaine (cardiac)	8
Atropine (cardiac)	4
Demerol (pain)	2

Pills and tablets in the medical kit were packaged in such a manner that the crewman had easy access to the medication at all times. The pills were sealed individually in cells in strips of 12 or 24 cells. Midway through the Apollo Program, the number of pills in the kit was increased. Pressure-related problems in medication packaging were resolved by puncturing each cell with a small pin; the hole made it possible for the air to vent when under reduced-pressure conditions.

The use of standard spray bottles in a weightless, reduced-pressure environment proved unsatisfactory. Sprays were therefore replaced by dropper bottles. However, the likelihood of overdosage from a dropper bottle and the need for more uniform distribution of decongestants than is possible with dropper bottles makes future development of a zero-gravity spray dispenser highly desirable.

General Adaptation

In general, Apollo astronauts adapted well to the world of zero gravity. It was, in many respects, a boon. Astronauts were able to move effortlessly about the spacecraft, and this enhanced the perceived volume of the vehicle.

The most frequently reported subjective sensation associated with initial orbital insertion was a feeling of fullness in the head. This sensation, reported by all but two crewmen, persisted for four hours to three days. Concomitantly, crewmen noticed a roundness of the face in one another and engorgement of the veins of the head and neck. One crewman reported that head fullness was similar to the feelings elicited by standing on one's head or hanging upside down.

Crews of the Apollo 7, 12, 14, and 15 missions reported some soreness of the back muscles. This condition was relieved by exercise and hyperextension of the back. No calibrated inflight exercise program was planned for any of the flights; however, an exercise device was provided. The crewmen typically used the exerciser several times a day for periods of 15 to 30 minutes when they were in the Command Module.

Insomnia was another frequent crew complaint. The principal reasons for insomnia were shifting the customary sleep time, altering circadian rhythm, and combating operational problems. When one considers the unfamiliar environment of space and the excitement this generated, as well as the onboard noise and other mission-related disturbances, it is not surprising that the astronauts in some cases failed to obtain sufficient restful sleep. Some crewmen found it was possible to obtain restful sleep with the aid of hypnotics.

The first American space crews to report any symptoms of motion sickness were the Apollo astronauts. The symptoms ranged from so-called "stomach awareness" to frank nausea and, in a few cases, vomiting. In most instances, the nausea appeared to be related to rapid body movement before adaptation to weightlessness occurred. Symptoms subsided or were absent when crewmen moved slowly during the initial period of weightlessness. Moreover, no recurrence of motion sickness symptoms was reported after this adaptation period was completed. Increased susceptibility to motion sickness is thought to be the result of the relatively enhanced effect of stimulation of the acceleration-detecting nerve ends in the semicircular canals that occurs during weightlessness. The otolith, the gravity-sensing component of the inner ear, is thought to bias the input of the semicircular canals to the brain center that controls vomiting. The removal of this bias in the weightless condition results in an alteration of the input to the brain from the semicircular canals. Then, in a susceptible individual, rapid head motions will result in motion sickness.

Adaptation of the inner ear to weightlessness, which occurs fairly rapidly in most individuals, can be hastened by appropriate head movements that produce a subthreshold stimulation of the semicircular canals. This technique was taught to all Apollo crewmen subsequent to the Apollo 9 mission. Although not all crewmen have used this technique to assist their adaptation to weightlessness, those crewmen who have used it have achieved fairly good results.

Considerable variation in susceptibility to motion sickness exists among individuals, and a prediction of individual susceptibility is not precise. A thorough understanding of the physiology of the inner ear is needed for better prediction and prevention of motion sickness.

Crew Illness and Medications

Table 15 lists medical problems experienced by Apollo crews in flight. The more important of these are discussed below.

Apollo 7. Three days prior to the Apollo 7 launch, the Commander and Lunar Module Pilot experienced slight nasal stuffiness and were successfully treated. They were medically certified fit for flight when launch day physical examinations of the crew failed to demonstrate any manifestations of illness.

Approximately 15 hours after lift-off, the crew reported that the Commander had developed a bad head cold. The flight surgeon recommended aspirin for symptomatic relief, and that one decongestant tablet (Actifed) be taken every eight hours until the Commander either felt better or had exhausted the onboard supplies. The Commander reported a normal temperature and no symptoms of sore throat, cough, or lung congestion. The Command Module Pilot and Lunar Module Pilot also experienced cold symptoms 24 hours later and the same treatment schedule was instituted.

The possibility of rupturing the eardrums during entry caused some concern because it was considered necessary for the crew to wear pressure suits during entry. With helmets on, the crewmen would not be able to perform the Valsalva maneuver and equalize pressure within the middle ear cavities. Forty-eight hours prior to entry, the crew made the decision not to wear helmets or gloves. The last nine decongestant tablets were taken during the last 24 hours of flight. The times for taking the tablets were selected so as to obtain the maximum benefit at the time of the deorbit maneuver and entry.

During entry, none of the crewmen had any difficulty in ventilating the middle ear and the Valsalva maneuver was not required. In the postflight physical examinations, the two crewmen who had experienced the most distressing inflight symptoms showed no residual evidence of their colds. The other crewman did exhibit a slight amount of fluid in the middle ear.

After the flight, the Commander stated that his cold symptoms began about one hour after lift-off (six hours after his prelaunch physical examination). In the zero-gravity environment, he reported, the drainage of nasal and sinus secretions ceases. The body's normal means of eliminating such secretions is lost because of the absence of gravity. There is no postnasal drip, and, because secretions do not reach the lower respiratory tract, they do not produce coughing. Forceful blowing is the only method available for purging nasal secretions, but blowing the nose is ineffective in removing mucoid material from the sinus cavities.

Apollo 8. After the Apollo 8 Commander's symptoms of motion sickness dissipated, he experienced additional symptoms of an inflight illness believed to be unrelated to the adaptation syndrome. When the Commander was unable to fall asleep two hours into his initial rest period, he took a sleeping tablet (Seconal) which induced approximately five hours of sleep, described as "fitful." Upon awakening, he felt nauseated and he had a moderate occipital headache. He took two aspirin tablets and then went from the sleep station to his couch to rest. The nausea, however, became progressively worse and he vomited twice. After termination of this first sleep period, the Commander also became aware of some increased gastrointestinal distress and was concerned that diarrhea might occur.

Table 15

Inflight Medical Problems in Apollo Crews

Symptom/Finding	Etiology	Number of Cases
Barotitis	Barotrauma	1
Cardiac arrhythmias	Undetermined, possibly linked with potassium deficit	2
Eye irritation	Spacecraft atmosphere	4
	Fiberglass	1
Dehydration (Apollo 13)	Reduced water intake during emergency	2
Flatulence	Undetermined	3
Genitourinary infection with prostatic congestion	Pseudomonas aeruginosa	1
Headache	Spacecraft environment	1
Head cold	Undetermined	3
Nasal stuffiness	Zero gravity	2
Pharyngitis	Undetermined	1
Rhinitis	Oxygen, low relative humidity	2
Respiratory irritation	Fiberglass	1
Rash, facial, recurrent inguinal	Contact dermatitis	1
	Prolonged wearing of urine collection device (Apollo 13)	1
Skin irritation	Biosensor sites	11
	Fiberglass	2
	Undetermined	1
Seborrhea	Activated by spacecraft environment	2
Shoulder strain	Lunar core drilling	1
Subungual hemorrhages	Glove fit	5
Stomach awareness	Labyrinthine	6
Nausea, vomiting	Labyrinthine	1
	Undetermined (possibly virus-related)	1
Stomatitis	Aphthous ulcers	1
Excoriation, urethral meatus (Apollo 13)	Prolonged wearing of urine collection device	2
Urinary tract infection	Undetermined	1
Dysbarism (bends) *		1

* Also occurred during Gemini 10; later incidences were reported by the same crewman five years after his Apollo 11 mission.

As the mission progressed, the flight surgeon had the impression that the Commander was experiencing an acute viral gastroenteritis. This tentative diagnosis was based upon the delayed transmission of a recorded voice report that the Commander had a headache, a sore throat, loose bowels, and had vomited twice. A conversation between the Senior Flight Surgeon and the Commander verified that the previous report was correct, but that the Commander was feeling much better. The Commander also stated that he had not taken any medication for his illness, which he described as a "24-hour intestinal flu." (Just prior to the Apollo 8 launch, an epidemic of acute viral gastroenteritis lasting 24 hours was present in the Cape Canaveral area.)

The Commander's temperature was $309^\circ K$ ($97.5^\circ F$) on two occasions subsequent to his nausea and vomiting. The Commander was advised to take one Lomotil tablet and to use Marezine if the nausea returned. Complete remission of the illness, however, made the use of further medications unnecessary.

Apollo 9. Three days before the scheduled Apollo 9 launch, the Commander reported symptoms of general malaise, nasal discharge, and stuffiness. These common cold symptoms were not present at the physical examination performed on the previous day. The Commander was treated symptomatically and his temperature remained normal throughout the course of the illness. Two days before the scheduled launch, the Command Module Pilot and the Lunar Module Pilot also became ill with common colds and were treated symptomatically. However, because the symptoms persisted, the launch was postponed for three days. The crew responded rapidly to rest and therapy and were certified fit for flight the day prior to the rescheduled launch.

The Lunar Module Pilot experienced motion sickness and vomited twice, once while preparing for transfer to the Lunar Module, and again after transfer. After about 50 hours of flight, he was still not feeling well but had experienced no further vomiting. He reported that his motion sickness symptoms subsided when he remained still. He was advised to take a Marezine tablet one hour before donning his pressure suit for extravehicular operations that were to be conducted at approximately 73 hours. The nominal plan called for the Lunar Module Pilot to spend two hours and 15 minutes outside the spacecraft, but, because of his symptoms, the plan was revised so that only the tasks having the highest priority were to be performed. The principal objectives were successfully accomplished in approximately 45 minutes. The Lunar Module Pilot took Seconal several times during the mission to induce sleep.

Apollo 10. All three crewmen experienced irritation of the skin, eyes, and upper respiratory passages when the fiberglass insulation in the Command Module tunnel became loosened and particles of fiberglass became suspended in the cabin air. This was treated symptomatically with good results. This crew complained of abdominal rumblings caused by the ingestion of hydrogen gas present in the potable water. Since they were concerned that diarrhea might develop, they decided on their own initiative to take Lomotil tablets. Medically, the use of the drug was not indicated.

Lomotil decreases the activity of the lower intestinal tract and reduces the amount of gas that can be expelled. Aspirin was taken occasionally by all crewmen.

Apollo 11. The Apollo 11 Commander and Lunar Module Pilot each took one Lomotil tablet to retard bowel movements before Lunar Module operations. They each carried extra Lomotil tablets into the Lunar Module but did not use them. Four hours before entry, and again after splashdown, the three crewmen each took scopolamine/dextroamphetamine (antimotion sickness) tablets. Aspirin tablets were also taken, but the number of tablets per individual was not recorded. The Lunar Module Pilot recalled that he had taken two aspirin tablets almost every night to aid his sleep. One interesting medical event that occurred on this flight was reported by the Command Module Pilot in his account of the Apollo Program.[*] He revealed that he had experienced dysbarism (bends) on his first space flight (Gemini 10) as well as on his second (Apollo 11). He described symptoms involving the left knee as a sharp, throbbing ache which gradually worsened and leveled off at a moderate, but very uncomfortable level of pain. The symptomatology was less painful on Apollo 11 than it had been on Gemini 10. Unfortunately this information was not made available to the medical team during either the Gemini or Apollo Programs.

Apollo 12. The Commander developed a mild contact dermatitis from the biosensor electrolyte paste. An analysis performed postflight on the batch of paste applied to the affected skin areas during the mission failed to identify any constituent not present in nonoffending batches of the electrolyte paste. To avoid similar occurrences, subsequent Apollo crewmen were tested with all materials of known allergenic potential, as has always been done with medical kit drugs. As a further precaution, the identical materials to be used in flight were used in training to provide for scrupulous observation and reporting of any skin reactions.

All three crewmen used Actifed decongestant tablets to relieve nasal congestion at various times throughout the flight. The Lunar Module Pilot also took Seconal throughout most of the mission to aid sleep. Aspirin was taken occasionally by all the crewmen. No motion sickness medications were taken prior to entry.

Apollo 13. The Lunar Module Pilot awoke on the second day of the mission with a moderately severe headache. He took two aspirin tablets with only fair results. After eating breakfast and engaging in physical activity, he became nauseated and vomited. His symptoms began to subside over the next 12 hours as adaptation to weightlessness took place. All crewmen took scopolamine/dextroamphetamine antimotion sickness medication prior to entry.

A urinary tract infection in one of the crewmen could have resulted in a serious inflight illness if the mission had lasted 24 hours longer. During the return flight following the inflight accident, the combined stresses of cold, dehydration (caused by voluntary rationing of water), and prolonged wearing of the urine collecting device (UCD) were

---

[*]Collins, Michael: Carrying the Fire: An Astronaut's Journeys. Farrar, Straus and Giroux (New York), 1974.

contributing factors. The other two crewmen had less serious problems, but the UCD was not designed for prolonged wearing.

Apollo 14. No medications were used during the Apollo 14 mission other than nose drops to relieve nasal stuffiness caused by the spacecraft atmosphere. On the third day of flight, the Commander and the Lunar Module Pilot used one drop in each nostril. Relief was prompt and lasted approximately 12 hours. The Command Module Pilot used the nose drops three hours prior to entry.

Apollo 15. The Commander developed a dermatitis from the deerskin lining of a communication carrier. This sensitivity was not recognized before the mission because a concomitant skin disorder (seborrhic dermatitis) existed.

Aspirin and nose drops were the only medications used during Apollo 15. The Commander took a total of 14 aspirin tablets over a period of days to relieve pain in his right shoulder that developed after difficult deep core-tube drilling on the lunar surface. The Command Module Pilot used nose drops just prior to Earth entry to prevent possible middle ear blockage.

Apollo 16. The Lunar Module Pilot used three Seconal capsules for sleep induction during the Apollo 16 mission. One capsule was taken on the night prior to lunar descent and the other two capsules were used for the first and second lunar surface sleep periods, respectively. In the postflight medical debriefing, the Lunar Module Pilot reported that the Seconal was effective in producing a rapid onset of good sleep.

Apollo 17. More medications were taken on Apollo 17 than on any of the previous missions. The intermittent use of Seconal for sleep by all three crewmen and the daily use of simethicone for symptomatic relief of flatulence by the Commander were the principal factors contributing to the high intake of medications. The Commander also took a scopolamine/dextroamphetamine capsule on the second day of flight for "stomach awareness."

The Command Module Pilot and the Lunar Module Pilot experienced one loose bowel movement each, on the eleventh and twelfth days of flight, respectively. In each case, Lomotil was taken and was effective.

Cardiac Arrhythmias

Apollo 15 was the first manned space flight in which cardiac irregularities other than occasional benign premature ventricular contractions were observed. A historical account precedes discussion of possible etiology and mechanisms.

An isolated premature ventricular contraction was observed on the Lunar Module Pilot 41 minutes prior to launch. Subsequently, while the Lunar Module Pilot was being monitored during the translunar coast phase of the mission, only infrequent premature ventricular contractions (approximate rate one to two per hour) were observed. These events were not considered significant since the Lunar Module Pilot had demonstrated occasional premature ventricular contractions during all of his ground-based altitude chamber tests and training sessions. The frequency of the Lunar Module Pilot's premature ventricular contractions remained constant at the same rate throughout the three periods of extravehicular activity, Lunar Module ascent, and docking.

Shortly after docking with the Command Module at 178 hours ground elapsed time (GET), the Lunar Module Pilot experienced five ventricular prematurities in a 30-second period. Approximately one hour later at 179:07 GET, while the crewmen were observing the Lunar Module tunnel leak rate in their couches, the Lunar Module Pilot suddenly converted from normal sinus rhythm to a nodal bigeminal rhythm. During the 14 seconds in which the abnormal rhythm persisted, a total of eleven coupled beats were observed. The Lunar Module Pilot's heart rate preceding and during the arrhythmia was approximately 95 beats per minute. One and one-half minutes prior to onset of the bigeminal rhythm, his heart rate had peaked at 120 beats per minute for a 20-second period. Following this bigeminal episode, the Lunar Module Pilot experienced approximately ten additional premature atrial contractions during the time he was monitored over the next 60 hours of the mission. The last atrial prematurity in the Lunar Module Pilot was observed at 240:24 hours GET. The Lunar Module Pilot's premature ventricular contractions, however, persisted at the previously cited rate of one to two per hour.

The Commander was completely eurhythmic until 286:22 hours GET, when he suddenly began to experience occasional supraventricular prematurities. The first of these occurred while the Commander was sound asleep and continued through the first hour after awakening. The Commander's heart rate at the time of onset was approximately 30 beats per minute. Approximately 30 aberrant beats occurred during a one and one-half hour period. No further prematurities were observed on the Commander after 288 hours GET.

Throughout the entire mission, no ectopic heart beats or arrhythmias were observed on the Command Module Pilot.

When questioned during the postflight medical debriefing, the Lunar Module Pilot recollected experiencing the sensation of extreme fatigue during the time when the bigeminal rhythm was noted. In fact, he required a short period of rest before he was able to carry on his assigned duties. Furthermore, the Lunar Module Pilot stated that he was puzzled about this feeling of extreme fatigue which he experienced and considered inappropriate; however, he did not express his concern to the flight surgeon in the Mission Control Center during the flight. Throughout the flight, the Lunar Module Pilot did not experience any symptoms referable to his heart, such as palpitations, sternal pressure or pain, and he was completely unaware that an arrhythmia had occurred.

The Commander also was unaware he had experienced ectopic heart beats during the last day of the mission and was unable to recall experiencing any cardiac symptoms inflight.

The etiology of episodic cardiac arrhythmias recorded on the two Lunar Module crewmen during this mission is unclear; however, a number of possible factors, acting independently or in concert, are considered to have predisposed the myocardium to ectopic behavior. Of principal interest is the magnitude of the total body potassium deficit and hypokalemia measured postflight. Whether the potassium concentrations recorded in the immediate postmission examination represented the true state of potassium balance at the time of the episodes of arrhythmias inflight cannot be determined. However, salt-wasting mechanisms predictably would have been at their peak during that period of the flight, thereby suggesting a total body potassium deficit considerably greater than that registered postflight.

While salt-wasting compensatory mechanisms operate to reestablish fluid and osmotic equilibrium in the adapted crewman, several other factors probably were operative which could upset this balance and lead to transient states of decompensation. For example, heavy workloads and the attendant heat stress could easily exacerbate the electrolyte deficit experienced by the lunar surface crewmen. Emotional stress, altered work/rest cycles, and fatigue are known to increase adrenal medullary activity and liberate large quantities of epinephrine which further aggravate the salt loss. Commensurate with the catecholamine-potentiated electrolyte loss, the resultant high epinephrine blood levels would exert a positive inotropic effect on the myocardium. Furthermore, these decompensating factors probably occurred in the presence of a marginal dietary intake of mineral which resulted in a clinical deficit of total body electrolyte.

Therefore, frank, yet transient periods of hypokalemia were considered to be of prime importance in the genesis of the observed arrhythmias. These postulates were further substantiated by the greater postflight deficits in total body and serum potassium recorded in the lunar surface crewmen and by the absence of cardiac irritability in the Command Module Pilot.

Accordingly, it is speculated that the adaptive processes alone resulted in sufficient salt loss (principally potassium) to have predisposed the crew to cardiac irritability, and that the additional stress characteristic of lunar surface operations was sufficient to enhance the electrolyte deficit and precipitate abnormal cardiac activity.

In order to prevent potassium deficits and to reduce the likelihood of inflight arrhythmias, both Apollo 16 and 17 crews were provided a high potassium diet commencing 72 hours prior to launch and continuing until 72 hours after recovery. As a precaution, antiarrhythmic medications were included in the Apollo 16 medical kit for the first time. As an added precaution, daily, high-resolution electrocardiograms were obtained for each crewman and an accurate metabolic input/output report was maintained during flight.

No medically significant arrhythmias occurred during either flight. The postflight exchangeable body potassium intake measurements indicated that a normal potassium balance had been maintained. The absence of arrhythmias in these last Apollo crews may be attributed in part to high dietary potassium intakes, but perhaps the fact that the Apollo 16 and 17 crews maintained a better fluid and electrolyte balance, obtained more adequate sleep, and experienced a lower level of fatigue is of equal or greater significance.

It must be noted that one of the Apollo 15 crewmembers who experienced a cardiac arrhythmia had undetected coronary artery disease at the time of the mission. Approximately two years after space flight, this particular astronaut suffered an acute myocardial infarction from which he completely recovered. The undetected coronary artery disease almost certainly interacted negatively with potassium deficiency and fatigue to precipitate the inflight bigeminal arrhythmia experienced by this astronaut.

Antihypotensive Garment Testing

While Apollo missions indicated no need for an antihypotensive garment during reentry into Earth's gravity or in the immediate postflight period, the effects of these garments were tested on the Apollo 16 and 17 missions in preparation for the long-term Skylab flights. The Apollo 16 Command Module Pilot and control subjects were fitted with waist-length leotards designed to produce gradient positive pressure along the lower half of the body. The Apollo 17 Command Module Pilot wore a lower body garment using the capstan principle to apply a gradient pressure to the lower limbs. Both garments appeared to furnish some protection against orthostatic hypotension following weightless flight. The capstan-type garment, however, proved to be considerably easier to don in flight. Section 3, Chapter 4 presents details of the antihypotensive garment experiment.

Postflight Procedures and Findings

Comprehensive medical examinations similar to the preflight F-5 exam were conducted immediately after recovery of the astronauts to document the physiological changes resulting from space flight and to detect and treat any medical problems. These medical evaluations included physical examinations, microbiology and blood studies, orthostatic tolerance tests, exercise response tests, urinalysis, and chest X-rays. Postflight testing was modified in those missions requiring postflight quarantine because of limited space in the Mobile Quarantine Facility.

Although all crewmen were in good health, they exhibited varying degrees of fatigue and weight loss. Functional tests consistently showed evidence of cardiovascular deconditioning.

Physical Examinations

The postflight physical examination involved obtaining a careful inflight history and a complete review of body systems. Laboratory studies included the following:

1. Urine culture and sensitivity
2. Complete blood count
3. Urinalysis
4. Serum electrolytes

Characterization of viral and mycoplasma flora was initiated with Apollo 14. State-of-the-art procedures were utilized. These included challenging tissue cultures, embryonated eggs, suckling mice, and mycoplasma media with specimens obtained at various times in preflight and postflight periods.

The detailed results of microbiological studies are presented in Section II, Chapter 2. In summary, considerable variation in the microfloral response was observed. *Staphylococcus aureus* increased in number in some crewmen and transfers were effected between crewmen. The variables of host susceptibility, external environmental factors, and ecological relationships between competing species of microorganisms were undoubtedly responsible for these findings. In one mission, an increase in the number and spread of *Aspergillus fumigatus* and beta hemolytic streptococci were found. Microbial analysis of samples obtained in the Command Module showed a loss of organisms during the course of the mission. Intracrew transfer of microbes appeared to be a regular occurrence. Finally, there was a buildup of medically important species, particularly *Proteus mirabilis* on the urine collection device. Contamination of the urine collection devices with this organism represented a significant medical hazard.

Clinical Findings

Weight loss was a consistent postflight finding for all crewmen except the Apollo 14 Commander and Lunar Module Pilot. These weight losses are shown in table 16. The major portion of these weight changes was attributed to loss of total body water; the remainder, to tissue mass loss.

Table 17 presents postflight medical findings and the following chronological list provides details concerning these findings.

Apollo 7. The residual effects of an inflight upper respiratory infection was definitely present in one of the Apollo 7 crewmembers at recovery.

Apollo 8. Six days after recovery, the Lunar Module Pilot developed a mild pharyngitis which evolved into a common cold and nonproductive cough. He recovered completely after six days of symptomatic therapy. The Commander developed a cold twelve days after the flight.

Apollo 9. The Commander suffered from bilateral barotitis media. This condition responded rapidly to decongestant therapy and cleared after two days. Four days after recovery, the Apollo 9 Lunar Module Pilot developed an upper respiratory infection with a secondary bacterial bronchitis. He was treated with penicillin and was well seven days later. The Commander developed a mild upper respiratory syndrome eight days after recovery. He was treated symptomatically and recovered four days later. The etiology of both of these cases was determined to be type-B influenza virus.

Apollo 10. The Commander and Lunar Module Pilot had mild rashes on their forearms which were caused either by exposure to the Fiberglas insulation or to the Beta cloth in their flight suits. Four days after recovery, the Lunar Module Pilot developed a mild infection in his left nasal passage which was probably caused by a small piece of Fiberglas to which the crew was exposed in flight. This responded rapidly to symptomatic therapy.

Apollo 11. The Commander had a mild barotitis media of the right ear; however, since he was able to clear the middle ear satisfactorily, no specific treatment was necessary.

Apollo 12. On initial examination, the Lunar Module Pilot had a small amount of clear fluid with air bubbles in the middle ear bilaterally. This disappeared after 24 hours of decongestant therapy. He also sustained a laceration over the right eye when a camera

Table 16

Apollo Astronaut Body Weights (kg)

Flight	Crewman	F-30 Days	F-15 Days	F-5 Days	Mean	± SD	F-0 Days	R+0 Hr	R+24 Hr	R+48 Hr	R+72 Hr
7	Schirra	87.1	88.0	88.2	87.8	0.59	88.0	86.1	86.4	—	—
	Eisele	69.4	69.4	69.8	69.5	0.23	71.2	66.7	68.3	—	—
	Cunningham	69.4	71.8	70.8	70.7	1.21	70.8	67.8	69.6	—	—
8	Borman	76.2	76.4	77.1	76.6	0.47	76.6	72.8	74.0	75.1	—
	Lovell	76.4	77.6	76.4	76.8	0.69	78.0	74.4	74.7	75.2	—
	Anders	66.0	67.1	66.0	66.4	0.64	64.4	62.6	62.8	—	—
9	McDivitt	73.5	72.8	72.8	73.0	0.40	72.1	69.6	70.9	71.7	—
	Scott	82.8	82.5	80.7	82.0	1.14	80.7	78.2	82.1	81.2	—
	Schweickart	74.7	74.5	73.7	74.3	0.51	71.2	69.4	71.3	72.3	—
10	Stafford	80.1	79.4	78.9	79.6	0.60	77.6	76.4	77.4	—	—
	Young	76.6	77.1	76.6	76.8	0.29	74.8	72.3	73.1	—	—
	Cernan	79.4	79.5	79.4	79.4	0.06	78.5	73.9	74.6	—	—
11	Armstrong	78.0	78.2	79.1	78.4	0.59	78.0	74.4	77.1	—	—
	Collins	74.4	75.3	77.1	75.6	1.37	75.3	72.1	72.1	—	—
	Aldrin	77.6	78.9	77.9	78.1	0.68	75.7	75.3	77.1	—	—
12	Conrad	66.2	—	66.9	66.6	0.49	67.7	65.8	66.7	66.7	—
	Gordon	71.0	70.3	—	70.7	0.49	70.4	67.1	68.9	68.9	—
	Bean	69.4	—	70.3	69.9	0.64	69.1	63.5	64.9	64.4	—
13	Lovell	79.8	77.8	78.5	78.7	1.01	80.5	74.2	—	—	—
	Swigert	89.1	—	89.7	89.4	0.42	89.3	84.4	—	—	—
	Haise	71.0	70.3	71.2	70.8	0.47	70.8	67.8	—	—	—

Table 16 (Continued)
Apollo Astronauts Body Weights (kg)

Flight	Crewman	F-30 Days	F-15 Days	F-5 Days	Mean	± SD	F-0 Days	R+0 Hr	R+24 Hr	R+48 Hr	R+72 Hr
14	Shepard	78.0	78.5	78.7	78.4	0.36	76.2	76.6	77.1	—	—
	Roosa	74.2	76.2	75.5	75.3	1.01	74.8	69.4	72.6	—	—
	Mitchell	83.5	83.1	83.2	83.2	0.21	79.8	80.3	80.7	—	—
15	Scott	80.5	81.2	81.5	81.1	0.51	80.2	78.9	—	81.0	80.7
	Worden	73.7	73.2	74.0	73.6	0.40	73.5	72.1	—	72.6	72.3
	Irwin	74.3	73.9	74.8	74.3	0.45	73.2	70.8	—	73.7	73.1
16	Young	80.8	80.5	78.9	80.1	1.02	78.9	75.5	76.6	—	76.4
	Mattingly	63.2	61.9	62.6	62.6	0.65	61.5	58.5	59.9	—	60.3
	Duke	73.1	73.8	72.6	73.2	0.60	73.0	70.5	71.7	—	71.3
17	Cernan	81.0	80.3	80.7	80.7	0.35	80.3	76.1	76.0	78.0	—
	Evans	78.2	76.6	77.0	77.3	0.83	75.7	74.6	73.9	73.9	—
	Schmitt	76.0	76.6	75.3	76.0	0.65	74.8	72.9	71.8	73.4	—
Apollo Crew Mean		75.90	75.09	76.12	75.96		75.26	72.45	73.05	73.44	72.35
Standard Deviation		5.849	5.213	5.786	5.792		5.727	5.866	5.763	4.781	6.826

Additional Postflight Weights

Apollo 15	R+121	R+137	R+210	R+311 hr
Scott	80.8			
Worden	72.5			
Irwin		73.7	75.0	73.0

Apollo 16	R+162 hr
Young	75.5
Mattingly	61.2
Duke	71.9

Apollo 17	R+90 hr
Cernan	78.5
Evans	75.8
Schmitt	72.8

F-0 Days = Launch Day

broke loose from the impact of landing and struck him. The cut was sutured onboard the recovery ship and healed normally. On the day after recovery, the Commander developed an acute left maxillary sinusitis which was treated successfully with decongestants and antibiotics.

Apollo 13. Postflight, all three crewmen showed extreme fatigue resulting from the severe environmental stresses imposed by their crippled spacecraft. The Lunar Module Pilot suffered an acute pseudomonas urinary tract infection which required two weeks of antibiotic therapy to resolve.

Table 17

Postflight Medical Findings in Apollo Mission Crews

Diagnosis	Etiology	Number of Cases
Barotitis media	Eustachian tube blockage	7
Folliculitis, right anterior chest	Bacterial	1
Gastroenteritis	Bacterial	1
Herpetic lesion, lip	Herpes virus	1
Influenza syndrome	Influenza B virus	1
	Undetermined	1
	Influenza A_2 virus	1
Laceration of the forehead	Trauma	1
Rhinorrhea, mild	Fiberglass particle	1
Papular lesions, parasacral	Bacterial	1
Prostatitis	Undetermined	2
Pulpitis, tooth No. 7		1
Pustules, eyelids		1
Rhinitis	Viral	3
Acute maxillary sinusitis	Bacterial	1
Ligamentous strain, right shoulder		1
Urinary tract infection	Pseudomonas	1
Vestibular dysfunction, mild		1
Rhinitis and pharyngitis	Influenza B virus	1
	Beta-streptococcus (not group A)	1
Rhinitis & secondary bronchitis	Influenza B virus	1
Contact dermatitis	Fiberglas	1
	Beta cloth	1
	Micropore tape	6
Subungual hemorrhages, finger nails	Trauma	3
Total		41

Apollo 14. The Commander and Command Module Pilot each exhibited a small amount of clear, bubbly fluid in the left middle ear cavity with slight reddening of the tympanic membrane. These findings disappeared in 24 hours without treatment. The Lunar Module Pilot had moderate eyelid irritation in addition to slight redness of the tympanic membranes. All crewmen showed a mild transient irritation from the micropore tape covering their biomedical sensors (figure 2).

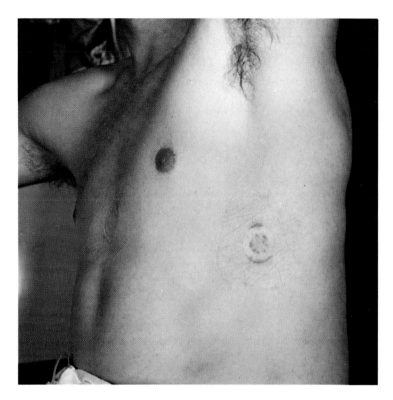

Figure 2. Example of skin irritation caused by
the micropore tape covering the biomedical sensors.

Apollo 15. The Commander had subungual hemorrhages of both hands and a painful right shoulder. These hemorrhages were caused by an insufficient arm length of the pressure suit forcing the fingertips too far into the gloves during pressurized suit operation. The Commander purposely had the arm length of his pressure suit shortened preflight to permit better tactile sensation and manual dexterity during mission EVA operations. Pain in the Commander's right shoulder was due to a muscle/ligament strain which responsed rapidly to heat therapy.

Apollo 16. All three crewmen suffered varying degrees of skin irritation at the biosensor sites. This skin irritation resulted principally from the crew's desire to wear the biosensor harnesses continuously in order to save the 15 to 20 minutes required to apply these bioharnesses. The irritation subsided in 48 hours without medical treatment. The Commander had some sinus congestion which responded to medication, and also a slight reddening and retraction of the right tympanic membrane.

Apollo 17. The two lunar surface crewmen developed subungual hematomas of both hands because of insufficient arm length of their pressure suits as in Apollo 15. The Commander also had a herpetic lesion on the right side of the upper lip, which was approximately 72 hours old at the time of recovery.

Postflight Visual Findings

Although numerous trends were noted, statistically significant changes between pre- and postflight testing were found only in the superior, superior-nasal, and temporal visual fields, each of which were constricted postflight. Only one other parameter approached significance: the unaided seven-meter (20-ft) visual acuity, which also was decreased postflight. Etiology of these changes is unknown at this time.

An additional point of interest is the result of a longitudinal study of changes in intraocular tension for Apollo astronauts and astronauts participating in the Mercury and Gemini missions. In the immediate postflight period, and for a short time thereafter, a statistically significant decrease in intraocular tension was found in all astronauts, when compared with their preflight tension. The postflight intraocular tension reverted to its preflight value at a much slower rate than expected. The reason for this slow return is unknown.

After Apollo 11, all crewmen except one observed bright flashes of light while in orbit. Retinal photography was considered to determine whether the high energy particles believed to be responsible for the phenomenon produced retinal lesions.

Photographs were first made of the Apollo 15 crew. Preflight photographs were taken as part of the F-30 physical examination, and postflight photographs were made three days after splashdown. Although no lesions were noted in the eye grounds, some decrease was observed in the size of the retinal vessels. No statistical comparison could be conducted, however, due to the low resolution of the film used.

Retinal photography was again conducted on the Apollo 16 crewmen using high resolution film. Comparison of the pre- and postflight films of this crew showed no change for the Lunar Module Pilot in the size of either retinal veins or arteries at approximately three hours postflight. The Command Module Pilot exhibited a significant decrease in the size of both the veins and arteries about three and one-half hours after flight, and the Commander showed a decrease in only the veins after four hours. The degree of constriction of retinal vasculature in this crew was greater and persisted for a longer time than could be accounted for by the vasoconstrictive effect of atmospheric oxygen alone. The reason for this finding in the crew of Apollo 16 is unknown.

Retinal photographs were not taken after the Apollo 17 flight because no lesions had been found on previous missions.

Special Studies

The results of the special studies conducted in the pre- and postflight periods are detailed in Section III of this text. Only a brief summary of the significant findings in the postflight examination are presented here.

The cardiovascular system showed the most significant and consistent changes in the Apollo crews. Resting and stressed heart rates were elevated in most all crewmen when compared to their preflight baseline tests. Blood pressures were labile; and the heart size as measured by the cardiothoracic ratio was decreased by 1.02 (approximately five percent). All crewmen demonstrated some degree of cardiovascular deconditioning during the lower body negative pressure tests in the immediate postflight period as compared to preflight measurements. They likewise showed a poorer work response on the bicycle ergometer. In both instances, the time required for return to preflight baselines was usually three days, but ranged from two days to one week. The Apollo 15 Commander and Lunar Module Pilot demonstrated a different response to exercise on the bicycle ergometer than observed in previous or subsequent flight crews. Their response at low heart rate levels of work was comparable to their preflight baseline tests; but at the higher heart rate levels of work on the ergometer, they showed the typical degraded work performance capability.

Summary and Conclusions

In summary, the twenty-nine Apollo astronauts accumulated 7506 hours of space flight experience without encountering any major medical problems. Perhaps the most significant postflight medical finding of Apollo was the absence of any pathology attributable to space flight exposure. Those physiological changes which did occur were all reversible within a two- to three-day period, with the exception of the Apollo 15 crew which required two weeks for complete return to preflight baselines. The most important physiological changes observed were cardiovascular deconditioning, reduction of red blood cell mass, and musculoskeletal deterioration. Since all medical objectives of the Apollo Program were successfully achieved, a sound medical basis existed for committing man to the prolonged space flight exposure of Skylab.

CHAPTER 2
MICROBIOLOGICAL INVESTIGATIONS

by

James K. Ferguson, Ph.D.
Gerald R. Taylor, Ph.D.
Bernard J. Mieszkuc

Lyndon B. Johnson Space Center

Introduction

The crew microbiology program was initiated in response to requirements made by the Interagency Committee on Back-Contamination[*] in recognition of the possibility of returning terrestrial contaminants in the lunar soil. In order to characterize contaminants as terrestrial, and not extraterrestrial, a catalog of the crew microflora was prepared prior to each Apollo mission. Since crewmen were the prime source for lunar soil contamination, this catalog provided an invaluable method to assist in establishing the terrestrial origin of a recovered contaminant.

Analysis of crew specimens was performed to satisfy three objectives in addition to lunar contaminant evaluation. The primary objective was to detect potentially pathogenic microorganisms so that associated medical problems could be identified early and preventive measures established. A second objective was to identify medically important microorganisms recovered from ill crewmen to aid in diagnosis and treatment. The third objective was to collect microbiological data that would aid in elucidating the response of the crew microbial autoflora to the space flight environment and in evaluating the resultant effect on the crewmember.

Microbiological sampling of selected sites in the Command Module (CM) was initiated in support of the quarantine program. These samples were also important from a medical standpoint because crewmen would be exposed to microorganisms in the closed spacecraft environment during space flight.

During lunar quarantine missions (Apollo 11 through 14), microbial screening was accomplished for all support personnel to be isolated with the returning crewmen.

---

[*]The Interagency Committee on Back-Contamination included members from the National Academy of Sciences and representatives from the U.S. Public Health Service, U.S. Department of Agriculture, and U.S. Department of Interior. See Section V, Chapter 1, *The Lunar Quarantine Program* for more detail.

Diagnostic microbiology was provided for all astronauts, their wives, and families; for personnel in the lunar (sample) processing area, and for personnel in the quarantine area. Microbiological support was also provided for the biological test systems used to screen the lunar materials for life forms and for maintenance of sterile Class III biological glove box systems.

Virology support for the Apollo Program consisted of characterization of the viral and mycoplasma flora of the crewmembers; performance of viral serology for crewmembers, crew contacts, and key mission personnel; and analysis of specimens obtained as a result of crew illnesses and from the conduct of the mission personnel surveillance program and the Flight Crew Health Stabilization Program. These programs were designed to ascertain the nature of illnesses in personnel who were either in contact with the crew or worked with lunar soil behind the biologic barrier. Serology studies were initiated with the Apollo 14 mission. The mission personnel surveillance program was in effect during the Apollo 11, 12, 13, and 14 missions, and the Flight Crew Health Stabilization Program was in effect during the Apollo 14, 15, 16, and 17 missions.

Procedures

Crew Microbiology

Each flight crewman and backup crewman assigned to Apollo missions 7 to 12, was sampled at four different time periods to provide the data needed to develop a catalog of microorganisms: 30 and 14 days before flight (F − 30 and F − 14, respectively), immediately before the flight (F − 0), and immediately upon recovery (R + 0). For the Apollo 13 to 17 missions, sampling times were varied according to mission constraints. Generally, an additional postflight sampling period was added at approximately two weeks following recovery.

Eleven samples were obtained from each crewmember on the morning of each preflight sampling date before initiation of personal hygiene activities, eating, or urination. Postflight samples were collected on board the recovery vessel immediately upon recovery and before other medical tests were performed. All specimens were analyzed by the microbiology laboratories at the NASA Lyndon B. Johnson Space Center. The body surface sites generally sampled were as follows.

1. A 13-cm^2 area of the scalp below the hairline at the base of the neck.

2. The auditory canals. (Two revolutions were made with each swab in each ear canal.)

3. The internal area of the umbilicus and a surrounding 13-cm^2 area. (Two revolutions were made with each swab.)

4. A 6.5-cm^2 area below the hairline of each axilla.

5. An area from front to rear of the left and right side of the groin.

6. An area between the first and large toe of each foot.

7. A 6.5-cm^2 area on each palm.

Both nostrils of each crewmember were sampled by making two revolutions with each swab in each nasal canal.

Each body surface site and the nasal passages were sampled separately with two sterile calcium alginate swabs moistened with a phosphate buffer. One swab from each sample area was placed in a screwcap tube containing 10.0 ml of sterile trypticase soy broth (TSB) for aerobic analysis. The second swab was placed in a tube of sterile veal infusion broth (VIB) for anaerobic analysis.

Each crewmember gargled with 60 ml of sterile phosphate buffer. The gargle was rinsed three times through the oral cavity to obtain a combination throat-mouth sample. The wash was then emptied into a sterile, widemouthed bottle.

A first-void, midstream urine specimen and a fecal specimen from each subject were collected in separate sterile containers on the morning of preflight sampling. Postflight specimens were collected as available.

The body surface samples, the nasal samples, the throat-mouth gargle, the urine, and the feces were maintained at $277^{o}K$ ($4^{o}C$) during transport to the laboratory. Approximately 12 hours elapsed between sampling and initial culture.

One-milliliter aliquots of the throat-mouth gargle and the urine were transferred to 9.0 ml each of TSB and VIB. Portions of fecal material weighing 0.1 gm each were transferred to TSB, VIB, and tetrathionate broth. In addition, a 0.1-gm portion of fecal material was heatshocked for five minutes at $353^{o}K$ ($80^{o}C$).

Dilution series from each TSB and VIB sample tube were prepared by aseptically transferring 1.0 ml aliquots to 9.0 ml of TSB or VIB. Body and nasal samples were diluted to 1 x 10^{4}; throat-mouth gargle samples, to 1 x 10^{5}; urine samples, to 1 x 10^{2}; and feces samples to 1 x 10^{10}. All tubes were maintained at $277^{o}K$ ($4^{o}C$) during the diluting process.

Aliquots of 0.1 ml from the initial sample tube and from the TSB and the VIB dilution series were transferred to agar media for quantitation and isolation of aerobic and anaerobic species (figures 1 and 2). Individual sterile glass rods were used to spread inoculum over the agar surface. Aerobic media were incubated for 48 hours at $308^{o}K$ ($35^{o}C$). Anaerobic media were incubated for 96 hours at $308^{o}K$ ($35^{o}C$) using an anaerobic Gas Pak (BBL, Division of Bio-Quest, Cockeysville, Md.) for generation of hydrogen gas. Colony counts were performed on the aerobic and anaerobic quantitation media. After 4.0 ml aliquots were transferred from each TSB sample tube to a labeled sterile screwcap tube for mycological analysis (figure 3), the TSB and VIB sample tubes were incubated for 24 hours at $308^{o}K$ ($35^{o}C$). Inocula from the sample tubes were then streaked on each isolation medium. The isolation streaks were prepared to culture organisms too few in number to be isolated on the quantitative agar media. Inoculated chocolate agar was incubated at $308^{o}K$ ($35^{o}C$) under an atmosphere of 8 to 10 percent carbon dioxide.

A portion of each colony type isolated on the quantitation and isolation media was transferred to a TSB or thioglycolate broth tube and incubated at $308^{o}K$ ($35^{o}C$) until turbid. The pure culture of each isolated organism was used to prepare stained slides and to inoculate biochemical media or to perform biochemical tests for identification.

State-of-the-art procedures that consisted of challenging tissue cultures, embryonated eggs, suckling mice, and mycoplasma media with specimens obtained at various times before and after flight were used in characterizing the viral and mycoplasma flora.

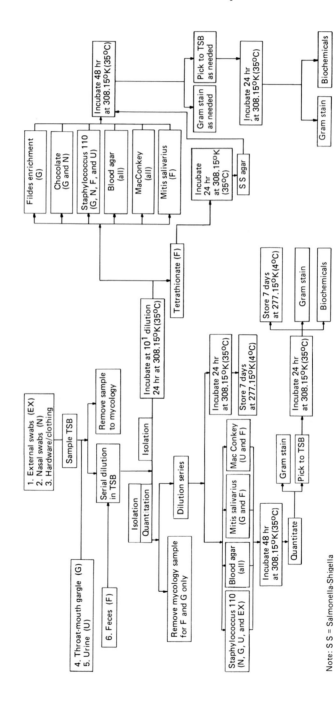

Figure 1. Crew bacteriology protocol for aerobic scheme.

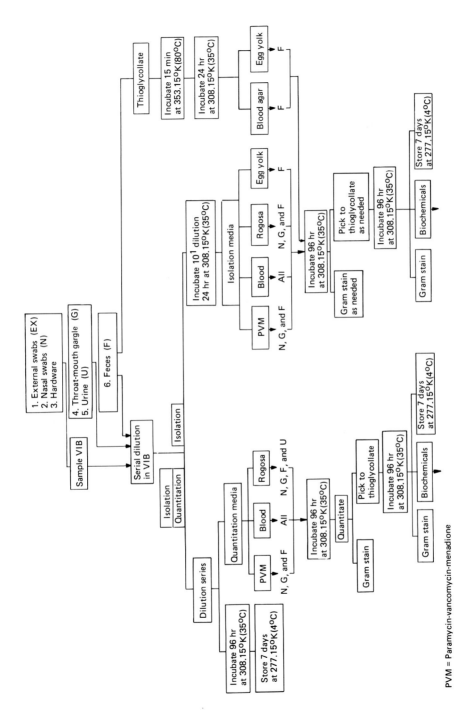

Figure 2. Crew bacteriology protocol for anaerobic scheme.

PVM = Paramycin-vancomycin-menadione

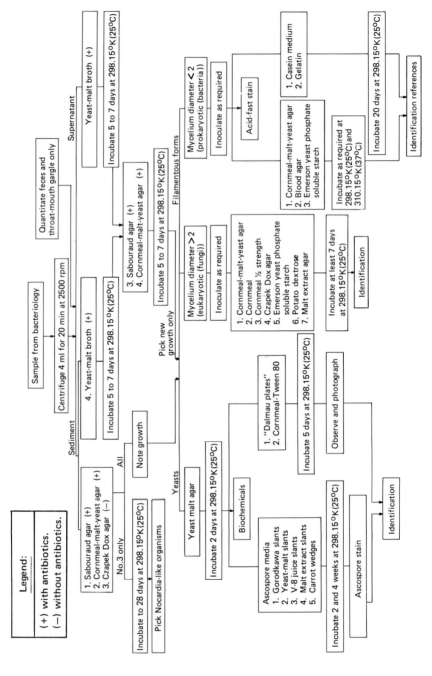

Figure 3.   Crew mycology protocol.

Spacecraft Microbiology

Immediately before and after flight, swab samples were obtained from four selected sites inside the Command Module. Sterile calcium alginate swabs were moistened with 0.85 percent saline containing 0.0003 molar phosphate buffer. Two swabs were used to sample each of the following sites: (1) the total surface area of the mouthpiece of the drink gun; (2) a 13-cm^2 area of each pistol grip of the Command Module Pilot (CMP) maneuver controller; (3) a 13-m^2 area of each head strut; and (4) a 26-cm^2 area of the floor beneath the foot of the center couch. After the sampling, one swab from each site was placed in 5.0-ml TSB and another in 5.0-ml VIB. The tubes were maintained at 277°K (4°C) during transport to the laboratory. Each tube was vortexed, and the appropriate medium was used to serially dilute the contents. An aliquot of each TSB dilution was plated onto five percent sheep blood agar and incubated aerobically at 308°K (35°C) for 48 hours. An aliquot of each VIB dilution was plated onto sheep blood agar containing 10 mg/liter vitamin K and 5 mg/liter hemin. Gas Paks (Bio-Quest) were used to obtain anaerobic conditions. The plates were incubated at 308°K (35°C) for 96 hours.

Four milliliters of the undiluted TSB samples were used for mycological analysis. Each sample was centrifuged at 2500 rpm for 15 minutes. The supernatant from each was mixed with 10 ml of yeast-malt broth containing 33 000 units/liter penicillin G and 62 mg/liter streptomycin. The sediment was sampled with sterile calcium alginate swabs. The swabs were used to streak the surface of cornmeal-malt-yeast agar (containing antibiotics), Sabouraud dextrose agar (containing antibiotics), and Czapek Dox agar. The swabs were then placed into 10 ml of yeast-malt broth (containing antibiotics). All mycological media were incubated at 298°K (25°C) for 120 hours.

Following identification of all microorganisms, the laboratory data on each isolate were stored in a Univac 1108 computer. A computer program was developed to provide a "match test" of all stored data with the data that would be gathered from a lunar soil isolate. The program was designed to search the catalog of data on known terrestrial microorganisms and to select those microorganisms with the greatest number of like characteristics and test results.

Results and Discussion

Crew Microbiology for Quarantine

The final identification of microorganisms isolated at the various sampling sites resulted in approximately 150 to 175 identifications per sampling period. Often, the same microorganism was isolated at more than one site. At the time the first lunar material was returned by the Apollo 11 crewmen, the catalog contained laboratory identification data of approximately 4000 microbial isolations.

Throughout the Apollo missions, no microorganism was isolated from the lunar soil. This result attests to the successful operation of the Lunar Receiving Laboratory and the development of adequate aseptic techniques in the handling and processing of the lunar soil.

Crew Medical Microbiology

Increased Incidence and Transfer of Microorganisms Between Crewmen. An increased incidence of medically important gram-positive cocci was found for the Apollo 7 and 12 missions. On the Apollo 7 flight, 16 postflight isolations of *Staphylococcus aureus* were made at the various sampling sites of all three crewmen. During the period immediately before flight, five isolations were made from the samples of only two crewmen (table 1). The isolation sites on crewmember C were different at the two preflight periods, and the *S. aureus* was not isolated at any time from throat or nasal samples of this crewman. It is likely that the *S. aureus* was a transient microorganism on crewmembers C and B, and that crewmember A was a carrier.

Table 1

Occurrence and Distribution of *Staphylococcus Aureus*
for the Apollo 7 Crewmembers

Sample Area	30-day Preflight			Immediate Preflight			Immediate Postflight		
	A[a]	B	C	A	B	C	A	B	C
Axilla	0[b]	0	0	0	0	0	0	0	0
Umbilicus	0	0	+[c]	0	0	0	+	0	+
Inguinal	0	0	0	0	0	+	+	0	+
Hands	+	0	0	+	0	+	+	+	0
Throat	0	+	0	+	0	0	+	+	0
Scalp	+	+	0	0	0	0	+	+	0
Nasal	+	+	0	+	0	0	+	+	0
Urine	0	0	+	0	0	0	0	+	0
Toes	0	0	0	0	0	0	+	0	+
Ears	0	0	I	0	0	0	+	0	0

[a]Crewmembers listed as A, B, and C.

[b]+ = isolation.

[c]0 = no isolation.

On the Apollo 7 flight, although no isolations of β-hemolytic streptococci were made from the throat samples of the crewmen at any preflight sampling period, β-hemolytic streptococci were present after the flight in the throat gargle sample of all three crewmen (table 2). Each sample contained 1×10^5 streptococcal cells per cubic centimeter of gargle. The presence and abundance of β-hemolytic streptococci and *S. aureus* on the Apollo 7 flight undoubtedly contributed to the nasal congestion and discomfort experienced by the crewmen.

Table 2

Occurrence and Distribution of Beta-hemolytic Streptococci
for the Apollo 7 Crewmembers

Sample Area	30-day Preflight			Immediate Preflight			Immediate Postflight		
	A[a]	B	C	A	B	C	A	B	C
Axilla	+[b]	0[c]	0	0	0	0	0	0	0
Umbilicus	+	+	+	0	0	0	0	0	0
Inguinal	+	0	+	+	0	+	+	0	+
Hands	0	0	0	0	+	0	0	0	0
Feces	0	0	+	+	0	+	0	+	+
Urine	0	0	0	0	0	+	0	0	+
Throat	0	0	0	0	0	0	+	+	+

[a]Crewmembers listed as A, B, and C.

[b]+ = isolation.

[c]0 = no isolation.

A third microorganism, *Aspergillus fumigatus,* increased in number and apparently spread over the body surfaces of the Apollo 7 crewmen (table 3). With a single exception, all preflight isolations of *A. fumigatus* were made from the samples obtained from crewmember A. After flight, three or more isolations were made from the samples of each crewman. The organism was apparently transferred in flight from crewman A to crewmembers B and C. No significant increase of *A. fumigatus* or of any other fungus occurred on any mission through the Apollo 12 mission.

After the apparent transfer of microorganisms between crewmen during the Apollo 7 mission, strain-specific bacteriophage typing was developed in the laboratory and performed on all *S. aureus* recovered from later missions to better substantiate the suspected transfer.

An increased incidence of *S. aureus* did not reoccur until the Apollo 12 flight (table 4). Although only two isolations of *S. aureus* were made from one crewmember immediately before flight, seven of the twelve crewmember samples analyzed after flight were positive for *S. aureus.* Six additional isolations were made from the clothing samples and the internal Command Module samples. The organisms obtained immediately before and after flight were phage typed (table 5). Both isolates of *S. aureus* obtained from crewmember A immediately before flight were typed 3A. The microorganism was evidently transferred to crewmember B, to the urine collection device (UCD) of crewmember C, and to the couch support struts of the Command Module. The *S. aureus* phage type 187 was possibly a spacecraft contaminant. Although no inflight samples were obtained and the pustules on the crewmen's skin had dried at the postflight examination, *S. aureus* may have been the causative agent of the skin infections on the Apollo 12 flight.

Table 3

Occurrence and Distribution of *Aspergillus Fumigatus* for the Apollo 7 Crewmembers

Sample Area	30-day Preflight			Immediate Preflight			Immediate Postflight		
	A[a]	B	C	A	B	C	A	B	C
Scalp	+[b]	0[c]	0	0	0	0	+	0	0
Exterior auditory canal	0	0	0	0	0	0	+	+	+
Umbilicus	0	0	0	0	0	0	+	0	+
Hands	0	+	0	0	0	0	0	0	+
Inguinal	+	0	0	0	0	0	+	+	+
Toes	0	0	0	+	0	0	+	0	+
Gargle	+	0	0	+	0	0	+	0	0
Axilla	0	0	0	0	0	0	0	+	0

[a]Crewmembers listed as A, B, and C.
[b]+ = isolation.
[c]0 = no isolation.

Table 4

Occurrence and Distribution of *Staphylococcus Aureus* for the Apollo 12 Crewmembers

Sample Area	30-day Preflight			Immediate Preflight			Immediate Postflight		
	A[a]	B	C	A	B	C	A	B	C
Axilla	+[b]	0[c]	0	0	0	0	−[d]	−	−
Inguinal	+	0	0	0	0	0	−	−	−
Scalp	+	0	0	0	0	0	−	−	−
Toes	0	0	0	+	0	0	−	−	−
Hands	+	0	+	0	0	0	0	+	0
Nasal	+	0	0	+	0	0	+	+	+
Throat	0	0	0	0	0	0	0	+	+
Ears	+	0	0	0	0	0	0	+	0

[a]Crewmembers listed as A, B, and C.
[b]+ = isolation.
[c]0 = no isolation.
[d]− = no culture made.

Table 5

Distribution of Phage Typed *Staphylococcus Aureus* for the Apollo 12 Crewmembers and Command Module

Sample Area	Immediate Preflight			Immediate Postflight		
	Crewmembers			Crewmembers		
	A	B	C	A	B	C
Toes	3A	0[a]	0	_[b]	—	—
Hands	0	0	0	0	3A	0
Nasal	3A	0	0	3A	3A	187
Throat	0	0	0	0	3A	187
Ears	0	0	0	0	3A	0
Gloves	0	0	0	3A	3A	0
UCD	0	0	0	3A	0	3A
	Command Module			Command Module		
Maneuver Control	0			187		
Struts	0			3A		

[a] 0 = no isolation.

[b] _ = not cultured.

An increase in *S. aureus* did not occur on the Apollo 8, 9, 10, or 11 missions, even though, on two of these missions, at least one crewmember was carrying a nasal *S. aureus*. The microorganism did not increase in number as observed on the Apollo 7 and 12 missions, and was not exchanged between crewmen.

During the Apollo 13 flight, the transfer of *S. aureus* was again demonstrated. The Commander (CDR) and the Command Module Pilot (CMP) each carried *S. aureus* before flight, but the organisms were of different strains. Both strains were recovered after flight from the Lunar Module Pilot (LMP), who had not exhibited either strain before flight (table 6).

The Apollo 15 flight was an example of a more common occurrence, in which one crewmember, exhibiting multiple strains, probably acted as a reservoir to effect a transfer of one strain to another previously uncolonized crewmember during the flight. The transfer was from the CDR to the LMP, who spent more time with the CDR during the mission than did the CMP (table 7). The occurrence of intercrew transfer of microorganisms was demonstrated on many Apollo missions.

Specific Medical Microbiological Problems Associated with the Apollo 13 and 17 Flights. Urinalyses were performed on specimens from the Apollo 14 CMP several times during the 26 months preceding lift-off in response to a recurrent urethritis of possible microbial origin. However, no microorganisms were recovered until seven months before launch. Urine samples were evaluated periodically through the day of launch, and seven different medically important microorganisms were isolated (table 8). Of the microorganisms listed, the *Haemophilus* species was the most likely to cause a bacteria-mediated recurrent urethritis. Clinical symptoms were not expressed during the Apollo 14 space flight, although *Haemophilus* species was again isolated two weeks following recovery. As was usually the case, the presence of potentially pathogenic microorganisms *Klebsiella pneumoniae*, *Proteus mirabilis*, and *Herellea vaginicola* in the postflight urine reflected the similar buildup observed in the urine collection device.

Table 6

Transfer of *Staphylococcus Aureus* Phage Types I and II
from Two Apollo 13 Crewmembers to the Third Crewmember

Subject	Types of Bacteriophage Groups Present	
	Preflight (F-0)	Postflight (R + 0)
CDR	I	I
CMP	II	II
LMP	Absent	I and II

Table 7

Distribution of *Staphylococcus Aureus* Phage Types
Among Apollo 15 Crewmembers

Subject	Sample Area	Sample Collection Period			
		F - 30	F - 5	F - O	R + O
CDR	Nasal	29/52	X[a]	X	X
	Throat	29	X	3A	29
	Gargle	X	N.T.[b]	29	29
LMP	Gargle	X	X	X	29/52
CMP	N.A.[c]	X	X	X	X

[a] Indicates no isolation of S. aureus.
[b] Nontypable S. aureus isolated.
[c] Not applicable.

An inflight malfunction of the Service Module, which caused early termination of the Apollo 13 mission, created a suboptimal environment and a stressful situation for the crew. Examination of the crew immediately after flight revealed that the LMP had a severe urinary tract infection from which *Pseudomonas aeruginosa* was isolated as the causative agent. Antibiotic therapy was administered and closely monitored for 48 days following recovery (figure 4). Viable microbes had disappeared in the midstream urine samples within nine days following splashdown, although *P. aeruginosa* could still be recovered following prostatic massage after 16 days.

Table 8

Isolates from Urine of Apollo 14 CMP

| Microorganisms | CMP Urinanalysis | | | | | | | | | | |
| | Preflight by Month | | | | | | | | | Postflight by Month | |
	26	13	7	4	3	2	1	0.5	0	0	0.5
Micrococcus species	–a	–	+b	–	–	–	–	–	–	–	–
Corynebacterium species	–	–	+	–	–	–	–	–	–	–	+
Haemophilus species	–	–	+	–	+	+	+	–	–	–	+
Staphylococcus epidermidis	–	–	–	+	+	+	–	–	–	–	–
Diphtheroid	–	–	–	+	–	–	–	–	–	–	–
Streptococcus species (β-hemolytic)	–	–	–	+	–	–	–	–	–	–	–
Klebsiella pneumoniae	–	–	–	–	–	–	+	–	+	+	–
Proteus mirabilus	–	–	–	–	–	–	–	–	–	+	–
Herellea vaginicola	–	–	–	–	–	–	–	–	–	+	–

a Indicates designated species not isolated.
b Indicates isolation of designated species.

The illness occurrence illustrates the types of infectious problems that can occur when the life support system is operating suboptimally for even a short period. Another example of the effect of unfavorable environmental conditions and poor hygiene was observed with the increased incidence of pathogenic microorganisms on the body surface. (figure 5). Whereas only three species (*Staphylococcus aureus*, *Escherichia coli*, and *Herellea vaginicola*) were recovered on the morning of launch, seven medically important species were recovered immediately after splashdown. In addition, the number of isolates of each species was generally higher after flight. Although there was generally a slight postflight increase in the incidence of pathogens in other crews, the Apollo 13 increase was significantly elevated. An average of 175 percent more medically important species was recovered from the seven Apollo 13 postflight skin swabs as compared with an average increase of only 33 percent for the same samples from the Apollo 14 flight.

It was not unusual to find at least one crewmember from each Apollo team harboring the pathogenic yeast *Candida albicans* in the mouth. The presence of this species generally does not pose a significant threat to healthy adults. However, the other fungi that normally exercise a controlling influence on *C. albicans* populations through

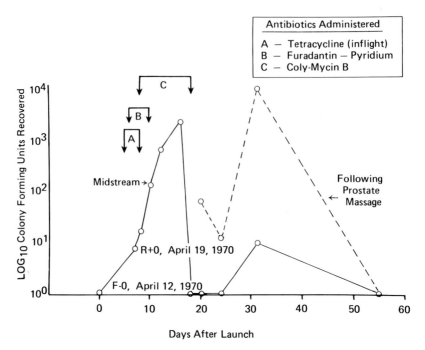

Figure 4. Presence of *Pseudomonas aeruginosa* in urine
of Apollo 13 Lunar Module Pilot.

microbial competition have decreased dramatically during space flight. This population shift creates a situation in which the natural resistance to infection may be decreased at a time when clinical diagnosis and treatment are most difficult.

The presence of *C. albicans*, as well as other species of *Candida* that have similarly been implicated in a variety of pathogenic situations, was carefully monitored during each Apollo flight. No anomalies were noted among any of the Apollo crewmembers that could be traced to yeast infections. Whether this lack of microbial competition could mediate a disease state during missions of longer duration is a matter of conjecture, but the Apollo data demonstrate the existing possibility.

The Apollo 17 Command Module Pilot exhibited a chronic dermatitis on the skin of the groin and both feet before and after flight. The pathogenic fungus *Trichophyton rubrum* was isolated as the causative agent at each sampling period. A similar dermatitis was present on the skin of the Commander's toes, although the causative agent could not be cultured. The presence of active dermatophyte infections on two of the Apollo 17 crewmembers afforded the opportunity to study the response of this type of disease condition to short-term space flight. Analysis of the lesions after flight revealed no discernible change from the preflight condition. Likewise, there was no evidence of transfer of *T. rubrum* to other parts of the body.

A potential avenue of secondary infection was carefully monitored in the Apollo 17 crewmen. The opportunistic pathogen *Pseudomonas aeruginosa* was present on the toes

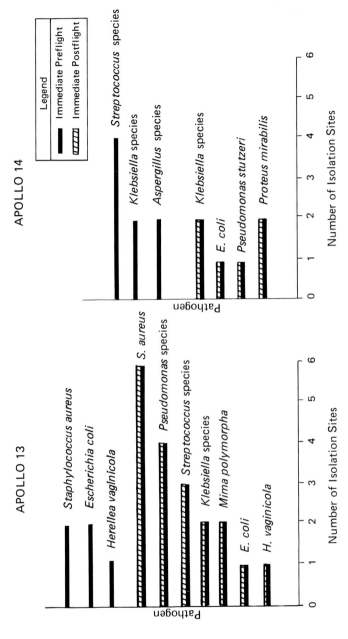

Figure 5. Incidence of pathogen isolation from Apollo 13 and 14 crew skin swabs.

of the CDR before flight and spread to the toes of the CMP and the LMP during flight. However, the presence of this species near the dermatophytic lesions did not result in a secondary, *P. aeruginosa* mediated infection.

Spacecraft and Clothing Microbiology

Spacecraft microbial samples from the Apollo 7 through 12 missions were evaluated. The microorganisms obtained from the four preflight and postflight Command Module samples were grouped according to morphological type (table 9). Although the sample population was small, a definite trend of increased numbers of potential pathogens was observed.

Table 9

Morphological Types Isolated From Four CM
Sampling Sites: Apollo 7 through 12

Morphological Type	Total Isolations	
	Immediate Preflight	Immediate Postflight
Gram-positive cocci	38	47
Bacillus species	13	4
Diptheroids	8	13
Gram-negative rods	0	9
Filamentous fungi	14	9
Yeasts	6	3

A potentially pathogenic microorganism (*Staphylococcus aureus*) was isolated at the preflight sampling period only on the Apollo 10 spacecraft (table 10). The organism, recovered in each of the four preflight samples collected, was not recovered after flight from any sampled site. However, several medically important organisms were isolated at the postflight period of most of the Apollo 7 through 12 missions.

Of the 79 morphological types isolated before flight, only ten species were reisolated after the flight on the same mission. The reisolated types were primarily *Staphylococcus epidermidis* and *Micrococcus* species. These isolates are predominant in the human microflora and their reisolation from spacecraft samples is probably attributable to recontamination of the sample sites by the crewmen rather than to survival in the Command Module.

The transfer of microorganisms between the crewmen and the Command Module or the extravehicular activity clothing became more obvious in the analysis of subsequent missions. The data obtained from the Apollo 14 flight illustrate what generally happens to the microbial load of selected Command Module sites during a space flight (table 11). The various sites sampled harbored a variety of microbial species. Command Module habitation did not generally affect a significant change in the number of contaminating species. However, there was an obvious loss of the original contaminants on each site with a concurrent invasion of microbes of different species.

Table 10

Medically Important Microorganisms Isolated From the Apollo CM

Micro-organism	Areas of Isolation by Apollo Mission											
	7		8		9		10		11		12	
	Preflight	Postflight	Preflight	Postflight	Preflight	Postflight	Preflight	Postflight	Preflight	Postflight	Preflight	Postflight
Aspergillus fumigatus	—[1]	M.C.[2]	—	M.C.	—	F.[3]	—	—	—	—	—	—
Coliform	—	F.	—	—	—	—	—	—	—	—	—	—
Herellea species	—	F.	—	—	—	—	—	—	—	—	—	F.
Klebsiella aerobacter	—	—	—	—	—	—	—	—	—	—	—	F.
Proteus mirabilis	—	S.A.[4]	—	—	—	—	—	—	—	—	—	—
Pseudomonas maltophilia	—	—	—	—	—	—	—	—	—	—	—	—
Pseudomonas	—	—	—	—	—	—	—	F.	—	—	—	—
Pseudomonas pseudomallei	—	—	—	—	—	—	—	—	—	—	—	—
Pseudomonas species	—	D.G.	—	D.G.[5]	—	F.	M.C. D.G. F. s.[6]	—	—	—	—	S.
Staphylococcus aureus	—		—	—	—	—		—	—	—	—	M.C.

[1] Indicates no pathogenic organism found.
[2] M. C. = Maneuver Controller
[3] F. = Floor
[4] S. A. = Shock Absorbers
[5] D. G. = Drink Gun
[6] S. = Strut

Table 11

Analyses of Aerobic Species Recovered From Apollo 14
CM Hardware Sites

Sample Site	Microorganisms Recovered	
	Preflight (F−0)	Postflight (R+0)
Floor	*Micrococcus* species 3	—[a]
	Micrococcus species 5	—
	Micrococcus species 14	—
	Pseudomonas maltophilia[b]	—
	Staphylococcus epidermidis	—
	—	*Herellea vaginicola*[b]
	—	*Klebsiella pneumoniae*[b]
	—	*Proteus mirabilis*[b]
	—	*Streptococcus faecalis*[b]
Head strut	*Gaffkya tetragena*	—
	—	*Staphylococcus epidermidis*
	—	*Bacillus* species
Rotational hand controller	*Micrococcus* species 10	—
	Micrococcus species 19	-
	—	*Staphylococcus epidermidis*
	Corynebacterium bovis	—
	Gaffkya species	—
	Micrococcus species 4	*Micrococcus* species 4
	Micrococcus species 29	—
	—	*Gaffkya tetragena*
	—	*Staphylococcus epidermidis*

[a] = Indicates designated species not recovered during this sampling period.
[b] = Medically significant species.

The Apollo 14 data also illustrate the general phenomenon of buildup of medically important species during the space flight. Only one potentially pathogenic species (*Pseudomonas maltophilia*) was recovered from the Command Module sites before lift-off, whereas four different potential pathogens, *Herellea vaginicola*, *Klebsiella pneumoniae*, *Proteus mirabilis*, and *Streptococcus faecalis*, were recovered after flight. This same pattern was generally noted in each of the flights for which the appropriate samples were collected.

The increased incidence of medically important microorganisms is even more obvious from urine collection device analysis. Table 12 illustrates a common pattern with the UCD samples. UCDs were first sampled in the clean room at the NASA John F. Kennedy Space Center the morning of launch, and were generally free of microbes. However, samples collected in the Command Module immediately upon recovery contained a variety of contaminants. All but one species (*Bacillus*) of the microbes recovered after flight from the Apollo 14 devices were potential pathogens. The buildup of *Proteus mirabilis* on the UCD reoccurred throughout most of the Apollo missions. Close contact of susceptible parts of the body with a contaminated UCD presented a significant medical hazard.

Table 12

Number of Aerobic Specimens Recovered From Samples of Three Apollo 14 UCSs

Organism	Preflight	Postflight
Bacillus species	—[a]	1
Klebsiella pneumoniae[b]	—	3
Proteus mirabilis[b]	—	1
Pseudomonas maltophilia[b]	—	2
Staphylococcus epidermidis	2	—

[a]Indicates designated species not isolated during this sampling period.
[b]Medically important species.

Statistical Analysis of Crew Microflora

Paired t-tests were performed on the crew bacterial flora of the Apollo 7 to 11 missions to identify significant changes in the number or occurrence of microorganisms in the postflight period as compared with the preflight period. Comparisons were made by testing both the sum of actual bacterial counts within a genus and the sum of occurrence of a particular genus at each sampling site. Times selected for comparison of the paired genera in the identified groups were F-30 and F-0; F-30 and R+0; and F-0 and R+0. The tests were performed on the microflora of the stool, urine, throat-mouth gargle, and inguinal region samples. All body surface samples, which included the inguinal region samples, were tested as a single group. The microflora of each sample area were further divided into groups of aerobic gram positives, anaerobic gram positives, aerobic gram negatives, and anaerobic gram negatives.

Significant alteration at the 0.05 level in the count, or occurrence, of microorganisms during these missions was indicated only in the inguinal region by this test method. Alteration of the microflora in this sample area was expected because of the poor personal hygiene measures available to the Apollo crewmen following defecation. In general, a high degree of variation was observed in the microflora between sampling periods, between crewmen, and between missions. No other consistent alteration to the microflora was observed by this test method.

Apollo Crew Virology

Serological titers were determined preflight on crewmen, crew contacts, and key mission personnel to ascertain immune status to mumps, rubella, and rubeola. The immune status of all astronauts to poliomyelitis virus types 1, 2, and 3 was also determined. In addition, complement-fixation antibody titers to influenza A, influenza B, ECHO virus (group), adenovirus (group), parainfluenza, herpes simplex, *Mycoplasma pneumoniae*, cytomegalovirus, and respiratory syncytial virus were determined for the crewmembers.

Poliomyelitis virus was isolated from the preflight stools of the Apollo 11 crewmen after the crewmen had been given poliomyelitis boosters. Herpes simplex virus was isolated from the throat specimen collected immediately before flight from one Apollo 15 crewmember. This virus was not isolated from postflight specimens.

An investigation of the postflight illness of Apollo 7 crewmen established A_2 Hong Kong influenza as the causative agent by serological confirmation. Postflight illnesses in two Apollo 9 crewmembers were confirmed as influenza B virus by virus isolation and identification.

A study of the rubella virus exposure of the Apollo 13 crewmembers definitely established that a backup crewmember was infected with rubella virus. The source of the backup crewmember's exposure was also identified. After the immune status of the Apollo 13 crew was determined, one crew reassignment was made and the scheduled initiation of the flight was permitted. The following viruses were isolated from personnel who either worked behind the biological barrier or were contacts of the crew: rhinovirus; herpes simplex; adenovirus type 2 and type 5; Coxsackie A6, A24, B1, and B3; and enteric cytopathogenic human orphan (ECHO) virus type 1. The crewmen remained free from manifestations of similar illnesses.

Mycoplasma species were routinely isolated from preflight and postflight specimens from all Apollo crewmen. Throat specimens frequently yielded *Mycoplasma salivarium* and *Mycoplasma orale I*, and *Mycoplasma hominis* was isolated from the urine. *Mycoplasma laidlawii A* was isolated from throat and urine specimens of Apollo 12 crewmen. Some evidence of cross infection was noted. Usually, *Mycoplasma* species were isolated from one or two crewmembers, and the same species were isolated before and after flight. The largest number of isolations was obtained from the Apollo 12 and 13 crewmen. *Mycoplasma* species were isolated from preflight and postflight specimens obtained from all crewmembers of these missions.

Summary and Conclusions

The return of sterile lunar soil indicated the success of measures developed to prevent lunar soil contamination. The likelihood of returning a lunar microorganism was recognized as being very small. However, the possibility of lunar soil contamination with terrestrial organisms was considerably greater. Had the soil become contaminated, the catalog developed before flight of microorganisms carried to the moon would have been extremely useful in identifying a terrestrial contaminant. The need for a premission microbial catalog will exist for future manned missions to other planets unless substantial advances can be made in the collection and transportation procedures of foreign soil, thus ensuring the return of the soil in its original state.

Considerable variation in the microfloral response was observed on the Apollo missions. The variables of host susceptibility, external environmental factors, and ecological relationships among competing species of microorganisms were undoubtedly responsible for the observed response of the microflora.

An increased incidence and spread of potentially pathogenic microorganisms between crewmen was demonstrated on several missions. In all cases, the organisms carried by each crewman were carefully monitored throughout the preflight and postflight phases in an effort to prevent, or control, infectious disease events. A major consideration for future missions of longer duration should be to develop improved preventive measures and inflight monitoring and diagnostic systems. Such systems will provide coverage for inflight illness events and will provide additional understanding of the microfloral response and its relationship to illness events.

Preflight and postflight microbial analysis of samples obtained from the Command Module showed a loss of the preflight microorganisms occurs during the mission. Microflora isolated at sampling sites before flight were replaced by microorganisms from the crew.

No observations made suggest the spacecraft environment predisposes the crewmen to viral or mycoplasma-induced illness.

CHAPTER 3
RADIATION PROTECTION AND INSTRUMENTATION

by

J. Vernon Bailey

Lyndon B. Johnson Space Center

Introduction

The solar and cosmic radiation found in space has long been recognized as a possible danger in space travel. Exposure to such radiation has the potential of causing serious medical problems. For example, radiation exposure can produce a number of significant changes in various elements of the blood, making an individual more susceptible to disease; also, ionizing radiations of the type found in space can produce significant damage to the lens of the eye. Radiation exposure can also cause temporary or lasting damage to the reproductive system ranging from reduced fertility to permanent sterility. The extent of damage depends upon the tissue involved, the duration of exposure, the dose received, and other factors.

Apollo missions placed men for the first time outside the Earth's geomagnetic shield, subjecting them to potentially hazardous particulate radiation of an intensity and frequency not encountered in the Earth's environment. In addition, various aspects of ground-based operations in support of Apollo missions involved some exposure to radioactive materials, for example during manufacture, testing, and installation of radioluminescent panels in the spacecraft. In flight, astronauts were exposed to both manmade radiations and those occurring naturally in space. Of the two, space radiations posed the larger hazard and were largely uncontrollable. Manmade radiation sources, while of appreciable strength, could be controlled.

The Apollo radiation protection program focused on both the natural radiations encountered in space and manmade radiations encountered on the ground and in the space environment. In both areas, the basic philosophy remained the same: to avoid harmful radiation effects by limiting the radiation dose to the lowest level judged consistent with the achievement of beneficial goals.

Radiation from Space

During a complete Apollo mission, astronauts were exposed to widely varying radiation sources. These included the Van Allen belts, cosmic rays, neutrons, and other subatomic particles created in high-energy collisions of primary particles with spacecraft materials. Spacecraft transfer from low Earth orbit to translunar coast necessitated traverse of the regions of geomagnetically trapped electrons and protons known as the Van Allen belts. When beyond these belts, the spacecraft and crewmen were continuously subjected to high-energy cosmic rays and to varying probabilities of particle bursts from the sun. In addition, the individual responsibilities of the crewmen differed, and with these, their radiation exposure. Free-space extravehicular activity, lunar surface activity, and intravehicular Command and Lunar Module activity imposed varying radiation doses.

Van Allen Belts

The problem of protecting astronauts against the radiation found within the Van Allen belts was recognized before the advent of manned space flight. These two bands of trapped radiation, discovered during the Explorer I flight in 1958, consist principally of protons and high-energy electrons, a significant part of which were, at that time, debris from high-altitude tests of nuclear weapons. The simple solution to protection is to remain under the belts [below an altitude of approximately 556 km ($\approx$300 nautical miles)] when in Earth orbit, and to traverse the belts rapidly on the way to outer space. In reality, the problem is somewhat more complex. The radiation belts vary in altitude over various parts of the Earth and are absent over the north and south magnetic poles. A particularly significant portion of the Van Allen belts is a region known as the South Atlantic anomaly (figure 1). Over the South Atlantic region, the geomagnetic field draws particles closer to the Earth than in other regions of the globe. The orbit inclination of a spacecraft determines the number of passes made per day through this region and, thus, the radiation dose.

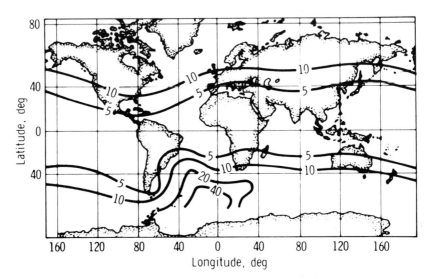

Figure 1. Isodose profile showing high-dose region
over South Atlantic.

Particles within the Van Allen belts, in spiraling around the Earth's magnetic lines of force, display directionality. This directionality varies continuously in angular relationship to the trajectory of the spacecraft. Therefore, dosimetry instrumentation for use in the Van Allen belts had relatively omnidirectional radiation sensors so that the radiation flux would be measured accurately. The Van Allen belt dosimeter (figure 2) was designed specifically for Apollo dosimetry within these radiation belts.

Figure 2. Van Allen Belt dosimeter.

Solar-Particle Radiation

No major solar-particle events occurred during an Apollo mission. Although much effort has been expended in the field of solar-event forecasting, individual eruptions from the solar surface have proved impossible to forecast. The best that can be provided is an estimate of particle dose, given visual or radio-frequency (RF) confirmation that an eruption has occurred. A system of solar-monitoring stations, the Solar Particle Alert Network (SPAN), provides a NASA-sponsored network of continuous data on solar-flare activity. SPAN consists of three multiple-frequency radio telescopes and seven optical telescopes. The network gives data for determining the severity of solar-particle events and the resultant possible radiation hazards to crewmen. After the appearance of particles is confirmed onboard a spacecraft, protective action can be taken.

In terms of hazard to crewmen in the heavy, well shielded Command Module, even one of the largest solar-particle event series on record (August 4-9, 1972) would not have caused any impairment of crewmember functions or ability of the crewmen to complete their mission safely. It is estimated that within the Command Module during this event, the crewmen would have received a dose of 360 rads[*] to their skin and 35 rads to their blood-forming organs (bone and spleen). Radiation doses to crewmen while inside the thinly shielded Lunar Module or during an extravehicular activity (EVA) would be extremely serious for such a particle event. To monitor particle activity, a nuclear-particle-detection system (figure 3) was designed to have a relatively narrow acceptance angle. It measured the isotropic proton and alpha particles derived from solar-particle events.

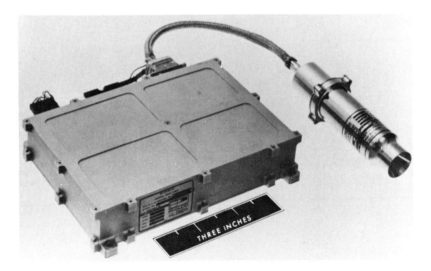

Figure 3. Nuclear-particle-detection system.

Cosmic Rays

Cosmic ray fluxes, consisting of completely ionized atomic nuclei originating outside the solar system and accelerated to very high energies, provided average dose rates of 1.0 millirads per hour in cislunar space[**] and 0.6 millirads per hour on the lunar surface. These values are expected to double at the low point in the 11-year cycle of solar-flare activity (solar minimum) because of decreased solar magnetic shielding of the central planets. The effect of high-energy cosmic rays on humans is unknown but is considered by most authorities not to be of serious concern for exposures of less than a few years. Experimental evidence of the effects of these radiations is dependent on the development of highly advanced particle accelerators or the advent of long-term manned missions outside the Earth's geomagnetic influence.

---

[*] Radiation absorbed dose. Corresponds to absorption of watts (100 ergs) per gram of any medicine.

[**] That region of space between the Earth and the moon or the moon's orbit.

Neutrons

Neutrons created by cosmic rays in collision with lunar materials were postulated to be a potential hazard to Apollo crewmen (Kastner et al., 1969). Two methods for neutron-dose assessment were used. These techniques of whole-body counting and neutron-resonant foil were initiated on the Apollo 11 mission. Later analyses indicated that neutron doses were significantly lower than had been anticipated. Both methods were retained because of the remaining potential for neutron production by solar-event particles and because of possible crewman exposure to neutrons from the SNAP-27 radioisotope thermal generator used to power the Apollo lunar surface experiments packages.

Detection Devices

To allow accurate determination of overall radiation exposure of the crewmen, each carried a personal radiation dosimeter (PRD) (figure 4) and three passive dosimeters (figure 5). The PRD provided visual readout of accumulated radiation dose to each crewman as the mission progressed. It is approximately the size of a cigarette pack, and pockets were provided in the flight coveralls as well as in the space suit for storage. The passive dosimeters were placed in the garments worn throughout the mission. By placing these detectors at various locations (ankle, thigh, and chest) within the garments, accurate radiation doses for body portions were determined.

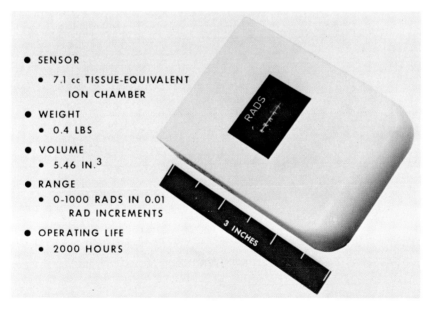

- SENSOR
  - 7.1 cc TISSUE-EQUIVALENT ION CHAMBER
- WEIGHT
  - 0.4 LBS
- VOLUME
  - 5.46 IN.^{3}
- RANGE
  - 0-1000 RADS IN 0.01 RAD INCREMENTS
- OPERATING LIFE
  - 2000 HOURS

Figure 4. Personal radiation dosimeter.

A radiation-survey meter (RSM) (figure 6) allowed crewmen to determine radiation levels in any desired location in their compartment. Crewmen could use the RSM, a direct-reading dose-rate instrument, to find a habitable low-dose region within the spacecraft in the event of a radiation emergency.

Figure 5. Passive dosimeter with component parts.

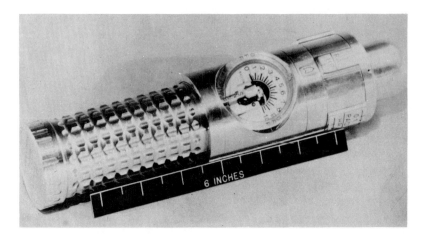

Figure 6. Radiation-survey meter.

Problems Involving Radiations of Manmade Origin

Protection against manmade sources of radiation is a ground support function concerned mainly with the protection of the ground personnel, the general public, and the environment against detrimental effects of radiation. Much of this effort involved routine health-physics procedures governed by U.S. Atomic Energy Commission regulations (Title 10, Code of Federal Regulations, 1971) and U.S. Department of Labor Standards (Title 29, Code of Federal Regulations, 1971). However, certain problems concerning spacecraft radioluminescent sources were peculiar to the Apollo Program. The chief problems were leakage of radioactive material from radioluminescent switch tips, and emission of excess soft X-ray radiation from radioluminescent panels. Both of these problems were solved.

A summary of all of the onboard instrumentation used during Apollo missions to assess radiation exposure is presented in table 1.

Table 1

Onboard Radiation Instrumentation

Instrument	Measurement	Location
Nuclear particle detection system	Alpha-proton spectrometer (4 channels proton, 15 to 150 MeV; 3 channels alpha, 40 to 300 MeV); telemetered	Service Module
Van Allen belt dosimeter	Skin and depth dose rates; telemetered	CM
Radiation survey meter	Portable, hand-held ratemeter: 4 linear ranges, 0 to 0.1 to 0 to 100 rad/hr; visual readout	CM (portable)
Personal radiation dosimeter	1/crewman; accumulated radiation dose; 0.01 to 1000 rad; visual readout	Suit
Passive radiation dosimeter	3/crewmen; emulsion/thermolumines-cent dosimeters; postflight analysis	Constant-wear garment

Results and Discussion

Average radiation doses were computed for each mission (table 2). Individual readings varied approximately 20 percent from the average because of differences in the shielding effectiveness of various parts of the Apollo spacecraft as well as differences in duties, movements, and locations of crewmen. Doses to blood-forming organs were approximately 40 percent lower than the values measured at the body surface. In comparison with the doses actually received, the maximum operational dose (MOD) limit for each of the Apollo missions was set at 400 rads (X-ray equivalent) to skin and 50 rads to the blood-forming organs.

Radiation doses measured during Apollo were significantly lower than the yearly average of 5 rem* set by the U.S. Atomic Energy Commission for workers who use

---

*Roentgen Equivalent, Man refers to the absorbed dose of any ionizing radiation which produces the same biological effects in man as those resulting from the absorption of 1 roentgen of X-rays.

radioactive materials in factories and institutions across the United States. Thus, radiation was not an operational problem during the Apollo Program. Doses received by the crewmen of Apollo missions 7 through 17 were small because no major solar-particle events occurred during those missions. One small event was detected by a radiation sensor outside the Apollo 12 spacecraft, but no increase in radiation dose to the crewmen inside the spacecraft was detected.

Table 2

Average Radiation Doses of the Flight
Crews for the Apollo Missions

Apollo Mission	Skin Dose, rads
7	0.16
8	.16
9	.20
10	.48
11	.18
12	.58
13	.24
14	1.14
15	.30
16	.51
17	.55

One particular effect possibly related to cosmic rays was the light-flash phenomenon reported on the Apollo 11 and subsequent missions. Although it is well known that ionizing radiations can produce visual phosphenes (subjective sensations best described as flashes of light) of the types reported, a definite correlation was not established between cosmic rays and the observation of flashes during the Apollo Program. The light flashes were described as starlike flashes or streaks of light that apparently occur within the eye. The flashes were observed only when the spacecraft cabin was dark or when blindfolds were provided and the crewmen were concentrating on detection of the flashes.

There is a possibility that visual flashes might indicate the occurrence of damage to the brain or eye; however, no damage has been observed among crewmen who experienced the light-flash phenomenon. During the Apollo 16 and 17 missions, a device known as the Apollo Light Flash Moving Emulsion Detector (ALFMED) was employed for the purpose of establishing if the flashes were indeed being caused by heavy cosmic rays. Further information regarding the light-flash phenomenon is contained in Section IV, Chapter 2 of this book.

Although Apollo missions did not undergo any major space radiation contingency, procedures for handling radiation problems were ready. The development of spacecraft dosimetry systems, the use of a space radiation surveillance network, and the availability of individuals with a thorough knowledge of space radiation assured that any contingency would be recognized immediately and would be coped with in a manner most expedient for both crewmember safety and mission objectives. The possible deterrent to manned space flight by large radiation doses was successfully avoided in the Apollo missions. More significantly, Apollo astronaut doses were negligible in terms of any medical or biological effects that could have impaired the function of man in the space environment.

The two key problems affecting safe operations with manmade radiation were resolved by design modifications. Leakage of radioactive materials from radioluminescent switch tips was eliminated by a change in encapsulating material. The problem of extensive emission of soft X-ray radiation from radioluminescent panels was resolved by applying a layer of plastic to the panels.

Summary and Conclusions

Radiation was not an operational problem during the Apollo Program. Doses received by the crewmen of Apollo missions 7 through 17 were small because no major solar-particle events occurred during those missions. One small event was detected by a radiation sensor outside the Apollo 12 spacecraft, but no increase in radiation dose to the crewmen inside the spacecraft was detected. Solar-particle releases are random events, and it is possible that flares, with the accompanying energetic nuclear particles, might hinder future flights beyond the magnetosphere of the Earth.

Radiation protection for the Apollo Program was focused on both the peculiarities of the natural space radiation environment and the increased prevalence of manmade radiation sources on the ground and onboard the spacecraft. Radiation-exposure risks to crewmen were assessed and balanced against mission gain to determine mission constraints. Operational radiation evaluation required specially designed radiation-detection systems onboard the spacecraft in addition to the use of satellite data, solar observatory support, and other liaison. Control and management of radioactive sources and radiation-generating equipment was important in minimizing radiation exposure of ground-support personnel, researchers, and the Apollo flight and backup crewmen.

References

Anon.: Occupational Safety and Health Standards. Title 29, Code of Federal Regulations, part 1910, May 1971.

Anon.: Standards for Protection Against Radiation. Title 10, Code of Federal Regulations, part 20, rev. July 15, 1971.

Kastner, Jacob; Oltman, B.G.; Feige, Yehuda; and Gold, Raymond: Neutron Exposure to Lunar Astronauts. Health Phys., vol. 17, no. 5, Nov. 1969, pp. 732-733.

CHAPTER 4
METABOLISM AND HEAT DISSIPATION DURING APOLLO EVA PERIODS

by

J.M. Waligora
D.J. Horrigan

Lyndon B. Johnson Space Center

Introduction

Extravehicular activity, particularly on the lunar surface, was a key and essential part of the Apollo Program. However, the physical capabilities of the crewmen in the performance of extravehicular activity (EVA) and the physiological cost to the crewmen were some of the significant uncertainties of the program.

The space environment imposed life support requirements during EVA: the maintenance of a minimum oxygen pressure, the removal of expired carbon dioxide, the provision for useful mobility, and the maintenance of body temperature. To meet these requirements, a composite pressure suit of many layers and complex joints was developed.[*] The result of the development was a pressure suit that provided excellent thermal insulation in a vacuum, but imposed a much greater workload on the wearer in a one-g environment than the work required to perform the same activity without a suit. In addition to the difficulty of working in a pressure suit, Apollo crewmen had to contend with either zero g for the free-space EVA or one-sixth g for the lunar surface EVA.

Zero-g extravehicular activities were performed during five Gemini missions, and considerable difficulty was experienced by the crewmembers. Crewmen experienced high work rates and apparent overheating during Gemini 4, Gemini 9, and Gemini 11 EVAs. The crewmen also encountered unexpected difficulty performing specific tasks on each of the Gemini missions (Roth, 1968). After the particularly exhausting experience on the Gemini 11 EVA, the Gemini 12 EVA was redirected to serve as an evaluation of zero-g EVA capability and restraint technology. It was found that adequate body restraints,

---

[*]See Section VI, Chapter 6, Extravehicular Mobility Unit.

The following individuals shared responsibility for development of measurement methods and real-time data analysis during extravehicular activities: G.F. Humbert, L. Kuznetz, L.J. Nelson, A.P. Schachter, S.J. Vogel, and R.J. Kelley.

115

realistic zero-g preflight training in a water immersion simulator and detailed preplanning of activity were essential to insure task performance and reduce fatigue (Machel, 1967). Although metabolic rates were not measured during the Gemini EVAs, it was clear in several instances that crewmen worked at levels above the heat removal capability of the gas cooled life support system (Kelley et al., 1968).

Several researchers reported on the effect of one-sixth g on the cost of work in a pressure suit. The results were inconclusive. Wortz and Prescott (1966), Margaria and Cavagna (1964), and Shavelson (1968) predicted metabolic costs would decrease with subgravity walking. Roth (1966), Springer and co-workers (1963), and Shevelson and Seminara (1968) indicated that a metabolic increase would accompany low traction exercise. Another factor of uncertainty was the terrain and surface composition of the moon and its effect on mobility and metabolic rate. In response to these uncertainties, conservative biomedical estimates of the life support requirements were defined on the basis of available data. Methods to measure metabolic rate during EVA were developed by using operational data from the portable life support system (PLSS).

EVA Life Support Equipment

Because the pressure suit was well insulated to protect the crewman from external high and low temperature extremes, the portable life support system of the pressure suit had to dissipate the crewman's heat production. A liquid cooling system was developed to accommodate high heat production in the suit as a result of the high EVA workloads. This system consisted of plastic cooling tubes on the inside of an undergarment. The garment could suppress sweating at work rates as high as 1670×10^3 J/hr (≈ 400 kcal/hr) and allowed sustained operation at rates as high as 2090×10^3 J/hr (≈ 500 kcal/hr) (Waligora & Michel, 1968).

The PLSS used for the Apollo 9, 11, 12, and 14 missions could support a total metabolic heat production of approximately 5020×10^3 J (1200 kcal), produced either at 1670×10^3 J/hr (≈ 400 kcal/hr) for three hours, or at 1260×10^3 J/hr (≈ 300 kcal/hr) for four hours. An expanded PLSS was used for the Apollo 15 through 17 missions that could support a total metabolic heat production of 7530×10^3 J (≈ 1800 kcal). This system provided for EVAs of seven hours at 1050×10^3 J/hr (≈ 250 kcal/hr) or eight hours at 942×10^3 J/hr (≈ 225 kcal/hr).

During the longer EVA periods a potential life support problem was dehydration. A drinking bag containing 100×10^{-5} m^3 of liquid was made available in the suit for replacement of water lost in sweat and respiration.

During the Apollo 15 through 17 missions, zero-g extravehicular activities were performed from the Command Module (CM) by means of an umbilical that provided approximately 0.3 m^3/min (10 ft^3/min) of gas for cooling. These extravehicular activities were limited to less than one hour.

Temperature Control

Suit temperature was controlled by a three-position manual valve that regulated the temperature of the coolant water flowing through the liquid cooling garment (LCG).

During the Apollo 11, 12, and 14 missions, the valve positions provided cooling water at temperatures of approximately 294°K (21°C) at the minimum position, 288°K (15°C) at the intermediate position, and 280°K (7°C) at the maximum position. Typically during these missions the temperature control valve was usually switched from minimum to intermediate and back again. The Apollo 11 Lunar Module Pilot was the only crewman who frequently used the maximum cooling position. The expanded portable life support system used on the Apollo 15 through 17 missions had a diverter valve that provided cooling water temperatures of approximately 300°K (27°C), 291°K (18°C), and 280°K (7°C). The minimum and intermediate cooling temperatures were increased to avoid overcooling during riding of the lunar roving vehicle. These temperature settings were quite satisfactory. Although the minimum and intermediate settings were most commonly used, the maximum setting was frequently used during high workload periods experienced during the Apollo 15 and 17 missions.

During two EVA periods, crewmen were instructed to change a diverter valve setting from minimum to intermediate as a preventive measure, but no crewman ever appeared to have a serious thermal problem. Despite variations in the frequency of diverter valve changes, each crewman maintained a suitable average temperature during the EVA periods. In all cases, 60 to 80 percent of the heat generated by metabolism was dissipated through the LCG. The LCG used during the lunar surface extravehicular activities undoubtedly minimized water loss from sweating and prevented dehydration and excessive fatigue.

For the Command Module extravehicular activities performed during the Apollo 15 through 17 missions, the only cooling available to the crewmen was from gas ventilation at a rate of $0.3 \text{ m}^3/\text{min}$ ($\approx 10 \text{ ft}^3/\text{min}$). This ventilation rate could not sustain prolonged work rates of more than 1050×10^3 J/hr (≈ 250 kcal/hr). Despite this limitation, no overheating problems were experienced because good restraint systems were available, training in the water immersion facility was adequate, and the EVA periods were short.

Metabolic Rate Measurement Methods

Since it was desirable to measure metabolic rate during extravehicular activies on the lunar surface and in free space, several measurement approaches were evaluated. The standard laboratory methods would have required breaking pressure suit integrity if used in space or during vacuum chamber training on the ground. Therefore, the operational data available from the crewman and from his life support system were assessed to determine their usefulness in approximating metabolic rate.

The data available from the crewmen during the EVA periods consisted of voice data, electrocardiogram (ECG) data from each crewman, oxygen bottle pressure, liquid cooling garment (LCG) coolant-water entry and exit temperatures, and suit-gas entry temperature. In addition, the sublimator water usage was available after the majority of the EVAs. Sublimator water usage provided a measure of the total heat loss from the suit. All of the heat removed from the pressure suit was first transferred to a heat sink maintained by the sublimator which rejected heat by the change of state involved in sublimating ice to water vapor in the vacuum of space.

Three methods were developed and used to estimate real-time metabolic rates:

1. The heart rate, counted from the electrocardiographic signal, was related to metabolism on the basis of a correlation with bicycle ergometer workload which was established before the flight (figure 1).

2. The oxygen usage, computed from the decrease in oxygen bottle pressure per unit time, was related to metabolism. A correction was made for an assumed rate of suit leakage.

3. The difference between the temperatures of the coolant water flowing into and out from the liquid cooling garment was multiplied by an assumed water flow rate and related to metabolism directly. This relationship is illustrated in figure 2, and it is based on the assumption that the crewman is maintaining a comfortable LCG inlet temperature. A second mode of computation was available in which crewman comfort is not assumed, but a steady-state of the coolant inlet temperature is assumed. An example of this mode of the LCG program is illustrated in figure 3. The basic difference between the two modes of computation, then, is the fact that the LCG inlet temperature is used in the second mode. This provided a greater degree of precision but required a constant inlet temperature. An operational procedure was established to select the appropriate LCG calculation mode as a function of the constancy of the inlet temperature.

In both the LCG computational modes, the metabolic rate was corrected by subtracting an estimate of heat leaked into the pressure suit from the environment from the total heat removed from the pressure suit.

After the mission was completed, the estimations made by each method of calculation were independently reassessed with respect to the information gained during the EVA including data on the sublimator feedwater remaining; real-time data were recalculated when required. The best metabolic rate estimate for the EVA and for EVA segments was then obtained by averaging the oxygen method and the LCG method. Because of apparent changes in the correlation of heart rate with metabolism, the heart rate method was not used independently. A postflight relationship of heart rate to metabolism was defined using the average heart and metabolic rates as a point and basing the slope of the relationship between heart rate and metabolic rate on the average of the preflight and postflight slopes.

Two types of task-identification methods were used for separating the activities performed during the EVA periods. The metabolic rate monitors divided the operational tasks into four types that were of interest to mission planners. These tasks consisted of overhead activities (that is, tasks required for each EVA, such as egressing and ingressing the vehicle, rather than those directed to a specific objective), deploying the Apollo lunar surface experiments package (ALSEP), making geological surveys, and riding in the lunar roving vehicle (LRV). Although these tasks were easy to separate according to time required for completion, the subtasks within a major task varied considerably from mission to mission. The oxygen and LCG methods could be used to obtain accurate metabolic rates for these activites. A more extensive task separation was accomplished in conjunction with a time and motion study.* This effort resulted in dividing the EVA

*Performed by Fordham University under contract to NASA.

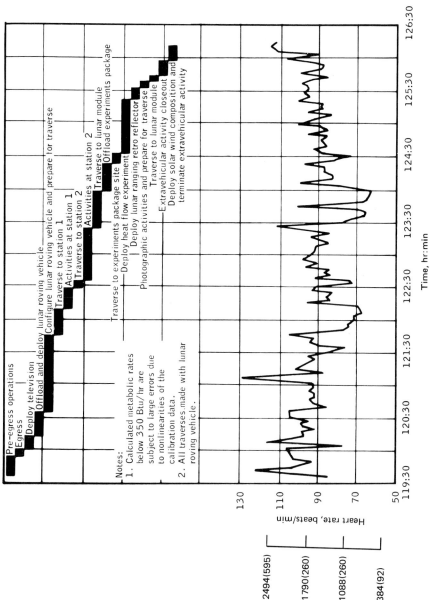

Figure 1. Heart rates and calculated metabolic rates of the Apollo 15 Commander during EVA-1.

timeline into as many definable activities as possible. Because of the short duration of some of these activities, metabolic rates could be assigned only by using the postflight heart rate method.

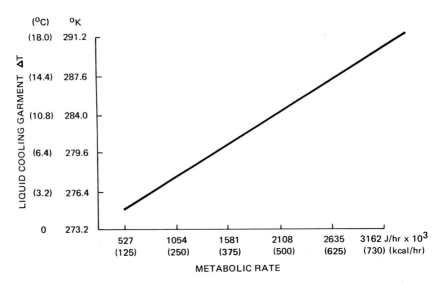

Figure 2. Example of mode 1 LCG program; metabolic rate plotted as a function of heat picked up by LCG. Relationship is based on the assumption that crewman is maintaining comfortable LCG inlet temperature.

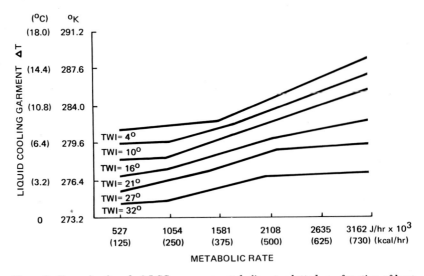

Figure 3. Example of mode 2 LCG program; metabolic rate plotted as a function of heat picked up by the LCG for each of a family of inlet temperatures. Relationship is based on the assumption that a steady-state exists; crewman comfort is not assumed.

Preflight data during one-g training was quite valuable in assessing the validity of the techniques of measurement but only of limited value in predicting actual workloads on the lunar surface and during free-space EVAs. Table 1 shows some of the data obtained prior to Apollo 15 as compared with the inflight data. As inflight data from previous missions became available, it became the best indicator of workloads to expect on succeeding missions.

Table 1

Metabolic Rate Measurement During Training and Flight — Apollo 15

Activity	KSC Training EVA 2 & 3 J/hr x 10^3 (kcal/hr)	Apollo 15 EVA 2 & 3 J/hr x 10^3 (kcal/hr)	Percent Difference
Overhead	359 (379)	261 (275)	+38
Station activity	422 (445)	216 (228)	+95
Lunar rover	192 (203)	463 (123)	+65
Average	372 (393)	218 (230)	+70

Energy Production

The metabolic rates experienced during the Apollo lunar surface extravehicular activities are summarized in table 2. Representative data for the first Apollo 15 EVA are given in table 3. The metabolic rates experienced during the EVA periods were lower than had been predicted before the Apollo missions, and the crewmen were able to move easily and confidently on the lunar surface. The overhead activities were the most energy consuming tasks performed. These activities included egress, offloading and setup of equipment around the Lunar Module (LM), ingress, and stowage of lunar samples. The ALSEP deployment and geological survey resulted in lower metabolic rates than did the overhead activity. This difference may have been attributable to the fact that the details of these activities as a group were less predictable and required more time for judgment and, in some cases, for precise manual manipulation.

The lowest metabolic rates occurred while astronauts drove and rode in the LRV (figure 4). This was the most clearly defined operational activity. Metabolic rates for this activity approached rates reported for shirt sleeve riding in an automobile (Webb, 1973). The low metabolic rates experienced during this lunar activity were important factors contributing to the success of the Apollo 15 through 17 missions through reduction in both the use of consumables and the fatigue experienced by crewmen during the long EVA periods.

The highest average metabolic rate during an EVA was exhibited by the Apollo 11 Lunar Module Pilot (LMP). This crewman had been assigned the task of evaluating modes of locomotion and was quite active in performing this task. Several crewmen experienced the minimum average metabolic rate of approximately 837×10^3 J/hr (200 kcal/hr) on different missions. The highest metabolic rates experienced during the performance of discrete activities were associated with LMP transport of the ALSEP pallet, LM ingress

Table 2

Metabolic Expenditures During Apollo
Lunar Surface Extravehicular Activities

Mission No.	EVA No.	Crewman	Metabolic Rate, J/hr x 10^3 (kcal/hr)					EVA Duration (hr)
			ALSEP Deployment	Geological Station Activity	Overhead	Lunar Roving Vehicle Operations	Total For Activities	
11	1	CDR	818 (195)	1023 (244)	899 (214)		949 (227)	2.43
		LMP	1267 (302)	1471 (351)	1269 (303)		1267 (302)	2.43
12	1	CDR	864 (206)	1017 (243)	1232 (294)		1028 (246)	3.90
		LMP	1006 (240)	1028 (245)	1119 (267)		1054 (252)	3.90
	2	CDR		913 (218)	902 (215)		922 (221)	3.78
		LMP		1058 (253)	1038 (248)		1054 (252)	3.78
14	1	CDR	762 (182)	1230 (294)	920 (219)		843 (202)	4.80
		LMP	947 (226)	729 (174)	1084 (259)		980 (234)	4.80
	2	CDR	494 (118)	996 (238)	895 (213)		959 (229)	3.58
		LMP	851 (203)	1120 (267)	894 (213)		1054 (252)	3.58
15	1	CDR	1182 (282)	1153 (275)	1417 (338)	639 (152)	1159 (277)	6.53
		LMP	1369 (327)	778 (186)	1226 (293)	435 (104)	1033 (247)	6.53
	2	CDR	1019 (243)	1227 (293)	1202 (287)	624 (149)	1054 (252)	7.22
		LMP	1110 (265)	792 (189)	1116 (266)	414 (99)	854 (204)	7.22
	3	CDR	1095 (261)	1013 (242)	1303 (311)	578 (138)	1086 (260)	4.83
		LMP	962 (230)	788 (188)	981 (234)	447 (106)	854 (204)	4.83
16	1	CDR	869 (207)	905 (216)	1146 (273)	725 (173)	917 (219)	7.18
		LMP	1081 (258)	1125 (268)	1154 (275)	666 (159)	1065 (255)	7.18
	2	CDR		933 (223)	1044 (249)	470 (112)	822 (197)	7.38
		LMP		1023 (244)	987 (236)	438 (105)	874 (209)	7.38
	3	CDR		966 (231)	983 (235)	518 (124)	854 (204)	5.67
		LMP		1013 (242)	1107 (264)	430 (103)	864 (207)	5.67
17	1	CDR	1192 (285)	1094 (261)	1267 (302)	506 (121)	1150 (275)	7.20
		LMP	1166 (278)	1255 (300)	1193 (285)	472 (113)	1139 (272)	7.20
	2	CDR		1094 (261)	1267 (302)	506 (121)	864 (207)	7.62
		LMP		1255 (300)	1193 (285)	472 (113)	874 (209)	7.62
	3	CDR		1094 (261)	1267 (302)	506 (121)	980 (234)	7.25
		LMP		1255 (300)	1193 (285)	472 (113)	990 (237)	7.25
Mean			1018 (244)	1018 (244)	1123 (270)	518 (123)	980 (234)	
Total time (hr)			28.18	52.47	52.83	25.28	158.74	

CDR = Commander
LMP = Lunar Module Pilot

with lunar samples, and drilling and removal of drill bits. The flight surgeon never had to limit the work rate of any crewman during an EVA. The lowest rates experienced for discrete activities were associated with riding the LRV, picture taking, and with periods of observation and description.

Table 3

Metabolic Expenditures for the Apollo 15 Commander During EVA-1

Surface Activity	End Time (hr:min)	Duration (min)	Average Metabolic Rate J/hr x 10³ (kcal/hr)
Preegress operations	119:51	12	1569 (374)
Egress	119:59	8	1726 (412)
Television deployment	120:11	12	1895 (452)
Lunar roving vehicle (LRV) offloading and deployment	120:32	21	1463 (349)
LRV configuration	121:45	73	1239 (296)
LRV traverse (LM to station 1)	122:11	26	513 (122)
Station 1 activities	122:29	18	1032 (246)
Geological site selection	122:15	4	1045 (249)
Radial sample	122:24	9	852 (203)
Traverse preparation	122:29	5	1343 (321)
LRV traverse (station 1 to station 2)	122:35	6	486 (116)
Station 2 activities	123:26	51	1196 (285)
Description and documented sample	122:57	22	1120 (267)
Comprehensive sample	123:05	8	1212 (289)
Double core tube	123:16	11	1112 (265)
500-mm photography and traverse preparation	123:26	10	1444 (345)
LRV traverse (station 2 to LM)	124:00	34	617 (155)
ALSEP offloading	124:24	24	1054 (252)
ALSEP traverse (LRV)	124:33	9	795 (190)
Heat flow experiment deployment	125:24	51	1184 (283)
Laser ranging retroreflector deployment	125:33	9	1393 (333)
Photography and traverse preparation	125:38	5	1394 (333)
LRV traverse (ALSEP site to LM)	125:43	5	1343 (321)
EVA closeout	125:58	15	1305 (311)
Solar wind composition experiment deployment and EVA termination	126:11	13	1701 (406)

During the Apollo 14 mission, which included some of the most extensive walking traverses (figure 5), a specific effort was made to relate walking speed to metabolic rate. The results of this effort are presented in table 4. These data indicate a very poor correlation between traverse rate and metabolic rate. During these operational traverses, the crewman apparently maintained a comfortable walking effort, and, to a large extent,

the rate of travel at this level of effort varied with the terrain and the operational
requirements of each traverse.

Figure 4. Apollo 17 astronaut riding in the lunar roving vehicle.

Figure 5. Apollo 17 astronaut walking on the lunar surface.

Table 4

Metabolic Analyses of Apollo 14 EVA Traverses

Traverse	Duration (min)	Traverse Distance (m)	Net Elevation Change (m)	Net Slope Percent	Traverse Rate (km/hr)	Metabolic Rate, $J/hr \times 10^3$ (kcal/hr)	
						CDR	LMP
EVA-1							
ALSEP out	15	172	0	0	.688	1039 (248)	1159 (277)
ALSEP return	16	204	0	0	.765	1344 (321)	1099 (262)
ALSEP overall	31	376	0	0	.728	1192 (285)	1130 (270)
EVA-2							
LM to A*	7.4	193	5	2.6	1.56	593 (142)	875 (209)
A to B	7.8	185	− 5	− 2.7	1.42	804 (192)	887 (212)
B to B1	7.2	319	15	4.7	2.65	1009 (241)	1144 (273)
B1 to B2	5.1	145	15	10.3	1.71	1438 (343)	1218 (291)
B2 to B3	14.4	399	45	11.3	1.66	1575 (376)	1321 (315)
B3 to C'	6.7	220	15	5.8	1.97	1911 (456)	2179 (520)
C' to C1	1.4	86	3	3.5	3.69	1024 (244)	1355 (323)
C1 to C2	5.6	240	− 33	− 13.8	2.57	998 (238)	1116 (266)
C2 to E	6.0	480	− 45	− 9.4	4.8	1314 (314)	1412 (337)
E to F	3.9	292	− 10	− 3.4	4.49	1353 (323)	1545 (367)
F to G	1.8	172	0	0	5.7	1180 (282)	1638 (391)
G to G1	2.5	110	5	4.5	2.64	1125 (268)	1588 (379)
G1 to LM	3.0	159	− 10	− 6.3	3.18	1277 (305)	1645 (393)
Subtotals							
LM to C1	50.0	1547	93	5.0	1.86	1247 (298)	1262 (301)
C1 to LM	22.8	1453	− 93	− 6.4	3.82	1205 (288)	1439 (343)
Totals							
LM to LM	72.8	3000	0	0	2.47	1233 (294)	1318 (315)

*Letter designations represent stations.

In general, both the speed and the efficiency of lunar walking were greater than could be achieved while wearing a pressure suit in a one-g environment; neither speed nor efficiency was equivalent to that of a shirt sleeve operation at one g.

Operational film and kinescope were used in performing a time and motion study of Apollo 15 and 16 activities. This study compared the facility for, and energy cost of performing several specific activities at one g during training wearing the Apollo space suit with one-sixth g on the lunar surface. One of the observations of this study was that tasks were completed more rapidly at one g than at one-sixth g, but that greater metabolic costs were involved (Kubis et al., 1972a; Kubis et al., 1972b).

In addition to the 14 periods of lunar surface activity, there were four periods of zero-g EVA. The metabolic data from these EVA periods are summarized in table 5. During the Command Module extravehicular activities performed during the Apollo 15 through 17 missions, the Command Module Pilot retrieved a film canister from the Service Module while the Lunar Module Pilot tended his umbilical in the doorway of the Command Module (figure 6). During the Command Module extravehicular activities, heart rate was the only data available for estimating metabolic rate. Because the errors in the heart rate method all tended to increase the metabolic rate estimate, these rates can be considered maximum values. Voice contact with crewmen during these periods did not indicate that they were working strenuously. The metabolic rates obtained from heart rate data were not used to constrain extravehicular activities; in some cases, the actual metabolic rates were much lower than the values obtained by means of heart rate calibration data. Elevation of these heart rates was attributed more to excitement than to exercise.

Table 5

Metabolic Expenditures
During Apollo Zero-G EVA Periods

Mission Number	Crewman	Metabolic Rate, J/hr x 10^3 (kcal/hr)	Duration (min)
9	LMP	634 (150)	59
15	CMP	< 992 (235)	40
	LMP*	< 486 (115)	40
16	CMP	<2108 (500)	85
	LMP*	**	85
17	CMP	<1267 (300)	67
	LMP*	<602 (145)	67
			Total 443

*Standup EVA
**Not measured
LMP = Lunar Module Pilot
CMP = Command Module Pilot

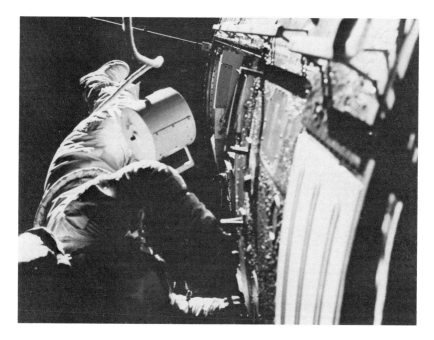

Figure 6. Apollo 17 CMP retrieving film canister from the Service Module.

Concluding Remarks

The Apollo crewmen were able to perform planned extravehicular activities and to extend them to the maximum time allowable without medical problems. The metabolic rates experienced during the lunar surface extravehicular activities were lower than conservative premission estimates.

A manually controlled liquid cooling garment was effectively used to minimize fatigue and water loss from sweating during lunar surface extravehicular activities.

Gas cooling was adequate during the short zero-g extravehicular activities performed from the Command Module.

The prediction of EVA workloads became more reliable as inflight data was accumulated. The prediction of the average metabolic cost of an EVA was more reliable than the cost of an individual short-term task.

References

Kelley, G.F.; Coons, D.O.; and Carpentier, W.R.: Medical Aspects of Gemini Extravehicular Activities. Aerosp. Med., vol. 39, June 1968, pp. 611-615.

Kubis, J.F.; Elrod, J.T.; Rusnak, R.; and Barnes, J.E.: (Final Report) Apollo 15 Time and Motion Study, NASA CR-128695, 1972a.

Kubis, J.F.; Elrod, J.T.; Rusnak, R.; Barnes, J.E.; and Saxon, S.C.: (Final Mission Report) Apollo 16 Time and Motion Study, NASA CR-128696, 1972b.

Machel, R.M., ed: Summary of Gemini Extravehicular Activity. NASA SP-149, 1967.

Margaria, R.; and Cavagna, G.A.: Human Locomotion in Subgravity. Aerosp. Med., vol. 35, Dec. 1964, pp. 1140-1146.

Roth, E.M.: Bioenergetics of Space Suits for Lunar Exploration. NASA SP-84, 1966, pp. 83-87.

Roth, E.M., ed.: Compendium of Lunar Responses to the Aerospace Environment. NASA CR-1205 (II), Nov. 1968.

Shavelson, R.J.: Lunar Gravity Simulation and its Effect on Human Performance. Human Factors, vol. 10, Aug. 1968, pp. 393-402.

Shavelson, R.J.; and Seminara, J.L.: Effect of Lunar Gravity on Man's Performance of Basic Maintenance Tasks. J. Appl. Physiol., vol 52, 1968, pp. 177-183.

Springer, W.E.; Stephens, T.L.; and Streimer, I.: The Metabolic Cost of Performing a Specific Exercise in a Low-Friction Environment. Aerosp. Med., vol. 34, June 1963, pp. 486-488.

Waligora, J.M.; and Michel, E.L.: Application of Conductive Cooling for Working Men in the Thermally Isolated Environment. Aerosp. Med., vol. 39, May 1968, pp. 485-487.

Webb, P.: Work, Heat, and Oxygen Cost. Bioastronautics Data Book. NASA SP-3006, 1973, pp. 847-879.

Wortz, E.C.; and Prescott, E.J.: Effects of Subgravity Traction Simulation on the Energy Costs of Walking. Aerosp. Med., vol. 37, Dec. 1966, pp. 1217-1222.

CHAPTER 5
ENVIRONMENTAL FACTORS

by

E.L. Michel, M.S.
J.M. Waligora, M.S.
D.J. Horrigan, M.S.
W.H. Shumate, Ph.D.

Lyndon B. Johnson Space Center

Introduction

Although many gaseous environments could have been used for the Apollo spacecraft, technological constraints existing in the early manned space flight program dictated the selection of the atmosphere ultimately used. Ideally, from a physiological point of view, the optimum spacecraft atmosphere would have simulated normal or near-normal sea level conditions. Because the state-of-the-art was not sufficiently advanced to cope with the weight and volume penalty imposed by maintaining such an atmosphere, and since spacecraft decompressions could not be precluded, compromises had to be made which resulted in the choice of a spacecraft atmosphere that was not optimum from all points of view, but which was adequate based on practical considerations and the results of appropriate validation tests (Michel et al., 1963).

In addition to establishing the acceptable range of atmospheric composition and pressure, consideration had to be given to the establishment of acceptable carbon dioxide levels, to thermal comfort criteria, and to acceleration and impact limits.

Atmosphere Selection Considerations

The prime design requirements in any spacecraft system are minimum weight, volume, and power usage; reliability, ease of maintenance, environmental compatibility, integration with other systems, and crew compatibility. In Project Mercury, a 100 percent oxygen, $34\,500\,\text{N/m}^2$ (5 psia) spacecraft atmosphere was selected. Although such physiological considerations as maintenance of adequate oxygen partial pressure and protection against decompression sickness were examined, the decision to use this atmosphere was based primarily on the engineering considerations described above and the fact that the longest Mercury mission was 34 hours in duration.

Atmospheric Pressure and Composition

During initial planning for the Apollo Program, biomedical experts of the NASA Space Task Group recommended a spacecraft atmosphere composed of 50 percent oxygen and 50 percent nitrogen, at a pressure of 48 300 N/m^2 (7 psia). This recommendation was approved, and contracts were awarded for the development of a suitable environmental control system (ECS). Research involving mixed gas atmospheres was initiated and mainly directed toward assessment of the potential dysbarism hazard following either planned operational or emergency decompressions to the space suit oxygen atmosphere of 25 500 N/m^2 (3.7 psia) (Damato et al., 1963).

Before the completion of Project Mercury, the decision was made to implement the Gemini Program which would bridge the gap between Project Mercury and the Apollo Program. The plan was one of minimum change and essentially involved enlarging the Mercury spacecraft to permit occupancy by two crewmembers. The mission of the Gemini Program was to obtain data and operational experience required for the Apollo Program. From an engineering aspect, it was desirable to continue using the 34 500 N/m^2 (5 psia), 100 percent oxygen atmosphere, provided that this atmosphere was physiologically adequate for periods of as long as 14 days.

Several questions arose concerning the physiological acceptability of the pure oxygen atmosphere for extended durations. At this time, the potential toxicity of oxygen at 34 400 N/m^2 (5 psia) had not been resolved. Additionally, it was felt that an inert gas should be included in any artificial atmosphere as protection against atelectasis. Accordingly, a comprehensive validation program was instituted by NASA in cooperation with the National Academy of Sciences Working Group on Gaseous Environments. Both industrial and Department of Defense laboratories were used in the program. Data obtained from these studies indicated that exposure of man for 14 days to the 100 percent oxygen, 34 500 N/m^2 (5 psia) atmosphere selected for the Gemini spacecraft would not impose any physiological problem (Morgan et al., 1965; Welch et al., 1965; Helvey et al., 1965; Mammen et al., 1965). As a result of these findings, the Apollo Program Office elected to use this atmosphere in the Apollo spacecraft.

Subsequent atmosphere validation tests up to thirty days in duration indicated that the 100 percent oxygen, 34 500 N/m^2 (5 psia) atmosphere was physiologically adequate (Herlocher, 1964; Robertson et al., 1964; Zalusky, et al., 1964). These studies clearly indicated, however, that this atmosphere was associated with nuisance findings such as aural atelectasis, eye irritation, and nasal congestion. Medical investigations associated with Gemini manned space flights resulted in suggestive, but not conclusive, evidence of hematologic changes resulting from exposure to a single gas atmosphere (Fischer et al., 1967). A consistent, time-related decrease in red cell mass was observed (Richardson et al., 1972). Although the causes and implications of this decrease in red cell mass were not completely understood they were not considered to be a deterrent to the use of 100 percent oxygen at 34 500 N/m^2 (5 psia) for Apollo spacecraft because of the limited duration of these missions.

Apollo preflight checkout procedures initially encompassed an overpressurization of the Command Module (CM) using 100 percent oxygen. After the Apollo fire, these procedures were modified, and a mixture of 60 percent oxygen and 40 percent nitrogen was used to reduce the fire hazard. The CM was launched with this gas composition, which eventually was built up to almost 100 percent oxygen, through leakage makeup with oxygen, in a time frame shown in figure 1. Additional decompression studies were performed to determine whether any dysbarism problems existed under these conditions (Maio et al., 1969; Maio et al., 1970; Allen et al., 1971). The results of these studies showed that potential dysbarism problems were minimal.

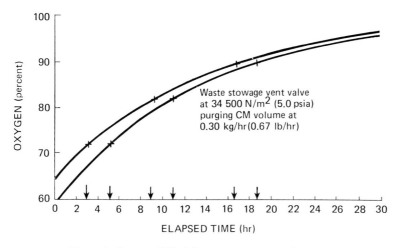

Figure 1. Command Module oxygen purge after launch.

The atmospheric pressure and composition after each launch remained between 32 406 and 35 164 N/m² (4.7 and 5.1 psia) at almost 100 percent oxygen for the duration of each mission, including the time in the Lunar Module (LM). During extravehicular activity (EVA), the suits were pressurized to 26 546 ± 1034 N/m² (3.85 ± 0.15 psia) with 100 percent oxygen. No untoward atmospheric effects, such as hypoxia, dysbarism, or oxygen toxicity, were experienced during any of the Apollo missions.

Carbon Dioxide Concentration

Because carbon dioxide has a powerful stimulatory effect on respiration as well as a marked influence on acid-base balance, the problems of carbon dioxide removal and the ability of man to perform adequately when exposed to various concentrations of carbon dioxide have become important. Synergistic interactions were considered independently in establishing acceptable levels of carbon dioxide for the Apollo Program. The optimal mission design level was established as 505.4 N/m² (3.8 torr) carbon dioxide partial pressure, with a maximum limit for continuous exposure of 1010.8 N/m² (7.6 torr). The emergency limit was set at 1995 N/m² (15.0 torr) carbon dioxide partial pressure.

The carbon dioxide levels recorded by sensors in the Command and Lunar Modules remained well below the limit of 1010.8 N/m² (7.6 torr) except for the return flight of the Apollo 13 spacecraft. The Lunar Module environmental control system was used for approximately 83 hours on this mission, and the first lithium hydroxide cartridge was used for approximately 83 man-hours. During this time, the carbon dioxide level was permitted to increase to an indicated 1981.7 N/m^2 (14.9 torr). Subsequently, four CM cartridges were used in a special arrangement devised and tested at the Lyndon B. Johnson Space Center during the mission. By using this arrangement of four lithium hydroxide cartridges, carbon dioxide levels were maintained between 13.3 and 239.4 N/m^2 (0.1 and 1.8 torr).

Space suit carbon dioxide levels were maintained within nominal limits by proper control of oxygen ventilation flow as predetermined by laboratory testing (Michel et al., 1969). The constant flow rate used was 0.15 m^3/min (5.5 ft^3/min).

Thermal Comfort

The space environment has no known effect on the thermoregulatory center, and there is no evidence that any effect might exist. However, it must be ensured that these environments do not exceed known limits within which thermoregulation can be maintained.

No major problems in thermoregulation were experienced during Project Mercury or the Gemini and Apollo Programs. However, thermal stress may have contributed to the shortening of some Gemini extravehicular activity. More extensive EVA and larger vehicles that permit more activity are conditions that will complicate the heat removal system design for future missions.

The design range for temperature and humidity control in the Apollo Command Module was 294° to 300°K (70° to 80°F) with a relative humidity of 40 to 70 percent. Similarly, the design range for the Lunar Module was 291° to 300°K (65° to 80°F) with a relative humidity of 40 to 70 percent. Thermal comfort and tolerance criteria were developed during the Apollo Program. Although these criteria did not replace the Apollo specifications, they were used frequently to assess the adequacy of pressure suit temperature control and in some instances to evaluate the acceptability of contingency cabin environments (Waligora, 1970). These criteria predicted a slightly cooler and expanded comfort range for the Apollo spacecraft environment compared to the 101 356 N/m^2 (14.7 psia) Earth environment.

Temperature in the CM was controlled through a combination of coldplate wall radiators and a cabin-gas heat exchanger. In practice, however, the gas heat exchanger was neither effective nor necessary and because it increased the ambient noise level it was seldom used. The ambient temperature sensor was located near the inlet to the heat exchanger and it was necessary that the heat exchanger be operating to provide a representative ambient temperature reading. Typically, when the heat exchanger was turned on the temperature reading immediately rose 2.2° to 3.3°K (4° to 6°F), although no constant offset can be assumed. The data from this sensor are presented in table 1.

No operational humidity measurements were made. Relative humidity was measured with a portable device on the Apollo 7 spacecraft and was found to be within the design range of 40 to 70 percent.

Table 1

Command Module Cabin Temperatures in °K (°F)
Measured at the Inlet to the Heat Exchanger (See Text)

Apollo Flight	Launch	Inflight			Reentry
		Average	Range		
7	294.3 (70)	294.3 (70)	290.9 to 299.3 (64 to 79)		291.5 (65)
8	291.5 (65)	295.4 (72)	289.3 to 300.4 (61 to 81)		289.3 (61)
9	291.5 (65)	294.3 (70)	291.5 to 295.4 (65 to 72)		292.6 (67)
10	297.0 (75)	295.9 (73)	290.9 to 299.8 (64 to 80)		287.6 (58)
11	294.3 (70)	290.4 (63)	285.9 to 295.9 (55 to 73)		285.9 (55)
12	294.3 (70)	292.6 (67)	287.6 to 299.8 (58 to 80)		288.7 (60)
13	294.3 (70)	290.9 (64)	287.6 to 294.8 (58 to 71)		297.0 (75)
14	294.3 (70)	296.5 (74)	288.7 to 298.2 (60 to 77)		288.1 (59)
15	294.3 (70)	293.7 (69)	288.1 to 300.4 (59 to 81)		288.1 (59)
16	294.3 (70)	294.3 (70)	287.0 to 299.8 (57 to 80)		287.0 (57)
17	294.3 (70)	293.7 (69)	289.3 to 300.4 (61 to 81)		289.8 (62)

Crew comments indicated that the Command Module was uncomfortably cool during several missions, especially during sleep periods. These occurrences were not serious problems and crewmen compensated by increasing their clothing insulation.

During the Apollo 13 mission, the LM environmental control system provided a habitable environment for approximately 83 hours (57:45 to 141:05 ground elapsed time). Cabin temperature remained low due to low electrical power levels. This caused crew discomfort during much of this time, with cabin temperatures ranging between 283° and 286°K (49° and 55°F).

During the Apollo 11 mission, the crewmen could not sleep in the Lunar Module following EVA because they were too cool. Contributing to the crewmen's discomfort were the sleep positions on the floor of the vehicle, the use by the crewmen, for some time after the EVA, of a cabin supply to their liquid cooling garments that had been provided against a hot-case contingency; and vehicle temperatures between 288° and 290°K (58° and 62°F). Hammocks were provided for sleeping after subsequent Apollo EVA's, and the cabin liquid cooling garment support system was not used before the sleep period; therefore, the problem did not recur.

At the conclusion of each of the missions, the Command Module was precooled prior to reentry to minimize the possible effect of the reentry thermal transients on the internal temperature of the Command Module. No elevated cabin temperatures were experienced during any of the reentries.

Acceleration and Impact

With the exception of Apollo 7, which used the Saturn IB, all Apollo missions used the Saturn V launch vehicle. Launch acceleration loads were well within Apollo system specifications, and crewmembers routinely reported that the launches produced no adverse physiological stresses. A typical Saturn V launch profile is presented in figure 2.

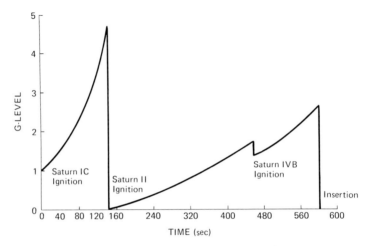

Figure 2. Typical Apollo launch profile — Saturn V launch vehicle.

Maximum reentry G levels for all Apollo missions are shown in table 2. As may be seen, deceleration levels for Earth orbital missions, Apollo 7 and 9, were about one-half those of lunar missions. Neither reentry mode resulted in any medically significant physiological stress. The greater reentry lift capability of the Apollo spacecraft over its predecessors accounts for the much lower acceleration forces. Reentry deceleration profiles of an Earth orbital and a lunar mission are presented in figures 3 and 4.

Table 2

Apollo Manned Space Flight
Reentry G Levels

Flight	Maximum G at Reentry
Apollo 7	3.33
Apollo 8	6.84
Apollo 9	3.35
Apollo 10	6.78
Apollo 11	6.56
Apollo 12	6.57
Apollo 13	5.56
Apollo 14	6.76
Apollo 15	6.23
Apollo 16	7.19
Apollo 17	6.49

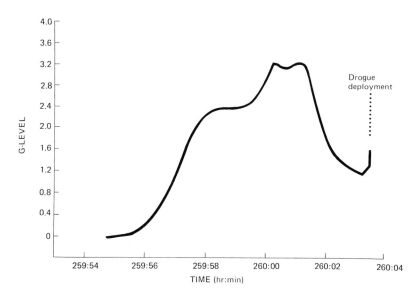

Figure 3. Earth orbital reentry profile — Apollo 7.

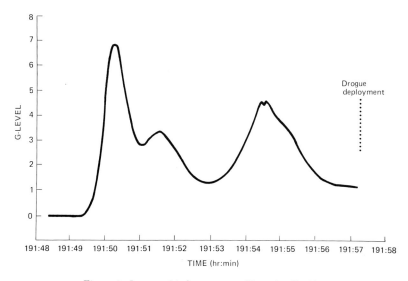

Figure 4. Lunar orbital reentry profile — Apollo 10.

While nominal reentry G levels had been well tolerated by the crew and posed no severe constraints on crew performance, an Apollo launch abort could have resulted in G_X acceleration levels as high as 16.2 G with an oscillating 1/2 Hz component ranging from $-1G_Z$ to $+3.2 G_Z$. Such abort acceleration levels in all probability could have been endured without injury by crewmembers experienced in acceleration tests and protected by the Apollo couch and restraint system. It is very doubtful that spacecraft control tasks could have been adequately performed under such conditions and, for this reason, crew tasks were minimized during a launch abort reentry. The Apollo spacecraft abort escape system was similar to that used in the Mercury Project, consisting of an escape rocket separated from the attached spacecraft by a tower. The rocket was provided, if required to lift the Command Module away from the booster to an altitude high enough for safe parachute deployment. The escape rocket can be seen at the very top of the spacecraft (figure 5).

Figure 5. Apollo 17 night launch showing abort escape system
at the top of the spacecraft.

The Apollo spacecraft landing system employed three parachutes and the repositioned Command Module system used in the Gemini Program (figure 6). The spacecraft entered the water at a 27 1/2° angle on a nominal landing. The most severe impact experienced in an Apollo space flight occurred with Apollo 12. It was estimated that the Command Module entered the water at a 20 to 22° angle which resulted in a 15 G impact. This abnormal entry angle occurred when the wind caused the spacecraft to swing and meet the wave slope at the more normal angle.

Figure 6. Apollo spacecraft parachute landing system.

While the 15 G impact of Apollo 12 was described as very hard by the crewmen, no significant physical difficulties were experienced. Apollo landing impact studies involving 288 human tests were conducted on a linear decelerating device at Holloman Air Force Base. These tests involved impact forces up to 30 G at various selected body orientations. Although significant effects to the neurological, cardiorespiratory, and musculoskeletal systems were recorded, none of the tests resulted in significant incapacitation or undue pain (Brown et al., 1966).

Summary

In summary, environmental factor considerations including atmospheric pressure and composition, thermal comfort, acceleration, deceleration and impact levels; for the most part, remained within physiologically acceptable ranges during the entire Apollo Program. At no time did an anomaly alter these factors to a point where crew health was jeopardized. The environmental changes following the Apollo 13 accident, if prolonged, would have endangered the crew. However, the quick and successful makeshift ECS modifications prevented this from occurring.

References

Allen, T.H.; Maio, D.A.; and Bancroft, R.W.: Body Fat, Denitrogenation and Decompression Sickness in Men Exercising After Abrupt Exposure to Altitude. Aerospace Med., vol. 42, no. 5, May 1971, pp. 518-524.

Brown, W.K.; Rothstein, J.D.; and Foster, P.: Human Responses to Predicted Apollo Landing Impacts in Selected Body Orientations. Aerospace Med. vol. 37, 1966, pp. 394-398.

Damato, Morris J.; Highly, Francis M.; Hendler, Edwin; and Michel, Edward L.: Rapid Decompression Hazards After Prolonged Exposure to 50 Per Cent Oxygen – 50 Per Cent Nitrogen Atmosphere. Aerospace Med., Vol. 34, no. 11, Nov. 1963, pp. 1037-1040.

Fischer, Craig L.; Johnson, Philip C.; and Berry, Charles A.: Red Blood Cell Mass and Plasma Volume Changes in Manned Space Flight. J. Am. Med. Assoc., vol. 200, no. 7 May 15, 1967, pp. 579-583.

Helvey, William M.; Albright, G.A.; Benjamin, F.B.; Gall, L.S.; et al.: Effects of Prolonged Exposure to Pure Oxygen on Human Performance. NASA TN D-2506, 1965, pp. 99-474.

Herlocher, James, E.: Physiologic Response to Increased Oxygen Partial Pressure. Part I – Clinical Observations. Aerospace Med., vol. 35, no. 7, July 1964, pp. 613-618.

Maio, Domenic A.; Allen, Thomas H.; and Bancroft, Richard W.: Decompression Sickness and Measured Levels of Exercise on Simulated Apollo Missions. Aerospace Med., vol. 41, no. 10, Oct. 1970, pp. 1162-1165.

Maio, Domenic A.; Allen, Thomas H.; and Bancroft, Richard W.: Decompression Sickness in Simulated Apollo Space Cabins. Aerospace Med., vol. 40, no 10, Oct. 1969, pp. 1114-1118.

Mammen, Robert E.; Critz, George T.; Dery, Donald W.; Highly, Francis M., Jr.; et al.: The Effect of Sequential Exposure to Acceleration and the Gaseous Environment of the Space Capsule on the Physiologic Adaptation of Man. NASA TN D-2506, 1965, pp. 475-518.

Michel, E.L.; Sharma, H.S.; and Heyer, R.E.: Carbon Dioxide Build-Up Characteristics in Spacesuits. Aerospace Med., vol. 40, no. 8, Aug. 1969, pp. 827-829.

Michel, Edward L.; Smith, George B., Jr.; and Johnston, Richard S.: Gaseous Environment Considerations and Evaluation Programs Leading to Spacecraft Atmosphere Selection. Aerospace Med., vol. 34, no. 12, Dec. 1963, pp. 1119-1121.

Morgan, Thomas E., Jr.; Cutler, Ralph G.; Shaw, Emil G.; Ulvedal, Frode; et al.: Physiologic Effects of Exposure to Increased Oxygen Tension at 5 psia. NASA TN D-2506, 1965, pp. 25-56.

Richardson, B., ed.: Hematologic Response to a Continuous 30-Day Exposure to Hypobaric Hyperoxia. Final Report. NASA MIPR 74401-G. USAF School of Aerospace Medicine, Brooks Air Force Base, Texas, 1972.

Robertson, William G.; Hargreaves, John J.; Herlocher, James E.; and Welch, B.E.: Physiologic Response to Increased Oxygen Partial Pressure, Part II – Respirator Studies. Aerospace Med., vol. 35, no. 7, July 1964, pp. 618-622.

Waligora, J.W.: Thermal Comfort and Tolerance Design Criteria. NASA JSC Report BRO DB-57-67B, 1970.

Welch, B.E.; Cutler, R.G.; Herlocher, J.E.; Hargreaves, J.J.; et al.: Effect of Ventilating Air Flow on Human Water Requirements. NASA TN D-2506, 1965, pp. 57-85.

Zalusky, Ralph; Ulvedal, Frode; Herlocher, James E.; and Welch, B.E.: Physiologic Response to Increased Oxygen Partial Pressure, Part III — Hematopoiesis. Aerospace Med., vol. 35, no. 7, July 1964, pp. 622-626.

CHAPTER 6

FLIGHT CREW HEALTH STABILIZATION PROGRAM

by

Bennie C. Wooley, Ph.D.[*]
Gary W. McCollum, M.S.

Lyndon B. Johnson Space Center

Introduction

When mission durations were increased during the Gemini Program, the possibility that an infectious disease occurrence would adversely affect mission success also increased. The problem did not seem one of major proportions for Project Mercury, because the risk of developing and manifesting a disease during such short duration flights was judged to be extremely low. Even so, crewmember activities were somewhat restricted in terms of contact with persons not directly involved in flight activities. While some cold and influenza symptoms were noted in crewmembers during the preflight period, no inflight illnesses occurred during Project Mercury.

When the training phase of the Gemini Program began, medical personnel were still providing active support for the Mercury flights. Little attention could, therefore, be given to implementing any program of strict isolation of Gemini astronauts during the prelaunch period. Medical personnel were successful in obtaining some reduction in the number of persons with whom the crewmembers had personal contact and were successful, to a limited extent, in having the flight crewmembers live in special quarters at the launch site. During the prelaunch period, access to these living quarters was closely controlled. While no direct illness erupted in flight, most Gemini crews experienced some preflight illness including colds, influenza, Beta-hemolytic streptococcus infections, and mumps.

The authors are grateful to those who helped establish the requirements of the program and participated in its successful implementation. Special acknowledgment is made to Dr. Charles A. Berry, Mr. Richard S. Johnston, Dr. W.W. Kemmerer, Dr. Charles Ross, Dr. Jack Teegen, Dr. John Elliott, Mr. Richard C. Graves, Dr. Howard Schneider, Mr. Larry Thompson, Mr. DeArmond Mathews, and Mr. Paul Hilk. The authors would also like to thank Dr. Alfred E. Evans of the National Academy of Sciences; Dr. Leslie Chambers, Dr. Harold Eitzen, Miss Kay Sue Blake, University of Texas School of Public Health; Northrop Services, Inc.; the Kelsey-Seybold Medical staff, Johnson Space Center; the Pan American Medical staff, Kennedy Space Center; Dr. T. Paul Haney and the Brevard County Health Department, Rockledge, Florida; Mr. William F. Muller and the Brevard County School Board, Titusville, Florida; and Dr. W.E. McConnell, USAF, who complemented the program as a Department of Defense physician to the Kennedy Space Center.

[*]Currently with Becton, Dickinson, and Company, Rutherford, N.J.

During the early development of the Apollo Program, steps were taken by medical personnel to document and implement a preventive medicine program to decrease the risk of illness during the prelaunch and flight periods. Because of early operational problems, no successful program could be developed for the Apollo 7 crewmembers. Perhaps in part as a consequence of this, two Apollo 7 crewmembers developed upper respiratory tract infections during the prelaunch period. These infections were successfully treated prior to launch. However, all crewmembers fell ill during the flight with symptoms which continued into the postflight period.

As a result of the Apollo 7 experience, a medical plan was developed for application to the prime and backup crews of future missions. The intent of the plan was to minimize exposure of crewmen to infectious diseases during the two-week period prior to launch for the crews of Apollo 8, 9, and 10, and during the three-week period preceding the Apollo 11 lunar landing launch. The program was designed to ensure optimal immunity, to reduce person-to-person contact, and to ensure rapid diagnosis and treatment of any diseases that might occur prior to flight. However, as had been the case in the Gemini Program, the Apollo training schedules had already been developed at the time a health stabilization program was conceived, and flight crewmembers, in seeking to maximize their training time and familiarity with spacecraft hardware, ran the risk of incurring greater than desirable disease exposure.

During the Apollo 8 preflight period, all crewmembers suffered viral gastroenteritis. Treatment appeared to be successful, and the spacecraft was launched on schedule. However, viral gastroenteritis reoccurred in the Commander in flight. Before the flight, crewmembers had attended a dinner at the White House, where, it later became known, several guests had had symptoms of influenza. While no rigid health stabilization program was to be established until the time of the Apollo 14 mission, increasing efforts in that direction commenced after the Apollo 8 illness episode.

The emphasis of the post-Apollo 8 health stabilization efforts involved constraint of crewmember activities that could impose the risk of disease exposure when such activities were not directly related to flight preparation. The residence of the crewmembers was limited to the crew quarters at the launch site, and control and screening were provided for personnel who had access to the quarters and conference rooms. The use of laminar airflow rooms for preflight press conferences was initiated in advance of the Apollo 11 mission. A proposed Presidential dinner prior to the Apollo 11 mission was cancelled because of the potential risk to the health of the crew. Activities of the crewmembers continued to be monitored closely. Despite these efforts, one of the primary Apollo 13 crewmembers was exposed to rubella by a backup crewman. Laboratory studies indicated that the Command Module Pilot alone had no immunity to the disease and he had to be replaced by one of the backup crew.

The Apollo 13 episode showed beyond question that the need existed for implementation of a meticulously conceived and strictly enforced program for minimizing and, hopefully, preventing exposure of flight crewmembers to infectious diseases during the prelaunch period. Such a program was developed and conceived for the Apollo 14 and subsequent missions. The program became known as the Flight Crew Health Stabilization Program.

Purpose

The purpose of the Flight Crew Health Stabilization Program finally conceived and implemented was to minimize or eliminate the possibility of adverse alterations in the health of flight crews during the immediate preflight, flight, and postflight periods. The elements of the program are indicated in figure 1. Each of these warrants discussion in terms of the direction taken for implementation in the Apollo Program and for subsequent missions.

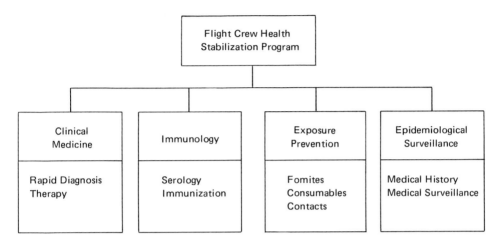

Figure 1. Elements of the Flight Crew Health Stabilization Program.

Clinical Medicine

Because it is critical that all astronauts be maintained in good health, the Government provided a clinical medicine program for Apollo crewmembers and their families and continues to do so for the astronaut corps. This health program is a continual one. It is initiated immediately upon selection of flight crewmembers and continues as long as astronauts are on flight status. The program provides both routine and emergency physical examinations. Rapid diagnosis and prompt effective treatment of any disease event in crewmembers and their families are ensured by complete virological, bacteriological, immunological, serological, and biochemical studies at the National Aeronautics and Space Administration's Lyndon B. Johnson Space Center. (Additional detail concerning the program is given in Chapter 2 of this section.)

Immunology

Ideally, one would desire to immunize crewmembers and their families against all disease agents to preclude the expression of disease symptoms. However, the number of diseases for which there are satisfactory immunizations is extremely limited. Indeed, immunizations are not available for the illnesses most likely to occur — viral and bacterial infections of the upper respiratory and gastrointestinal tracts. The immunizations listed in table 1 were those administered in conjunction with Apollo missions. These were selected after careful review of all known immunizations by NASA medical personnel and a microbiology advisory committee of the National Academy of Sciences. Other immunizations were excluded on the following bases: (1) questionable effectiveness; (2) traumatic side reactions; and (3) low probability of disease agent exposure. Serological tests were conducted to determine immunity levels prior to immunizations. Tuberculin skin tests were given and serological tests were performed for tetanus, syphilis, typhoid, mumps, polio, rubella, rubeola, and yellow fever.

Table 1

Apollo Program Immunization Requirements[a]

Disease	Required Immunization of Astronaut	Required Immunization of Family Members of Astronaut
Diphtheria	Yes	Yes
Pertussis	No	Yes
Tetanus	Yes	Yes
Typhoid	Yes	No
Influenza	Yes	No
Mumps	Yes[b]	Yes
Poliomyelitis	Yes	Yes
Rubella	Yes[b]	Yes
Rubeola	Yes[b]	Yes
Smallpox	Yes	Yes
Yellow fever	Yes	No
Other	(c)	(c)

[a]Schedule recommended by personnel of the USPHS and of the American Public Health Association.

[b]Immunization if no serologic response was obtained.

[c]Only as indicated for travel to endemic areas.

Exposure Prevention

Disease exposure prevention was the most important aspect of the Apollo preventive medicine program. If exposure to infectious diseases had not been minimized or eliminated, the program would have been unsuccessful regardless of the effectiveness of all other aspects combined. Diseases can be transmitted by fomites (contaminated inanimate objects), contaminated consumables (air, food, water, etc.), and personal contacts. Fomites probably represented the least important source of infectious diseases. Nevertheless, the precaution of using separate headsets, microphones, and so forth, for crewmembers was observed. Contaminated consumables posed a greater danger. To prevent transmission of an infectious disease through the air, a closely controlled living environment was provided during the prelaunch period.

All areas in which crewmembers resided or worked were equipped with ultra-high efficiency bacterial filters in all air supply ducts. This precluded exposure to microbial agents from adjacent non-medically controlled areas and individuals. Air conditioning systems were also balanced to provide air pressure in those areas inhabited by crewmembers, as compared with areas outside. Air leakage around windows, doors, floors, walls, and ceilings was directed outward rather than inward toward crewmembers.

The food supply consumed by flight crewmembers was a source of potentially infectious microorganisms. As a precautionary measure, no set or publicized pattern of food procurement was established. Crew quarters food procurement was supervised by members of the medical team. Portions of each lot of food were subjected to microbiological evaluations and all food preparation areas were inspected daily for cleanliness and maintenance of satisfactory sanitary conditions. Drinking water sources were limited to drinking fountains provided in the quarters and working spaces. Water samples were taken daily from all areas visited by the crewmembers and subjected to microbiological evaluations.

By far the most important means of preventing crew exposure to infectious diseases was to minimize exposure to personal contacts during the critical preflight period. The areas which could be visited by crewmembers were strictly limited and the number of individuals allowed contact with the crewmembers was reduced to slightly over one hundred people with mission-related responsibilities. A medical surveillance program of primary contacts was conducted to ensure that those people who did have contact with the flight crewmembers represented a low probability of disease transmission. Additionally, crewmembers were isolated from potential carriers, such as transient populations (launch site visitors), high incidence groups (children), and uncontrolled contacts (maintenance and other personnel about whom no medical information was known). Launch site visitors came from all over the United States and from many foreign nations and brought with them a flora that differed significantly from that normally experienced by the astronauts. Children are the most common carriers and transmitters of upper respiratory and gastrointestinal infections. Astronauts were therefore isolated for 21 days prior to flight even from their own children. The need for this measure was borne out by epidemiological data obtained during initial implementation of the health stabilization program.

Several options were available to minimize crew exposure to infectious agents. Building facilities to house crews and primary contacts for the prelaunch period or modifying existing ones to this end would have been effective approaches, but they were economically prohibitive. The more economical solution provided for strict isolation of flight crewmembers, both prime and backup, in crew quarters and limiting their contacts to medically approved individuals only. These latter individuals were permitted to maintain their residence at home. However, their health status was continually monitored to minimize the possibility of their exposing flight crewmembers to any infectious disease agent. This monitoring of primary contacts resulted in the epidemiological surveillance program.

Epidemiological Surveillance

The medical surveillance program, initiated three months prior to launch, began with the taking of medical histories and other critical information from each primary contact. Each was then subjected to an extensive physical examination approximately 60 days prior to launch, and microbiological samples were obtained to identify carriers. Based on this information, certain individuals were medically approved for access to flight crewmembers during the 21-day prelaunch period.

Each primary contact and all his family members were subjected to medical surveillance during the F-21 (flight day minus 21 days) period. Primary contacts were instructed to report to the medical examination facility whenever they or any of their family became ill or had been exposed to any infectious diseases. Reports of illness events were also obtained from all schools attended by primary contacts' or astronauts' children. Daily reports were solicited from each school of interest concerning the total number of absences, including absences of the children of any crewmember or primary contact. Additional daily reports were obtained from public health authorities in the launch site area to determine trends and incidence of specific disease events within the population where primary contacts may have had exposure. A computerized data processing system was developed to maintain complete and up-to-date records on all crewmembers, primary contacts, and their families. The system linked the medical analyses laboratories at the NASA Lyndon B. Johnson Space Center in Houston, Texas, with the Medical Surveillance Office at the Kennedy Space Center, Florida. Medical information on any individual was immediately available by this system.

Results

The success of the Flight Crew Health Stabilization Program implemented in support of the Apollo 14 through 17 missions was evidenced by absence of preflight, inflight, and postflight illnesses. A comparison of the illness incidents for astronauts, primary contacts, and their families, and for the control group, their spouses and children for each mission is tabulated in table 2. A comparison of the type of illness event occurring in the primary contacts and dependent group is given in table 3. Monitoring the health of primary-contact children proved to be valuable because in approximately 30 percent of the cases of illness in primary contacts, similar illnesses had occurred previously in one or more of the family members. The most common type of illness reported was upper respiratory tract infection.

Summary and Conclusions

The Flight Crew Health Stabilization Program, developed to minimize exposure of flight crewmembers to infectious microorganisms in the prelaunch period, had three basic aspects. These were:

1. Control of locations to which flight crewmembers had access during the three-week period before launch.

Table 2

Apollo Flight Crew Health Stabilization Program Comparison
of Illness Incidence for the Apollo 14 to 17 Missions

Population	Mission Number							
	14[a]		15[b]		16[c]		17[d]	
	Number of Persons	Percentage of Illness Incidence	Number of Persons	Percentage of Illness Incidence	Number of Persons	Percentage of Illness Incidence	Number of Persons	Percentage of Illness Incidence
Astronauts (prime & backup)	12	0	15	0	15	0	13	0
Primary contacts	161	22	151	13	180	35	176	28
Spouses	130	6	132	1	139	15	147	10
Children	242	56	241	8	226	28	263	26
Control group	—	—	145	10	149	32	—	—
Spouses	—	—	127	5	121	12	—	—
Children	—	—	230	5	241	18	—	—

[a] Surveillance period was from December 7, 1970 to February 9, 1971.
[b] Surveillance period was from June 11, 1971 to August 7, 1971.
[c] Surveillance period was from February 28, 1972 to April 27, 1972.
[d] Surveillance period was from October 16, 1972 to December 19, 1972.

2. Control of the number of personal contacts of the astronauts during the three-week prelaunch period.

3. Careful monitoring of the health of individuals required to be in contact with flight crewmembers.

Table 3

Apollo Flight Crew Health Stabilization Program Characterization of Illnesses for the Apollo 14 to 17 Missions[*]

(values are number of illnesses)

Illness	Mission Number			
	14	15	16	17
Upper respiratory infections	156	32	89	77
Gastrointestinal infections	12	1	28	24
Ear infections	7	3	5	2
Chicken pox	3	0	3	0
Pneumonia	3	1	1	1
Measles	0	1	0	0
Primary contacts and dependents under surveillance	575	569	590	644

[*]Primary contacts and dependents only.

In summary, the Flight Crew Health Stabilization Program was an unequivocal success. No crewmember illness was reported for the missions for which the program was in effect. Statistics recorded for prior Apollo missions indicated that 57 percent of the prime crewmembers experienced some illness during the 21 days prior to launch, as well as illness events inflight and postflight.

The importance of a health stabilization program was clearly demonstrated by the Apollo experience. The importance of such a program will become more critical for manned missions of longer durations, and it is anticipated that a stricter isolation program may be necessary to prevent the potential threat of infectious disease and compromise of mission success.

References

Downs, T.D.; Eitzen, H.E.; and Labarthe, D.R.: Apollo 16 Surveillance Report (NAS 9-12640). University of Texas School of Public Health (Houston, Texas), June 1, 1972.

Eitzen, H.E.: Apollo 15 Final Surveillance Report (NAS 9-11384). University of Texas School of Public Health (Houston, Texas), September 1, 1971.

Eitzen, H.E.: Apollo 14 Flight Crew Health Stabilization Program Analysis (NAS 9-11384). University of Texas School of Public Health (Houston, Texas), March 1, 1971.

McCollum, G.W.: Apollo 17 Flight Crew Health Stabilization Program Mission Report. NASA (Houston, Texas), January 17, 1973.

Wooley, B.C.: Apollo Experience Report – Protection of Life and Health. NASA TN D-6856, 1972.

CHAPTER 7
THE ROLE OF TOXICOLOGY IN THE APOLLO SPACE PROGRAM

by

Wayland J. Rippstein, Jr.
Lyndon B. Johnson Space Center

Introduction

It had been determined from experiences with manned chamber tests and submarine operations that human exposure to trace levels of a significant number of gases presented a threat, both to man and to the successful completion of closed-loop operations. It was therefore of major concern that adequate protection be provided for space crews. This protection could be accomplished by eliminating, or at least minimizing, crew exposures to possible harmful levels of trace contaminant gases contained in the spacecraft cabin.

A review of the offgassing characteristics of nonmetallic materials used in the manufacture and fabrication of pre-Apollo spacecraft indicated that, without proper safeguards, a potential toxicological problem could develop in the Apollo spacecraft cabin. The offgassing from man and nonmetallic materials, such as surface coatings, adhesives, elastomers, cleaning agents, solvents, and spacecraft fluids systems (heat exchanger liquids, fire extinguishers, etc.), were all known to contribute to the overall spacecraft trace contaminant burden. The trace contamination problem in the spacecraft atmosphere was further complicated by the introduction of a new generation of fire retardant materials following the Apollo 204 fire. Most of these materials were of the halogenated polymeric type and had undergone few or no toxicity investigations.

Toxicological Considerations

When toxicology is discussed, lethality is generally the major concern. It was equally important, however, in the Apollo Program, to ensure that a crew's exposure to a contaminated atmosphere created no irreversible physiological changes. Irreversible decrements in any physiological function were considered completely unacceptable. Had this criterion not been met, the ability of the crew to properly perform their duties throughout the mission could have been seriously hampered and the success of the mission jeopardized.

Most of the available inhalation toxicity information concerning man is based on the eight-hour work period of the industrial worker. Such data presumes an eight-hour daily

151

exposure, followed by a 16-hour recovery period prior to re-exposure, and a 48-hour weekend recovery. New exposure limits had to be established for space missions since these involved uninterrupted exposure for two weeks with no daily or weekend recovery periods. Information concerning the possible resultant cumulative damage was unavailable.

Two major toxicological situations were considered to develop a toxicology program that could best be used to evaluate the factors involved in extended human exposures. These were the potential contaminant levels that could occur during (1) "normal" spacecraft operating conditions, that is all spacecraft systems functioning properly, and (2) the "emergency" situation, that is when any spacecraft system experienced an upset condition or a failure mode. In the normal condition, the major concern was generation of trace contaminant gases by the normal offgassing of nonmetallic materials both at ambient temperatures and at elevated temperatures during equipment operation. Other sources of contaminant gases under normal conditions were the breathing gas supply reservoirs onboard the spacecraft and, to a lesser extent, the crewmembers themselves. Under emergency conditions, contaminant gas levels could be quantitatively much greater because of overheating, spills, ruptures, and so forth. Rupture of the coolant loop, for example, could have introduced a dangerous contaminant, ethylene glycol. Pyrolysis of some of the electronic nonmetallic materials could have produced a host of particulates and toxic gases.

Provisions were made in the spacecraft carbon dioxide removal unit for the removal of trace levels of contaminant gases. The unit consisted of two parallel canisters, each containing lithium hydroxide for removal of carbon dioxide, and activated carbon for the removal of trace contaminant gases. The parallel flow configuration permitted the canisters to be alternately exchanged for fresh ones after 12 hours of continuous operation. While activated carbon is the best all-purpose trace contaminant gas removal agent, it does not remove carbon monoxide. The only means for removing carbon monoxide from the spacecraft cabin was by cabin leakage. Since leakage rates were very low, the presence of carbon monoxide in the spacecraft cabin was a major concern for all the Apollo missions.

In summary, two major areas of emphasis in the toxicology program were (1) sources of contaminant gases and (2) control or removal of these gases. The trace gas source problem was dealt with by implementing a spacecraft materials control program to either eliminate or minimize the acceptance of materials with undesirable offgassing properties. A trace gas removal capability was incorporated in the spacecraft environmental control system to maintain an acceptable trace gas level in the spacecraft cabin. Before either of these programs could be intelligently implemented, however, maximum acceptable concentrations had to be determined for trace contaminant gases in the spacecraft cabin.

Maximum Allowable Concentrations of Spacecraft Trace Gas

A major difficulty existed in deriving a set of maximum allowable concentrations (MAC) for spacecraft trace contaminant gases. "New" toxicity values had to be determined with a dearth of data concerning increased exposure time and human responses to different compounds or mixtures of compounds.

Thomas (1968)[*] characterized human toxicity responses in a generalized manner, in the following ways:

1. *Equilibrium – (intake equals excretion).* The total organism appears to maintain equilibrium, since the excretion of the contaminant equals the intake or input. There is no apparent biochemical reaction.

2. *Adaptation – (desensitization, cross tolerance).* There may be chemical reactions, but these are countered by an adaptation of the organism to the contaminant exposure.

3. *Cumulative – (summation of interests).* The adsorbed contaminant damages one or more internal organs, with concomitant biochemical derangement and probable physiological dysfunction.

4. *"All or None" – (carcinogens, sensitizers, irritants).* Response may be immediate, as with irritant substances, or delayed, as with sensitizing substances. Some materials may be involved in cancer production. (Carcinogenic reactions were not considered in the Apollo toxicity program.)

Considering these generalized response descriptions in relation to the differences in the maximum allowable concentration values for the eight-hour work day exposure versus the approximately 350 hours of lunar space mission exposure, it is noteworthy that, in most cases, one or all four types of these responses were significant in determining new MAC values for the lunar mission. In the cases for the "equilibrium," "adaptation," and "all or none" responses, the alterations of the MAC values could be theoretically small or none at all. In the case of the "cumulative" response, the MAC value required a major reduction since the change in exposure duration was increased by a factor of approximately 44 times the original exposure time value. It was realized that it was virtually impossible to consider the synergistic effects of two or more compounds in establishing the spacecraft MAC levels.

Establishment of Spacecraft Materials Selection Criteria

During the initial phases of the Apollo Program, a procedure was adopted that served as a toxicological screening test for spacecraft candidate nonmetallic materials. This test was used to determine the toxic effects of the offgassed products on laboratory animals. The test consisted of heating materials to $341^\circ K$ ($68^\circ C$) and allowing the offgassed products to flow over rats and mice for a period of 14 days. Weight losses of each material were recorded, and the exposed animals were observed for their responses. The animals were observed periodically for 30 days after exposure, and histopathological studies were made.

In all, 150 materials were tested at the Wright-Patterson Air Force Base Toxicology Facility. Approximately 10 percent of the materials tested were rejected because they produced unsatisfactory responses in animals. Approximately 90 percent of the materials tested offgassed significant amounts of carbon monoxide.

---

[*]A.A. Thomas: Man's Tolerance to Trace Contaminants. AMRL-TR-67-146, Aerospace Medical Research Laboratories, Wright-Patterson Air Force Base, Ohio, Jan. 1968.

With the change of materials specification after the Apollo 204 fire, only about 20 percent of the information previously obtained was applicable for the fabrication of subsequent spacecraft. The revised materials program emphasized the requirement for low flammability characteristics. At that phase in the program, there was insufficient time to conduct toxicological studies on the newly developed materials as had been done earlier. A new screening test was adopted that included offgassing considerations so that appropriate information would be available for the selection of the candidate materials. As before, the candidate material was heated to 341°K (68°C) but animal exposures were replaced with analytical analyses. The material was kept at 341°K (68°C) for 72 hours in a dessicator filled with oxygen to a pressure of $337 \times 10^2 N/m^2$ (253 mm Hg). At the end of the 72-hour period, samples of the dessicator atmosphere were withdrawn for determination of the amounts of total organics (TO) and carbon monoxide (CO). Results were reported as micrograms of TO or CO per gram of material offgassed. Any material tested was considered acceptable if it offgassed less than $100\mu g$ TO or $10\mu g$ CO per gram of material.

An odor test was also employed to test for those materials considered undesirable because they generated offensive odors. This test was accomplished by allowing a specially qualified panel of laboratory personnel to grade their odor responses to an administered sample of the atmosphere from the candidate material.

In cases where it was known that a candidate material might undergo overheating in the actual spacecraft application, pyrolysis studies were employed using laboratory animal exposures and analytical chemistry. The final decision, from a toxicological standpoint, was then made for the data obtained.

Materials Acceptance

One of the main functions of the Johnson Space Center Toxicology Laboratory was to provide a rapid response capability for handling emergency toxicity problems. Most often the emergency problems resulted in one of three resolutions. A material usage or procedure was either (1) approved, (2) disapproved, or (3) approved after modification.

During the Apollo Program some thirty of these emergency problems were resolved. Some examples are listed below:

Disapproved. Carboxynitroso rubber was submitted as a candidate material for use as an electrical insulator. Upon pyrolysis, the material was found to produce a very toxic vapor. A flight log ink was found to produce toxic volite vapors at room temperature.

Approved. Ethylene glycol was selected as the candidate heat exchanger fluid for the Command/Service Module. It was feared that even a minute leak in the spacecraft coolant loop could result in a hazardous breathing atmosphere. A series of contractual and in-house studies proved the problem could be handled by training the astronauts to detect trace levels of the glycol vapor. Several paints and adhesives were found to offgas excess quantities of total organics. These materials were all approved for usage after a qualitative analysis proved the offgassed species to be nontoxic at the levels offgassed.

Approved After Modification. A special paint developed for the space program was found to offgas excessive quantities of total organics and carbon monoxide. The paint was approved for usage by employing a procedural change in the curing process. A quartz window was installed in the Command/Service Module for conducting special ultraviolet photographic work. The quartz window permitted the production of ozone in the cabin atmosphere when the spacecraft orientation allowed sunlight to pass into the interior of the vehicle. The use of the quartz window was allowed by requiring the use of an ultraviolet filter over the window when photographic work was being done.

In general, the time required to conduct these special toxicity assessments was from two to six weeks. The investigation on the use of ethylene glycol was the major exception. Approximately 18 months were required for the ethylene glycol evaluation.

Atmospheric Assessment

Preflight Assessment

Prior to the first Earth orbital flights of the Apollo spacecraft, a series of solar simulator–altitude chamber tests was accomplished to determine the overall performance characteristics of the spacecraft systems. This included testing of the prototypes of the Command/Service Module (designated as 2TV-1) and the Lunar Module (designated LTA-8). These tests were conducted at the Johnson Space Center's High Altitude Chamber Test Facility. During the testing of both vehicles, trace contaminant analyses were performed on the crew cabin atmospheres to ensure the safety of the test crew and to assess the performance of the spacecraft's environmental control system in maintaining an acceptable breathing gas environment.

The atmospheric samples were taken both by whole gas sampling and by cryogenic trapping techniques. Chemical analyses were accomplished by employing the latest methods in gas chromatography, mass spectrometry, and infrared spectrophotometry.

The final atmospheric assessment of the flight Command and Lunar Modules was accomplished at the Kennedy Space Center during final checkout of the spacecraft. Atmospheric samples were taken from both vehicles prior to their acceptance for space flight. Sampling and analytical methods similar to those described previously were employed at the Kennedy Space Center for assuring the atmospheric quality of these spacecraft.

Postflight Analyses

Inflight cabin trace gas composition was determined by chemical analysis of the activated carbon canisters returned from the Apollo 7 through 17 spacecraft. The carbon dioxide concentration calculated from conversion of lithium hydroxide in the canisters was utilized to study crew metabolic performance.

Samples of activated carbon were removed from each of the canisters for trace gas analysis. The trace gas samples were obtained by employing high vacuum and thermal desorption techniques. Both qualitative and relative quantitative chemical data were obtained by performing gas chromatographic–mass spectrometric analyses on the activated carbon desorbate. A list of the identified compounds from Apollo 7 through 17 is presented in table 1. (An "X" under the mission number indicates that the compound listed was present in the desorbate taken from that mission.)

Table 1

Apollo Spacecraft Contaminants

Contaminant Name	Flights in Which Detected										
	7	8	9	10	11	12	13	14	15	16	17
Amyl Alcohol											
Butyl Alcohol	x	x	x	x	x	x	x	x	x	x	
Capryl Alcohol					x	x	x	x	x		
Ethyl Alcohol	x	x	x	x	x	x	x	x	x	x	x
Isoamyl Alcohol					x	x	x	x	x	x	
Isobutyl Alcohol	x	x	x	x	x	x	x	x	x	x	x
Isopropyl Alcohol	x	x	x	x	x	x	x	x	x	x	x
Methyl Alcohol	x	x	x	x	x	x	x	x	x	x	x
Propyl Alcohol	x				x	x			x	x	x
Sec-Butyl Alcohol	x	x	x	x			x				
Tert-Butyl Alcohol	x	x	x			x					
Acetaldehyde	x	x	x	x	x	x	x	x	x	x	x
Butyraldehyde	x										
N-Butane					x	x	x	x	x	x	x
Cyclohexane	x	x	x	x	x	x				x	x
Cyclopentane	x		x		x	x		x	x	x	
Ethane					x	x	x		x	x	x
Heptane	x	x	x	x		x					
Hexane	x	x	x	x	x	x	x		x	x	
Isobutane					x	x			x	x	
Isopentane	x	x	x	x							x
Methylcyclohexane	x	x	x	x	x	x	x	x	x	x	
Methylcyclopentane	x		x	x		x	x	x	x	x	x
N-Octane	x										
Pentane	x	x	x	x	x	x					
Propane					x	x			x	x	x
Trimethylbutane	x			x							
Trimethylhexane	x		x		x		x			x	
Allene						x	x				
Benzene	x	x	x	x	x	x	x	x	x	x	x
1, 3,-Butadiene						x	x				
1-Butene					x	x	x	x	x	x	x
2-Butene (cis)					x	x			x	x	x
2-Butene (trans)					x	x			x	x	x
Cyclohexane		x				x	x		x	x	
Cyclopentene		x		x							
Ethylbenzene		x	x	x	x	x	x	x	x	x	x
Ethylene	x	x		x	x	x	x	x	x	x	x
2-Hexene			x	x	x	x	x	x	x	x	x
Indene	x	x			x	x	x	x	x	x	x
Isoprene			x		x	x	x	x	x	x	x
Mesitylene	x		x		x	x	x	x	x	x	x
Methylacetylene					x	x	x		x	x	
1-Pentene	x		x	x					x		
2-Pentene						x	x		x	x	

Table 1 (Continued)
Apollo Spacecraft Contaminants

Contaminant Name	Flights in Which Detected										
	7	8	9	10	11	12	13	14	15	16	17
Dichloroethane					x				x	x	x
Dichloroethylene					x	x					
Dichlorofluoromethane					x	x					
Difluoroethylene							x		x		x
Ethyl chloride					x	x				x	x
Ethylene dichloride	x										
Ethylfluoride						x	x	x	x	x	x
Fluoroethane					x		x		x	x	
Fluoropropane						x	x		x	x	
Freon 11	x	x	x	x	x		x		x	x	
Freon 12					x	x	x	x		x	x
Freon 22					x	x	x	x		x	
Freon 113	x	x	x	x	x	x		x	x	x	x
Freon 114					x						
Methylchloride							x	x	x	x	x
Methylchloroform	x	x	x	x	x	x					x
Methylene chloride	x	x	x	x	x	x		x	x	x	x
Mono-Chloroacetylene					x						
Pentafluoroethane					x	x	x		x	x	x
Tetrachloroethane		x		x			x	x			
Tetrachloroethylene	x	x	x	x	x	x				x	x
Tetrafluoroethylene					x	x	x		x	x	x
Trichloroethylene	x	x	x	x	x	x		x	x	x	x
Trifluorochloroethylene		x						x	x	x	
Tetrahydrofuran									x	x	
Methylfuran										x	
Freon 21									x	x	
Hexafluoroethane										x	
Trifluoroethylene					x	x	x	x	x	x	x
Trifluoromethane					x	x		x	x	x	
Trifluoropropane						x	x		x	x	
Trifluoropropene					x		x	x	x		
Vinyl Chloride						x	x	x	x	x	x
Vinylidene Chloride				x	x	x	x		x	x	x
Dimethyldiflurosilane						x	x	x		x	
Trimethylfluorosilane					x	x	x	x	x	x	x
Diethyldisulfide					x						
Dimethyldisulfide				x					x	x	
Dimethylsulfide			x	x	x	x		x	x	x	x
Vinyl Fluoride							x	x	x	x	x
1, 1, 1-Trichloroethane							x	x	x	x	x
Tetrafluorochloroethane							x				
Chlorodifluoroethylene							x	x	x		
Naphthalene							x		x		
Pentyl alcohol							x	x			
Cellosolve acetate							x				
Decahydronapthanlene							x	x			

Table 1 (Continued)
Apollo Spacecraft Contaminants

Contaminant Name	Flights in Which Detected										
	7	8	9	10	11	12	13	14	15	16	17
Propylene	x	x	x	x	x	x	x	x	x	x	x
Styrene	x	x	x	x	x	x	x	x	x		
Toluene	x	x	x	x	x	x	x	x	x	x	x
Trimethyl Benzene					x				x		
M-Xylene	x	x	x	x	x	x	x	x	x	x	x
O-Xylene	x	x	x	x	x	x	x	x	x	x	
P-Xylene	x	x				x	x	x	x	x	
N-Propyl Benzene									x	x	
Ethylacetylene									x		
Trimethylbenzene									x		
2-Methyl Pentane										x	x
Dimethyl Butane										x	x
3 Methylpentane											x
Acetylene					x	x	x			x	x	x
Octyne						x	x	x	x		
Diisopropylamine			x								
Butyl Acetate	x	x	x	x	x				x		
Butyl Lactate						x		x			
Ethyl Acetate	x	x	x	x	x	x			x	x	
Ethyl Lactate						x	x	x			
Methyl Acetate	x	x	x	x	x	x	x				
Propyl Acetate	x						x				
Dimethyl Ether					x	x			x	x	x
Dioxane			x	x	x	x	x		x	x	x
Furan		x	x	x	x	x	x	x	x	x	x
Sulfur Dioxide				x							x
Acetone	x	x	x	x	x	x	x	x	x	x	x
Cyclohexane	x										
Methyl lethyl Ketone	x	x	x	x	x	x	x	x	x	x	x
Methyl Isobutyl Ketone	x	x	x	x	x	x	x	x	x	x	x
2-Pentanone	x	x									
Acetonitrile		x	x	x	x			x	x	x	
Methoxy Acetic acid				x				x			
Carbon Tetrachloride	x							x			
Chloroacetylene						x					
Chlorobenzene		x	x	x	x	x			x	x	
Chlorofluoroethylene						x			x	x	x	x
Chloroform	x	x			x	x				x	x
Chloropropane	x										
Chlorotetrafluoroethane					x	x			x		x
Chlorotrifluoroethylene					x	x			x	x	x
Dichlorobenzene		x	x	x		x					x
Dichlorodifluoroethylene						x		x	x	x	x

Table 1 (Continued)

Apollo Spacecraft Contaminants

Contaminant Name	Flights in Which Detected										
	7	8	9	10	11	12	13	14	15	16	17
Chlorotrifluoromethane								x			
Fluoroform								x			
Trifluoroacetonitride									x		
Octalfluorobutane								x			
Propadiene								x			
Dichlorodifluoroethane								x		x	x
Dimethylcyclohexane								x		x	
Cyclohexyl alcohol									x		
1-Hexene									x	x	x
Octafluoropropane									x		
Ethyl fluoride									x		
Hexafluoropropene									x		
Vinylidenefluoride									x		

Quantitative information is not included in this chapter because of the uncertainties associated with the adsorption-desorption efficiencies of the compounds listed.

Summary

This chapter has presented some of the major considerations that governed the formation and application of the toxicology program employed in support of the Apollo Program. The overriding concern of the program was the safety of crews exposed to trace contaminant gases for extended periods of time. The materials screening program employed, in conjunction with a well designed spacecraft environmental control system, helped to attain the goals set forth for the Apollo Program.

The knowledge gained from working with the toxicity problems and the identification of compounds in the space cabin atmosphere are of much importance for continued efforts in the realm of manned space flight.

Preflight and Postflight

Medical Testing

It was apparent at an early point in the Gemini Program that exposure to the environment of space produces some changes in man. These changes included postflight orthostatic intolerance, a loss of red cell mass, some loss of bone mineral, and other effects. While the fact of these changes was certain, their medical significance was not. For this reason, a number of medical experiments and evaluations were conducted during the Apollo Program. The purpose was to gain additional information concerning the physiological response of astronauts to the stresses of space flight. The chapters within this section describe the principal medical experiments of Apollo. Conclusions from these experiments are based on a comparison of postflight measures with baseline information obtained during preflight testing.

CHAPTER 1

ENDOCRINE, ELECTROLYTE, AND FLUID VOLUME CHANGES ASSOCIATED WITH APOLLO MISSIONS

by

Carolyn S. Leach, Ph.D.
W. Carter Alexander, Ph.D.

Lyndon B. Johnson Space Center

P.C. Johnson, M.D.

Baylor College of Medicine

Introduction

As a result of medical observations during the American and Soviet manned space flight programs, it is now known that complex physiological changes occurred in crewmen returning from space missions (Berry & Catterson, 1967; Kakurin, 1971). These changes have been associated with severe operational demands coupled with exacting mechanical tasks, acceleration, weightlessness, sleep loss, changing circadian rhythms, confinement, periods of relative inactivity alternating with strenuous physical activity, and a cabin atmosphere which is both hyperoxic and hypobaric. The urgent need to study the physiological changes in exact mechanistic terms led to the development of the endocrine/metabolic program in support of manned space flight.

Before the Apollo 7 mission, considerable knowledge had been accumulated concerning the fluid and endocrine changes associated with Mercury and Gemini Earth-orbital missions (Leach, 1971; Dietlein & Harris, 1966). It was known that astronauts always weighed less after a mission than they did before the mission. This decrease in weight was associated with modest decreases in plasma volume. These results showed that, although cardiovascular deconditioning resulting from space flight was similar in extent to that found after bed rest, the weight changes after space flight were greater but the plasma volume changes were smaller. There is evidence from Gemini

The authors would like to thank Drs. Edgar Haber, John Potts, Bonnalie Campbell and Myron Miller for their scientific consultations. Additionally, the following individuals are responsible for the conduct of the analyses in this report: Margaret Patton, Libby Troell, Vernell Fesperman, Dorothy Hatton, Sylvia Wilson, Sandra Seals, Charles Shannon, Richard Long, Douglas Fogel, George Green, Theda Driscoll, Karen Windler, Karen Swensen and Lee Bertam.

studies that the reentry sequence is associated with a sudden increase in epinephrine release as shown by a short-lived granulocytosis. This finding indicated that reentry for Gemini crewmen was a stressful experience. Before Project Mercury, certain segments of the scientific community were apprehensive that certain aspects of weightlessness might produce life-threatening conditions including hypercalcemia and hypercalciuria. This apprehension subsided when no evidence of a calcium abnormality was found. Even after the 14-day Gemini 7 mission, X-ray bone densitometry showed absent to slight loss of bone mineral (Mack et al., 1967).

Using this background, more extensive endocrine and metabolic studies were planned for the Apollo Program. As with other portions of the medical program, these studies were designed to provide data relative to the maintenance of flight crew health and well-being during a mission. The purpose of this chapter is to summarize and discuss the endocrine and metabolic results obtained before and after the Apollo missions and the results of the limited inflight sampling. From these studies, it is possible to obtain an idea of the nature and the extent of endocrine responses by the crewmen who flew the Apollo missions.

As part of the overall operational medical program, the endocrinological and metabolic studies were designed to evaluate the biochemical changes in the returning Apollo crewmembers. The areas studied were balance of fluids and electrolytes, regulation of calcium metabolism, adaptation to the environment, and regulation of metabolic processes.

Methods

The same general protocol was followed for most of the Apollo missions. Deviations from the procedures occurred when the quarantine program was imposed upon the Apollo 11,12, and 14 missions.

With the crewmembers reclining for 30 minutes, approximately 45 ml of peripheral venous blood were drawn three times (thirty, fifteen, and five days) before space flight. Blood was drawn approximately two hours after recovery (as soon as possible) and one, seven, and fourteen days later. All blood samples were drawn with the subject fasting from midnight until 7:00 a.m. except for the postrecovery sample, which was drawn regardless of the time of day or prior food intake by the crewmen. Generally, the crewmen had not eaten for six hours before recovery and had been awake for at least eight hours. For the preflight control samples, the crewmen had been awake less than one hour.

The 24-hour urine samples were collected preflight and postflight from each crewman on the same days as were the blood samples. The pooled urine was collected without additive, aliquoted, stablized with acid, and frozen for analysis. Urine samples were collected inflight by means of a biomedical urine sampling system (BUSS). Each BUSS consisted of a large (four liters) pooling bag in which urine was collected. Each contained 10 gm of boric acid for stabilization of certain organic constituents. One entire 24-hour urine sample from each Apollo 16 crewman was returned. For Apollo 17 collections, a sampling bag was used. In this bag a sample of urine (as much as 120 cm^3) was stored for later analysis. The collection bags contained 30 mg of lithium chloride. The final lithium concentration was used to estimate total urine volume.

Ground control subjects were used during each mission to determine the effects of collection and transportation of blood and urine samples. The control results showed that transportation of the endocrine samples to the NASA laboratories produced no change in values. Analyses of the blood samples (plasma or serum) included osmolality, sodium, potassium, chloride, adrenocorticotrophic hormone (ACTH), angiotensin I, cortisol, human growth hormone (HGH), insulin, parathormone thyroxine, and triiodothyronine. The 24-hour urine samples were analyzed for electrolytes, osmolality, volume, aldosterone, cortisol, antidiuretic hormone (ADH), total and fractionated ketosteroids, and amino acids. Procedures for these analyses have been previously reported (Leach et al., 1973; Alexander et al., 1973). Radionuclide studies were performed according to the schedule shown in table 1. The methods used for the radionuclide studies were described by Johnson and co-workers (1973). Table 2 contains the calculated radiation exposures from these radionuclide studies. The data in table 2 indicate that these exposures added only modestly to total radiation exposure of the astronauts and that the exposure levels are well within occupationally prescribed limits. All preflight data were averaged, and the standard error (SE) of the mean was calculated. The data taken immediately postflight were also averaged, and the percent deviation from the preflight level given. Inflight data are presented in figures 1 to 16. Prolonged exposure to increased temperature and to the boric acid preservative made the urine voided inflight unsuitable for catecholamine or ADH analyses.

Table 1

Schedule of Apollo Radionuclide Studies

Test Schedule	Total Body Potassium	Plasma Volume	Extracellular Fluid	Total Body Water
30 days preflight	X			
15 days preflight	X	X	X	X
5 days preflight	X			
As soon as possible after recovery	X	X	X	X
1 day after recovery	X	X	X	X
7 days after recovery	X	X	X	X

Table 2

Calculated Radiation Exposure of Apollo Crewmen

Nuclide and Physical Form		Critical Organ (rem/μCi)		Total Body (rem/μCi)	Total μCi	Total Body (rem)
Iodine-125	Albumin	Thyroid	− 0.0625–0.1875	0.00050	8	0.0040
Sulfur-35	Sulfate	Total body	− 0.00009	0.00009	100	0.0090
Hydrogen-3	Water	Total body	− 0.00017	0.00017	200	0.0340
Potassium-42	Chloride	Muscle	− 0.00134	0.00086	300	0.2580
						0.3050

Results

Postmission body fluid losses have been found in both American and Russian space flight crewmen (Webb, 1967). Apollo crewmen showed an average of five percent decrease in body weight after flight when the mean of the preflight results (thirty, fifteen, and five days) was compared to the individual postflight values. The average loss was 3.51 kg, approximately one-third of which was regained within the first 24 hours after recovery. These data are given in table 3.

Table 3

Summary of Apollo Crewmen Body Weight Data

Preflight Mean, kg (lb)	N*	Immediate Postflight Mean kg (lb)	One Day Postflight Mean kg (lb)	Percent Change
75.96 (167.50)	33	72.45 (159.75)	—	−4.6
—		72.45 (159.75)	73.05 (161.08)	+0.8

*Number of crewmen tested.

Body weight changes indicate significant fluid changes among all crewmembers exposed to weightlessness. Loss of fluid does not seem to be related to the duration of the mission. Because of this fact, studies were undertaken to investigate cations and anions, both of which have critical roles in the regulation of fluid volume. Serum electrolyte data from the Apollo crewmen are summarized in table 4. Significant differences were observed in a 7.3 percent decrease in potassium and a 4.5 percent decrease in magnesium immediately after flight. These changes were accompanied by no significant change in serum sodium or chloride.

Table 4

Summary of Apollo Serum Electrolyte Results

Electrolyte	N*	Preflight Mean ± SE	Immediate Postflight Mean ± SE	Percent Change
Sodium (mEq/l)	33	141 ± 0.1	141 ± 0.3	0
Potassium (mEq/l)	33	4.1 ± 0.03	3.8 ± 0.05	−7.3
Chloride (mEq/l)	32	104 ± 0.3	104 ± 0.5	0
Magnesium (mg/100 ml)	32	2.2 ± 0.04	2.1 ± 0.05	−4.5

*Number of crewmen tested.

The 24-hour urine electrolyte results are given in table 5. These samples exhibited significant decreases in sodium, potassium, chloride, and magnesium values. The results from Apollo 17 inflight collections are shown in figures 1 to 4.

Table 5

Apollo Twenty-Four Hour Urine Electrolyte Results

Electrolyte	N*	Preflight Mean ± SE	First 24 Hours Postflight Mean ± SE	Percent Change
Sodium (mEq/vol)	30	169 ± 15	87 ± 12	−49
Potassium (mEq/vol)	30	79 ± 4	42 ± 3	−47
Chloride (mEq/vol)	30	155 ± 7	60 ± 7	−61
Magnesium (mg/vol)	23	9 ± 0.5	6 ± 0.5	−36

*Number of crewmen tested.

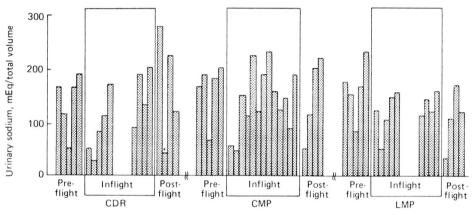

Note: CDR = Commander
CMP = Command Module Pilot
LMP = Lunar Module Pilot

* Indicates one 12-hour sample

Figure 1. Apollo 17 urinary sodium results.

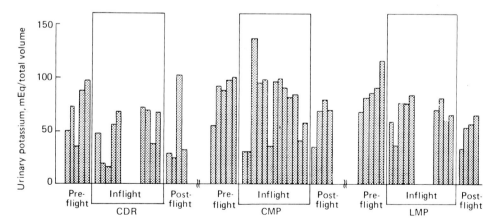

Figure 2. Apollo 17 urinary potassium results.

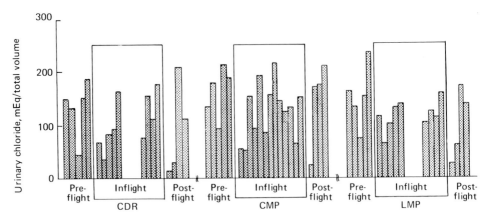

Figure 3. Apollo 17 urinary chloride results.

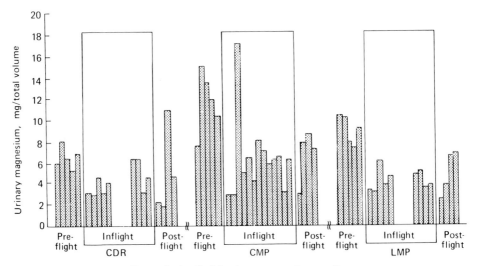

Figure 4. Apollo 17 urinary magnesium results.

To aid in the understanding of water and electrolyte balance and of renal function, renin activity was measured as angiotensin I in blood samples, and aldosterone was measured in urine. Table 6 contains these results. The plasma angiotensin I values show a 488 percent increase in the crewmen tested on the day of recovery. This elevation was followed by a significant increase (57 percent) in urinary aldosterone during the first day following recovery. In figures 5 and 6, the inflight aldosterone results for the Apollo 16 and 17 missions, respectively, are shown.

Table 7 contains summary data on urinary volume, ADH, and osmolality. These results indicate a 32 percent decrease in urine volume after flight with significant increases in osmolality (20 percent) and ADH (152 percent). The inflight volume and

Table 6

Apollo Sodium Retaining Hormone Results

Hormone	N*	Preflight Mean ± SE	First Postflight Examination ± SE	Percent Change
Plasma Angiotensin I (mμg/ml/hr)	21	1.7 ± 0.2	9.9 ± 2.0	+488
Urinary Aldosterone (μg/volume)	28	12.2 ± 0.8	19.9 ± 2.0	+ 57

*Number of crewmen tested.

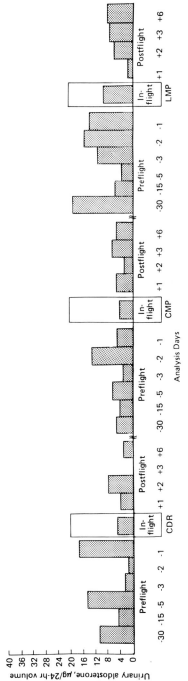

Figure 5. Apollo 16 urinary aldosterone results.

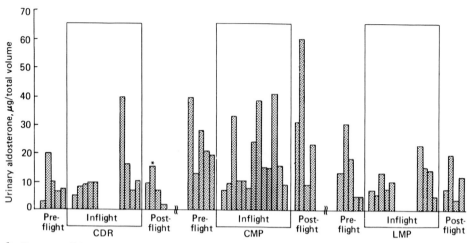

Figure 6. Apollo 17 urinary aldosterone results.

Table 7

Apollo Urine Volume Data

Test	N*	Preflight Mean ± SE	First 24 hours Postflight Mean ± SE	Percent Change
Urine Volume (ml)	30	1602 ± 77	1089 ± 109	− 32
Osmolality (milliosmols)	30	696 ± 24	833 ± 45	+ 20
ADH (milliunits/vol)	26	28 ± 3	72 ± 17	+152

*Number of crewmen tested.

osmolality values for the Apollo 17 mission are shown in figures 7 and 8, respectively. A summary of the measured body fluid volumes is given in table 8. These same data are also expressed as milliliters per kilogram of body weight. Table 9 contains the total body exchangeable potassium data as measured by potassium-42. Table 10 contains blood urea nitrogen (BUN) and creatinine clearance data. The creatinine clearance results show no significant change in renal function after flight as indicated by this test. A slight but significant increase in BUN was found. Apollo 17 inflight creatinine values are shown in figure 9.

The calcium, phosphorus, and parathormone (PTH) changes are summarized in table 11. It is believed that the calcium, phosphorus, and PTH results not only reflect normal bone metabolism but would seem to reflect normal renal function. These results are in agreement with the results of photon absorptiometry studies performed on several Apollo flights which s showed small to insignificant losses of bone calcium after flight (Vogel, 1971).

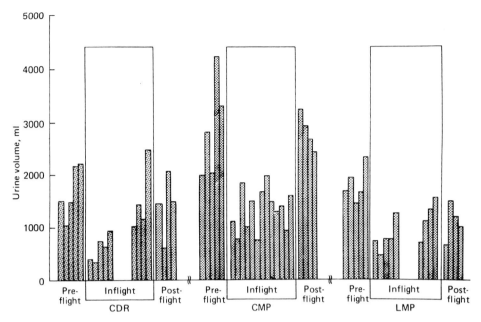

Figure 7. Apollo 17 urine volume data.

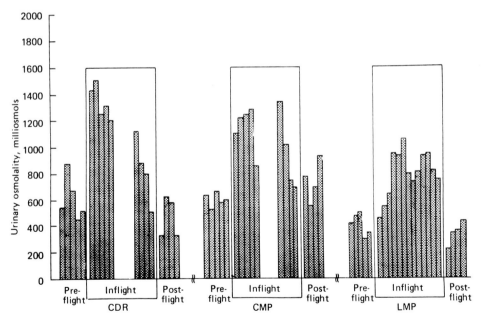

Figure 8. Apollo 17 urinary osmolality.

Table 8

Apollo Body Fluid Compartment Data
Mean Percent Change ± SE

	Volume			ml/kg		
	Immediately Postflight	One Day After Recovery	>7 Days After Recovery	Immediately Postflight	One Day After Recovery*	>7 Days After Recovery
Plasma volume	−4.4 ± 1.7	+4.8 ± 2.2	+3.4 ± 1.4	−0.1 ± 1.4	+8.2 ± 1.9	+5.3 ± 1.6
Total body water	−2.4 ± 0.4	−0.1 ± 0.6	−0.5 ± 0.3	+1.6 ± 0.4	+2.9 ± 0.8	+1.2 ± 0.6
Extracellular fluid	−2.7 ± 1.0	+0.2 ± 1.3	−0.5 ± 0.8	+1.1 ± 0.9	+2.8 ± 1.5	+1.5 ± 1.4
Intracellular fluid	−2.1 ± 0.8	+0.2 ± 1.1	−0.6 ± 0.9	+1.9 ± 0.9	+3.2 ± 1.2	+0.8 ± 0.7
Interstitial fluid	−2.2 ± 1.0	−1.3 ± 1.6	−1.5 ± 1.1	+1.7 ± 1.0	+1.6 ± 1.8	+0.3 ± 1.6

* Used R +2 values for Apollo 15.

Table 9

Apollo Total Body Exchangeable Potassium

Mean Percent Change in Total mEq Potassium		
Dilution Time in Hours	24	48
Apollo 15	−15.3	−13.8
Apollo 16	+ 3.8	+ 2.3
Apollo 17	−16.3	− 5.2

Mean Percent Change in mEq Potassium/kg Body Weight		
Dilution Time in Hours	24	48
Apollo 15	−12.7	−12.6
Apollo 16	+ 7.7	+ 7.0
Apollo 17	−13.5	− 0.3

Table 10

Index of Apollo Renal Function

Test	N*	Preflight Mean ± SE	Immediate Postflight Mean	Percent Change
BUN (mg/100 ml)	33	18.5 ± 0.6	20.7 ± 0.7	+ 12
Creatinine clearance (liters/24 hr)	29	151 ± 8	133 ± 8	− 12

*Number of crewmen tested.

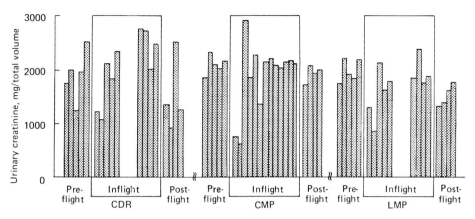

Figure 9. Apollo 17 urinary creatinine results.

Table 11

Apollo Calcium Metabolism Results

Test	N*	Preflight Mean ± SE	First Postflight Examination ± SE	Percent Change
Calcium serum (mg/100 ml)	33	9.6 ± 0.05	9.7 ± 0.05	+ 1.0
Urine (mEq/vol)	30	9.3 ± 0.8	7.8 ± 0.8	−15
Phosphorus serum (mg/100 ml)	33	3.5 ± 0.07	3.6 ± 0.1	+ 3
Urine (mg/vol)	30	966 ± 64	956 ± 67	− 4
Parathormone serum (pg/ml)	12	0.44 ± 0.03	0.42 ± 0.05	− 5

*Number of crewmen tested.

Plasma cortisol and ACTH results are given in table 12. Although no significant change was found, a mean decrease was demonstrated in both hormones. The urinary hormonal data indicating adrenal activity are also given in table 12. Cortisol demonstrated a 24 percent increase, whereas the total 17-hydroxycorticosteroid excretion was decreased 30 percent. The inflight values for these measurements for Apollo 17 crewmen are shown in figures 10 and 11. Both catecholamine compounds show decreases after flight when the data from all crewmen are grouped for analysis. Some individual preflight values are often elevated. This is believed to be due to premission stress. The total and fractionated ketosteroid data are given in table 13. These results demonstrate a 30 percent decrease in the total component, which is spread over four fractions: androsterone, etiocholanolone, dehydroepiandrosterone (DHEA), and 11 = OH etiocholanolone. A slight increase was observed in pregnanediol and 11 = O etiocholanolone. Figures 12 and 13 demonstrate the typical inflight component of these results for Apollo 17 crewmen.

Table 12

Apollo Adrenal-Pituitary Hormone Concentration

Test	Sample	N*	Preflight Mean ± SE	First Postflight Examination ± SE	Percent Change
Cortisol (μg/100 ml)	Plasma	30	16.7 ± 0.5	12.2 ± 2.0	−27
ACTH (pg/ml)	Plasma	12	37 ± 5	28 ± 5	−24
Cortisol (μg/vol)	Urine	27	60.3 ± 3.0	74.7 ± 7.0	+ 24
Epinephrine (μg/vc l)	Urine	24	26.3 ± 2.0	24.1 ± 4.0	− 8
Norepinephrine (μg/vol)	Urine	24	55.5 ± 3.0	55.8 ± 8.4	+ 0.5
Total 17-Hydroxycorticosteroids (mg/vol)	Urine	6	6.1 ± 0.5	4.3 ± 1.2	−30

*Number of crewmen tested.

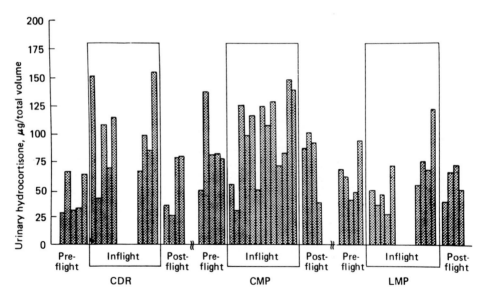

Figure 10. Apollo 17 urinary hydrocortisone results.

The serum and plasma values for various hormones and related parameters are summarized in table 14. Glucose showed a 10 percent increase after flight, and insulin increased 32 percent after flight. Human growth hormone demonstrated a 304 percent increase after flight. The postflight increase in thyroxine was statistically significant, whereas slight change was noted in percentage of triiodothyronine binding.

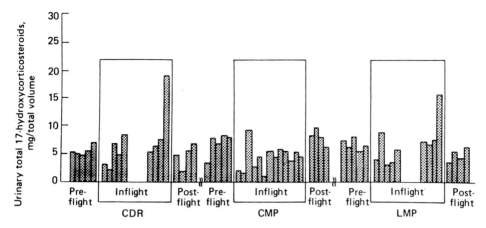

Figure 11. Apollo 17 urinary total 17-hydroxycorticosteroids.

Table 13

Apollo Total and Fractionated
17-Ketosteroid Excretion Results

| | | mg/Total Volume | | |
Compound	N*	Preflight Mean ± SE	First Day Postflight Mean ± SE	Percent Change
Pregnanodiol	9	0.33 ± 0.05	0.38 ± 0.08	+ 14
Androsterone	9	2.28 ± 0.53	1.57 ± 0.13	−49
Etiocholanolone	9	3.47 ± 0.51	2.25 ± 0.27	−35
Dehydroepiandrosterone	9	1.15 ± 0.46	1.10 ± 0.29	− 5
11-Ketoetiocholanolone	9	0.34 ± 0.13	0.38 ± 0.09	+ 10
11-Hydroxy Androsterone	9	0.15 ± 0.05	0.15 ± 0.06	0
11-Hydroxyetiocholanolone	9	0.33 ± 0.19	0.18 ± 0.06	−44
TOTAL mg/TV	9	8.66 ± 1.54	6.05 ± 0.72	−30

* Number of crewmen tested.

Table 15 is a summary of the urinary amino acid results for six representative amino acids from a total of 39 analyzed. The comparison of postflight to preflight control levels has been variable. However, taurine has been consistently elevated after flight (140 percent). The inflight data for Apollo 17 crewmen are presented in figures 14 to 16.

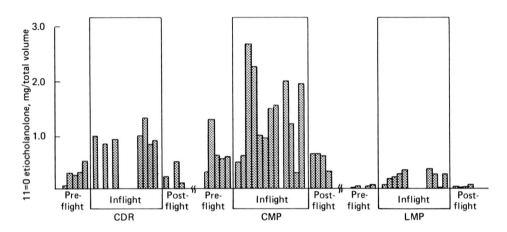

Figure 12. Apollo 17 urinalysis of 11 = 0 etiocholanolone.

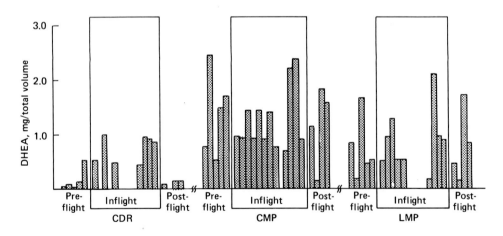

Figure 13. Apollo 17 urinalysis of dehydroepiandrosterone (DHEA).

Table 14

Summary of Plasma Hormones
and Related Parameters for Apollo Crewmen

Hormone	N*	Preflight ± SE	Postflight ± SE	Percent Change
Thyroxine (T_4) (µg/100 ml)	30	6.8 ± 0.1	7.6 ± 0.5	+ 12
Tri-iodothyronine (T_3) (% uptake)	30	32.4 ± 0.1	32.1 ± 0.1	− 1
Insulin (µU/ml)	22	6.8 ± 1.2	9. 0 ± 1.4	+ 32
Glucose (mg/100 ml)	33	95.7 ± 1.3	105.1 ± 2.2	+ 10
Human Growth Hormone (ng/ml)	10	2.6 ± 0.2	10.5 ± 3.1	+304

*Number of crewmen tested.

Table 15

Summary of Apollo Amino Acid Excretion Results

Amino Acid	N*	mg/Volume Preflight Mean ± SE	mg/Volume First Day Postflight Mean	Percent Change
Phosphoethanolamine	12	6.1 ± 0.4	7.2 ± 2.6	+ 18
Taurine	12	126.2 ± 18.5	304.0 ± 89.5	+140
Glycine	12	53.7 ± 6.8	45.7 ± 11.2	− 15
Alanine	12	30.2 ± 6.8	25.3 ± 3.2	− 15
Tyrosine	12	18.4 ± 1.8	16.8 ± 2.1	− 9
β-Alanine	12	5.25 ± 2.0	5.8 ± 1.8	+ 13

*Number of crewmen tested.

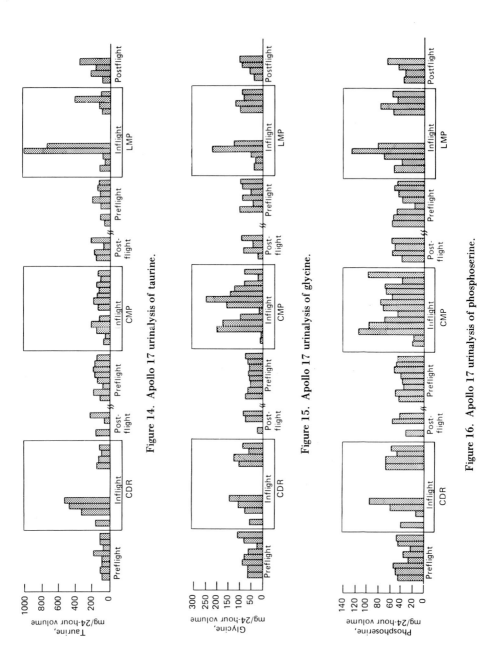

Figure 14. Apollo 17 urinalysis of taurine.

Figure 15. Apollo 17 urinalysis of glycine.

Figure 16. Apollo 17 urinalysis of phosphoserine.

Discussion

After considering all previously mentioned data together with the clinical condition of the returning Apollo crewmen, the following hypothesis was proposed to explain the changes. As a crewman enters the weightless environment, his circulating blood volume and extracellular fluid shift from the extremities and the lower abdomen and are redistributed equally throughout the vascular space. This alteration of the blood volume is interpreted as a relative volume expansion. The fluid redistribution necessitates a compensatory change in water balance with a net loss of fluid and electrolytes. The extent of the fluid and electrolyte loss is related also to food consumption, which has been variable and generally below basal requirements during the first 24 hours of a mission. The changes in water balance are believed to occur principally in the first or second day of flight just as they do in bed rest (Hyatt et al., 1970). This theory explains why crewmembers showed weight decreases even after short duration Mercury and Gemini missions (Webb, 1967). On return to Earth and the one-g environment, a portion of the weight loss is regained within the first 24 hours. A rapid weight gain of this magnitude indicates a renal and endocrine response to the new environment. The remainder of the weight loss could be attributed to tissue loss. Consistently measured decreases in red cell mass and decreases in individual cell electrolyte content, determined by the electron microprobe, add support to this hypothesis. Furthermore, significant decreases in serum magnesium during the postflight period suggest previous losses of intracellular electrolyte, since magnesium is concentrated in the intracellular space along with potassium.

Postflight decreases in total body potassium of the Apollo 12 to 14 crewmen were determined by gamma spectrometric measurement of the total body potassium-40. Seven of the nine men showed a significant decrease (three to ten percent) for this measurement (Benson & Bailey, 1971). Beginning with the Apollo 15 mission, total body exchangeable potassium was measured (Leach et al., 1972). The results are expected to differ from total body potassium because slow-to-equilibrate pools may not be completely exchanged in the 24- and 48-hour periods analyzed. However, because comparisons of measurements before and after space flight of the same individuals are being made, the relative changes are meaningful. Crewmembers of the Gemini 7 mission demonstrated positive potassium balance before and after the flight and negative balance during the flight. Results from Gemini missions and data available from Apollo crewmen confirm that aldosterone is elevated during space flight. This elevation could have been produced by decreases in renal blood flow or in carotid artery or right-heart pressures: the specific etiology must await further experimentation.

All Apollo missions were followed by a change in the plasma volume of returning crewmen. The overall mean of the crewmen's plasma volume decrease for the Apollo missions was considerably less than the 10 percent mean decrease associated with an equivalent period of bed rest. Only three of the twenty-one crewmembers tested showed losses greater than the average bed rest results. A smaller decrease in plasma volume could be one manifestation of an inflight increase in adrenal activity, particularly aldosterone secretion. Because no plasma volume measurements for Apollo missions were taken during flight, it was not known whether plasma volume was actually lower during flight and increased slightly before being recorded immediately after flight or whether plasma volume remained essentially stable after the 4.4 percent decrease (table 8) had occurred.

Even with adequate calories available, most crewmen showed a weight loss after flight. Part of this weight loss was made up during the first 24 hours after recovery, but it took from several days to weeks for crewmen to return fully to their premission weight. This fact suggests that part of the weight loss during a mission is tissue and another part fluid. Only fluid loss could be made up in the first 24 hours; recovery of tissue losses takes considerably longer. Weight loss from short term dieting is generally followed by an increase in extracellular fluid, which compensates for the tissues lost. This extra fluid is ordinarily lost by diuresis at irregular intervals of several days to several weeks. The increased extracellular fluid volume seen after these missions could be explained as a compensation for tissue losses. The water retention associated with weight loss is probably accomplished by increased aldosterone secretion.

During recovery operations, crewmen were exposed to increased ambient temperatures in the spacecraft, in the helicopter, and on the carrier deck because of the tropical location of recovery operations. The crewmen did not eat or drink between the time they left the spacecraft and the time of blood sampling; thereafter, they could eat or drink anything they desired. The postrecovery diet was generally high in salt, protein, and calories. The postrecovery urine generally showed increased osmolality with a decrease in electrolyte content, a combination that indicated increased excretion of nonelectrolyte osmotic substances. Part of this increase in osmolality might have been a result of the increased blood urea nitrogen (BUN) found after recovery. The clinical laboratories found postflight elevations in uric acid. Because of the increased environmental temperatures during the first four hours after recovery, a slight increase in serum sodium was to be expected then, and in osmolality later. However, serum sodium was actually less after flight than before flight, and osmolality was unchanged; therefore, serum sodium may have been even lower before reentry. This discovery, coupled with the BUN change, suggests that renal blood flow is decreased during weightlessness, and this decrease could be partly responsible for the increased aldosterone excretion by way of the renin-angiotensin system.

Balakhovskiy and others (1971) have suggested that the postflight weight loss in American astronauts was due to dehydration caused not by space flight but by environmental temperatures in the tropical recovery zones. Apollo data do not substantiate dehydration as the causative factor for the fluid/electrolyte results because serum sodium and osmolality were not increased at recovery.

Prolonged bed rest is associated with a negative calcium balance beginning in the second week (Deitrick et al., 1948). It was postulated that exposure to weightlessness would produce similar losses of calcium from the skeleton. The results of the Apollo missions did not appear to indicate significant changes in calcium metabolism. First, no change in parathormone was found in recovery specimens; second, urine and serum calcium were elevated; and third, bone densitometry failed to show consistent decreases in bone mass. Therefore, for missions of 14 days or less, it was apparent that significant calcium losses did not occur. Hypercalcemia does not account for the loss of sodium, as has been suggested (Griffith, 1971). However, if changes in calcium dynamics had occurred, they would have probably just begun during the last few days of the missions.

Current data show no evidence of plasma cortisol and adrenocorticotrophic hormone (ACTH) increase after flight. The stress of reentry is assumed to be not great enough to produce a change in these hormones. The time of recovery, however, generally is at a different point in the diurnal cycle of the pituitary-adrenal axis than in the preflight control (Leach & Campbell, 1971). Without stress, higher values were to be expected at the time of the control specimens (8:00 a.m.) than at the time of recovery (between morning and early afternoon). Reentry stress may have elevated these hormones higher than they were 24 hours before recovery.

The Apollo 16 mission was the first after Gemini 7 in which inflight urine samples were returned for analysis. The 17-hydroxycorticosteroids were found to be significantly decreased during the 14-day Gemini 7 mission (Lutwak et al., 1969). Likewise, total 17-hydroxycorticosteroid values were decreased in second-day inflight specimens from Apollo 16 crewmen and were normal to decreased in the more comprehensive sample collection of the Apollo 17 mission. Ordinarily, if total 17-hydroxycorticosteroid excretion decreases, a decrease in cortisol is to be expected; however, cortisol excretion during the inflight phase of both missions was normal to elevated or, stated differently, no value was lower than preflight or postflight values. This divergence of results could be related either to a sample storage program that affected the 17-hydroxycorticosteroid analyses or, possibly, to changes in blood flow to the liver that altered the conjugation rate of the free hormone resulting in decreased excretion of 17-hydroxycorticosteroids.

In several endocrine-related diseases, the determination of urinary 17-ketosteroids, either fractions or total, has been helpful in both diagnosis and understanding the pathophysiology of these diseases. The decrease in the total 17-ketosteroid fraction agrees with the decrease in the total 17-hydroxycorticosteroid data. The mechanism is believed to be related to the liver conjugation of these steroids. The inflight increase in specific fractions reflects the heightened adrenal activity during the flight phase. The dehydroepiandrosterone (DHEA) increases shown on the Apollo 16 and 17 missions inflight are considered significant since they had been shown to occur in potassium-depleted subjects (Leach et al., 1973). The exact function of this steroid is not known, but it appears to be related to stress responses as well as to nitrogen and mineral metabolism.

Bed rest, the most frequently used analog of weightlessness, alters glucose metabolism (Lipman, 1970). Studies have shown that glucose and insulin are elevated after two weeks of absolute bed rest. Apollo results suggest that space flight may have a similar effect with an apparent decrease in the efficiency of insulin to lower plasma glucose concentrations. However, increased growth hormone may be a factor in these observed increases. A significant change in plasma thyroxine (T_4) may represent the thyroid gland's response to increases in plasma proteins.

To assess metabolic responses in the area of nutrient use as well as stress, human growth hormone (HGH) was measured. This hormone was significantly increased (table 14) postflight. Because HGH acts to increase blood sugar and plasma-free fatty acids, and to lower plasma amino acids by incorporating them into proteins, these results after space flight are compatible with the evidence of muscle breakdown discussed previously.

The changes in amino acid excretion patterns are thought to be related to diet as well as to muscle metabolism. However, as in every study of amino acid excretion, renal threshold, glomerular filtration rate, and cellular use enter into the full explanation. Furthermore, the relationship between adrenal steroid activity and amino acid excretion must be considered because adrenal steroids alter urinary excretion patterns of amino acids (Zinneman et al., 1963). Glycine, significantly elevated in the inflight samples, is required by the body for formation of nucleic acid, porphyrins, creatinine, hippuric acid, and bile acid conjugates (Searcy, 1969). Therefore, the increased excretion of this amino acid could be related to cellular mass loss or to the suspected decrease in liver blood flow. The significant increases in taurine after flight could be an indication of a decrease in bile acid formation and hence in liver function. Sarcosine, another amino acid that was increased during flight, is related to muscle protein and is believed to be a further indication of muscle breakdown during flight.

Summary

Biochemical analyses were performed on samples of blood and urine obtained from astronauts at various intervals before and after each Apollo space mission. During the Apollo 16 and 17 missions, urine samples from the inflight phase were also obtained, and a similar series of biochemical analyses was performed.

The observed universal loss in body weight was accompanied by decreases in intracellular water and by increases in extracellular water after flight with a resultant net loss in total body water. Water losses, however, appeared to account for only about one-third of the total mass loss. That losses in cellular mass also occurred was evident from decreases in the body's potassium-40 content and in its exchangeable potassium pool. The loss of tissue was further supported by increases in blood and urinary nitrogenous components after flight as well as in decreases in serum potassium and magnesium.

The observed losses in potassium and retention of fluid were generally reflected in appropriate postflight elevations in renin activity, aldosterone, and antidiuretic hormone (ADH). Changes in excretion patterns inflight were also observed. Elevation of aldosterone during flight supports the concept that the electrolyte changes were hormonally induced. Hydroxycortisone was normal to increased, whereas total 17-hydroxycorticosteroids and total 17-ketosteroids were low normal to decreased during flight. A change in the metabolism of these hormones is suggested by these results.

The following hypothesis is presented to explain the mechanisms underlying the observed electrolyte and fluid compartment changes. In a weightless environment, there is a tendency for plasma volume to be distributed more evenly within the vascular system and away from the gravity-dependent extremities. This shift is interpreted by receptors, probably in the right atrium, to be an increase in vascular volume. The increase in vascular volume is counteracted by an increased water loss, followed by a compensatory, adrenal-pituitary-mediated retention of water and sodium and by a continued loss of potassium. Other hormone changes observed are tentatively ascribed to the stresses associated with the condition of the Apollo space flights, to the well-known consequences of hypokinesis, and to the metabolic effects of hypocaloric nutritional intake.

References

Alexander, W.C.; Leach, C.S.; Fischer, C.L.; Lambertsen, C.J.; and Johnson, P.C.: Hematological, Biochemical, and Immunological Studies During a 14-Day Continuous Exposure to 5.2% O_2 in N_2 at Pressure Equivalent to 100 FSW (4 ata). Aerospace Med., vol. 44, no. 7, July 1973, pp. 850-854.

Balakhovskiy, I.S.; Natochin, U.V.; and Kozyrevskaya, G.I.: Status of Water-Salt Metabolism Under Space Flight Conditions. NASA TT F-14029, 1971.

Benson, R.E.; and Bailey, V.: Personal Communication. March 15, 1971.

Berry, C.A.; and Catterson, A.D.: Pre-Gemini Medical Predictions Versus Gemini Flight Results. Section 16 of Gemini Summary Conference, NASA SP-138, 1967, pp. 210-218.

Deitrick, J.E.; Whedon, G.D.; and Shorr, E.: Effects of Immobilization Upon Various Metabolic and Physiological Functions of Normal Men. Am. J. Med., vol. 41, no. 1, Jan. 1948, pp. 3-36.

Dietlein, L.F.; and Harris, E.: Experiment M-5, Bioassays of the Body Fluids. Section 42 of Gemini Midprogram Conference, NASA SP-121, 1966, pp. 403-406.

Griffith, D.P.: Immobilization Hypercalciuria: Treatment and a Possible Pathophysiologic Mechanism. Aerospace Med., vol. 42, no 12, Dec. 1971, pp. 1322-1324.

Hyatt, K.H.; Smith, W.M.; Vogel, J.M.; Sullivan, R.W.; Vetter, W.R.; Calder, B.E.; Bohnn, B.J.; and Haughton, V.M.: A Study of the Role of Extravehicular Dehydration in the Production of Cardiovascular Deconditioning by Simulated Weightlessness (Bedrest), Part II. Final Report. NASA CR-114809, 1970.

Johnson, P.C.; Driscoll, T.B.; Alexander, W.C.; and Lambertsen, C.J.: Body Fluid Volume Changes During a 14-Day Continuous Exposure to 5.2% O_2 in N_2 at Pressure Equivalent to 100 FSW (4 ata). Aerospace Med., vol. 44, no. 7, July 1973, pp. 860-863.

Kakurin, L.I.: Medical Research Performed on the Flight Program of the Soyuz-Type Spacecraft. NASA TT F-14026, 1971.

Leach, C.S.: Review of Endocrine Results: Project Mercury, Gemini Program, and Apollo Program. Proceedings of the 1970 Manned Spacecraft Center Endocrine Program Conference, NASA TM X-58068, 1971.

Leach, C.S.; Alexander, W.C.; Fischer, C.L.; Lambertsen, C.J.; and Johnson, P.C.: Endocrine Studies During a 14-Day Continuous Exposure to 5.2% O_2 in N_2 at Pressure Equivalent to 100 FSW (4 ata). Aerospace Med., vol. 44, no. 7, July 1973, pp. 855-859.

Leach, C.S.; Alexander, W.C.; and Johnson, P.C.: Adrenal and Pituitary Response to the Apollo XV Crewmembers. J. Clin. Endocrinol. Metab., vol. 35, no. 5, Nov. 1972, pp. 642-645.

Leach, C.S.; and Campbell, B.O.: Hydrocortisone and ACTH Levels in Manned Spaceflight. Rhythms in Special Environments. Proceedings of the International Society for the Study of Biologic Rhythms (Little Rock, Arkansas), Nov. 1971.

Leach, C.S.; Hyatt, K.H.; and Johnson, P.C.: Increased Dehydroepiandrosterone Excretion During a Low Potassium Diet. Clin. Res., vol. 21, no. 1, 1973, p. 87.

Lipman, R.L.: Impairment of Peripheral Glucose Utilization in Normal Subjects by Prolonged Bedrest. J. Lab. Clin. Med., vol. 76, no. 2, Aug. 1970, pp. 221-230.

Lutwak, L.; Whedon, G.D.; LaChance, P.A.; Reid, J.M.; and Lipscomb, H.S.: Mineral, Electrolyte and Nitrogen Balance Studies of the Gemini-7 Fourteen-Day Orbital Space Flight. J. Clin. Endocrinol. Metab., vol. 29, no. 9, Sept. 1969, pp. 1140-1156.

Mack, P.B.; LaChance, P.A.; Vose, G.P.; and Vogt, F.B.: Bone Demineralization of Foot and Hand of Gemini – Titan IV, V, and VII Astronauts During Orbital Flight. Am. J. Roentgenol., vol 100, no. 3, July 1967, pp. 503-511.

Searcy, R.L.: Diagnostic Biochemistry. McGraw-Hill Book Co., Inc., 1969, p. 50.

Vogel, J.M.: Bone Mineral Measurement, Apollo XV. NASA T-93591, 1971.

Webb, Paul: Weight Loss in Men in Space. Sci., vol. 155, no. 3762, Feb. 1967, pp. 558-560.

Zinneman, H.H.; Johnson, J.J.; and Seal, U.S.: Effect of Short-Term Therapy with Cortisol on the Urinary Excretion of Free Amino Acids. J. Clin. Endocrinol., vol. 23, no. 10, Oct. 1963, pp. 996-1000.

CHAPTER 2
CLINICAL BIOCHEMISTRY

by

W.C. Alexander, Ph.D.
Carolyn S. Leach, Ph.D.
Craig L. Fischer, M.D.*

Lyndon B. Johnson Space Center

Introduction

An extensive group of biochemical tests was instituted in support of the Apollo Program. These tests were conducted for each flight by the Clinical Laboratories of the Lyndon B. Johnson Space Center (JSC), and gave investigators their first documentation of the normal biochemistry of the astronauts who flew the Apollo missions. The results were especially meaningful since comparable data were not consistently available from the Mercury and Gemini Programs. The biochemical studies significantly increased the understanding of man's adaptation to the spaceflight environment and of the resultant physiological cost of spaceflight.

The biochemical evaluation of the Apollo crewmen was designed to document the physical qualification of the invididual for each mission and to detect problems which might require remedial or preventive action. Accordingly, the primary purpose of the laboratories during the Apollo missions was to support the crew by providing clinical biochemical and immuno-hematology data to the flight surgeon for evaluations of pre- and postflight health status. The chemical measurements of various blood and urine constituents were one portion of a comprehensive medical examination intended to disclose a state of well-being or the presence of occult disease processes. The biochemical studies furnished data which, when integrated with the facts obtained from a complete history and physical examination, permitted an objective assessment of crew physical status.

---

*Now at Eisenhower Medical Center.

The authors wish to especially thank the following technical personnel in the Clinical Laboratory at the Johnson Space Center for their support throughout the many missions of the Apollo Program: A. Carmona, K. Brown, E. Coleman, N. Funderburk, C. Johnson, M. Johnson, H. Knippa, Jr., C. Lassiter, R. Landry, H. Owens, N. Pettit, Jr., J. Potter, J. Terrell, L. Wallace, N. Whitecotton, and J. Wright.

The second objective of the biochemical studies was to elucidate and describe the physiological changes attributable to the spaceflight environment. Continued examination over extended periods of time established normal ranges for the astronaut population. The significance of subtle biochemical changes and the relationship of these changes to the influence of the spaceflight environment were thereby assessed.

Procedures

Blood Sample Collection

The preflight samples of blood were acquired depending on the location of the crew. Normally the serum, acquired at Johnson Space Center, or Kennedy Space Center was frozen immediately and transported to the JSC Clinical Laboratories for analysis. The immediate postflight samples were acquired on the Prime Recovery Ship, stabilized and returned to JSC for analysis. In both instances time critical analyses were performed prior to freezing in remote site laboratories.

The biochemical studies in Apollo varied somewhat between missions depending on overall mission objectives. In general, Apollo missions 7, 8, 9, and 10 were supported in the same manner, except that the number of 24-hour urine collections increased as the importance of these data became more evident. Apollo missions 11, 12, and 14 were characterized by a postflight quarantine and therefore received similar laboratory emphasis. Apollo missions 15, 16, and 17 were supported with an expanded protocol characterized by an increasing number of biochemical studies. The general methods included the withdrawal of 20 ml of venous whole blood at least three times, approximately thirty, fifteen, and five days before each mission. Similar amounts of blood were withdrawn within two hours after recovery, one day, six days, and thirteen days later. Fasting blood samples were obtained with the crewman recumbent and at approximately the same time each day except for the sample immediately after splashdown. The crews' intake of food and water prior to splashdown was varied, and operational considerations dictated the actual time and place of recovery.

Urine Sample Collection

Twenty-four hour urine samples were collected on each crewman beginning with Apollo 8 and coincident with each blood collection. The urine was aliquoted, stabilized, and frozen for transport to the JSC for subsequent analysis.

Overall Procedural Plan

The crews generally consumed a conventional diet during the pre- and postflight periods and Apollo flight food throughout the mission. Fluids were available *ad libitum* during all phases. In order to evaluate the data obtained, certain information from the clinical history of each crewman was required. This information included medication history one month prior to, during, and postflight; radiation; exposure to toxic products, if known; and description of the pertinent history and physical examination findings. Approximate dietary intake, and the amount and time of any alcohol consumption were also noted. The biochemistry program was judged successful based on the criteria that the samples were obtained at the appropriate time and in the amount specified, and were processed and delivered to the laboratory in specified conditions.

Ground-based control subjects participated in the same procedural plan used for the flight crew evaluations. Before each mission, three men in good health and in approximately the same physical conditions as the crewmen were selected as control subjects. The goal of the ground-control program was to supply controls for the hematology evaluation and to predict any complex interactions with other phases of the preflight and postflight evaluation protocols. These individuals were utilized also for each mission to prevent misinterpretation of data due to sample preparation or artifacts resulting from sample manipulation and transport from remote site laboratories to the JSC facility for processing. The controls demonstrated that neither the blood sampling nor transport had any demonstrable effect on the measured parameters.

In addition, each crewman served as his own control, with the preflight period as baseline. The backup crew assigned to each flight participated in the biochemical evaluations to the same degree as the prime crew in the preflight interval. These data, provided no member of the backup crew actually flew, were used as adjunctive control data for comparative purposes.

The clinical biochemical methods were selected specifically for a given determination utilizing minimal sample volume. Standard biochemical laboratory techniques were used (table 1). Whenever possible, an aliquot of serum was frozen and stored for subsequent or retrospective analysis. The data were subjected to statistical analysis. The mean of preflight data (three crewmen, three sample dates) was obtained and the standard deviation of the mean calculated. The mean value of the postflight data (three crewmen, one sample date), the standard deviation, and the percent deviation from the preflight level were recorded. The results were submitted to student's paired t test (Snedecor, 1956). Annual comprehensive biochemical examinations were conducted also on the entire group of individuals selected for the astronaut program. The normative values for the astronaut population are defined in table 2.

Results

A summary of serum biochemical measurements from all Apollo crewmen is presented in table 3. There are no values which are out of normal range established for the astronaut population for the variables considered. However, when postflight values were compared with preflight levels, significant changes were found, as listed in table 4. This comparison described consistent and significant decreases in potassium, magnesium, lactic dehydrogenase (LDH), creatine phosphokinase (CPK), albumin, uric acid, triglycerides and cholesterol. Increases were described in creatinine, total protein, blood urea nitrogen (BUN), and glucose.

The 24-hour urine results are shown in table 5. Since the diet consumed in the pre- and postflight phases was not controlled, there was variation between means which resulted in large standard deviations; however, significant changes did occur, as shown in table 6. Significant postflight increases were measured in specific gravity and osmolality. Decreases were measured in the 24-hour urine volume, and in the 24-hour excretion of sodium, potassium, chloride, magnesium, and uric acid.

Table 1

Apollo Biochemical Laboratory Techniques

Serum Chemistries		
Constituent	Unitage	Method
Sodium	mEq/L	Flame photometry (Henry)
Osmolality	milliosmols	Freezing point depression (Gambino)
Cholesterol	mg%	AutoAnalyser (Lieberman-Burchard)
Triglycerides	mg%	AutoAnalyser (Kessler & Lederer)
Magnesium	mg%	Atomic absorption (Willis)
Glucose	mg%	AutoAnalyser (Ferrocyanide reduction)
Inorganic phosphate	mg%	AutoAnalyser (Fiske & Subbarow)
Potassium	mEq/L	Flame photometry (Willis)
Chloride	mEq/L	Titration (Buchler-Cotlove)
Total bilirubin	mg%	AutoAnalyser (Jendrassic)
Direct bilirubin	mg%	AutoAnalyser (Jendrassic)
Calcium	mg%	Atomic absorption (Willis)
Uric acid	mg%	AutoAnalyser (Hawk)
Urea nitrogen	mg%	AutoAnalyser (Diacetyl monoxime/Marsh et al.)
Creatinine	mg%	AutoAnalyser (Jaffe)
Alkaline phosphatase	International units	AutoAnalyser (Babson)
Creatine phosphokinase	milliunits/ml	Robot chemist (Oliver)
Creatine phosphokinase	International units	Rate reaction analysis (Boehringer-Mannheim)
Lactic dehydrogenase	milliunits/ml	Robot chemist (Wroblewski & LaDue)
Lactic dehydrogenase	International units	Rate reaction analysis (Boehringer-Mannheim)
Glutamic oxaloacetic transaminase	milliunits/ml	Robot chemist (Karmen, Wroblewski, & LaDue)
Glutamic oxaloacetic transaminase	International units	Rate reaction analysis (Boehringer-Mannheim)
Urine Chemistries		
Osmolality	milliosmols/24 hrs	Freezing Point Depression (Gambino)
Calicum	mEq/24 hrs	Atomic absorption (Willis)
Inorganic phosphate	mg/24 hrs (P)	AutoAnalyser (Fiske & Subbarow)
Specific gravity	None	Total solids
Chloride	mEq/24 hrs	Titration (Buchler-Cotlove)
Creatinine	mg/24 hrs	AutoAnalyser (Jaffe)
Volume	ml/24 hrs	Volumetric
Sodium	mEq/24 hrs	Flame photometry (Henry)
Magnesium	mEq/24 hrs	Atomic absorption (Willis)
Potassium	mEq/24 hrs	Flame photometry (Henry)
Uric acid	mg/24 hrs	AutoAnalyser (Hawk)

Table 2
Normal Biochemistry Values for Apollo Astronaut Population

A. Serum		
Parameter	Number of Crewmen	Two Standard Deviation Range
Osmolality	112	267.2-313.7
Sodium	127	115.8-164.9
Potassium	126	3.5-4.7
Chloride	127	98.4-111.2
Calcium	126	8.9-10.3
Magnesium	128	1.7-2.7
Inorganic phosphate	128	2.3-4.7
Blood urea nitrogen	126	11.3-25.7
Creatinine	125	0.9-1.5
Total protein	131	6.2-7.8
Albumin	131	3.7-5.3
Glucose	98	85.4-111.5
Triglycerides	86	26.9-195.9
Cholesterol	125	113.1-261.1
Uric acid	126	4.4-7.9
Total bilirubin	122	0.1.5
Alkaline phosphatase	128	7.8-37.1
Lactic acid dehydrogenase (RC)	59	29.8-65.4
(LKB)	66	134.1-263.0
Serum glutamic oxaloacetic transaminase (SGOT) (RC)	59	14.2-44.8
(LKB)	67	9.5-22.1
Creatine phosphokinase (RC)	59	0.68.4
(LKB)	62	2.6-110.7
B. Urine		
24-hr urine volume	87	102-2746
Specific gravity	85	1.007-1.031
Osmolality	73	282-1110
Sodium	88	20.1-306.9
Potassium	88	18.6-128.4
Chloride	88	20.8-278.9
Calcium	88	0.8-16.9
Magnesium	88	-30.5

Table 3

Summary of Apollo Serum Biochemistry Results

Parameter	Unit	N*	Preflight Mean ± S.D.	Recovery							
				+2 hrs	Δ%***	+1 Day	Δ%***	+7 Days	Δ%***	+14 Days	Δ%***
Osmolality	Mosmo	32	291 ± 3	289 ± 6	− 0.7	290 ± 6	− 0.3	293 ± 6	+ 0.7	294 ± 6	+ 1
Na	mEq/l	33	141.5 ± 0.9	140 ± 2.3	− 0.4	140.9 ± 1.8	− 0.4	142.8 ± 1.6	+ 0.9	143.0 ± 2.8	+ 1.1
K	mEq/l	33	4.1 ± 0.3	3.8 ± 0.3	− 7.3	4.1 ± 0.3	0	4.1 ± 0.3	0	4.2 ± 0.2	+ 2.4
Cl	mEq/l	33	104.6 ± 2.2	104.0 ± 3.3	− 0.6	104.2 ± 1.8	− 0.4	105.7 ± 2.9	+ 1.1	106.6 ± 2.3	+ 1.9
Ca	mg/100 ml	33	9.6 ± 0.3	9.7 ± 0.4	+ 1.0	9.5 ± 0.3	− 1.0	9.5 ± 0.4	− 1.0	9.6 ± 0.3	0
Mg	mg/100 ml	33	2.2 ± 0.2	2.1 ± 0.2	− 5.0	2.2 ± 0.2	0	2.2 ± 0.1	0	2.3 ± 0.1	+ 5.0
PO$_4$	mg/100 ml	33	3.6 ± 0.4	3.6 ± 0.6	0	3.4 ± 0.5	− 6.0	3.8 ± 0.4	+ 6.0	3.7 ± 0.4	+ 2.8
BUN	mg/100 ml	33	18.5 ± 2.6	20.7 ± 3.8	+11.9	19.1 ± 3.4	+ 3.2	14.9 ± 2.4	−19.5	16.0 ± 2.9	−13.5
Creatinine	mg/100 ml	33	1.2 ± .1	1.3 ± 0.2	+ 8.3	1.2 ± 0.2	0	1.3 ± 0.2	+ 8.3	1.2 ± 0.2	0
Total protein	gm/100 ml	33	7.1 ± 0.3	7.3 ± 0.4	+ 2.8	6.9 ± 0.3	− 2.8	6.7 ± 0.3	− 5.6	6.8 ± 0.3	− 4.2
Albumin	gm/100 ml	33	4.6 ± 0.3	4.5 ± 0.4	− 2.2	4.3 ± 0.4	− 6.5	4.3 ± 0.2	− 6.5	4.2 ± 0.4	− 8.7
Glucose	mg/100 ml	33	95.7 ± 7.3	105.1 ± 13.6	+ 9.8	93.4 ± 13.8	− 2.4	99.1 ± 9.9	+ 3.6	94.2 ± 7.5	− 1.6
Triglycerides	mg/100 ml	28	119.7 ± 77.4	90.6 ± 23.5	−24.3	95.0 ± 37.9	−20.6	113.2 ± 37.7	− 5.4	157.9 ± 15.0	+31.9
Cholesterol	mg/100 ml	33	185.6 ± 36.3	174.4 ± 33.2	− 6.0	149.8 ± 26.2	−19.3	165.9 ± 27.1	−10.6	179.6 ± 33.8	− 3.2
Uric acid	mg/100 ml	33	6.1 ± 1.1	5.2 ± 0.9	−14.8	5.5 ± 1.0	− 9.8	5.6 ± 1.1	− 8.2	5.7 ± 0.9	− 6.6
Total bilirubin	mg/100 ml	33	0.8 ± 0.5	0.9 ± 0.9	+12.5	0.7 ± 0.5	−12.5	0.5 ± 0.3	−37.5	0.6 ± 0.3	−25.0
Alkaline phosphatase	Int. units	33	21.8 ± 4.0	22.4 ± 4.4	+ 2.8	21.8 ± 4.1	0	21.9 ± 4.8	+ 0.5	20.9 ± 5.1	− 4.1
**Lactic acid dehydrogenase	mμ/ml										
Missions 7 - 13		21	46.5 ± 7.7	46.0 ±	− 1.1	46.5 ± 8.5	0	46.5 ± 8.5	0	42.3 ± 5.4	− 9.0
Missions 14 -17		12	207.3 ± 24.2	186.4 ± 27.9	−10.1	196.7 ± 14.5	− 5.1	189.5 ± 27.7	− 8.6	180.0 ± 16.8	−13.2

Table 3 (Continued)
Summary of Apollo Serum Biochemistry Results

Parameter	Unit	N	Preflight Mean ± S. D.	+2 hrs	Δ%***	Recovery +1 Day	Δ%***	+7 Days	Δ%***	+14 Days	Δ%***
**SGOT	mμ/ml										
Missions 7 - 13		21	29.5 ± 5.5	31.1 ± 6.6	+ 5.4	35.1 ± 9.9	+ 18.9	31.8 ± 5.9	+ 7.8	32.9 ± 6.9	+ 11.5
Missions 14 - 17		12	16.5 ± 3.7	15.8 ± 3.5	− 4.2	16.3 ± 3.0	− 1.2	13.3 ± 2.4	−19.4	14.0 ± 3.5	−15.2
**Creatine phosphokinase	mμ/ml										
Missions 7 - 13		21	25.3 ± 22.7	18.7 ± 7.5	−26.1	35.2 ± 19.2	+ 39.1	16.3 ± 11.3	−35.6	16.8 ± 16.6	−33.6
Missions 14 - 17		12	70.9 ± 24.1	62.9 ± 45.4	−11.3	81.0 ± 62.2	+ 14.3	43.1 ± 21.8	−39.2	38.3 ± 12.9	−45.9

*Number of crewmen.
**Procedural change.
***% means percent change when compared to preflight mean.

Table 4

Significant[*] Serum Biochemistry Changes

(Pre $\bar{x}$ vs. Recovery Day)

Parameter	Direction of Change
Potassium	Decreased
Magnesium	Decreased
Creatinine	Increased
Lactic acid dehydrogenase	Decreased
Creatine phosphokinase	Decreased
Total Protein	Increased
Albumin	Decreased
Blood urea nitrogen	Increased
Glucose	Increased
Triglycerides	Decreased
Cholesterol	Decreased
Uric acid	Decreased

*Significant change is defined as $p < .05$.

Discussion

The clinical biochemical investigations conducted on the Apollo crewmen showed no preflight or postflight abnormalities of clinical significance. Some transient changes, however, were observed postflight which occurred consistently and merit discussion.

Blood Constituent Measurements

Postflight decreases in serum potassium, although not significant clinically, were found in 24 of the 33 crewmen. This early finding was an important factor in the decision to conduct more extensive electrolyte studies on the later Apollo flights (Leach et al., 1970). Based on measurements in Apollo 16 and 17 the increase in aldosterone which occurred during flight was believed to be partly responsible for the decrease in serum potassium, and for the lack of change in serum sodium postflight. Decrease in serum magnesium was interpreted as evidence of a reestablishment of ionic equilibrium principally in muscle tissue occuring while in space.

Immediate postflight creatinine and blood urea nitrogen (BUN) levels were increased over preflight mean values with return toward preflight levels by one day after recovery. These increases often are associated with prerenal diversion of water, increased protein catabolism, and impaired renal function. Although no evidence of renal impairment was suggested in the associated chemistry data, it could not be ruled out. Increased protein catabolism or dietary factors probably influenced the creatinine and BUN levels, as well as the state of hydration of the returning crewmen.

Table 5

Apollo Twenty-four Hour Urine Results

Parameter	Units	N*	Preflight Mean ± S.D.	Recovery							
				+24 Hrs	Δ%**	+48 Hrs	Δ%**	+72 Hrs	Δ%**	+6 Days	Δ%**
Specific gravity	SpGr	30	1.019 ± .005	1.024 ± .006	+ .5	1.018 ± .007	— .1	1.016 ± .005	— .3	1.017 ± .004	— .2
Osmolality	Mosmo	30	789 ± 238	1017 ± 569	+28.9	1373 ± 163	+74.0	1170 ± 996	+48.3	750 ± 288	— 4.9
Urine volume	ml	30	1989 ± 494	1090 ± 599	-49.2	1541 ± 691	-22.5	1370 ± 674	-31.1	1805 ± 860	— 9.3
Sodium	mEq/24 hr	30	173 ± 61	90 ± 60	-48.0	106 ± 45	-38.7	156 ± 75	— 9.8	206 ± 57	+19.1
Potassium	mEq/24 hr	30	73 ± 19	43 ± 17	-41.1	54 ± 15	-26.0	50 ± 23	-31.5	68 ± 23	— 6.9
Chloride	mEq/24 hr	30	156 ± 53	60 ± 42	-61.5	97 ± 51	-37.8	137 ± 67	-12.2	181 ± 60	+16.0
Calcium	mEq/24 hr	30	9.3 ± 3	7.8 ± 4.4	-16.1	9.5 ± 4.7	+ 2.2	9.9 ± 4	+ 6.5	12.4 ± 5.8	+33.3
Magnesium	mEq/24 hr	30	8.6 ± 2.7	5.7 ± 2.7	-33.7	5.7 ± 2.4	-33.7	6.9 ± 3.4	-19.8	9.7 ± 4.5	+12.8
IPO₄	mg/24 hr	30	965 ± 267	956 ± 361	— .9	804 ± 340	-16.7	832 ± 381	-13.8	1107 ± 211	+14.72
Creatinine	mg/24 hr	30	1852 ± 468	1842 ± 660	— .5	1669 ± 703	— 9.9	1779 ± 565	— 3.9	1945 ± 641	+ 5.0
Uric acid	mg/24 hr	30	825 ± 303	638 ± 268	-22.7	688 ± 346	-16.6	675 ± 274	-18.2	761 ± 249	— 7.8

* Number of crewmen tested.

** Percent change from preflight mean.

Table 6

Significant[*] Twenty-four Hour Urine Biochemistry Changes
(Pre $\bar{x}$ vs. Recovery Day)

Parameter	Direction of Change
Specific gravity	Increased
Osmolality	Increased
Volume	Decreased
Sodium	Decreased
Potassium	Decreased
Chloride	Decreased
Magnesium	Decreased
Uric acid	Decreased

*Significant change is defined as $p < .05$.

The serum creatine phosphokinase (CPK) levels were reduced immediately postflight, and mild elevations were evident by 24 hours after recovery. This alteration was probably a result of muscle inactivity incident to weightlessness and to increased muscular activity during the first 24-hour postflight interval. The decrease in LDH could not be as readily explained, since this enzyme would be expected to increase with exercise (Halonen & Koltinen, 1962). However, it is likely that preflight LDH levels were atypically elevated due to rigorous physical conditioning by the crew, such that the postflight reduction in LDH may simply have been a return to normal enzyme balance.

The postflight elevation of blood glucose may have been related to stress associated with reentry. In support of this prediction the epinephrine and steroid increases correlated well with the hematologic findings of a transient postflight neutrophilia, eosinopenia, and lymphopenia. However, short-term bedrest is associated also with glucosemia (Lutwak & Whedon, 1959), which raises the possibility that the increased glucose seen after the Apollo missions was not entirely a result of stress. As in bedrest, the finding may be a result of diminished uptake of glucose by inactive muscle cells (Lipman, 1970).

The decrease in cholesterol, triglycerides and uric acid may have been a result of the low residue, high fat and carbohydrate diet consumed during the Apollo flights However, these values did not return to preflight levels in two weeks after the mission, even though the crewmen began eating a conventional diet immediately after recovery. This fact suggested possibly that other metabolic consequences were involved. Adrenal steroids have been shown to be elevated during flight which may have accounted for the decrease in the stores of precursor cholesterol, particularly if not replaced by the diet (see Section III, Chapter 1). The decreased cholesterol was in agreement with elevated thyroxine levels, and contributed to the evidence for increased thyroid function during flight (Sheinfeld et al., 1975); (see also Section III, Chapter 1 of this book).

The increase in total protein at recovery, and subsequent decrease in the days following, portrayed the immediate postflight state of hydration of the individual crewmen and the redistribution of fluid compartments which occurred throughout the postflight interval. The immunological proteins were elevated also in many of the crewmen, which perhaps contributed also to total protein elevation (Fischer et al., 1972); (see also Section III, Chapter 3).

Urine Constituent Measurements

The postflight 24-hour urine collections revealed significant retention of sodium, potassium, and chloride ions associated with a reduced total urine volume and hyperosmolality. These findings are consistent with the reestablishment of preflight fluid and electrolyte balance and with hormonal adjustments required for readaptation from the space flight environment. The decrease in urinary uric acid predictably reflects the anabolism which occurs during the postflight period. Although dietary factors cannot be ruled out in uric acid metabolism, by six days postflight the crewmen should have consumed diets sufficient to return those levels to the preflight mean. For a more detailed review of the urinary constituents, the reader is referred to Section III, Chapter 1 of this book.

Summary

The objectives of the biochemical studies conducted for the Apollo Program were (1) to provide routine laboratory data for assessment of preflight crew physical status and for postflight comparisons; (2) to detect clinical or pathological abnormalities which might have required remedial action preflight; (3) to discover as early as possible any infectious disease process during the postflight quarantine periods following certain missions; and (4) to obtain fundamental medical knowledge relative to man's adjustment to and return from the space flight environment. The accumulated data suggest that these requirements were met by the program described. All changes ascribed to the space flight environment were subtle, whereas clinically significant changes were consistent with infrequent illnesses unrelated to the space flight exposure.

References

Fischer, C.L.; Gill, C.; Daniels, J.C.; Cobb, E.K.; Berry, C.A.; and Ritzmann, S.E.: Effects of the Space Flight Environment on Man's Immune System: I Serum Proteins and Immunoglobulins. Aerospace Medicine, vol. 43, 1972, pp. 836-860.

Halonen, P.I.; and Koltinen, A.: Effect of Physical Exercise of Some Enzymes in the Serum. Nature, vol. 193, pp. 942-944.

Leach, C.S.; Johnson, P.C.; and Alexander, W.C.: The Endocrine, Electrolyte and Fluid Volume Changes Associated with Apollo. In: Apollo Medical Experiments. Washington, D.C.: U.S. Government Printing Office, 1974.

Leach, C.S.; Alexander, W.C.; and Fischer, C.L.: Compensatory Changes During Adaptation to the Weightlessness Environment. Physiologist, vol. 13, 1970, p. 246.

Lipman, R.: Impairment of Peripheral Glucose Utilization in Normal Subjects by Prolonged Bedrest. Journal of Laboratory and Clinical Medicine, vol. 76, 1970, pp. 221-223.

Lutwack, L.; and Whedon, G.D.: The Effect of Physical Conditioning on Glucose Tolerance. Clinical Research, vol. 7, 1959, p. 143.

Sheinfeld, M.; Leach, C.S.; and Johnson, P.C.: Plasma Thyroxine Changes in the Apollo Crewmen. Aviation Space and Environmental Medicine, vol. 46, no. 1, 1975, pp. 47-50.

Snedecor, G.W.: Statistical Methods. Iowa State University Press, Ames, Iowa, 1956.

CHAPTER 3
HEMATOLOGY AND IMMUNOLOGY STUDIES

by

Stephen L. Kimzey, Ph.D.
Craig L. Fischer, M.D.[*]

Lyndon B. Johnson Space Center

Philip C. Johnson, M.D.

Baylor College of Medicine

Stephan E. Ritzmann, M.D.

University of Texas Medical Branch

Charles E. Mengel, M.D.

University of Missouri School of Medicine

Introduction

The hematology and immunology program conducted in support of the Apollo missions was designed to acquire specific laboratory data relative to the assessment of the health status of the astronauts prior to their commitment to space flight. A second, equally important objective was to detect and identify any alterations in the normal functions of the immunohematologic systems which could be attributed to space flight exposure, and to evaluate the significance of these changes relative to man's continuing participation in space flight missions. Specific changes observed during the Gemini Program formed the basis for the major portion of the hematology-immunology test schedule. Additional measurements were included when their contribution to the overall interpretation of the flight data base became apparent.

Detailed hematologic investigations had been conducted in support of selected flights in the Gemini Program. Although the data collected were sparse and incomplete, certain trends were noted and are worthy of comment (Fischer et al., 1967). Radioisotope—derived plasma volume measurements, performed on the crew of Gemini 4, yielded

---

[*]Now at Eisenhower Medical Center.

The authors would like to thank the following individuals for their technical and scientific support of these studies: J. Bailey, L. Brannon, L. C. Burns. H. R. Cantu, E. K. Cobb, H. Conrad. B. S. Criswell, J. Daniels, T. Driscoll, B. Edwards. C. Gill, P. C. Gouch, M. Graham, R. C. Hirasaki, L. Hollaman, T. Jefferson, H. Jordan, A. D. LeBlance. J. Lopez, T. D. Rogers, H. Sakai, C. Tuchman, D. G. Winkler.

calculated red cell mass deficits of about 12 percent after four days in orbit. Based on this observation, direct measurements of red cell mass were performed on the crew of Gemini 5 using a ^{51}Cr tag. The data derived from this study showed a 20 percent decrease in red cell mass following eight days in orbit, accompanied by an abnormally low red cell ^{51}Cr half-life in both pilots. These studies suggested that a hemolytic process was responsible for the observed red cell loss.

Affirmation of a hemolytic reduction in red cell mass was obtained from the crew of the 14-day Gemini 7 mission. In this case, one pilot showed a modest decrease in red cell mass, whereas the other crewman lost 20 percent. Special hematology tests, accompanying the isotope studies, revealed that the reduction in red cell mass was associated with increases in mean corpuscular volume and osmotic fragility. Reticulocyte counts before and after the mission revealed no actual depression of bone marrow activity incident to flight; however, no reticulocytosis appeared until the fourth day after landing. These data imply that the erythropoietic mechanisms were insensitive to the red cell mass reduction which occurred over the 14-day interval. The red cell mass was recovered in both men by three weeks postflight.

Additional biochemical analyses of blood samples from returning Gemini crewmen reflected significant decreases in plasma alpha-tocopherol levels, total red cell membrane lipids, specifically the long chain of fatty acids of cephalin and lecithin, and red cell phosphofructokinase activity. All of these compounds influence red cell integrity. Indeed, the Gemini findings provided a new impetus in red cell investigation, with emphasis directed at the red cell membrane itself and not solely at intracellular enzyme systems.

The Gemini findings formed the basis of a working hypothesis for the influence of space flight on red cell function and survival. This hypothesis, comparable to that of Jacob (1969) for microspherocyte formation, proved to be actually applicable only to the Gemini environment, but it strongly influenced both the selection and interpretation of test data of the earlier Apollo flights. As more information was collected in the later Apollo missions, it became apparent that the hemolytic damage characteristic of the Gemini flights was not the only hematologic consequence of space flight.

Hematology Studies

The hematology analyses conducted in support of Apollo missions ranged from routine procedures (table 1) intended primarily to provide basic information to the crew surgeon to more specialized tests (table 2) designed to elucidate the effects of space flight on the normal functioning and integrity of the red blood cell. For the most part, standard laboratory techniques were employed. Some specific procedures are discussed in more detail in the text or are referenced where details are necessary for a more complete comprehension of the results. Blood samples were obtained by venipuncture beginning approximately 30 days prior to launch. No blood samples were acquired during the inflight phase of the missions. The first postflight sample was collected onboard the recovery vessel within one to three hours after splashdown, after which sampling continued for about two weeks. A typical blood sampling schedule for an Apollo mission is illustrated in table 3. The logistics involved with the postflight quarantine of Apollo 11, 12, and 14 made it impractical to perform some of the analyses on those missions.

Table 1

Routine Hematology Tests

Red blood cell count

Reticulocyte count

Hemoglobin

  Oxyhemoglobin
  Carboxyhemoglobin
  Methemoglobin

Hematocrit

Red cell indicies

  Mean corpuscular volume
  Mean corpuscular hemoglobin
  Mean corpuscular hemoglobin concentration

White blood cell count

White blood cell differential

Platelet count

Total eosinophil count

Table 2

Special Hematology Tests

Blood Volume Measurement

  RBC mass
  Plasma volume
  Blood volume (calculated)
  Serum iron turnover
  RBC survival
  Whole body hematocrit

RBC Metabolism

  Hexokinase
  Phosphofructokinase
  Glucose-3-phosphate dehydrogenase
  Phosphoglyceric kinase
  Pyruvate kinase
  Adenosine triphosphate
  2, 3-diphosphoglycerate
  Reduced glutathione
  Glucose-6-phosphate dehydrogenase
  Lipid peroxides

Cellular Analysis

  RBC electrolyte distribution (electron probe analysis)
  RBC hemoglobin distribution (microspectrophotometry)
  RBC morphology and ultrastructure (electron microscopy)
  RBC age density separation
  RBC sodium/potassium flux (isotope exchange)
  RBC sodium/potassium concentration
  RBC volume distribution

Table 3

Blood Sampling Protocol[a]

(Values in ml)

Sample Day	Hematology	Clinical Chemistry Endocrinology	Immunology	Fluid and Electrolyte Isotope	Type and Cross-Match
F-30[c]	5	25	10	b	
F-29					
F-15[d]	5	25	10	12[b]	
F-14					
F-5[c]	5	25	10	b	20
F-4					
R+0[d]	5	25	10	12[b]	
R+1[c]	5	25	10	12[b]	
R+6[d]	5	25	10	12[b]	
R+7					
R+13[d] days	5	25	10	12[b]	
R+14					

[a]From *Apollo 16, Medical Requirements*. NASA Document MSC-05259, February 17, 1972.
[b]K^{42} (radioactive potassium).
[c]One venipuncture required on F-30, F-5, and R+1.
[d]Two venipunctures required on F-15, R+0, R+6, and R+13. (Second sample must be taken exactly 30 minutes following injection of isotope.)

On each mission, a group of three male subjects of comparable age, weight, and general physical condition to the crew formed a ground-based control group. These individuals were examined simultaneously with the crew to ensure that the sampling schedule, transfer of blood samples from remote sites, and the overall medical protocol did not influence laboratory results. The data from these subjects will be referred to as control data or simply "controls" throughout the following discussion, and should not be confused with laboratory "standard samples" which were routinely used to verify procedures.

Routine Hematology

Routine hematological data from the Apollo missions are summarized in table 4. Details concerning some of the results mentioned here are presented in subsequent sections of this chapter. There were no changes in RBC count or hematocrit following the flights. However, there was a modest (significant in one-third of the crewmen) elevation

Table 4

Summary of Apollo Hematology Results

Parameter	Preflight Mean ± SD	Postflight Mean ±SD			
		R+2 Hrs	R+1 Day	R+7 Days	R+14 Days
Red cell	5.01 ± 0.31	4.92 ± 0.53	4.55 ± 0.34	4.56 ± 0.37	4.60 ± 0.30
Reticulocyte	0.98 ± 0.45	0.62 ± 0.23	0.58 ± 0.22	1.06 ± 0.39	1.18 ± 0.31
Hemoglobin	14.9 ± 0.7	15.4 ± 0.9	14.6 ± 0.9	13.9 ± 1.1	14.2 ± 0.9
Hematocrit	44.2 ± 2.2	44.2 ± 2.8	41.9 ± 3.1	40.9 ± 2.7	41.7 ± 2.6
MCV[a]	88.3 ± 3.7	90.5 ± 6.2	92.3 ± 5.5	90.2 ± 4.2	90.9 ± 4.3
MCH[b]	29.8 ± 1.3	31.5 ± 2.6	32.1 ± 2.3	30.5 ± 1.9	29.4 ± 6.7
MCHC[c]	33.8 ± 1.0	34.9 ± 1.6	34.4 ± 1.7	34.1 ± 1.0	34.2 ± 1.5
Platelet	218000	287000	225000	238000	261000
White cell	7000 ± 1800	8900 ± 3000	7300 ± 1900	6500 ± 1700	6500 ± 2200
Neutrophil	3900 ± 1100	6200 ± 2600	4000 ± 1100	3500 ± 1300	3900 ± 1800
Lymphocyte	2600 ± 700	2300 ± 1300	2700 ± 1100	2400 ± 800	2300 ± 800

[a]Mean corpuscular volume.

[b]Mean corpuscular hemoglobin.

[c]Mean corpuscular hemoglobin concentration.

The preflight mean represents the average of approximately 99 determinations (3 per crewman). The postflight means are average of 33 determinations or less (1 per crewman). Units in each case are standard with respect to routine hematology parameters.

in the hemoglobin concentration, resulting in an increase in the calculated mean corpuscular hemoglobin (MCH) and the MCH concentration (MCHC) immediately postflight in those crewmen. Determinations of concentration-dependent parameters were complicated during the recovery day (R+0) examination by the often inadequate laboratory facilities on the recovery vessel and by the changes in red cell mass and plasma volume which occurred during the mission. There were rapid postflight shifts in body fluid compartment sizes, which influenced particularly the plasma volume.

In contrast to the Gemini findings (Fischer et al., 1967) a slight, but statistically significant, reduction in the reticulocyte count was observed at R+0. The significance of this finding relative to changes in blood volume is discussed in the next section.

There was a postflight (R+0) leukocytosis generally associated with an absolute neutrophilia and a complicated lymphocyte response. This finding was also consistently observed during the Gemini missions. In all cases, the changes in the white blood cell count and differential were transient and reverted to normal within 24 to 48 hours after flight. The elevations in the neutrophil count were modest. In most crewmen, elevations did not exceed the 10 000 count required for the classical definition of neutrophilia. While these changes were possibly a consequence of increased blood epinephrine and/or steroid levels associated with mission stresses, they were highly variable among individuals.

It should be noted that none of the changes observed in hematologic parameters were outside accepted normal ranges, and therefore were not indicative of significant medical events.

Blood Volume

Measurement of red cell mass was of particular interest in the early Apollo flights because of the significant decreases observed in red cell mass during the Gemini flights. The procedures used to measure red cell mass and plasma volume have been reported previously (Fischer et al., 1967; Johnson et al., 1971). The red cell mass loss in the first two Apollo flights was negligible in five of six crewmen tested. This deviation from the pattern of the Gemini crewmen was attributed to a change in the Apollo spacecraft atmosphere composition at launch — from 100 percent oxygen in Gemini to a 60 percent oxygen 40 percent nitrogen mixture at $346 \times 10^2 \mathrm{N/m^2}$ (260 torr) in Apollo. Therefore, the Apollo 7 and 8 missions were characterized by an oxygen concentration of less than 100 percent during the entire flight interval, though it did approach the 95 percent level by the end of the flight.

On the Apollo 9 mission, the crew opened the spacecraft hatches to perform extravehicular activity. Even though denitrogenation began at the time of repressurization and the crew lived in 100 percent oxygen for the next five days, only a seven percent mean decrease in crew red cell mass was observed. This was a significant, but not dramatic, change. However, the crew was not denitrogenated before the mission in the manner of the crews in the Gemini Program. Gemini crewmen breathed 100 percent oxygen at $101 \times 10^3 \mathrm{N/m^2}$ (760 torr) for three hours before the mission, again on the launch complex for several hours before lift-off, and then proceeded with a mission in which a 100 percent oxygen, $346 \times 10^2 \mathrm{N/m^2}$ (260 torr) atmosphere was used. Thus, the

Apollo 7 and 8 oxygen-nitrogen profiles differed considerably from those of the Gemini missions. The atmosphere profile of the Apollo 9 mission was also different, but it was somewhat similar to the Gemini type atmosphere profile during the later stages of the flight.

The results of Apollo 9 and subsequent chamber study at Brooks Air Force Base (Larkin et al., 1972) seemed to confirm the hypothesized toxic effect of oxygen on the circulating red blood cells. These data were integrated into a hypothesis that hyperoxia (even at low atmospheric pressures) can induce the loss of red cell mass by inhibition of red cell production and/or increased destruction of circulating red cells. The details of this hypothesis, which have been reported (Fischer & Kimzey, 1971; Fischer, 1971), are summarized in figure 1.

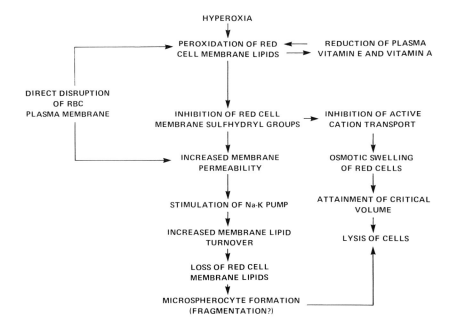

Figure 1. Hypothesis to explain loss of red cell mass as a result of a hyperoxic breathing atmosphere.

Hyperoxia can cause peroxidation of red cell lipids (all membrane-bound), resulting in one or both of the following: (1) the plasma vitamin E and vitamin A levels can be reduced by virtue of the fact that these sterols are lipid antioxidants and are consumed in this type of reaction, and (2) peroxidated lipids can physically compromise red cell membrane integrity. Lipid peroxides are very effective and efficient red cell membrane sulfhydryl group inhibitors, as is oxygen directly. Thus, if red cell lipid peroxides were formed, inhibition of red cell membrane sulfhydryl groups would be expected. The sulfhydryl groups are essential in maintaining the integrity of passive red cell membrane cation transport. If active cation transport is poisoned by the same mechanism, one would observe osmotic swelling of red cells resulting in attainment of critical volume and lysis. Altered active and passive transmembrane cation transport may, therefore, be occurring simultaneously. If the integrity of the red cell membrane is disrupted, changes in shape and/or compliance of the membrane will result in the cell's removal by the reticuloendothelial system (RES).

On Apollo 9, the sodium-potassium flux in the red cell was measured before the mission, immediately afterward, and one day after recovery. The procedure used has been described previously (Larkin & Kimzey, 1972). The controls showed essentially no change, but a significant reduction in the active component (as defined by ouabain inhibition) of potassium flux was observed in the oxygen-exposed flight personnel. This change would compromise the osmoregulatory capacity of the cells, making them more susceptible to osmotic hemolysis. No changes in cation flux were observed on Apollo 10, a mission with a normal oxygen/nitrogen profile.

The Apollo 9 mission was characterized by other changes consistent with the proposed hypothesis; specifically, (1) a reduction in plasma vitamin E and vitamin A levels, (2) a decreased phosphofructokinase activity, (3) a reduction in total red cell lipids, especially lecithin, and (4) abnormal red cell morphology characterized by acanthrocytoid cells, spherocytes and schistocytes (Fischer & Kimzey, 1971).

No measurements of red cell mass were made on Apollo flights 10 through 13 due to operational constraints imposed by the quarantine requirements. On Apollo 14, small but significant red cell mass losses were observed postflight. The mean decrease of -4.7 percent is greater than the changes found in Apollo 7 (-3.4 percent) and Apollo 8 (-1.4 percent), but less than the -7.2 percent after Apollo 9. The Apollo 14 data are somewhat misleading since one crewman had no loss of red cell mass during the flight.

A significant decrease in red cell mass (-10 percent) was measured after Apollo 15. The red cell loss during this mission was more than half recovered by the R+13 examination. The atmosphere to which the Apollo 15 crew was exposed was also higher in oxygen due to a more rapid than nominal leak rate early in the flight, an extended stay on the lunar surface, and extravehicular activity during the transearth coast.

On Apollo 16, as in other similar missions, there was a decreased red cell mass postflight when compared to preflight (F-15) values. If the Apollo 16 results are compared with data from previous missions, we find that the percent changes in red cell mass of the three crewmembers (average of -14.2 percent) were greater than 15 of 16 other Apollo crewmembers. This loss had not been recovered by R+7. When expressed as milliliters per kilogram of body weight, the red cell mass change was greater after Apollo 16 than in all previous Apollo missions. It would appear from data collected on the Apollo flights, that the crewmen judged to be in the best physical condition (based on their exercise testing performance) exhibited the greatest loss of red cell mass.

The crew of Apollo 17 showed an 11 percent decrease in red cell mass at recovery. One week later at R+8 the red cell mass was still nine percent below the control values of F-15. When the red cell mass is corrected for body weight loss, the decrease was seven percent at recovery. The changes in this crew were approximately the same as in crews of the other lunar flights.

Changes in plasma volume following space flight have been more variable, but with a general tendency to be reduced following the Apollo flights. The rapidity with which the plasma volume can equilibrate, combined with the varying length of time following recovery at which the plasma volume was measured and the less than optimal conditions for these tests on the recovery vessel, make these results somewhat less meaningful relative to the inflight condition. Nevertheless, the reduction in plasma volume after space flight might be expected based on similar studies of subjects during comparable periods of bed rest (Hyatt, 1969).

In contrast to the Gemini flights, the red cell survival (as measured by the ^{51}Cr half-life) was not significantly altered during the inflight or postflight phases of the Apollo flights.

To summarize, table 5 compares the percent change in red cell mass, plasma volume, and red cell survival of the crews of the Apollo and Gemini missions in which these studies were performed. The red cell mass decrease of the Apollo 7 and 8 crews was significantly less than the decrease after the lunar missions 14 through 17. The flight duration of the Apollo 7 and 8 missions was less than the average duration of the moon landings; however, it is improbable that flight duration was the reason for the difference since large red cell mass decreases were found after the shorter Gemini 5 mission.

Table 5

Blood Volume Studies

Mission	Plasma Volume (mean % change)	Red Cell Mass (mean % change)
Gemini 4	− 9	− 13 *
Gemini 5	− 7	− 21
Gemini 7	+ 11	− 14
Apollo 7-8	− 8	− 2
Apollo 9	− 9	− 7
Apollo 14-17	− 4 ± 2	− 10 ± 1
Apollo Controls	+ 10 ± 2	− 1 ± 1

Red Cell Survival
(^{51}Cr T ½ in Days)

	Preflight	During Flight	Postflight
Apollo 7-8	25	28	25
Apollo 14-17	24	23	27

* Calculated

Apollo 7 and 8 also differ from other Apollo missions in that the Lunar Module purged the Command Module's atmosphere of nitrogen. After that maneuver, the Apollo atmosphere was equivalent to a Gemini atmosphere. Small amounts of residual nitrogen were present throughout Apollo 7, the only mission in which atmosphere composition was measured. The difference between these two types of missions was further evidence to support the concept that a nitrogen-free atmosphere was the cause of the red cell mass decreases. The red cell survival as measured by ^{51}Cr half-life was not shortened to the extent found in three of four Gemini crewmen, suggesting that hemolysis did not occur or was very slight.

While it was not possible within the framework of the Apollo Program to test this hypothesis extensively, all of the Apollo, Gemini, and supporting ground-based studies can be ranked according to the mean red cell mass loss that was measured in the subjects (table 6). These data include the percent loss, the atmosphere composition, the number of subjects, and the exposure duration. What is noteworthy is that anytime a 100 percent oxygen atmosphere was used, significant red cell mass loss occurred. However, if a diluent gas was present, no significant red cell loss was observed.

The initial hypothesis (figure 1) predicted an intravascular hemolysis of the cells as a result of failure to maintain osmotic balance. Based upon additional data collected in support of the Apollo Program, this hypothesis may need to be modified. The consistent elevation of haptoglobin in all of the crewmen following Apollo flights is inconsistent with intravascular hemolysis. Red cell survival was not significantly shortened in the Apollo flights, and this finding does not support the concept of intravascular hemolysis.

It is possible that the alteration of red cell membrane lipids and/or sulfhydryl groups would alter the cells' structural configuration leading to fragmentation of cells and their subsequent destruction by the reticuloendothelial system. Shape changes have been observed in red cells collected inflight (Kimzey et al., 1974).

However, the lack of any change in the ^{51}Cr survival time suggests that the loss may not be due to red cell destruction at all, but to a reduction in the production of cells. Regardless of the exact cause of the red cell mass decrease, compensatory erythropoiesis is not evident. There are data from later flights to suggest that initiation of the recovery of red cell mass after completion of the mission may be delayed for up to two weeks (Johnson et al., 1974; 1975). In order to account for the loss seen in some of the Apollo flights, red cell production would have to be totally inhibited for the duration of the flight (assuming a normal loss of approximately one percent per day), and even this could not account for the large loss in the Gemini missions. It is obvious that the exact mechanism of this red cell mass loss has not been established; oxygen undoubtedly is a contributory agent, but is probably not the only one.

Special Hematology

The measurement protocol for red cell glycolytic enzymes and intermediate compounds varied from mission to mission. Operational constraints associated with quarantine prevented this protocol from being applied with any degree of consistency. The changes in red cell metabolic function during space flight as determined by analysis of selected compounds are summarized in table 7.

The energy-related enzymes in general showed a postflight elevation, but adenosine triphosphate (ATP) levels were unchanged. The stability of red cell 2, 3-diphosphoglycerate (2, 3-DPG) is indicative of the maintenance of normal hemoglobin-oxygen affinity. During a chamber study with a high oxygen atmosphere [100 percent at $34 \times 10^3 N/m^2$ (5 psi)], red cell ATP and 2, 3-DPG were reduced during the exposure period. The ATP decline during this study resulted in a significant reduction in the active component of potassium influx in the erythrocytes (Larkin & Kimzey, 1972). The decline in potassium influx noted in the Apollo 9 samples was not accompanied by a reduction in ATP.

Table 6
Summary of Red Cell Mass Data

Study	% RBC Mass Change		Atmospheric Oxygen Partial Pressure		Exposure (days)	No. of Subjects
	Mean	Range	% Oxygen (minimum-maximum)	(Psia)[*]		
Tektite I	− 2.0	+ 8.0 to − 7.4	15	3.09	60	4
Apollo 8	− 2.0	+ 3.0 to − 4.0	60 − 95	3.7 − 5.1	7	3
Apollo 7	− 3.0	− 2.0 to − 9.0	60 − 95	3.7 − 5.1	11	3
2TV-1 chamber	− 3.0	− 1.6 to − 7.3	60 − 94	3.7 − 5.1	11	3
BAFB chamber	− 3.0	+ 6.0 to −10.0	91	5.0	21	4
Apollo 14	− 4.7	− 1.7 to − 9.1	60 − 99	3.7 − 5.1	10	3
Sealab 111	− 5.0	+ 4.0 to − 9.0	2	4.0	12	3
Apollo 9	− 7.0	− 4.0 to −10.0	60 − 99	3.7 − 5.1	10	3
Apollo 15	−10.1	− 7.0 to −13.7	60 − 99	3.7 − 5.1	12	3
Apollo 17	−11.2	− 8.4 to −14.9	60 − 99	3.7 − 5.1	13	3
BAFB chamber (1970)	−12.7	− 7.0 to −22.0	100	5.0	30	8
Gemini 4	−13.0	−12.0 to −13.0	100	5.0	4	2
Gemini 7	−14.0	− 8.0 to −19.0	100	5.0	14	2
Apollo 16	−14.2	−11.9 to −17.0	60 − 99	5.0	12	3
Gemini 5	−21.0	−20.0 to −22.0	100	5.0	8	2
Phila chamber	−27.0	−19.0 to −31.0	5	3.1	14	6

[*]1 psia = 6.0×10^3 N/m^2

Studies are arranged in order of increasing loss of red cell mass. The atmospheric oxygen profile is based on estimates in most cases instead of actual measurements. All results were collected using the ^{51}Cr procedure (Fischer et al., 1967 and Johnson et al., 1971) except Gemini 4, which was estimated from measurement of plasma volume and the hematocrit.

Although some moderate changes were observed during Apollo in some of the glycolytic enzymes, no trend was evident and the magnitude of the changes did not represent a significant alteration in the functional capacity of the cells.

Decreases were observed after the Apollo 9 mission in the plasma vitamin E and vitamin A levels, as compared with three controls. The reductions in the plasma vitamin E are statistically significant. Concomitant changes in the red cell membrane vitamin E or vitamin A were not observed. Total phospholipid, neutral lipid, and fatty acids of several major phospholipids of the red cell membrane were measured.

The red cell lecithin, a major component of the red cell membrane, showed a dramatic change both quantitatively and qualitatively. There was a quantitative change in the phospholipids and a qualitative change in the fatty acids of the phospholipids. These changes did not appear to be related to diet. Lecithin and other phospholipids showed a shortening of the fatty acid chains, particularly the long-chain, unsaturated fatty acids, such as C_{24}, C_{22}, and C_{18}, suggesting lipid peroxidation.

Table 7

Summary of Changes in Red Cell Metabolic Constituents
(Preflight vs Immediate Postflight Periods)

Parameter	Apollo Mission						
	7	8	9	14	15	16	17
Hexokinase	+	0	0	ND	ND	ND	+
Phosphofructokinase	0	—	0	ND	ND	ND	+
Glucose-3-phosphate dehydrogenase	0	—	+	ND	ND	ND	+
Phosphoglyceric kinase	+	0	—	ND	ND	ND	+
Pyruvate kinase	ND	ND	ND	ND	ND	ND	0
Adenosine triphosphate	0	+	0	0	0	0	0
2,3-diphosphoglycerate	ND	ND	ND	0	0	0	0
Reduced glutathion	—	0	+	ND	ND	ND	—
Glucose-6-phosphate dehydrogenase	ND	ND	ND	ND	ND	ND	0
Lipid peroxides	0	0	0	ND	ND	0	0

0 = no change, + = significantly increased, — = significantly decreased, ND = not done.

Both changes can be explained on the basis of peroxidation. However, on those missions where red cell membrane lipid peroxides were assayed (Apollo 7, 8, 9, 16, 17), none were detected. The lack of detectable lipid perioxidation implied that the possibility of overt red cell damage was unlikely.

Methemoglobin concentrations in blood samples collected immediately postflight after Apollo missions 7, 8, and 16 were substantially elevated and remained high in subsequent postflight samples. The magnitude of this elevation was too great to be indicative of the *in vivo* situation, and therefore must be assumed to have occurred *in vitro* during sample storage. It is perhaps significant that the level of methemoglobin in the crew samples was substantially greater than in control samples collected at the same time, and the conversion rate would have to be many times in excess of that reported for stored blood samples (Jaffe, 1964). The significance of this finding is unknown, but could have been related to the reverse capacity of the reductase mechanism in the cells *in vitro*.

There would appear to be no compromise of red cell metabolic function as a consequence of space flight. The elevation of several energy related enzymes following Apollo 17 could have been indicative of a transient response of the cell to a stressful condition, or could have been indicative of a younger population of red cells known to have a higher enzyme activity overall. However, both of these suggestions remain speculative in the absence of additional data.

In Apollo 13 through 17, the erythrocytes were examined individually by electron probe microanalysis for cellular sodium (Na), potassium (K), and sulfur (S) content. These procedures were designed to evaluate changes in the population distribution of the two major osmotically active cations (Na and K) of the red blood cell. In general, the method consisted of focusing a beam of high energy electrons onto a single red cell and determining the Na, K, and S content by detection of the resultant characteristic X-ray photons emitted from the red cell structural matrix (figure 2). The precision and usefulness of the technique for analyzing blood cells have been described in detail elsewhere (Kimzey & Burns, 1973; Burns & Kimzey, 1973).

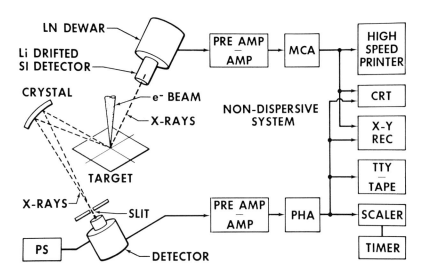

Figure 2. Diagrammatic representation of X-ray detection systems utilized to examine red blood cells with an electron probe microanalyzer.

The results of these studies on Apollo 13 and 14 showed a transient postflight shift in the red cell Na/K ratios, reflecting an elevated cellular Na content and/or reduced cellular K. This change was not detected on Apollo 15. A significant transient drop in erythrocyte K, as measured by electron probe microanalysis, occurred postflight in all three crewmen of Apollo 16; K levels returned to preflight values within one day following recovery. A reduction in erythrocyte S (representative of cellular hemoglobin content) occurred at R+0 on this mission and continued through R + 1 in samples obtained from one of the three crewmen. No change was observed in the other two.

Evaluation of K/S ratios showed that a highly probable direct relationship existed in all three crewmen at R+0. In view of the reduction in cellular K seen at R+0, these data implied either the increased presence of smaller cells in the erythrocyte population or a concomitant loss of hemoglobin at this sampling period.

On Apollo 17, red cells were analyzed individually with the electron probe to determine the intracellular content of K, S, and P as well as to measure the relative mass-density of the cell by X-ray absorption. The trend in Apollo 17 was different from that noted on previous Apollo flights. For this flight, the cells were separated prior to analysis by density centrifugation, using a modification of the procedure of Herz and Kaplan (1965), into a young cell fraction (lightest 10 percent fraction of red cell column) and an old cell fraction (heaviest 10 percent fraction). Thirty cells from each fraction on each sample day were examined individually for their K, S, and P X-ray intensities. The cells' ability to absorb silicon (Si) X-rays from the substrate was also measured as representative of the cell dry mass. These four measurements were made simultaneously on each cell. The S X-ray intensity (reflecting the cellular hemoglobin moiety) and P X-ray intensity (primarily cellular metabolites and phospholipids) did not change significantly during the mission in either the young or old cell fractions. The older cell K did show a postflight drop from a steady increase during the preflight period, but these changes were paralleled by shifts in red cell dry mass (ΔSi intensity).

When the K intensity was corrected for cellular dry mass (thereby reflecting concentration), there was essentially no change following the flight. Red cell K was also measured by conventional emission flame photometry using an internal Li standard. These data for Apollo 17 whole blood, young cells, and old cells were consistent with the results of X-ray microanalysis.

Previously, visualization of red cell shape and structure has been limited to the use of the light microscope with a resolution of .2 micron. Transmission electron microscopy, while providing information on intracellular ultrastructure, is of no help in delineating the three-dimensional structure of the cell. With the use of the scanning electron microscope, details of the cell can be visualized with a tenfold greater resolution .01 to .02 micron than with the light microscope, and with a large depth of field.

Because of the physiological importance of the red cell shape and the variety of pathological conditions in which red cells can undergo shape changes, a characterization system for red blood cells using the scanning electron microscope was established during the latter Apollo missions to evaluate changes in red blood cell morphology. This classification scheme is similar to that described by Bessis (1973) and is reported in detail elsewhere (Kimzey et al., 1974).

Six categories of red cell morphology were defined from examination of normal human red cell preparations; these cell types and representative photographs are indicated in table 8 and figures 3 through 7. Baseline data were obtained from control subjects, the backup crew, and prime crewmembers preflight. No significant abnormalities were found as a result of the space flight exposure to Apollo. However, extensive examination of red cell shape changes in other studies has indicated that red cell morphological alterations do occur during space flight (Kimzey et al., 1974). These changes were rapidly (within hours) reversed after recovery. Thus, with only the pre- and postflight sampling characteristic of the Apollo Program, any inflight changes might not be detected.

Examination of postflight crew and control buffy coat (leukocyte) samples by transmission electron microscopy indicated no noticeable changes in intracellular ultrastructure as compared with preflight samples. Mitochondria were intact, cytoplasmic granules were well preserved, nuclear membranes were intact, and cell membranes appeared normal.

Table 8
Red Cell Shape Classification

Designation	Characteristic	Comments	SEM Criteria
Discocyte	Disc	Normal biconcave erythrocyte	Shallow but visible round depression in central portion of cell.
Leptocyte	Thin, flat	Flattened cell	No visible depression and no evidence of cell sphering (cell diameter normal or larger than normal).
Codocyte	Bell	Bell-shaped erythrocyte (appearance depends upon side of cell uppermost)	Single concavity with extruded opposite side or flattened ring around elevated central portion of cell.
Stomatocyte	Single concavity	Various stages of cup shapes	Swollen cell periphery with smaller concavity or concavity flattened on one side, indicating the beginnings of sphering.
Knizocyte	Pinch	Triconcave erythrocyte	Triconcave depression or cell with pinched area in center.
Echinocyte	Spiny	Various stages of crenation	Deformed and angular cell periphery with spicule formation.

(From Kimzey et al., 1974)

Red blood cell samples were processed by microspectrophotometry on Apollo missions 15 through 17 using techniques designed by Wied and co-workers (1968). Samples were taken from both crew and controls on F-30, F-15, F-5, R+0, and R+8. A minimum of 25 red cells was scanned from each sample at a wavelength of 280 mm. The step size of 0.5 micron resulted in 150 to 200 measurements of optical density within each red cell, providing quantitative measurements of protein (hemoglobin) content and distribution within individual cells.

Comparisons of relative cell cross-sectional area, total extinction (at 280 nm), and mean extinction values in the crew and control samples, both before and after flight, indicated no significant differences. Two-dimensional (area and total extinction) cluster analyses of these data also failed to reveal any changes attributable to space flight. Evaluation of these data using a multidimensional space analysis whereby multiple variables from the microspectrophotometric data are used for hyperspace comparisons also failed to separate any distinct population changes.

From the data analyzed to date, there would seem to be no significant changes in the structure or function of the blood cells, as measured by the procedures described, that could be attributed to the space flight environment of Apollo. There were difficulties with preparation of critical samples which left some gaps in the data, especially with respect to analysis of the R+0 blood samples. Nevertheless, the conclusion from the

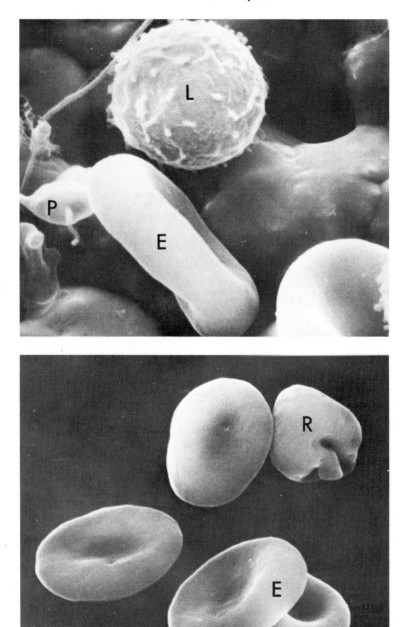

Figure 3. Scanning electron microscope (SEM) photograph of normal blood cells. Shown in these photographs are erythrocytes (E), a lymphocyte (L), a platelet (P) and a reticulocyte (R). The cell to the left of the reticulocyte is probably a more mature reticulocyte.

results is that man's red cell function was not compromised during space flight and that the formed elements of the blood had no compromising structural abnormalities.

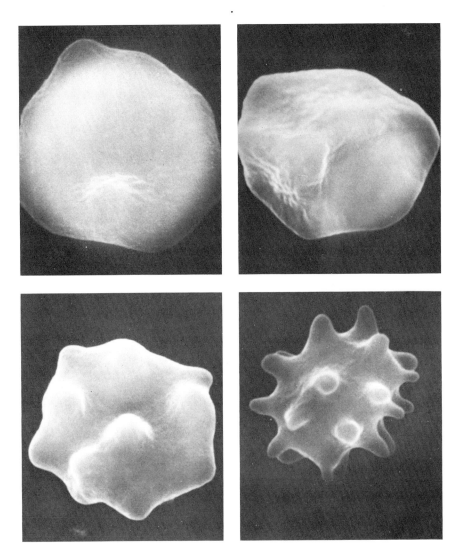

Figure 4. Progressive stages in the discocyte (normal biconcave shaped erythro-cyte)--echinocyte (crenated cell) transformation as viewed by SEM. This transformation is readily reversible in most situations.

Immunology Studies

The assessment of man's immunologic integrity is of particular importance in evaluating the health status of potential space flight crewmen prior to launch and in

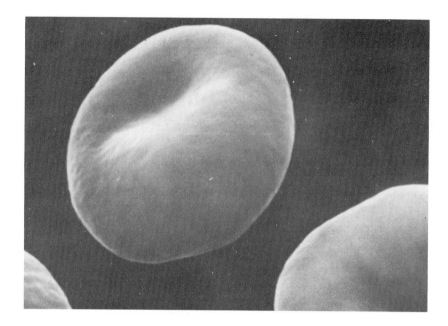

Figure 5. Two stages of stomatocyte (lower image)—spherocyte transformation. Only a slight depression remains in the upper cell of the deep cup prevalent in the stomatocyte.

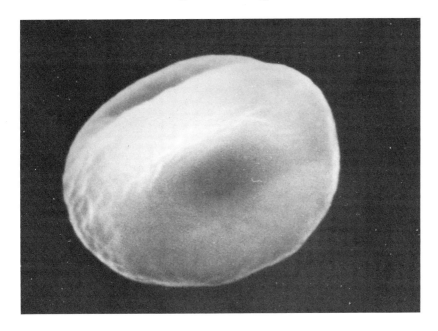

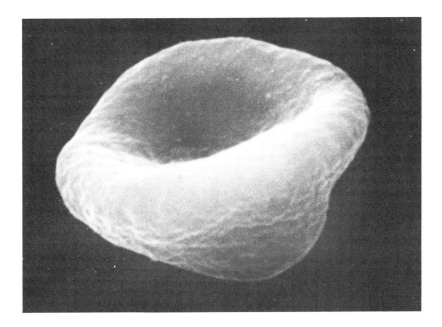

Figure 6. The upper SEM image is a knizocyte ("pinched" cell) and the lower one is a codocyte with a very deep depression. These cells normally comprise less than 2 percent of the circulating red cells.

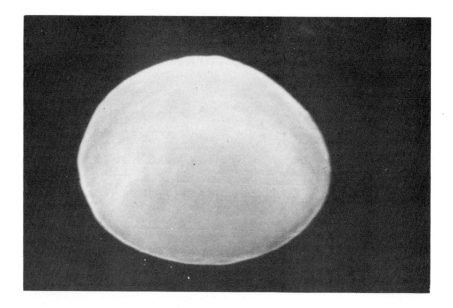

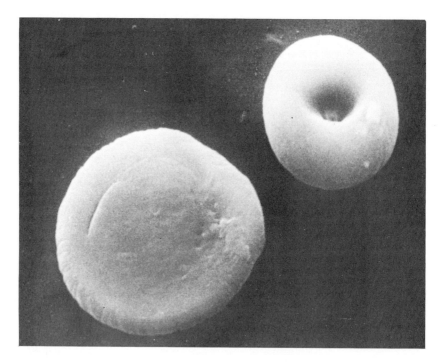

Figure 7. Leptocytes (flattened cells). The lower photograph also contains a microstomatocyte (often identified under the light microscope as a microspherocyte). Leptocytes usually have a greater diameter than discocytes.

determining the medical consequences of space flight. The objectives of the immunology program were to assess the health status of the crews during the preflight period to assist in determining fitness for flight, and, in doing so, to establish individual baseline data for later comparisons. Another objective was to detect any aberrations in immune function resulting from exposure to the space flight environment, both from the standpoint of a response to the environment and the capacity for an adequate immune response after the flight.

The immune system is usually considered as being composed of two basic functional branches. The humoral system consists of immunoglobulins, complement factors, related serum proteins, and the B-lymphocytes. The T-lymphocytes, which when sensitized are capable of performing the tasks of antigen recognition and repulsion, are a major component of the cellular immune system. The T-lymphocytes are responsible for delayed allergic reactions and the initiation of graft-versus-host reactions. They play a major role in the body's defense against certain microorganisms and are also important in the detection and destruction of malignant cells.

Like most biological systems, neither the humoral nor the cellular immune system functions independently of the other. The response to certain antigens requires both T-cell and B-cell interactions to achieve antibody synthesis. Although the differentiation of the immune system into separate classes is somewhat artificial, it will be utilized in the following discussion for the purposes of organization and clarity.

Humoral Immunology

The serum proteins were assayed serially before flight, immediately after recovery, and for varying periods of time (up to two weeks) after flight. Serum protein electrophoretic patterns were obtained by cellulose acetate electrophoresis, from which albumin, α_2-globulin and γ-globulin fractions were computed. Individual serum proteins were quantitated by radial immunodiffusion (RID), using specific antisera (Ritzmann et al., 1973). Proteins assayed by RID include immunoglobulins G, A, and M (IgG, IgA, IgM), the third component of complement (C3), the carrier proteins transferrin, haptoglobin and ceruloplasmin, the antiproteases, α_1-antitrypsin and α_2-macroglobulin, and α_1-acid glycoprotein. The results of the serum protein assays conducted during the Apollo 7 through 17 missions are summarized in table 9 (Fischer et al., 1972a).

The total concentration of serum proteins is typically increased after space flight, with the α_2-globulin fraction responsible for this change. It is of significance that the mean concentrations of the albumin fraction and the total γ-globulin fraction remained unchanged in postflight as compared with preflight values. This elevation was statistically significant in some individuals, but the overall assessment of any meaningful change was complicated by substantial individual variation. Alterations in the plasma volume during the first few hours postflight also contributed to some of the variations observed.

The immunoglobulin profiles in the Apollo astronauts showed a varied response to space flight. Serum levels of IgG and IgM were unchanged over the flight intervals. Individual crewmen occasionally demonstrated IgG values in the low normal range, but these levels were consistent throughout the mission timeline. Serum IgA, which includes

Table 9

Summary of Apollo Serum Protein Results

Parameter	Preflight Mean ± SD	Postflight Mean ± SD			
		R+2 Hrs	R+1 Day	R+7 Days	R+14 Days
Total protein	7.1 ± 0.1	7.3 ± 0.4	6.9 ± 0.3	6.7 ± 0.3	6.8 ± 0.3
Albumin	4.5 ± 0.1	4.5 ± 0.4	4.3 ± 0.4	4.3 ± 0.2	4.2 ± 0.4
α1-globulin	0.2 ± 0.01	0.2 ± 0.01	0.3 ± 0.07	0.2 ± 0.08	0.2 ± 0.09
α2-globulin	0.6 ± 0.02	0.7 ± 0.14	0.6 ± 0.18	0.6 ± 0.09	0.6 ± 0.08
β-globulin	0.8 ± 0.02	0.8 ± 0.10	0.7 ± 0.09	0.7 ± 0.06	0.7 ± 0.10
γ-globulin	1.0 ± 0.03	1.1 ± 0.21	1.0 ± 0.22	0.9 ± 0.17	1.0 ± 0.19
IgG	1022 ± 228	1076 ± 274	954 ± 235	949 ± 194	970 ± 188
IgA	187 ± 73	205 ± 86	174 ± 58	176 ± 62	221 ± 90
IgM	159 ± 73	164 ± 75	118 ± 37	157 ± 74	174 ± 64
C3	84 ± 23	101 ± 28	84 ± 32	86 ± 29	103 ± 16
Transferrin	231 ± 31	225 ± 45	219 ± 32	218 ± 27	218 ± 17
Haptoglobin	136 ± 79	240 ± 121	189 ± 136	189 ± 120	180 ± 97
Ceruloplasmin	31 ± 5	38 ± 14	31 ± 7	35 ± 13	33 ± 11
α1-antitrypsin	255 ± 61	283 ± 60	280 ± 69	263 ± 73	247 ± 66
α2-macroglobulin	232 ± 91	282 ± 117	182 ± 33	226 ± 86	187 ± 31
α1-glycoprotein	66 ± 17	74 ± 21	70 ± 21	77 ± 34	81 ± 25

The preflight mean represents the average of approximately 99 determinations (3 per crewman). Postflight means are averages of 33 determinations (1 per crewman). Values are expressed as gm% for first 6 parameters and mg% for the remainder.

immunoglobulins responsible for antitoxic, antibacterial, antiviral and isoagglutinin activities, was significantly elevated in about one-half the crewmen on the day of recovery, with a return to preflight levels within a few days. No definitive concentration changes were detected in IgD (measured on Apollo 14 through 17 only).

No significant changes were observed in α_1-antitrypsin levels, but there was wide variation among crewmen. The α_2-macroglobulin had a distinctive pattern characterized by a significant postflight increase at R+0, followed by a rapid drop until rather low levels were obtained by R+14. Concentrations of α_1-glycoprotein were unchanged at R+0 from preflight levels, but tended to rise during the postflight period.

The increased postflight α_2-globulin fraction was a result of hyper-α_2-macro-globulinemia and hyperhaptoglobinemia. The consistent postflight elevation of the α_2-macroglobulin is puzzling. In the clinical setting, such a change would suggest an underlying nephrotic syndrome; however, in the Apollo crewmen there was no evidence for this disorder. Therefore, another etiopathogenic relationship, possibly associated with the basic function of this protein as a moderator of certain proteolytic enzyme reactions must be sought. The possibility must be considered that the concentration changes of α_2-macroglobulin are correlated with alterations in the coagulation mechanism, such as accelerated plasmin production, possibly in response to a hypercoagulable predisposition secondary to the hypodynamic state of space flight.

Of the three transport proteins assayed, transferrin, haptoglobin, and ceruloplasmin, haptoglobin showed the most consistent and significant postflight change. The mean increase in haptoglobin concentration on R+0 was almost double the preflight levels and was generally still elevated 14 days following recovery. A postflight increase in ceruloplasmin was also observed, but it was not as consistent, nor was it as significant as the change in haptoglobin. Transferrin showed no significant difference between the immediate postflight value and the preflight mean, but there was a tendency for the concentration to decrease during the two-week postflight period in several of the crewmen.

The causes of postflight hyperhaptoglobinemia are elusive. Although haptoglobin may respond "non-specifically" as an acute phase reactant, the trigger mechanism for such a response pattern is unknown. Haptoglobin is the specific carrier of free hemoglobin, and haptoglobin-hemoglobin complexes are eliminated by the reticuloendothelial system (RES). Thus, hemolysis may lead to increased consumption of haptoglobin and decreased serum levels. However, in patients with severe thermal burns and hemolysis, there is a paradoxical increase of serum haptoglobin levels. Such a contradiction may be due to an RES blockage by tissue breakdown products following thermal injury, preventing the uptake of hemoglobin-haptoglobin complexes and resulting in their accumulation in the circulation. The elevation in haptoglobin levels was confusing in light of the consistent loss of red cell mass during the Apollo flights.

The astronauts as a group demonstrated certain characteristic serum profiles following exposure to the space flight environment; specifically, elevated α_2-globulin due to increases of haptoglobin, ceruloplasmin and α_2-macroglobulin, elevated IgA and C3 without evidence of compromised humoral immunity, and a delayed postflight depression of α_2-macroglobulin, which was transiently elevated after splashdown and recovery.

Transferrin possibly tended to decrease toward the end of the second week of postflight observation. The mechanisms responsible for these observed changes are unknown.

While these patterns prevailed for the astronauts as a group, individual astronauts demonstrated interesting exaggerations or mitigations of these mean changes. One crewman exhibited a marked increase of acute phase reactants such as haptoglobin and α_1-antitrypsin, with a depression of transferrin levels. This pattern contrasted with that of the other astronauts in the group, for which changes in α_1 antitrypsin were insignificant. This crewmember had experienced a pyelonephritis secondary to a Pseudomonas infection. Another crewmember experienced an episode of mild otitis media which was coincident with a decrease of IgG to approximately two-thirds of normal levels. The possibility cannot be excluded that this reduced IgG level may have contributed to this individual's susceptibility to infection.

It would appear that there were no consistent abnormalities relative to the humoral immune system as a result of exposure to the space flight environment of the Apollo missions. There were unexplainable characteristic alterations in some of the proteins, haptoglobin and α_2-macroglobulin in particular. However, the medical consequences of these changes relative to man's immune competence during and after space flight would appear to be minimal. There were no indications from these data to suggest that the functional capacity of the immune system is restrictive to man's participation in lunar and orbital space flights of the duration and type of the Apollo missions.

Cellular Immunology

Techniques for assessing the cellular immune status utilize the ability of small lymphocytes to undergo morphologic changes in response to in vitro antigenic stimulation. These morphological alterations are accompanied by characteristic patterns of biochemical changes which provide a useful measure of cellular immunocompetence. The studies discussed here represent the application of such methods to lymphocytes obtained from Apollo astronauts in an attempt to evaluate the effects of the environment of space flight on cellular immunity.

Lymphocytes from astronauts and control subjects were analyzed for their in vitro antigenic responsiveness by quantitating the rates of synthesis of ribonucleic acid (RNA) and dioxyribonucleic acid (DNA) both in the presence and absence of the mitogen, phytohemagglutinin P (PHA). The details of this technique have been previously described (Daniels et al., 1970a; Fischer et al., 1972b). Lymphocytes were separated from heparinized venous blood by a nylon reticulum column and cultured, with and without PHA, in appropriate media. At the times of maximal RNA and DNA synthesis, 24 and 72 hours respectively, cultures were pulsed for one hour with either ^{3}H-uridine or ^{3}H-thymidine; and incorporation of radioactivity into the lymphocytes measured by liquid scintillation spectrometry. Lymphocyte viability at the time of harvest was assessed by supravital fluorescent staining. The results were calculated as ^{3}H-disintegrations per minute (DPM) per million viable cells. This technique, with appropriate modifications for maintaining cellular functional capacity, yields valid data in the face of the various modes of transport over considerable distances necessary for collecting lymphocyte samples from the Apollo crews (Daniels et al., 1970b).

Absolute lymphocyte counts were determined for each of the 33 astronauts three times during the 30 days prior to launch (at approximately F-30, F-15, and F-5), as soon as possible after recovery (R+0), and various days after recovery. The lymphocyte counts of individual astronauts fluctuated rather widely, but there was a definite trend in many of the crewmen (18 of 33) to exhibit a postflight lymphocytosis at either the R+0 or R+1 sampling periods. However, because of individual variations, this increase was not statistically significant when all flights were considered.

Normal *in vitro* lymphocyte synthesis of nucleic acids, in both the basal unstimulated state and in response to the stimulating agent PHA, tended to remain well confined within relatively narrow ranges of variability, irrespective of the lymphocyte counts in the individual astronauts. The RNA and DNA synthesis rates for lymphocytes cultured before and after flight from the astronauts of Apollo 7 through 13 remained well within the normal ninetieth percentile ranges (Fischer et al., 1972b).

In Apollo flights 14 through 17, the data were somewhat less consistent. The data for the crews of Apollo 14 and 17 were all within normal ranges, both pre- and postflight, and therefore fit the general trend. The data from Apollo 15 were confusing and were complicated by sample handling problems.

Evaluation of the cellular immune response of lymphocytes from pre- and postflight blood samples of the Apollo 16 crew strongly suggested the presences of a subclinical viral infection in both the prime and backup crewmen. These indications were based on (1) abnormal rates of RNA and DNA synthesis in unstimulated lymphocytes as indicated by radioactivity count levels above and below the normal ranges, and (2) abnormal high or low values for rates of RNA and DNA synthesis in PHA stimulated lymphocytes. Electron microscope studies of lymphocytes from the prime crew (R+3 sample) provide a supplemental evidence of subclinical viral infection, based on increased protein-synthesizing capacity (increase in number of polyribosome aggregates and rough endoplasmic reticulum) (Bethard, 1974). These conclusions were supported by preflight and postflight incidences of lymphocytosis and a high percentage of atypical lymphocytes.

While individual astronauts exhibited a variability in lymphocyte patterns preflight and postflight, the majority exhibited a significant but fluctuating increase in lymphocyte numbers shortly after, but not coincident with recovery. The mean lymphocyte count for all Apollo astronauts, however, reflected a value which remained within the normal range. Based on a normal human peripheral blood lymphocyte mean count of 2400/mm^3 and a range of approximately 1500 to 4000/mm^3, 20 of the 33 astronauts exhibited early postflight increases above the normal mean, and five of the 33 above the upper limit of the normal range. Five astronauts experienced lymphocyte counts below the normal range.

The significance of the lymphocyte pattern is unknown. Several factors must be considered in the context of the normal environment during space flights. Among these are demargination and mobilization of lymphocytes from sequestered pools, adrenal corticosteroid influences, possible effects of radiation, and impaired recirculation pathways.

The second parameter studied was the ability of small lymphocytes to respond to antigenic stimulation by the kidney bean extract phytohemagglutinin (PHA) with increased synthesis of RNA and DNA. The phenomenon, associated with characteristic morphologic changes, is generally accepted as an *in vitro* indicator of *in vivo* immunocompetence of T-cells. These morphologic alterations are paralleled by functional changes, such as increased RNA and increased DNA synthesis rates.

The rates of spontaneous unstimulated and PHA-stimulated synthesis of both RNA and DNA by lymphocytes cultured preflight and postflight from the Apollo astronauts remained with the ninetieth percentile normal ranges with the exception of the Apollo 15 and 16, crews which were discussed. The most meaningful mode of data presentation for such determinations, which are based on liquid scintillation counting of radiolabeled nucleotide precursor incorporation, is absolute radioactivity per million viable lymphocytes.

While lymphocyte numbers fluctuated significantly shortly after return from space flight and tended to exhibit a delayed increase, the immunocompetence of these cells, as judged by *in vitro* stimulation techniques, remained stable throughout the preflight and postflight observation periods. This finding is of significance in engendering confidence that the human immune system, particularly such vulnerable components as circulating antigen-sensitive small lymphocytes, can maintain functional integrity in the environments of space flights of the duration of the Apollo missions (10 to 12 days). The influence of longer duration space flights may be more complicated and could influence the lymphocyte responsiveness postflight (Kimzey et al., 1975a, 1975b).

Cytogenetic Studies

It has been appreciated for some time that increased frequency of chromosomal aberration occurs in man following exposure to ionizing radiation. Structural chromosomal aberrations are also known to occur following exposure to other environmental factors such as viruses (both DNA and RNA), to various chemicals such as benzene, and to numerous drugs, including aspirin.

Concern over the possible harm of low levels of radiation exposure centers mostly around it's association with hereditary damage or malignancy. Essentially no information is available concerning radiation effects on the chromosomes of gonadal or meiotic cells of man, and estimates of hereditary damage are based in large part on theoretical views. It should be remembered that one cannot extrapolate findings in somatic cells (in the case under discussion, circulating lymphocytes) to gametic chromosomal patterns. However, studies of patients receiving irradiation treatments as a part of a therapeutic profile suggest a strong correlation between irradiation, chromosome damage, and cancer (Buckton et al., 1962; Bender, 1969).

It is clearly established that many agents which produce tumors in man and animals can also produce chromosomal aberrations in their cells. This information, coupled with the fact that in several rare human disorders (Bloom's syndrome, Fanconi's anemia and ataxia telangiectasia) there is a constitutional predilection for increased chromosomal aberrations as well as an increased incidence of leukemia and lymphoma, has suggested that an increase in structural chromosome aberrations cannot be ignored.

Chromosomal aberrations of concern are structural in nature, that is, they arise through breakage of the strands of chromatin. These breaks may occur either in one or in both chromatids of a single chromosome, or multiple breaks may occur in several chromosomes within an individual cell. Following such accidents, the strands may or may not recombine with themselves, and the broken ends of several chromosomes may combine with each other. Two general types of aberrations occur depending on the stage of the cell cycle in which the break occurs. If the cell is in the pre-DNA synthesis period, chromosome strands are single (chromatids); if the accident occurs after synthesis, the chromosome consists of two chromatids. Chromosomes are technically examined in the metaphase stage of division because that is when they can be separated as individuals, so replication may not have occurred when the chromosomes of peripheral lymphocytes are examined, depending in part on the time in culture. Generally, these two types of aberrations may be morphologically separated. However, in several instances it is impossible to tell whether the break occurred in the pre-DNA synthesis, and was replicated, or whether both strands were affected after replication. A break will produce a fragment that is generally lost in the next cell division. Separation of the aberrations into chromatid-type chromosome-type is useful, since the type of structural defect occurring in humans as a response to a specific exposure has varied with the agent to which the person is exposed.

The results of the Gemini Program have been summarized elsewhere (Gooch & Berry, 1969). The percentage of breaks before flight ranged from zero to 9.5 percent, with a mean of 4.4 percent. The postflight values ranged from 0.5 to 11 percent, with a mean of 8.3 percent or almost twice the preflight mean. More significantly, there were eleven values which increased, five values which decreased, and one value which remained unchanged.

The Apollo flights were marked by a greater magnitude increase in postflight chromosome breaks in every crewmember tested. However, cultures obtained from the missions associated with lunar quarantine did not yield sufficient well-spread mitoses for analyses.

In the Apollo studies, peripheral blood samples were collected and heparinized. After centrifugation, the buffy coat was preserved for chromosome cultures and the serum and erythrocytes were used for other laboratory experiments. The cultures were harvested after 66 hours incubation at $310°K$ ($37°C$). Slides were prepared by the air-dry method and the cells stained with Giemsa. Preflight blood samples were collected from 30 days to one day prior to lift-off. Postflight samples were drawn on the day of recovery or within four days postrecovery. From 200 to 1000 metaphase cells were scored for each individual.

Chi-square tests on preflight versus postflight aberration rates showed that approximately 50 percent of the crewmen tested had significant increases in chromatid-type changes postflight. Fewer tests showed significant chromosome-type increases. If the Apollo astronauts are divided into two groups based on the presence or lack of previous flight experience, an interesting fact emerges. Only one out of six astronauts who were on their first mission had a preflight value above four percent, whereas all but one of the nine experienced astronauts had preflight values of four percent or more.

The postflight break rates were frequently higher for Apollo than for Gemini, and the overall means were nearly double (7.73 percent versus 3.94 percent). With the longer duration of the Apollo missions compared to Gemini, there was a corresponding increase in postflight aberration yields. Although there was wide variation in individual values, the trend is apparent.

In order to evaluate the significance of these findings in terms of astronaut health and safety and in terms of permanent genetic change, more information will be required. Scattered data have been reported in the literature for spontaneous chromosome breakage in man. The values vary from laboratory to laboratory, and among observers in the same laboratory. Standardized slide preparation and cell selection are hopes for the future. Automated chromosome analysis and measurement will hopefully provide data on minute chromosomal changes which are not detectable by the cytologist.

Several investigators have reported correlations between chromosome loss or hypodiploidy and age. It is not yet known whether chromosome loss increases with age or with variables such as increased mild radiation exposure from medical examinations or other environmental factors.

In summary, the chromosome analysis of Gemini and Apollo astronauts from preflight and postflight blood samples suggest three tentative conclusions:

1. Postflight aberrations are approximately double preflight values.

2. There is a rather constant postflight aberration yield which seems to be dependent on the duration of flight.

3. Baseline or preflight values in experienced astronauts appear to be higher than in the other crewmen.

Conclusions

From the standpoint of the normal functioning of the hematological and immunological systems, it appears that space flight has only minimal impact of as yet undetermined significance. The most striking and consistent finding is the loss of red cell mass, but this event might well be due to the hyperoxic atmosphere of the Apollo Command and Lunar Modules, and not to some external factor unique to the space flight environment. However, the red cell mass loss in the later Apollo missions (Apollo 14 through 17) was not characterized by alterations in the red cell which would suggest hemolysis as the primary cause of the drop in blood volume. This finding differentiates these missions where red cell mass is concerned from the earlier Gemini flights and chamber studies conducted with pure oxygen atmospheres. Clearly, more studies must be completed to fully understand the cause and the significance of the red cell mass loss.

Although there were subtle alterations on other aspects of erythrocyte function, plasma protein profiles, lymphocyte response patterns, and chromosome aberrations, none of these changes compromise man's performance capacity while in space or should limit his stay in space. While questions remain unanswered, especially with respect to longer duration missions, no drastic alterations were observed during the Apollo Program for the hematological and immunological systems which would cause serious concern for the health and safety of the crewmen on longer space journeys. As man has adapted to other extremes of his normal environment, both by natural physiological processes and by ingenious engineering fabrications, so it would seem that he is equally capable of surviving and functioning in the artificial environment he has created for himself in space.

References

Bender, M.A.: Human Radiation Cytogenetics. Advanced Radiation Biology, vol. 3, 1969, pp. 215-275.

Bessis, M.: Red Cell Shapes. An Illustrated Classification and Its Rationale. In: Red Cell Shape, M. Bessis, R.I. Weed and P.F. Leblond (eds.), Springer Verlag (New York), 1973, pp. 1-25.

Bethard, B.A.; Granholm, N.A.; Sakai, H.A.; and Ritzmann, S.E.: Ultrastructural Alterations in Peripheral Blood Lymphocyte Profiles Following Acute Thermal Burns. Clin. Immunol. Immunopathol., vol. 2, 1974, pp. 488-500.

Buckton, K.E.; Jacobs, P.A.; Court Brown, W.M.; and Doll, R.: A Study of the Chromosome Damage Persisting After X-Ray Therapy for Ankylosing Spondylitis. Lancett II, 1962, pp. 676-682.

Burns, L.C.; and Kimzey, S.L.: Electron Probe Microanalysis of Age Differences in Human Red Blood Cells. Proc., VIII Nat. Conf. Electron Probe Analysis, 1973, pp. 64A-64E.

Daniels, J.C.; Sakai, H.; Cobb, E.K.; Remmers, R.; Sarles, H.E.; Fish, J.C.; Levin, W.C.; and Ritzmann, S.E.: Altered Nucleic Acid Synthesis Patterns in Lymphocytes From Patients with Chronic Uremia. Amer. J. Med. Sci., vol. 259, 1970a, pp. 214-227.

Daniels, J.C.; Cobb, E.K.; Fischer, C.; Levin, W.C.; and Ritzmann, S.E.: Lymphocyte Cultures Under Varied Logistical Conditions: Stability of Nucleic Acid Synthesis. Aerospace Med., vol. 41, 1970b, pp. 1298-1301.

Fischer, C.L.: Aerospace and Underwater Pathology. In, Pathobiology. An Introduction, J. Minckler, H.B. Anstall and T.M. Minkler (eds.), C.V. Mosby Co. (St. Louis), 1971, pp. 455-466.

Fischer, C.L.; Johnson, P.C.; and Berry, C.A.: Red Blood Cell Mass and Plasma Volume Changes in Manned Space Flight. JAMA, vol. 200, 1967, pp. 579-583.

Fischer, C.L.; and Kimzey, S.L.: Effects of Oxygen on Blood Formation and Destruction. In: Underwater Physiology. C.J. Lambertsen (ed.), Academic Press (New York), 1971, pp. 41-47.

Fischer, C.L.; Gill, C.; Daniels, J.C.; Cobb, E.K.; Berry, C.A.; and Ritzmann, S.E.: Effects of the Space Flight Environment on Man's Immune System: I. Serum Proteins and Immunoglobulins. Aerospace Med., vol. 43, 1972a, pp. 856-859.

Fischer, C.L.; Daniels, J.C.; Levin, W.C.; Kimzey, S.L.; Cobb, E.K.; and Ritzmann, S.E.: Effects of the Space Flight Environment on Man's Immune System: II. Lymphocyte Counts and Reactivity. Aerospace Med., vol. 43, 1972b, pp. 1122-1125.

Gooch, P.C.; Berry, C.A.: Chromosome Analyses of Gemini Astronauts. Aerospace Med., vol. 40, 1969, pp. 610-614.

Herz, F.; and Kaplan, E.: A Microtechnic for the Separation of Erythrocytes in Accordance with their Density. Amer. J. Clin. Path., vol. 43, 1965, pp. 181-183.

Hyatt, K.H.: Hemodynamic and Body Fluid Alterations Induced by Bed Rest. Proc. of Conference on Hypogravic and Hypodynamic Environments. NASA SP-269, 1969, pp. 187-199.

Jacob, H.S.: The Defective Red Blood Cell in Hereditary Spherocytosis. Ann. Rev. Med., vol. 20, 1969, pp. 41-46.

Jaffe, E.R.: Metabolic Processes Involved in the Formation and Reduction of Methemoglobin in Human Erythrocytes. In: The Red Blood Cell. C. Bishop and D.M. Surgenor (eds.), Academic Press (New York), 1964, pp. 397-422.

Johnson, P.C.; Driscoll, T.B.; and Fischer, C.L.: Blood Volume Changes in Divers of Tektite I. Aerospace Med., vol. 42, 1971, pp. 423-426.

Johnson, P.C.; Driscoll, T.B.; and LeBlance, A.D.: Blood Volume Changes. Proc., Skylab Life Sci. Symp. NASA TM X-58154, 1974, pp. 495-505.

Johnson, P.C.; Kimzey, S.L.; and Driscoll, T.B.: Postmission Plasma Volume and Red-Cell Mass Changes in the Crews of the First Two Skylab Missions. Acta Astronautica, 1975 (in press).

Kimzey, S.L.; and Burns, L.C.: Electron Probe Microanalysis of Cellular Potassium Distribution. Proc., N.Y. Acad. Sci., vol. 204, 1973, pp. 485-501.

Kimzey, S.L.; Burns, L.C.; and Fischer, C.L.: Experiment M115—Special Hematologic Effect: Dynamic Changes in Red Cell Shape in Response to the Space Flight Environment. Proc., Skylab Life Science Symposium. NASA TM X-58154, 1974, pp. 519-544.

Kimzey, S.L.; Johnson, P.C.; Ritzmann, S.E.; and Mengel, C.E.: Skylab Hematology and Immunology Studies: A Summary of the Second Mission. Aerospace Med., 1975a (in press).

Kimzey, S.L.; Ritzmann, S.E.; Mengel, C.E.; and Fischer, C.L.: Skylab Experiment Results: Hematology Studies. Acta Astronautica, 1975b (in press).

Larkin, E.C.; Adams, J.D.; Williams, W.T.; and Duncan, D.M.: Hematologic Responses to Hypobaric Hyperoxia. Amer. J. Physiol., vol. 79, 1972, pp. 541-549.

Larkin, E.C.; and Kimzey, S.L.: The response of Erythrocyte Organic Phosphate Levels and Active Potassium Flux to Hypobaric Hyperoxia. J. Lab Clin. Med., vol. 79, 1972, pp. 541-549.

Ritzmann, S.E.; Alami, S.Y.; Vanfossan, D.D.; and McKay, G.G.: Electrophoresis, Immunoelectrophoresis, Quantitative Immunodiffusion, and Thermoproteins. In: Laboratory Medicine. G.J. Race (ed.). Harper and Row (New York), 1973, Chap. 12A.

Wied, G.L.; Bartels, P.H.; Bahr, G.H.; and Oldfield, D.C.: Taxonomic Intra-cellular Analytic System (TICAS) for Cell Identification. Acta Cytol., vol. 12, 1968, pp. 100-204.

CHAPTER 4
APOLLO FLIGHT CREW CARDIOVASCULAR EVALUATIONS

by

G. W. Hoffler, M.D.
Robert L. Johnson, M.D.

Lyndon B. Johnson Space Center

Introduction

The Apollo Program was designed to fulfill the specific operational goals of landing man safely on the moon, enabling him to explore the lunar surface, and successfully returning him to Earth. The engineering and operational complexity of this effort necessarily limited inflight physiological studies of man to those measurements considered vital to crew safety and health assessment. Limited availability of astronaut time during busy preflight and postflight periods constrained evaluations significantly; therefore, only examinations believed to have the greatest relevance to the understanding of man's physiological responses to the space flight environment were undertaken.

Reductions in orthostatic tolerance following space flight were first observed with the late flights of Project Mercury. Tilt table tests revealed moderate orthostatic hypotension in the Mercury-Atlas 9 Pilot after only 34 hours of orbital flight. Because of this finding, tilt table tests for orthostatic tolerance were incorporated into routine preflight and postflight evaluations and continued throughout the Gemini Program. The results of these tests confirmed consistent but variable losses of orthostatic tolerance following three- to fourteen-day flights. Elevated heart rate, reduced pulse pressure, and increased pooling of fluid in the lower extremities were found consistently during 70° upright tilts in the early postflight period. Responses to this stress usually returned to normal within 50 hours after splashdown, regardless of flight duration (NASA, 1963; 1967).

The advent of the Apollo Program presented new questions and uncertainties. Fundamental differences in the Apollo spacecraft, in its operational environment, and in program goals were expected to produce physiological responses that differed from those

The authors are grateful for the technical assistance of R. A. Wolthuis, J. T. Baker, M. E. Taylor, D. P. Golden, and M. M. Ward. The authors also thank T. A. Beale, S. A. Bergman, J. Day, J. A. Donaldson, J. G. Groves, M. M. Jackson, N. A. Lee, S. McKamie, A. E. Nicogossian, R. A. Schiffman, and E. Sloan. All associates of various tenure were affiliated with the NASA Lyndon B. Johnson Space Center Cardiovascular Laboratory during the Apollo Program.

seen after the Gemini flights. The two-gas (oxygen and nitrogen) atmosphere and the capability to move about in the spacecraft led to speculation that returning Apollo crewmen might show little or no change in orthostatic tolerance. On the other hand, there was some concern regarding the ability of the cardiovascular system to withstand acceleration stresses associated with lunar descent and ascent. Headward acceleration ($+G_z$) was imposed during the Lunar Module descent after three to four days of weightlessness, and a near one-g ($+G_z$) force was produced by the ascent profile after a day or more of 1/6-g exposure. Also, the results of postflight tests were expected to show important differences in cariovascular responsiveness between crewmen who walked on the moon and those who remained in weightless flight. These speculations and many other unanswered questions emphasized the need to gain as much understanding as possible about the cardiovascular system and its adaptation, first to zero g and, later, to one g.

For several years before the first manned Apollo flight, investigators had studied the effects on the cardiovascular system of the application of lower body negative pressure (LBNP). Lower body negative pressure involves the application of reduced pressure usually to that portion of the body below the level of the iliac crests. Evaluations of its use as a simulator of orthostatic stress (Samueloff et al., 1966; Brown et al., 1966; Gilbert et al., 1966; Murray et al., 1967) and as a preventer of cardiovascular deconditioning (Stevens et al., 1966a; 1966b) had been made. Lower body negative pressure, at levels ranging from -40 to -60 mm Hg (-53×10^2 to -80×10^2 N/m^2) as determined by individual tolerance, produced changes in heart rate and blood pressure similar to those resulting from upright tilting. Clearly, the cardiovascular responses initially induced by either stress procedure depended primarily on displacement of blood, chiefly from central blood volume reservoirs, to the lower extremities.

Although qualitatively alike, differences in the magnitude of cardiovascular compensatory responses induced by LBNP have been reported. Stevens (1966) and Stevens and Lamb (1965) found a greater increase in heart rate during upright tilting than during LBNP adjusted to produce the same cardiac output reduction (-19 percent). Later, Musgrave and co-workers (1969; 1971) reported that even though LBNP at -40 mm Hg (-53×10^2 N/m^2) and the upright posture displaced essentially equal volumes of blood to the lower extremities, negative pressure levels of -50 mm Hg (-67×10^2 N/m^2) were required to produce equivalent elevations of heart rate. Both groups of investigators attributed the smaller heart rate response during LBNP to the absence of stimulation of carotid and other baroceptors by gravity-induced hydrostatic pressure and flow changes. Further, the absence of hydrostatic pressure gradients along the lower extremities during LBNP caused displaced blood to be distributed differently than during tilt.

In addition to the capability to induce cardiovascular responses similar to those resulting from orthostasis, several advantages over the tilt table test were offered by the LBNP procedure. No movement of the subject was required; therefore, instrumentation was easier to apply and maintain, and physiological signals remained more stable. Stress could be applied at several levels and the magnitude of stress could be adjusted with greater ease and precision with the LBNP procedure. Because it could be used in weightless conditions and tilt table testing could not, LBNP testing of Apollo crewmen furnished a valuable data base for future application to the understanding of Skylab results. LBNP studies were performed for most Apollo crewmen for missions not encumbered by postflight quarantine restrictions. In some instances, a static stand procedure was performed in conjunction with, or instead of LBNP evaluations. Admittedly, these techniques had limitations. The response of the cardiovascular system during weightlessness can only be inferred from studies performed before and after flight. In addition, many variables, including climatic and emotional factors, complicated interpretation of the results (Hoffler et al., 1974).

On the last two Apollo missions, experimental antihypotensive garments were tested. Although the Gemini and earlier Apollo missions revealed no need for such postflight support, planners of the 28- and 56-day Skylab flights envisioned the possible need for such postflight protection. This concern was in part engendered by reports that crewmen of the 18-day Soyuz 9 orbital mission had to be assisted from their spacecraft after flight because of difficulty standing, and that anti-G suits had been provided for Soyuz 11/Salyut crewmen for use following flight if necessary.

In this chapter, the results of the lower body negative pressure and passive stand tests are presented, and the efficacy of the experimental antihypotensive garments is evaluated. Many answers will be required before the entire picture of man's cardiovascular adaptation to weightlessness can be clarified and understood. The Apollo cardiovascular studies constitute a small but important step in the acquisition of this knowledge.

Methods and Conditions

As noted previously, an LBNP protocol was used in conjunction with missions not encumbered by postflight quarantine restrictions. To assess the comparability of the LBNP and passive stand procedures, both tests were performed on the Apollo 9 crewmen. The passive stand protocol alone was used for evaluating the orthostatic tolerance of the Apollo 10 and 11 crewmen. The Apollo 10 to 14 missions included postflight quarantine, which precluded use of the LBNP. The types and durations of each of the eleven manned Apollo missions and the orthostatic evaluation techniques employed for each are described in table 1. Total mission duration varied from 143 to 302 hours; for the lunar landing missions, the length of crew time in 1/6 g varied from 22 to 75 hours.

The Command Module Pilot (CMP), his backup crewmember, and two control subjects were fitted for Jobst waist-length leotards before the flight of Apollo 16. These garments were to be donned during postflight orthostatic evaluations to assess their antihypotensive effect. A garment employing the capstan principle for the application of lower body positive pressure was designed to be worn by the Apollo 17 CMP during postflight tests.

The following subsections will describe the methodological aspects and conditions affecting orthostatic evaluation with and without the use of countermeasure garments.

Equipment and Measures

Lower Body Negative Pressure Device. The device for accomplishing LBNP consisted of a chamber of sufficient size to accommodate the lower body, an airtight waist seal, and

Table 1

Apollo Mission Characteristics and Orthostatic
Evaluation Techniques Employed

Apollo Mission	Type of Mission	Time From Lift-off to Lunar Landing, Hr	Length of Lunar Stay, Hr	Time From Lunar Lift-off to Splashdown, Hr	Total Mission Duration		Type of Orthostatic Evaluation Performed
					Hours	Days	
7	Earth orbital				260.1	10.8	LBNP
8	Lunar orbital				147.0	6.1	LBNP
9	Earth orbital				241.0	10.0	LBNP, Stand
10	Lunar orbital				192.0	8.0	Stand
11	Lunar landing	102.7	22.2	70.9	194.0	8.1	Stand
12	Lunar landing	110.5	31.5	102.0	244.5	10.2	—
13	Lunar-abort				142.9	6.0	—
14	Lunar landing	108.2	33.5	74.3	216.0	9.0	—
15	Lunar landing	104.7	67.0	123.6	295.0	12.3	LBNP
16	Lunar landing	104.5	71.0	90.3	265.8	11.1	LBNP
17	Lunar landing	110.3	75.0	116.5	301.8	12.6	LBNP

a regulated vacuum source (Wolthuis et al., 1970; Wolthuis et al., 1972). The LBNP device is shown in figure 1. The type of physiological measurements taken during the LBNP protocol varied slightly from mission to mission. Measurements made in conjunction with the Apollo 7 to 9 missions included continuous axillary and sternal lead electrocardiograms, indirect blood pressure taken every 30 seconds by the Korotkov sound technique [using the NASA Gemini blood pressure measuring system (NASA, 1968)], and changes in calf circumference measured by double-strand, mercury-in-Silastic strain gages.

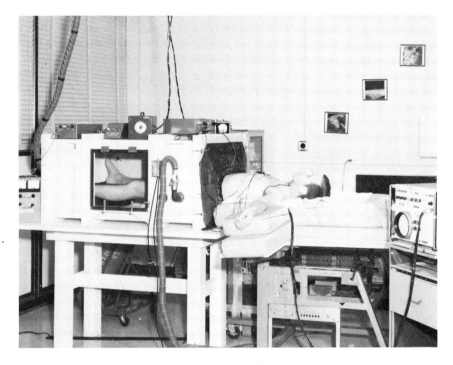

Figure 1. Subject undergoing test
in lower body negative pressure device.

For the Apollo 15 to 17 evaluations, the limited two-lead electrocardiogram (ECG) was replaced with a modified Frank lead vectorcardiogram (VCG), and wide-band precordial heart sounds (vibrocardiogram) were recorded with a capacitance microphone system (LTV Research Center, Anaheim, Calif.). The respiration rates of the Apollo 16 and 17 crewmen were measured with a mercury strain gage attached to the lower thorax. The carotid pulse trace was recorded for Apollo 17 crewmen.

Antihypotension Garments. A Jobst waist-length elastic leotard was used in conjunction with the Apollo 16 mission. This garment was designed to produce a pressure at the ankle of 40 to 45 mm Hg (53×10^2 to 60×10^2 N/m²) that decreased linearly to approximately 10 mm Hg (13×10^2 N/m²) at the waist. To accommodate the reduction in limb size expected to occur during flight, garments in three separate sizes were made for the CMP. They were, respectively, 0.5, 1, and 1.5 cm smaller in circumference at the calf with proportionate reductions throughout the lower limbs.

A lower body garment using the capstan principle to apply pressure to the lower limbs was designed, fabricated, and sized for the Apollo 17 CMP to use following splashdown. The garment is pictured diagrammatically in figure 2. Capstan pressure was read from an aneroid gage and the capstan was inflated with a hand bulb, both of which were concealed in a zippered pocket. The capstan exerted the pressure of the garment over the skin at the ankle in a 2:1 ratio. This pressure diminished linearly to approximately 10 mm Hg (13×10^2 N/m²) at the waist. Preflight testing with pressure sensors between the garment and the skin verified the ratio and the diminishing gradient of pressure from ankle to waist. To accommodate anticipated loss of limb girth, laces were provided for reducing the garment size slightly before stowage in the Command Module. The capstan itself accommodated moderate changes (±2.5 cm) in limb girth.

Physical Examinations

Major medical examinations of space flight crewmembers were performed at approximately 30, 15 and 5 days before flight (F-30, F-15 and F-5, respectively). Orthostatic tolerance evaluations performed as an integral part of these medical examinations provided baseline information for comparison with postflight evaluation results. These preflight orthostatic tolerance evaluations took place at the NASA Lyndon B. Johnson Space Center (JSC) Cardiovascular Laboratory, Houston, Texas, and at the NASA John F. Kennedy Space Center (KSC) Medical Operations Facility, Kennedy Space Center, Florida. As part of the major medical examinations, postflight orthostatic tolerance evaluations were performed shortly after splashdown and at intervals of approximately 24-hours thereafter. The number of postflight evaluations and the time at which they were performed (table 2) were dictated partly by operational constraints and partly by the length of time required for individual crewmembers to regain their preflight status. As indicated in table 2, either two or three postflight orthostatic evaluations were completed on each crewman; a fourth evaluation of the Apollo 15 to 17 crewmembers differed in that it did not necessarily include orthostatic stress tests. Immediately postflight, the first evaluations took place on the recovery ship; subsequent postflight evaluations were performed on the recovery ship, at KSC, or at the JSC Cardiovascular Laboratory.

Control Subjects

To ensure comparability of test conditions and operability of test equipment, several members of the attending support team assigned to each Apollo mission participated in preflight and postflight orthostatic evaluations identical to those used on crewmembers. These control subjects were evaluated a day or two before the Apollo crewmen were evaluated. The data collected helped ensure the validity of postflight changes observed in space flight crewmembers and the operational readiness of test teams and equipment.

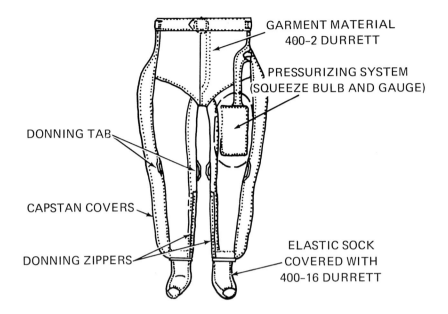

GARMENT MATERIAL
400-2 DURRETT

PRESSURIZING SYSTEM
(SQUEEZE BULB AND GAUGE)

DONNING TAB

CAPSTAN COVERS

DONNING ZIPPERS

ELASTIC SOCK
COVERED WITH
400-16 DURRETT

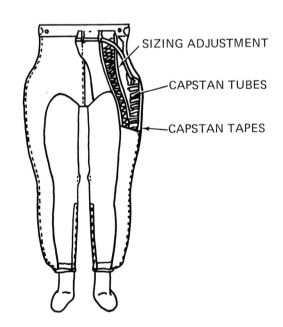

SIZING ADJUSTMENT

CAPSTAN TUBES

CAPSTAN TAPES

Figure 2. Lower body positive pressure garment
employing the capstan principal.

Table 2

Time of Apollo Postflight Orthostatic Tolerance Evaluations

Apollo Mission	Crew-member	Time of Postflight Evaluations (hours following splashdown)			
		First	Second	Third	Fourth
7	CDR	3	34		
	CMP	2	35		
	LMP	5	32		
8	CDR	3	26	51	
	CMP	4	27	53	
	LMP	5	26	52	
9	CDR	2	31	53	
	CMP	4	33	55	
	LMP	3	32	54	
10	CDR	2	26		
	CMP	3	27		
	LMP	2	28		
11	CDR	6	25		
	CMP	7	25		
	LMP	8	26		
15	CDR	3	43	73	122
	CMP	4	42	71	121
	LMP	5	44	72	137
16	CDR	4	24	68	162
	CMP	6	26	70	162
	LMP	5	25	71	162
17	CDR	6	24	48	90
	CMP	5	26	50	91
	LMP	7	25	51	91

Test Protocols

The protocols for the two orthostatic stress procedures are shown in figure 3. The supine LBNP protocol consisted of a five-minute resting control period, a five-minute period at each of three distinct reduced-pressure levels, and a five-minute recovery period. The first five-minute period of reduced pressure included one minute at -8 mm Hg (-11×10^2 N/m^2) and one minute at -16 mm Hg (-21×10^2 N/m^2), followed by three minutes at -30 mm Hg (-40×10^2 N/m^2). The two short-duration, relatively low levels of reduced pressure were adopted to obtain additional information regarding the responsiveness of lower limb capacitance vessels. The three levels of sequentially applied reduced pressure used were chosen on the basis of previous experience in the JSC Cardiovascular Laboratory (Wolthuis et al., 1970). As reported, the use of an incremental LBNP protocol produced physiological responses for each level of reduced pressure applied and ensured a measurable, quantitative stress response in both the normal preflight and the orthostatically intolerant postflight conditions.

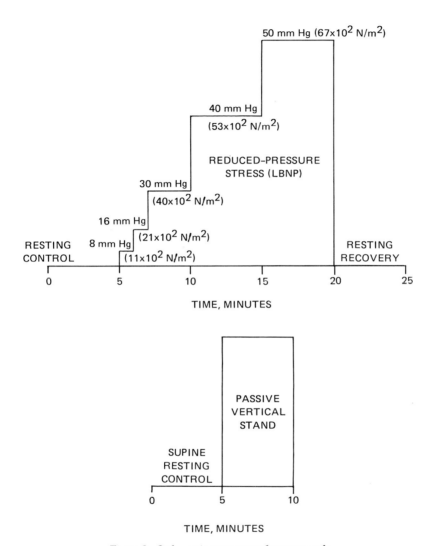

Figure 3. Orthostatic stress procedure protocols.

The passive stand protocol consisted of a five-minute resting supine control period followed by a five-minute passive stand. For the passive stand, the subject leaned against a wall in a relaxed manner with his heels spaced 15 cm (6 in.) away from the wall. Physiological measurements made during this protocol included continuous sternal and axillary lead ECG's, and indirect blood pressure taken by the Korotkov sound technique at 30-second intervals.

The Apollo 16 tests, utilizing the Jobst leotard, were performed pre- and postflight. Passive stand tests were performed at the F-15 tests on the Command Module Pilot, the backup CMP, and the two control subjects, and were repeated on the CMP and the controls at their respective recovery day examinations. The tests followed the LBNP test and consisted of a five-minute supine rest period followed by a five-minute stand period in the manner of the earlier Apollo passive stand tests. The leotards were then donned, and, after a ten-minute period of supine rest, the stand test was repeated. Blood pressure and heart-rate data were obtained by using the instrumentation of the earlier LBNP test.

Approximately one-half hour before Apollo 17 deorbit, the Command Module Pilot donned but did not inflate the antihypotensive garment. After splashdown, while still reclining in the couch, he inflated the capstan to a pressure of 130 mm Hg (173×10^2 N/m^2) and, thus, furnished 65 mm Hg (87×10^2 N/m^2) pressure over the ankle region. This pressure was maintained until a stand test could be performed. The suit was tested by performing a stand test four hours after splashdown and before LBNP testing. Crew time restraints prohibited repetition of the preflight protocol, which included separate tests with and without the garment, each separated by an appropriate recovery period. Therefore, the crewman spent five minutes in the supine position with the capstan inflated, five minutes passive standing with the capstan inflated, five minutes standing with the garment depressurized, and four minutes standing with the capstan reinflated to the original capstan pressure of 130 mm Hg (173×10^2 N/m^2). The total duration of the continuous stand was 15 minutes, including approximately 45 seconds for reinflation of the capstan. Heart rate was obtained continuously from the VCG; blood pressure was measured every 30 seconds by a Skylab automatic blood pressure measuring system.

Ancillary Indicators of Orthostatic Tolerance

Accessory cardiovascular and related measurements were made in conjunction with orthostatic evaluations. Before orthostatic evaluation of the Apollo 7 to 11 and 15 to 17 crewmen, the circumference of the calf at its maximum girth was measured during supine rest. An assessment of total lower limb volume made on the Apollo 16 and 17 crewmembers consisted of multiple leg circumference measurements at discrete intervals from the ankles to the groin while the crewman was supine with the legs extended and slightly elevated. Limb volume was computed by summing sequential, truncated, assumed-circular cones. Standard 1.8-m (6-ft) posterior-anterior chest X-rays were taken of every crewmember at his last major preflight medical examination and first postflight evaluation. The cardiothoracic (C/T) ratio was determined by standard clinical methods. The ambient temperature and the oral temperature and body weight of each crewman were recorded at each evaluation.

Ambient Conditions and Other Variables

Ambient temperatures and oral temperatures were recorded during preflight and postflight orthostatic evaluations because sufficiently high temperatures can affect orthostatic tests in an adverse way. While ambient temperatures during preflight orthostatic evaluations were acceptably low, temperatures during the first postflight evaluations were generally markedly higher. Ambient temperatures during orthostatic evaluations for the Apollo 15 Commander are illustrative. During preflight testing, the mean ambient temperature derived from measurements made on three separate days of testing was 297°K (24°C). On the first postflight day, the ambient temperature during orthostatic evaluation was 301°K (28°C). The significant elevation in group mean ambient temperature at the first postflight evaluation reflected the recovery zone climate (usually tropical) and inadequate air conditioning of the recovery ships. Group mean ambient temperatures for subsequent postflight evaluations were not significantly different from preflight temperatures.

Preflight examinations employing the Apollo 16 antihypotensive garment were performed under adequately controlled temperatures of 295° to 296°K (22° to 23°C). However, environmental temperatures during the first and second postflight examinations were the highest of any encountered during the Apollo shipboard tests, ranging from 305° to 306°K (32° to 33°C) during the postflight stand tests of the CMP. Apollo 17 crewmen were exposed to high environmental temperatures during transfer to the recovery vessel and during subsequent ceremonies, but their tests were performed in the air-conditioned Skylab Mobile Laboratory at a temperature of 296°K (23°C).

Table 3 is a tabulation of group mean oral temperature. Here, too, the preflight mean was based on three separate determinations, thirty, fifteen and five days before flight. The elevation in this parameter noted at the first postflight evaluation continued for succeeding postflight days.

The effects of elevated ambient and oral temperatures within the postflight evaluation periods may be altered by the presence of certain additional variables. For example, although most Apollo crewmembers reported a normal amount of sleep before each preflight evaluation, there was a significant group mean reduction in the amount of sleep on the night before splashdown. Further, the interval between venipuncture for biochemical analysis (30 to 80 cm^3 withdrawn) and time of orthostatic evaluation varied widely (15 minutes to many hours) within preflight and postflight time frames. Finally, the interval between food ingestion and orthostatic evaluation also varied widely (15 minutes to 17 hours).

Data Collection and Reduction

The various physiological measurements were recorded in real time on a strip chart recorder and on frequency modulation magnetic tape. The strip chart data were used for real-time assessment of crewmember well-being and safety. The appearance of presyncopal symptoms in some crewmen during orthostatic stress caused early termination of the procedure. Analog tape data were subsequently converted to digital data and analyzed by specially developed software on a Sigma 3 computer system.

Minute heart rates were derived from an analysis of electrocardiogram or vector-cardiogram R-R intervals; systolic blood pressure and diastolic blood pressure values were read at the appearance of the first and last Korotkov sounds, respectively, on the calibrated descending arm cuff pressure ramp. Percentage change in calf volume was measured by calculating the change from initial, resting-calf circumference and converting this value to percentage change in calf volume using the method of Eagan (1961). Two

Table 3

Tabulation of Apollo Group Mean Oral Temperatures

(Arrows Indicate p<0.05)

Apollo Mission	Crew-member	Preflight Summary Mean °K	(°C)	±SD	Postflight Evaluations First °K	(°C)	Second °K	(°C)	Third °K	(°C)
7	CDR	309.6	(36.5)	0.12	310.7	(37.6)←	309.9	(36.8)←		
	CMP	309.8	(36.7)	0.12	309.7	(36.6)	310.1	(37.0)←		
	LMP	309.6	(36.5)	0.38	310.5	(37.4)	309.9	(36.8)		
8	CDR	309.6	(36.5)	0.17	310.2	(37.1)←	309.7	(36.6)	309.9	(36.8)
	CMP	309.9	(36.8)	0.32	310.2	(37.1)	310.2	(37.1)	310.0	(36.9)
	LMP	309.7	(36.6)	0.25	309.9	(36.8)	309.7	(36.6)	309.8	(36.7)
9	CDR	309.5	(36.4)	0.15	309.5	(36.4)	309.3	(36.2)	310.3	(37.2)←
	CMP	309.4	(36.3)	0.15	309.7	(36.6)	309.3	(36.2)	309.6	(36.5)
	LMP	309.7	(36.6)	0.21	309.9	(36.8)	310.3	(37.2)←	309.9	(36.8)
10	CDR	309.6	(36.5)	0.36	309.3	(36.2)	309.4	(36.3)	—	—
	CMP	309.8	(36.7)	0.31	309.9	(36.8)	309.9	(36.8)	—	—
	LMP	309.6	(36.5)	0.15	310.2	(37.1)←	309.7	(36.6)	—	—
11	CDR	309.6	(36.5)	0.12	309.5	(36.4)	—	—	—	—
	CMP	309.6	(36.5)	0.49	309.8	(36.7)	—	—	—	—
	LMP	309.8	(36.7)	0.06	310.2	(37.1)←	—	—	—	—
15	CDR	309.4	(36.3)	0.23	—	—	309.2	(36.1)	309.4	(36.3)
	CMP	309.6	(36.5)	0.17	—	—	—	—	310.4	(37.3)←
	LMP	309.6	(36.5)	0.21	—	—	309.8	(36.7)	309.7	(36.6)
16	CDR	308.9	(35.8)	0.40	—	—	—	—	309.6	(36.5)
	CMP	309.1	(36.0)	0.10	—	—	—	—	309.7	(36.6)←←
	LMP	308.8	(35.7)	0.46	—	—	—	—	310.2	(37.1)←
17	CDR	309.8	(36.7)	0.40	309.8	(36.7)	309.7	(36.6)	309.8	(36.7)
	CMP	310.0	(36.9)	0.35	310.4	(37.3)	309.8	(36.7)	310.5	(37.4)
	LMP	309.4	(36.3)	0.46	309.9	(36.8)	310.0	(36.9)	309.3	(36.2)
Group Mean		309.61	(36.42)		310.01	(36.86)	309.81	(36.66)	309.92	(36.77)
±SD		0.334			0.345		0.316		0.353	
		t-Test			p<0.001		n.s		p<0.005	

successive heart sound complexes were analyzed from the vibrocardiogram each minute; computation of stroke volume followed the method of Agress and co-workers (1967).

For each crewman evaluation, heart rate, systolic blood pressure, diastolic blood pressure, pulse pressure, and stroke volume values were averaged within each of the five five-minute LBNP periods and within the two five-minute passive stand periods to produce the respective mean values within each of these periods. These mean values for each crewmember, during each period and by each measurement, were subsequently used as the best estimate of measurement within that period in the compilation of data tables. In the case of percentage, maximal calf volume change rather than mean values within each level of LPNP was used.

Data Analysis

Data were analyzed statistically by individual crewmember and by group mean. For individual crewmembers, the mean and the standard deviation of the three preflight values for each measurement in each distinct protocol condition were calculated (preflight summary). From these values, fiducial limits of the normal range at the 95-percent confidence level were determined. Individual postflight values lying outside these limits were defined as statistically significant changes and are indicated appropriately in the tables. Group means and standard deviations were calculated for each discrete measurement within each protocol condition for every evaluation day and for the preflight summaries. Preflight summary group means were compared with each postflight counterpart by using the independent t-test.

It should be noted that four astronauts flew two Apollo missions each. The Apollo 8 Command Module Pilot (CMP) flew as the Apollo 13 Commander (CDR); the Apollo 9 CMP flew as the Apollo 15 CDR; the Apollo 10 CMP flew as the Apollo 16 CDR; and the Apollo 10 Lunar Module Pilot (LMP) flew as the Apollo 17 Commander.

Results

Heart Rates

Of the various cardiovascular measurements obtained from Apollo crewmembers during their evaluations, heart rate was the most easily measured and yielded the most accurate and predictable values. Table 4 contains heart-rate data on individual crewmembers during three conditions of orthostatic stress evaluations: (1) resting supine control, (2) the highest level of LBNP [-50 mm Hg (-67 x 10^2 N/m^2)], and (3) passive standing. Resting supine heart rate is elevated significantly in 13 of 24 crewmen (54 percent) at the first postflight evaluation; the group response is elevated at the two-percent level of confidence. A trend toward preflight values is subsequently evident. By the third postflight evaluation, only three of fifteen individuals (20 percent) show significant elevations in resting supine heart rate, and the group mean value is not statistically different from the preflight group mean heart rate (n = 15, paired).

Following the same comparisons, the application of -50 mm Hg (-67 x 10^2,N/m^2) LBNP produced significantly elevated heart rates in 14 of 17 Apollo crewmen (82 percent) at the first postflight evaluation, with a group elevation significant at the 0.1-percent level. The Apollo 15 LMP experienced presyncope during the last seconds of

Table 4

Individual Apollo Crewmember Heart Rate Data

(Arrows Indicate p<0.05)

Protocol Condition	Apollo Mission	Crew member	Preflight Evaluations			Preflight Summary		Postflight Evaluations		
			F-30 Days	F-15 Days	F-5 Days	Mean	± SD	First	Second	Third
Resting Supine Control Period	7	CDR	56	59	54	56	2.6	77	59	
		CMP	81	74	78	78	3.1	78	76	
		LMP	57	64	66	62	4.4	75	70	
	8	CDR	74	69	70	71	2.6	87	70	80
		CMP	84	69	66	73	9.7	94	76	66
		LMP	77	74	72	74	2.4	91	81	71
	9	CDR	76	63	68	69	6.8	64	78	80
		CMP	56	59	58	57	2.0	57	54	53
		LMP	59	55	57	57	2.1	50	50	50
	10	CDR	62	70	59	64	5.7	81	73	—
		CMP	65	59	55	60	5.0	65	62	—
		LMP	59	62	52	58	5.1	80	79	—
	11	CDR	61	62	67	63	3.2	69	79	—
		CMP	53	46	51	50	3.6	67	65	—
		LMP	68	69	70	69	1.0	62	81	—
	15	CDR	51	50	55	52	2.6	54	50	52
		CMP	66	69	70	68	2.1	83	84	73
		LMP	52	56	57	55	2.6	66	66	66
	16	CDR	57	57	55	56	1.2	70	60	61
		CMP	49	49	45	48	2.1	56	48	56
		LMP	60	53	54	56	3.9	57	61	60
	17	CDR	55	62	59	59	3.2	67	70	64
		CMP	78	76	68	74	5.1	67	64	69
		LMP	50	50	51	50	0.6	55	56	52
	Group Mean		62.8	61.5	60.7	61.6		69.7	67.2	63.5
	±SD		10.47	8.53	8.41	8.60		12.19	10.90	9.88
	LMP					t-Test		p<0.02	n.s.	n.s.

Table 4 (Continued)

Individual Apollo Crewmember Heart Rate Data

(Arrows Indicate p<0.05)

Protocol Condition	Apollo Mission	Crew-member	Preflight Evaluations			Preflight Summary		Postflight Evaluations		
			F-30 Days	F-15 Days	F-5 Days	Mean	± SD	First	Second	Third
−50 mm Hg* LBNP	7	CDR	72	61	59	64	6.7	90	67	—
		CMP	94	92	90	92	2.1	137	94	—
		LMP	76	74	76	75	1.1	108	87	—
	8	CDR	100	86	94	93	6.7	159	108	101
		CMP	116	89	94	99	14.5	129	121	88
		LMP	97	105	106	103	4.8	146	137	102
	9	CDR	82	67	78	76	7.9	100	94	93
		CMP	63	73	76	71	6.9	81	70	68
		LMP	74	70	67	70	3.3	87	75	65
	15	CDR	62	59	61	61	1.5	76	—	65
		CMP	79	81	81	80	1.2	131	109	93
		LMP	58	56	64	59	4.2	—	84	78
	16	CDR	79	71	72	74	4.1	109	101	83
		CMP	62	67	58	62	4.2	99	74	79
		LMP	82	72	83	79	5.9	112	98	98
	17	CDR	67	78	71	72	5.3	112	91	78
		CMP	87	86	79	84	4.3	87	78	90
		LMP	59	69	60	63	5.4	82	80	60
	Group Mean ±SD		78.3 15.97	75.3 12.61	76.1 13.70	76.5 13.27 t-Test		108.5 24.58 $p<0.001$	92.2 18.85 $p<0.02$	82.7 13.76 n.s.

*—67 x 10^2 N/m^2

Table 4 (Continued)

Individual Apollo Crewmember Heart Rate Data

(Arrows Indicate p<0.05)

Protocol Condition	Apollo Mission	Crew-members	Preflight Evaluations			Preflight Summary		Postflight Evaluations		
			F-30 Days	F-15 Days	F-5 Days	Mean	± SD	First	Second	Third
Passive Stand	9	CDR	81	73	79	78	4.2	93 ◄	100 ◄	96 ◄
		CMP	66	75	72	71	4.6	88 ◄	72	70
		LMP	71	67	69	69	2.0	93 ◄	79 ◄	65
	10	CDR	86	93	86	88	4.0	111 ◄	92 ◄	—
		CMP	88	85	70	81	9.6	100	81	—
		LMP	80	74	70	75	5.0	121 ◄	109 ◄	—
	11	CDR	73	83	85	80	6.4	112 ◄	105 ◄	—
		CMP	76	69	65	70	5.6	91 ◄	88 ◄	—
		LMP	73	76	79	76	3.0	89 ◄	100 ◄	—
	Group Mean		77.1	77.2	75.0	76.4		99.8	91.8	77.0
	±SD		7.22	8.29	7.48	6.11		11.99	12.71	16.64
						t-Test		p<0.001	p<0.001	n.s.

-40 mm Hg (-53 x 10^2 N/m^2) LBNP and was not tested at -50 mm Hg (-67 x 10^2 N/m^2) LBNP on recovery day. Five other crewmembers (the Apollo 8 CMP, the Apollo 8 LMP, the Apollo 9 LMP, the Apollo 16 CMP, and the Apollo 16 LMP) developed presyncopal symptoms at some point before protocol completion during their immediate postflight -50 mm Hg (-67 x 10^2 N/m^2) stress; the Apollo 15 Commander experienced similar symptoms during his second postflight evaluation. Although more crewmembers, immediately postflight, demonstrated a larger heart rate increment over preflight values during LBNP stress than during the resting control period, statistically significant group differences disappeared by the third postflight evaluation. Passive vertical standing results indicated a similar increase in heart rate immediately postflight, with eight of nine crewmembers (89 percent) having heart rates above their 95-percent preflight envelope, and the group mean value being elevated at the 0.1 percent level.

In table 5, heart rates of Apollo crewmembers are compared with those of control subjects for three protocol conditions. Significant "postflight" heart rate changes among the control subjects onboard the recovery ship were not observed. Although the control subjects were exposed to similar environmental conditions, all had a five- to ten-day acclimatization period onboard the recovery ship preceding their evaluations.

Table 5

Apollo Crewmember Versus Control Subject Heart Rate Data

Protocol Condition	Apollo Group	Preflight Summary				Postflight Evaluations					
		Response				First			Second		
		N	$\overline{X}$	SD_i	SD_t	N	$\overline{X}$	p	N	$\overline{X}$	p
Resting supine	Crew	24	61.6	8.60	1.06	24	69.7	0.02	24	67.2	0.05
	Controls	22	69.7	6.93	1.00	22	69.4	n.s.	10	70.4	n.s.
-50 mm Hg* LBNP	Crew	18	76.5	13.27	1.55	17	108.5	0.001	17	92.2	0.02
	Controls	16	85.1	8.14	1.49	14	87.3	n.s.	9	84.2	n.s.
Stand	Crew	9	76.4	6.11	1.24	9	99.8	0.001	9	91.8	0.01
	Controls	7	79.6	6.40	2.72	7	81.1	n.s.	—	—	—

*-67 x 10^2N/m^2

Note: N   = Number of subjects
$\overline{X}$ = Group mean
SD_i = Standard deviation of crewmember preflight summary means
SD_t = Standard deviation of three preflight group means
p   = Probability level

Heart Rate and Other Measures During Several LBNP Protocols

Table 6 contains group mean values for several physiological measurements by protocol condition. Preflight summary group means are shown with two different standard deviations. The first (SD_i) is an expression of variability between the crewmember preflight summary means; the second (SD_t) is a measure of variability among the three preflight group means. Accompanying each postflight evaluation group mean is the t-test probability that it differs from the preflight summary group mean. For the resting supine control condition, heart rate is significantly elevated at the first and second postflight evaluations. The reciprocal of this response is seen in the stroke volume data. No significant differences are noted after flight in the resting systolic, diastolic, or pulse pressures. During the three conditions of reduced pressure [-30, -40, and -50 mm Hg (-40 x 10^2, -53 x 10^2 and -67 x 10^2 N/m^2) LBNP], heart rates are significantly elevated at the first postflight evaluation, with a trend toward preflight summary response values in subsequent postflight evaluations. Again, stroke volume followed a reciprocal pattern. Significant decreases in systolic and pulse pressures are seen during LBNP only in the first postflight evaluations. Changes during the passive stand condition parallel changes during LBNP. Postflight changes during the recovery condition are not significant. All postflight alterations return to preflight summary values by the third postflight evaluation.

Calf Volume Changes Induced by LBNP

No significant postflight changes in calf volume are observed during the three conditions of reduced-pressure stress at any of the postflight evaluations (table 6). Table 7, which includes data on individual calf volume change during Apollo LBNP maximal stress, is presented because plethysmographic data from Gemini tilt table tests indicated increased postflight calf volume during tilt stress. Seven of seventeen Apollo crewmembers (41 percent) showed significantly decreased postflight calf volume changes during the maximal [-50 mm Hg (-67 x 10^2 N/m^2)] LBNP level, and the total group mean also decreased from the preflight value, although not to a statistically significant degree.

Body Weight Changes

Significant body weight changes occurred in virtually all astronauts regardless of flight duration. If a significant part of the weight change is due to a reduction in blood volume or loss of body fluids, cardiovascular function might be affected. Consequently, weight changes were considered in conjunction with orthostatic evaluations. Table 8 contains data on individual body weights at each evaluation date. Preflight summary means are based on three weights taken on the days of the major medical examinations. Launch day (F-0) weights are also listed because the postflight weight of United States space crewmen has been previously based on these data (Berry, 1973). The launch day group mean is clearly decreased (0.7 kg) from the preflight summary group mean. The t-test probability for postflight weight change is referenced to the preflight summary group mean rather than to the single launch day group mean, because the preflight mean is more representative of true crew weight change. The first postflight group mean weight shows a 3.4-kg (4.4 percent) decrement that is not regained at 90 to 160 hours after splashdown by the nine crewmen (Apollo 15 to 17 missions) weighed that long after recovery.

Resting Calf Circumference and Volume of the Lower Limbs

The simple and relatively accurate supine measurement of maximal calf circumference was performed before and after flight on 24 crewmen. The first section of table 9

Table 6

Apollo Group Mean Values for Preflight Summary and
Postflight Orthostatic Evaluations

Measurement	Protocol Condition	Preflight Summary Response				Postflight Evaluations First			Second			Third		
		N	X̄	SD_i	SD_t	N	X̄	p	N	X̄	p	N	X̄	p
Heart rate (bpm)	Control	24	61.6	8.60	1.06	24	69.7	0.02	24	67.2	n.s.	15	63.5	n.s.
	−30 ⎫ mm Hg*	18	65.7	11.11	1.42	18	84.3	0.005	18	72.7	n.s.	15	68.5	n.s.
	−40 ⎬ LBNP	18	70.7	11.20	1.40	18	96.7	0.001	18	79.8	0.05	15	74.5	n.s.
	−50 ⎭	18	76.5	13.27	1.55	17	108.5	0.001	17	92.2	0.02	15	82.7	n.s.
	Recovery	18	59.1	8.66	1.08	18	67.4	n.s.	18	64.1	n.s.	15	60.5	n.s.
	Stand	9	76.4	6.11	1.24	9	99.8	0.001	9	91.8	0.001	3	77.0	n.s.
Systolic blood pressure (mm Hg*)	Control	24	115.3	8.31	0.74	24	111.6	n.s.	24	118.0	n.s.	15	118.5	n.s.
	−30 ⎫ mm Hg*	18	110.5	10.04	1.86	18	101.5	0.02	18	112.3	n.s.	15	112.7	n.s.
	−40 ⎬ LBNP	18	107.7	10.66	1.15	18	96.3	0.01	18	109.7	n.s.	15	109.3	n.s.
	−50 ⎭	18	104.8	11.09	1.86	17	91.5	0.01	17	107.4	n.s.	15	107.2	n.s.
	Recovery	18	117.1	10.03	1.55	18	116.4	n.s.	18	123.2	n.s.	15	120.5	n.s.
	Stand	9	118.8	6.24	3.40	9	105.8	0.001	9	123.9	n.s.	3	120.7	n.s.
Diastolic blood pressure (mm Hg*)	Control	24	67.0	6.61	1.51	24	67.1	n.s.	24	67.7	n.s.	15	66.3	n.s.
	−30 ⎫ mm Hg*	18	69.7	6.63	1.31	18	66.5	n.s.	18	67.4	n.s.	15	67.9	n.s.
	−40 ⎬ LBNP	18	70.7	6.21	1.25	18	66.3	0.05	18	68.3	n.s.	15	70.0	n.s.
	−50 ⎭	18	71.8	6.84	2.01	17	66.6	n.s.	17	69.1	n.s.	15	70.9	n.s.
	Recovery	18	71.0	6.32	0.89	18	73.4	n.s.	18	70.9	n.s.	15	69.4	n.s.
	Stand	9	81.0	5.22	4.46	9	80.2	n.s.	9	82.8	n.s.	3	80.7	n.s.

*1 mm Hg = 1.33 × 10² N/m²

Note: N = Number of subjects
X̄ = Group mean
SD_i = Standard deviation of crewmember preflight summary means
SD_t = Standard deviation of three preflight group means
p = Probability level

Table 6 (Continued)

Apollo Group Mean Values for Preflight Summary and
Postflight Orthostatic Evaluations

Measurement	Protocol Condition	Preflight Summary				Postflight Evaluations								
			Response			First			Second			Third		
		N	X̄	SD_i	SD_t	N	X̄	p	N	X̄	p	N	X̄	p
Pulse Pressure (mm Hg*)	Control	24	48.3	6.34	0.81	24	44.6	n.s.	24	50.2	n.s.	15	52.1	n.s.
	−30 ⎫ mm Hg*	18	40.9	6.09	0.61	18	35.2	0.01	18	44.8	n.s.	15	44.8	n.s.
	−40 ⎬ LBNP	18	37.2	6.52	0.06	18	30.2	0.02	18	41.4	n.s.	15	39.4	n.s.
	−50 ⎭	18	33.1	6.59	0.06	17	24.8	0.02	17	38.2	n.s.	15	36.3	n.s.
	Recovery	18	46.4	6.76	1.07	18	43.1	n.s.	18	52.2	0.05	15	51.0	n.s.
	Stand	9	37.8	6.44	7.47	9	25.6	0.02	9	41.0	n.s.	3	40.0	n.s.
Calf circumference (cm)	Control	24	37.47	1.626	0.072	24	36.38	0.05	21	36.85	n.s.	15	37.05	n.s.
Calf volume Change (% Δ)	−30 ⎫ mm Hg*	18	1.62	0.512	0.060	18	1.45	n.s.	18	1.49	n.s.	15	1.45	n.s.
	−40 ⎬ LBNP	18	2.32	0.597	0.050	18	2.09	n.s.	18	2.26	n.s.	15	2.21	n.s.
	−50 ⎭	18	3.08	0.679	0.042	18	2.71	n.s.	17	3.04	n.s.	15	3.04	n.s.
	Recovery	18	0.54	0.270	0.029	17	0.27	0.02	18	0.66	n.s.	15	0.53	n.s.
Stroke volume (ml)	Control	9	85.8	4.49	0.15	7	74.1	0.02	9	79.2	0.05	9	80.4	n.s.
	−30 ⎫ mm Hg*	9	73.7	6.00	1.05	7	60.3	0.01	9	64.9	0.05	9	66.3	n.s.
	−40 ⎬ LBNP	9	63.8	6.96	1.58	6	49.3	0.025	9	56.4	n.s.	9	58.0	n.s.
	−50 ⎭	9	57.6	7.02	0.78	5	41.4	0.05	8	47.9	n.s.	9	50.2	0.05
	Recovery	9	86.9	3.37	1.36	7	79.4	n.s.	9	81.6	n.s.	9	82.7	n.s.

*1 mm Hg = 1.33 x 10^2 N/m²

Note: N = Number of subjects

X̄ = Group mean

SD_i = Standard deviation of crewmember preflight summary means

SD_t = Standard deviation of three preflight group means

p = Probability level.

Table 7

Individual Calf Volume Percent Change Data During Apollo
LBNP Maximal Stress. (Arrows Indicate $p<0.05$).

Apollo Mission	Crew-member	Preflight Evaluations			Preflight Summary		Postflight Evaluations		
		F-30 Days	F-15 Days	F-5 Days	Mean	SD	First	Second	Third
7	CDR	1.74	1.73	2.24	1.90	0.294	2.21	2.01	
	CMP	2.49	2.30	2.50	2.43	0.120	1.96 →	2.21	
	LMP	3.60	3.41	2.85	3.13	0.392	2.78	3.87	
8	CDR	3.06	2.86	2.54	2.83	0.262	2.37	2.75 →	2.91
	CMP	2.74	2.98	2.98	2.90	0.140	2.29 →	2.54 →	2.55
	LMP	3.54	4.09	3.45	3.70	0.350	2.61 →	4.25	3.34
9	CDR	2.45	2.16	2.42	2.34	0.159	2.72	2.53	2.40
	CMP	2.59	3.86	2.16	2.87	0.884	3.40	2.83	2.71 →
	LMP	2.90	—	3.50	3.20	0.424	2.31	2.59	2.55
15	CDR	4.16	3.93	4.28	4.12	0.178	3.55 →	—	3.28 →
	CMP	2.71	2.85	3.03	2.86	0.160	3.27 →	3.50 →	2.91
	LMP	3.98	3.86	4.28	4.04	0.216	—	3.90	3.94
16	CDR	4.02	4.02	3.90	3.98	0.069	3.37 →	3.98	4.18 →
	CMP	3.69	3.78	3.16	3.54	0.335	2.32 →	3.11	4.03
	LMP	3.89	3.94	3.68	3.83	0.135	2.99 →	3.37 →	3.71
17	CDR	2.47	2.81	3.08	2.79	0.306	2.71	2.85	2.84
	CMP	1.97	1.84	2.13	1.98	0.145	2.37 →	2.44 →	1.58 →
	LMP	3.05	2.92	3.25	3.07	0.166	2.80	2.98	2.69
Group Mean		3.06	3.14	3.08	3.08		2.71	3.04	3.04
±SD		0.729	0.796	0.679	0.679		0.472	0.666	0.708
					t-Test		n.s.	n.s.	n.s.

Table 8

Individual Body Weights at Each Orthostatic Evaluation Date

(Arrows Indicate p<0.05)

(Values are in kg)

Apollo Mission	Crew-member	Preflight Evaluations			Preflight Summary		Launch Day	Postflight Evaluations			
		F-30 Days	F-15 Days	F-5 Days	Mean	± SD		First	Second	Third	Fourth
7	CDR	87.1	88.0	88.2	87.8	0.59	88.0	86.1 →	86.4		
	CMP	69.4	69.4	69.8	69.5	0.23	71.2 ←	66.7 →	68.3		
	LMP	69.4	71.8	70.8	70.7	1.21	70.8	67.8	69.6		
8	CDR	76.2	76.4	77.1	76.6	0.47	76.8	72.8 →	74.0 →	75.1 →	
	CMP	76.4	77.6	76.4	76.8	0.69	78.0	74.4 →	74.7 →	75.2	
	LMP	66.0	67.1	66.0	66.4	0.64	64.4 →	62.6 →	62.8 →	—	
9	CDR	73.5	72.8	72.8	73.0	0.40	72.1	69.6 →	70.9 →	71.7 →	
	CMP	82.8	82.5	80.7	82.0	1.14	80.7	78.2 →	82.1	81.2	
	LMP	74.7	74.4	73.7	74.3	0.51	72.1 →	69.4 →	71.3 →	72.3 →	
10	CDR	80.1	79.4	78.9	79.5	0.60	77.6 →	76.4 →	77.4 →		
	CMP	76.6	77.1	76.6	76.8	0.29	74.8 →	72.3 →	73.1 →		
	LMP	79.4	79.5	79.4	79.4	0.06	78.5 →	73.9 →	74.6 →		
11	CDR	78.0	78.2	79.1	78.4	0.59	78.0	74.4 →	77.1		
	CMP	74.4	75.3	77.1	75.6	1.37	75.3	72.1 →	72.1 →		
	LMP	77.6	78.9	77.9	78.1	0.68	75.7 →	75.3 →	77.1		
12	CDR	66.2	—	66.9	66.6	0.49	67.7	65.8 →	66.7	66.7	
	CMP	71.0	70.3	—	70.7	0.49	70.4	67.1	68.9	68.9	
	LMP	69.4	—	70.3	69.9	0.64	69.1	63.5 →	64.9	64.4	
13	CDR	79.8	77.8	78.5	78.7	1.01	80.5	74.2 →			
	CMP	89.1	—	89.7	89.4	0.42	89.3	84.4 →			
	LMP	71.0	70.3	71.2	70.8	0.47	70.8	67.8 →			

Table 8 (Continued)

Individual Body Weights at Each Orthostatic Evaluation Date

(Arrows Indicate p<0.05)

(Values are in kg)

Apollo Mission	Crew-member	Preflight Evaluations			Preflight Summary		Launch Day	Postflight Evaluations			
		F-30 Days	F-15 Days	F-5 Days	Mean	± SD		First	Second	Third	Fourth
14	CDR	78.0	78.5	78.7	78.4	0.36	76.2 ↓	76.6 ↓	77.1 ↓		
	CMP	74.2	76.2	75.5	75.3	1.01	74.8	69.4 ↓	72.6 ↓		
	LMP	83.5	83.1	83.2	83.2	0.26	79.8 ↓	80.3 ↓	80.7 ↓		
15	CDR	80.5	81.2	81.5	81.1	0.51	80.2	78.9 ↓	—	81.0	80.7 ↓
	CMP	73.7	73.2	74.0	73.6	0.40	73.5	72.1 ↓	—	72.6	72.3 ↓
	LMP	74.3	73.9	74.8	74.3	0.45	73.2	70.8 ↓	—	73.7	73.1 ↓
16	CDR	80.8	80.5	78.9	80.1	1.02	78.9	75.5 ↓	76.6 ↓	—	76.4 ↓
	CMP	63.2	61.9	62.6	62.6	0.65	61.5	58.5 ↓	59.9 ↓	—	60.3 ↓
	LMP	73.1	73.8	72.6	73.2	0.60	73.0	70.5 ↓	71.7 ↓	—	71.3 ↓
17	CDR	81.0	80.3	80.7	80.7	0.35	80.3	76.1 ↓	76.0 ↓	78.0 ↓	78.5 ↓
	CMP	78.2	76.6	77.0	77.3	0.83	75.7	74.6 ↓	73.9 ↓	73.9 ↓	74.8 ↓
	LMP	76.0	76.6	75.3	76.0	0.65	74.8	72.9 ↓	71.8 ↓	73.4 ↓	72.8 ↓
Group Mean		75.90	75.09	76.12	75.96		75.26	72.45	73.05	73.44	73.36
±SD		5.849	5.213	5.786	5.792		5.727	5.866	5.763	4.781	5.787
					t-Test			$p<0.02$	n.s.	n.s.	n.s.

contains values of the average of both calves for individual crewmembers at each test date. In the first postflight evaluation, 16 of 24 crewmembers (67 percent) showed significantly reduced calf circumference. Group mean values showed a statistically significant probability ($p < 0.05$) immediately postflight of a decrement of 1.1 cm (3 percent) that was not totally regained at approximately 120 hours after splashdown by two of the three crewmen tested at that time.

Total leg volume was calculated for the six crewmen of the last two Apollo missions (Apollo 16 and 17). The last section of table 9 contains data on total leg volume as the sum of both legs. Although not statistically significant, a one-liter (5.8 percent) group mean decrement was seen in the first two postflight evaluations. No clear trend toward restitution was seen as late as 90 to 160 hours after splashdown; subsequent measurements were not performed.

Cardiothoracic Ratios

To determine whether a change in heart size had occurred, cardiothoracic (C/T) ratios were calculated. Once before and once after flight, posterior-anterior chest X-rays were taken of each crewmember. The C/T ratios given in table 10 provided a measure of heart size to amplify the preceding weight and leg-size data. Accurate cardiothoracic ratios could not be obtained from three postflight films. Synchronization at peak systolic and peak diastolic cardiac phases for X-rays taken on the last six Apollo crewmembers (Apollo 16 and 17 missions) enabled achievement of greater accuracy by providing two films for each preflight and postflight comparison, and by eliminating random X-ray exposure in the cardiac cycle. Twenty-four of thirty crewmembers (80 percent) showed a decrease in postflight C/T ratios with a group mean cardiothoracic ratio decrement of 0.021 (5 percent), highly significant at $p < 0.001$. The Apollo 17 CMP, who showed a postflight increase in C/T ratio, wore a special antihypotensive pressure garment from splashdown until LBNP evaluation five hours later.

Special Measures for Apollo 15, 16, and 17

Vectorcardiographic data for Apollo 15, 16, and 17 crewmen showed no changes of clinical significance. An analysis of the phonocardiographic findings derived from the vibrocardiogram and of the systolic time intervals obtained with carotid pulse and VCG measurements was incomplete at the time of this writing.

Antihypotensive Garment Efficacy

Seven hours after splashdown, orthostatic evaluations were made of the Apollo 16 CMP wearing the antihypotensive garment. The garment was 0.5 cm smaller at the calf than the one worn during preflight testing to compensate for the expected loss of lower limb girth from disuse in zero g. The results are shown in table 11. Blood pressure and heart rate data are expressed as mean values with one standard deviation, for each five-minute period.

As noted earlier, ambient temperatures during postflight testing of Apollo 16 astronauts were high [305°K (32°C) to 306°K (33°C)]. During the same tests on two control subjects one day earlier, the temperature was somewhat lower: 301°K (28°C) for

Table 9

Individual Resting Supine Calf Circumference
and Lower Limb Volume Data (Arrows Indicate p<0.05)

Resting Supine Mean Calf Circumference, cm

Apollo Mission	Crew-member	Preflight Evaluations			Preflight Summary		Postflight Evaluations			
		F-30 Days	F-15 Days	F-5 Days	Mean	±SD	First	Second	Third	Fourth
7	CDR	40.7	40.9	40.8	40.8	0.10	40.1→	40.1→	—	—
	CMP	35.9	35.9	35.9	35.9	0.00	34.7	35.6	—	—
	LMP	36.6	36.9	36.1	36.5	0.40	35.1→	36.0	—	—
8	CDR	35.2	35.3	35.4	35.3	0.10	34.9→	35.2	34.4→	—
	CMP	39.7	39.4	39.4	39.5	0.17	39.1	39.1	39.1	—
	LMP	37.3	36.8	37.2	37.1	0.26	36.8	36.7	37.2	—
9	CDR	37.0	37.0	36.8	36.9	0.12	35.2→→	35.9→	36.4→	—
	CMP	40.5	40.2	40.1	40.3	0.21	38.9→→	40.2	40.4	—
	LMP	36.4	—	36.2	36.3	0.14	34.7→→	38.1←	36.1	—
10	CDR	36.3	35.1	35.9	35.8	0.61	34.6→	35.6	—	—
	CMP	37.8	37.1	37.0	37.3	0.44	36.2→	37.1	—	—
	LMP	38.1	37.5	37.0	37.5	0.55	35.6	36.5	—	—
11	CDR	36.6	36.0	36.2	36.3	0.31	35.6	—	—	—
	CMP	37.2	36.8	38.1	37.4	0.67	37.0	—	—	—
	LMP	37.9	38.3	37.6	37.9	0.35	37.6	—	—	—
15	CDR	40.3	40.5	40.5	40.4	0.12	39.3→→	39.4→→	40.1	40.8 ←→
	CMP	36.5	36.3	36.5	36.4	0.12	35.6→→	35.1→→	35.9→	35.9 →
	LMP	37.5	37.1	37.4	37.3	0.21	36.0→→	36.5→	36.7	36.3 →
16	CDR	38.1	37.9	38.0	38.0	0.10	36.6→→	36.6	36.5→	—
	CMP	34.4	34.4	34.8	34.5	0.23	33.5	33.5→	33.2→	—
	LMP	36.3	36.3	36.3	36.3	0.00	35.5	35.6	35.4	—

Table 9 (Continued)

Individual Resting Supine Calf Circumference
and Lower Limb Volume Data (Arrows Indicate p<0.05)

Apollo Mission	Crew-members	Preflight Evaluations			Preflight Summary		Postflight Evaluations			
		F-30 Days	F-15 Days	F-5 Days	Mean	± SD	First	Second	Third	Fourth
		Resting Supine Mean Calf Circumference, cm (Continued)								
17	CDR	38.0	38.2	38.5	38.2	0.25	37.3	36.6	38.1	37.3
	CMP	38.8	38.1	38.6	38.5	0.36	37.0	37.0	38.1	37.0
	LMP	38.6	39.1	38.9	38.9	0.25	37.4	37.5	38.1	37.6
Group Mean		37.57	37.44	37.45	37.47		36.43	36.85	37.05	37.48
±SD		1.621	1.724	1.625	1.634		1.688	1.719	1.995	1.743
					t-Test		p<0.05	n.s.	n.s.	n.s.
		Lower Limb Volume, ml								
16	CDR	15 929	15 485	15 669	15 694	223	14 108	14 146	13 770	13 812
	CMP	12 577	12 492	12 798	12 622	158	12 150	11 898	12 005	12 146
	LMP	14 556	14 794	14 741	14 697	125	14 482	14 033	14 068	13 806
17	CDR	17 265	17 685	17 991	17 647	365	16 772	16 427	17 238	16 706
	CMP	17 426	17 132	17 357	17 305	154	15 964	16 366	17 028	16 424
	LMP	17 944	18 542	18 030	18 172	323	17 084	17 692	17 878	17 189
Group Mean		15 950	16 022	16 098	16 023		15 093	15 094	15 331	15 014
±SD		2 059	2 218	2 089	2 113		1 873	2 116	2 371	2 035
					t-Test		n.s.	n.s.	n.s.	n.s.

Table 10

Apollo Crewmen Cardiothoracic Ratios
During Orthostatic Evaluations
(Ratios based on X-radiographs)

Apollo Mission	Crew-member	Preflight F-5 Days	First Post-flight	Change in C/T
7	CDR	0.46	0.44	−0.02
	CMP	0.45	0.41	−0.04
	LMP	0.39	0.36	−0.03
8	CDR	0.44	0.40	−0.04
	CMP	0.44	0.41	−0.03
	LMP	0.38	0.32	−0.06
9	CDR	0.37	0.36	−0.01
	CMP	0.43	0.39	−0.04
	LMP	0.36	0.33	−0.03
10	CDR	0.43	0.39	−0.04
	CMP	0.43	0.39	−0.04
	LMP	0.50	0.40	−0.10
11	CDR	0.40	0.40	0.00
	CMP	0.35	−	−
	LMP	0.40	0.39	−0.01
12	CDR	0.37	0.39	+0.02
	CMP	0.41	−	−
	LMP	0.40	−	−
13	CDR	0.42	0.41	−0.01
	CMP	0.43	0.42	−0.01
	LMP	0.43	0.39	−0.04
14	CDR	0.39	0.42	+0.03
	CMP	0.41	0.40	−0.01
	LMP	0.46	0.44	−0.02
15	CDR	0.42	0.43	+0.01
	CMP	0.40	0.37	−0.03
	LMP	0.48	0.51	+0.03
16	CDR	0.41	0.40	−0.01
	CMP	0.44	0.41	−0.03
	LMP	0.36	0.34	−0.02
17	CDR	0.50	0.44	−0.06
	CMP	0.43	0.45	+0.02
	LMP	0.37	0.36	0.00
Group Mean		0.417	0.399	−0.021
±SD		0.0383	0.0384	0.0281
	t-Test		n.s.	$p < 0.001$

control subject 1, and 303°K (30°C) for control subject 2. The results of their tests also appear in table 11.

Table 11

Preflight and Postflight Passive Stand Test Data With and Without
Jobst Antihypotensive Garment

Subject Position	Measurement	Without Garment		With Garment	
		Preflight Mean ±SD	Postflight Mean ±SD	Preflight Mean ±SD	Postflight Mean ±SD
Apollo 16 Command Module Pilot					
Supine	Heart rate, bpm	45.8 ± 0.96	57.8 ± 0.84	44.8 ± 0.84	54.6 ± 0.89
	SBP, mm Hg*	113.5 ± 2.64	119.2 ± 4.80	117.9 ± 7.09	112.6 ± 6.17
	DBP, mm Hg*	74.3 ± 2.00	80.8 ± 2.90	67.2 ± 4.21	67.5 ± 3.89
Erect	Heart rate, bpm	55.8 ± 1.79	87.6 ± 0.89	55.2 ± 3.56	78.4 ± 1.34
	SBP, mm Hg*	121.6 ± 5.62	112.6 ± 6.17	117.8 ± 4.02	110.2 ± 5.24
	DBP, mm Hg*	77.2 ± 4.37	67.5 ± 3.89	77.8 ± 5.27	75.2 ± 6.02
Control Subject 1					
Supine	Heart rate, bpm	77.6 ± 0.89	60.2 ± 1.30	81.4 ± 1.52	63.4 ± 2.70
	SBP, mm Hg*	118.0 ± 2.71	102.8 ± 4.77	118.4 ± 2.50	111.3 ± 4.47
	DBP, mm Hg*	57.4 ± 2.95	62.1 ± 2.81	58.0 ± 4.45	58.4 ± 4.12
Erect	Heart rate, bpm	85.8 ± 0.84	76.8 ± 1.48	78.4 ± 2.70	70.4 ± 1.34
	SBP, mm Hg*	119.1 ± 0.72	104.4 ± 8.38	122.7 ± 4.79	109.6 ± 3.95
	DBP, mm Hg*	74.9 ± 2.66	75.8 ± 4.02	75.1 ± 3.60	76.5 ± 3.24
Control Subject 2					
Supine	Heart rate, bpm	67.2 ± 0.84	72.4 ± 0.89	64.0 ± 1.87	71.2 ± 1.30
	SBP, mm Hg*	134.3 ± 3.11	127.7 ± 5.58	137.1 ± 2.85	124.2 ± 5.55
	DBP, mm Hg*	71.8 ± 5.03	74.9 ± 5.21	81.3 ± 5.01	75.0 ± 1.63
Erect	Heart rate, bpm	76.8 ± 2.05	92.2 ± 2.17	70.6 ± 1.95	85.0 ± 1.22
	SBP, mm Hg*	145.0 ± 7.44	132.7 ± 8.74	149.7 ± 5.25	136.0 ± 8.01
	DBP, mm Hg*	82.8 ± 2.57	81.4 ± 5.52	90.4 ± 3.47	84.4 ± 7.95

*1 mm Hg = 1.33 x 10^2 N/m^2

The Apollo 17 CMP, as noted previously, inflated his antihypotensive garment one-half hour before deorbit and kept it inflated [which provided a pressure of 65 mm Hg (87 x 10^2 N/m^2) over the ankle area] until a standard orthostatic evaluation could be made. Under the conditions of testing, his heart rate increased slightly and tended to climb after the garment was deflated. Heart rate declined slightly upon reinflation (figure 4). Heart rate and blood pressure data are shown in table 12 as mean values for the three five-minute periods and for the single four-minute period.

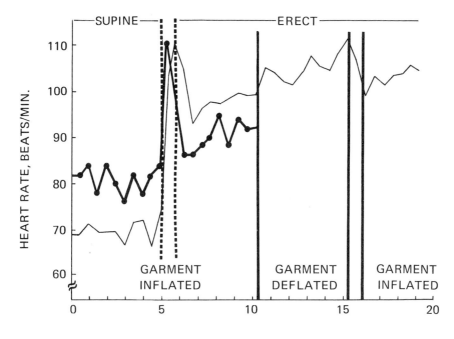

Figure 4. Passive Stand test
with antihypotensive garment — Apollo 17 CMP.

Table 12

Heart Rate and Blood Pressure Data
for Apollo 17 Command Module Pilot During Passive Stand Test
Utilizing Antihypotensive Garment

Measurement	Supine	Erect		
	Garment Inflated	Garment Inflated	Garment Deflated	Garment Reinflated
	Mean ±SD	Mean ±SD	Mean ±SD	Mean ±SD
Heart rate, bpm	70.1 ± 3.50	98.3 ± 3.43	105.2 ± 3.82	103.5 ± 3.72
SBP, mm Hg*	115.5 ± 8.28	128.8 ± 3.27	131.0 ± 3.89	129.1 ± 5.92
DBP, mm Hg*	64.6 ± 3.92	82.7 ± 4.22	84.4 ± 4.93	85.4 ± 2.88
Pulse pressure, mm Hg*	49.4 ± 6.90	46.9 ± 7.25	46.6 ± 5.46	43.3 ± 7.16

*1 mm Hg = 1.33×10^2 N/m^2.

Discussion

The objective of Apollo preflight and postflight cardiovascular evaluations was to determine the effects of space flight on human physiological functions. These studies were performed within the context of transporting man safely to the moon and returning him to Earth while ensuring his well-being and functional capability in an unnatural environment. It would be naive, however, to ascribe the cardiovascular findings reported here to the effects of weightlessness alone. The observed postflight cardiovascular changes reflect the total effect of the environmental conditions encountered by each crewman within a given space flight mission. In addition to stresses of the weightless state, these conditions included stresses of launch, inflight deviations from normal work and rest cycles, variations in duration and magnitude of lunar activity, changes in diet, and stresses of entry, splashdown, and recovery. Unfortunately, the relative contribution of each of these environmental conditions cannot be established.

Significant postflight changes in cardiovascular measurements have included elevated resting and orthostatically stressed heart rate, similar but reciprocal decreases in stroke volume, and decreases in pulse pressure during orthostatic stress caused almost exclusively by decreases in systolic blood pressure. These changes are characteristic of decreased orthostatic tolerance. In addition, several presyncopal episodes occurred postflight during orthostatic stress. To properly assess the postflight decrease in crew orthostatic tolerance, however, one must consider the set of variables that existed during the recovery period.

1. Crewmen were launched and maintained in a temperate environment but were recovered and evaluated immediately after flight at significantly elevated ambient temperatures (Apollo 10, 11, and 17 missions excepted).

2. Crewmen were physically more active in the time periods immediately preceding and following splashdown. This activity tended to augment any postflight thermal stress.

3. Preflight evaluations were always performed in the morning hours, whereas postflight evaluations were usually performed in the afternoon or evening hours with respect to the preflight work and rest cycles established at the Kennedy Space Center and normally maintained in flight. This change in the time of day postflight evaluations were performed could have produced diurnal variations in body temperature, heart rate, and orthostatic tolerance.

4. Returned crewmen were exposed for varying time periods to orthostatic stress in one-g prior to orthostatic testing.

5. Vestibular effects associated with readaptation to the one-g environment were compounded by sea motion (not expressly evaluated).

6. Neurohumoral forces were altered by the excitement and the emotion of return to Earth.

These stresses and uncontrolled variables undoubtedly affected the postflight cardiovascular changes reported here.

Certain relationships suggest that all the factors listed contributed significantly. A positive, though statistically insignificant, correlation (r = 0.27) exists between change (preflight to postflight) in resting heart rate and change in oral temperature (figure 5). Also, there is a significant positive correlation (r = 0.52) between postflight change in orthostatically stressed heart rate and postflight change in resting heart rate (figure 6). In concert with similar data from Gemini crew evaluations, these Apollo findings suggest that, for flights of eight to fourteen days, postflight resting or orthostatically stressed heart rates do not increase in conjunction with increasing mission duration.

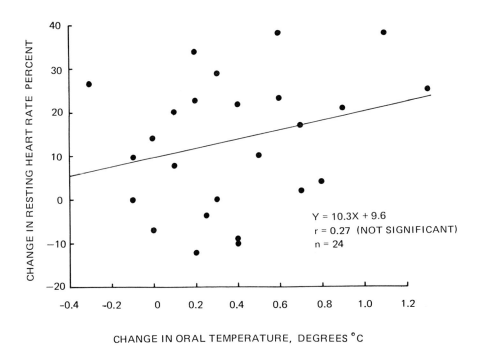

Figure 5. Positive correlation between preflight to postflight change
in oral temperature and change in resting heart rate.

Weight loss was a universal finding among Apollo flight crews, but the cause and the specific body tissues involved are not readily apparent. A positive correlation between weight loss and change in total blood volume (r = 0.77) was obtained from Apollo data. Fluid losses or changes, however, did not fully explain the weight loss. The relatively inactive role of the lower extremities during space flight predisposes them to significant loss of tissue substance, especially in muscle; consistent postflight reductions in maximal calf girth on 24 Apollo crewmen and in total leg volume on the last six Apollo crewmen showed significant soft-tissue decrements (table 9). The magnitude of these decrements in the maximal calf circumference measurement taken immediately after recovery showed a positive correlation (r = 0.42) with the time of the measurement following splashdown (figure 7). Assuming rapid changes to be due to fluid shifts to the lower extremities postflight, a better correlation would be expected had the physical activities of the crewmen between splashdown and time of calf measurement been controlled. Continued decrements in leg size for several days after splashdown indicate that they were not exclusively caused by fluid changes. On the other hand, a true flight-related tissue deterioration was suggested by a negative and significant correlation (r = -0.47) between the decrement in calf size and the length of exposure to weightlessness (figure 8). When both Apollo data and Gemini data (from missions shorter and longer than Apollo missions) are used, weight loss reveals a leveling off with flight duration, if not a reversed trend, after a peak at approximately 200 hours of flight time (figure 9). The relative contributions of muscle, fatty, and interstitial tissues to weight loss have not yet been determined.

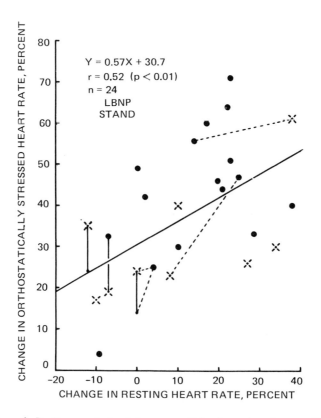

Figure 6. Positive correlation between postflight change in orthostatically stressed heart rate and postflight change in resting heart rate.

Perhaps more specific are data obtained from preflight and postflight chest roentgenograms. Although a decrease in the frontal plane cardiac silhouette size may

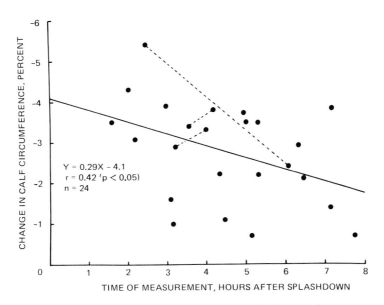

Figure 7. Positive correlation between maximal calf circumference
taken immediately after recovery and time of measurement following splashdown.

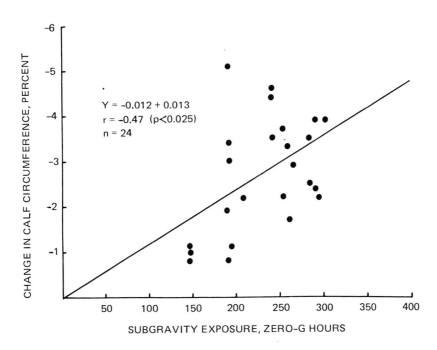

Figure 8. Negative correlation between decrement in calf size
and length of exposure to weightlessness.

represent either a decrement of myocardial tissue, a decrement of intrachamber blood content, or positional change such as rotation of the heart with reference to the chest wall, changes in the cardiothoracic ratio show a very definite rise and subsequent reversal with the duration of zero-g exposure; the peak decrement occurs between 100 and 200 hours (figure 10). The relationship between the cardiothoracic ratio and the duration of zero-g exposure is definite, whereas correlations of the C/T ratio with weight loss or change in blood volume are only vaguely suggested. A most unexpected finding, however, is the significant difference (p<0.01) between the mean C/T ratio of the 12 lunar explorers and the mean of those Apollo crewmen who were continuously exposed to weightlessness. With 11 useful postflight data points, the lunar-walking group mean postflight cardiothoracic ratio was essentially unchanged from the preflight ratio, whereas the other 19 Apollo crewmen incurred a decrease in the group mean C/T ratio of -0.03. Because changes explicitly caused by exposure to the space environment are of great importance and concern, any opportunity to detect them is eagerly explored. Other similar comparisons between these same groups have revealed no difference in postflight weight loss or changes in resting and stressed postflight heart rate. Despite some use of the lower extremities on the lunar surface, no difference in resting-calf circumference changes was detected between the groups. These findings imply that exposure to the lunar environment somehow maintains the preflight cardiothoracic ratio.

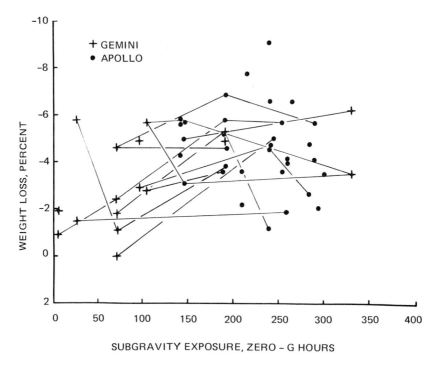

Figure 9. Apollo and Gemini data indicating a leveling off of weight loss after 200 hours of flight.

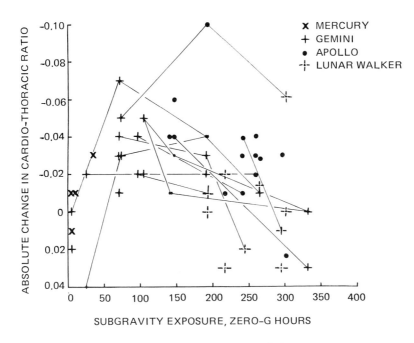

Figure 10. Roentgenogram showing peak decrement
in cardiothoracic ratio.

These Apollo data have also provided a comparison of cardiovascular responses to LBNP and to vertical passive standing (the true orthostatic stress reference). For 18 crewmen evaluated with -50 mm Hg (-67 × 10^2N/m^2) LBNP and for nine tested with the passive stand (both procedures for three of each group), heart rates were almost identical before flight, and postflight values for LBNP stress were slightly greater. In contrast, and as noted in prior studies comparing orthostatic techniques, preflight and postflight systolic and diastolic blood pressure values were higher during stand stress than during LBNP. Thoracic and carotid pressure sensors differentially responding to the two stressors may partly account for the difference. Pulse pressure during LBNP, however, differed very little from pulse pressure during passive stand. These findings supported the use of LBNP as an orthostatic stress procedure and provided a reference for the integration of data from the Skylab inflight LBNP evaluations.

Of the two garments designed to offer protection against orthostatic hypotension. the garment employing the capstan principle proved to be the more suitable for use in the space flight environment. Although the elastic garment worn by the Apollo 16 CMP appeared to furnish moderate protection against orthostatic hypotension following weightless flight and heat stress, this type of garment seemed to be unsuitable for use in the operational setting. The crewman was unable to don the leotards in zero g before reentry or following splashdown in the confined volume of the spacecraft. Consequently, any protection the garment afforded could not be made available until the postflight testing phase. It was also impossible to ensure a garment of proper fit for postflight use because the decline in limb girth was neither uniformly distributed nor predictable in magnitude.

The design of the pressurized garment used by the Apollo 17 CMP included features intended to overcome the difficulty of predicting change in limb girth during flight. The CMP reported that the garment was easier to don in flight than he had anticipated, due in part perhaps to a relatively large reduction in limb girth. He wore the garment for more than four hours and reported it relatively comfortable.

The heart rate while reclining with the suit inflated was ten beats per minute slower than during the preflight test 15 days before launch (70.1 ± 3.5 compared to 81 ± 2.12 beats per minute). Although uncommon, a reduction of the supine resting heart rate from preflight values had been seen previously in Apollo crewmen. Mean heart rate during the first five minutes of standing with the garment inflated after flight was 98.3 ± 3.43 beats per minute compared to 91 ± 2.35 beats per minute in the preflight test.

When the garment was deflated, heart rate increased and was still increasing after five minutes. Garment reinflation, which required approximately 40 seconds, was associated with an interruption of the rising slope of heart rate and a modest reduction of mean heart rate, suggesting a protective effect from the garment.

Aside from the antihypotensive effect of using the garment, other physiological processes that occurred during readaptation to one g may have been modified. The Apollo 17 CMP was the only crewman of the 18 tested whose mean heart rate at R+0 during exposure to a pressure of -50 mm Hg ($-67 \times 10^2 N/m^2$) was within the preflight envelope. In the other stress procedure, bicycle ergometry, he again showed no decrement of performance from preflight levels. His pattern of postflight limb volume changes, estimated from multiple circumferential measurements, was somewhat different from that shown by the other five crewmen who received such measurements. Postflight X-rays, taken before deflation of the garment, showed an increased cardiothoracic ratio in contrast to the other 20 Apollo crewmen exposed to continuous weightlessness, for whom data exist demonstrating postflight decreases in C/T ratios.

Summary and Conclusions

In summary, postflight orthostatic evaluations during the Apollo Program appear to indicate that reduction in orthostatic tolerance is a consequence of space flight exposure. Heart rate, the most reliable index, was increased, while systolic and pulse pressures were decreased during immediate postflight evaluations using lower body negative pressure and passive standing as the orthostatic stress. Elevation in resting heart rate was a less frequent finding. There was considerable variability in the magnitude of these changes between individual crewmembers and in the persistence of the changes over subsequent postflight evaluations. Postflight changes in leg volume during LBNP were equal to or less than those seen during preflight baseline evaluations. Body weight, resting calf girth, supine leg volume, and cardiothoracic ratios were all diminished immediately postflight, and return to preflight values was not complete within the postflight testing time frame.

The reported changes in orthostatic tolerance and other related measurements must be interpreted with care in view of the conditions under which the data were obtained.

The priority of operations during Apollo missions did not allow optimal control over a number of important variables during preflight and postflight evaluations. Preflight evaluations had to be scheduled and completed within narrow time limits and in competition with the training and launch preparation of crewmembers. Postflight evaluations were performed among intensive debriefing sessions, public appearances, and other ceremonies. Relative degrees of sleep loss and high ambient temperatures also undoubtedly influenced the findings.

Wearing of a lower body positive pressure garment during the reentry and immediate postflight period appeared to offer some protective benefit by way of reducing extravascular lower body pooling of fluid. It would, however, be premature to conclude that the garment was the primary factor responsible for improved orthostatic tests for the Apollo 17 Command Module Pilot. As was the case in all missions and for all crewmen, individual variables cloud interpretation of the data. Other studies will be necessary to determine the effects of such protective garments under space flight-type readaptive conditions.

Man's physiological adaptation to the space environment and his readaptive alterations upon return to Earth are complex. The orthostatic evaluations performed in conjunction with the Apollo missions provide some insight into these changes. But a more complete understanding of the physiological role, especially for missions of longer duration, requires a thorough analysis of the effects of the space environment with special emphasis upon inflight evaluations, control of environmental conditions, and interrelating findings from many study disciplines.

References

Agress, Clarence M.; Wegner, Stanley; Fremont, Robert P.; Mori, Izumi; and Day, Dixie J.: Measurement of Stroke Volume by the Vibrocardiogram. Aerospace Med., vol. 38, no. 12, Dec. 1967, pp. 1248-1252.

Berry, Charles A.: Weightlessness. Bioastronautics Data Book. Second ed. NASA SP-3006, 1973, pp. 349-415.

Brown, Ellen; Goei, J.S.; Greenfield, A.D.M.; and Plassaras, G.C.: Circulatory Responses to Simulated Gravitational Shifts of Blood in Man Induced by Exposure of the Body Below the Iliac Crests to Sub-Atmospheric Pressure. J. Physiol., vol. 183, no. 3, Apr. 1966, pp. 607-627.

Eagan, C.J.: The Physics of the Mercury Strain Gauge and of its Use in Digital Plethysmography. Alaskan Air Command, Arctic Aeromedical Laboratory Tech. Note AAL-TN-60-17, 1961.

Gilbert, Charles A.; Bricker, Lee A.; Springfield, W. Thaxton, Jr.; and Stevens, Paul M.: Sodium and Water Excretion and Renal Hemodynamics During Lower Body Negative Pressure. J. Appl. Physiol., vol. 21, no. 6, Nov. 1966, pp. 1699-1704.

Hoffler, G.W.; Wolthuis, Roger A.; and Johnson, Robert L.: Apollo Space Crew Cardiovascular Evaluations. Aerospace Med., vol. 45, no. 8, Aug. 1974, pp. 807-820.

McCally, Michael S.; Pohl, Shirley, A.; and Sampson, Plummer A., Jr.: Relative Effectiveness of Selected Space Flight Deconditioning Countermeasures. Aerospace Med., vol. 39, no. 7, July 1968, pp. 722-724.

Miller, Perry B.; Hartman, Bryce O.; Johnson, Robert L.; and Lamb, Lawrence E.: Modification of the Effects of Two Weeks of Bed Rest Upon Circulatory Functions in Man. Aerospace Med., vol. 35, no. 10, Oct. 1964, pp. 931-939.

Miller, Perry B.; Johnson, Robert L.; and Lamb, Lawrence, E.: Effects of Four Weeks of Absolute Bed Rest on Circulatory Functions in Man. Aerospace Med., vol. 35, no. 12, Dec. 1964, pp. 1194-1200.

Murray, Raymond H.; Krog, John; Carlson, Loren D.; and Bowers, John A.: Cumulative Effects of Venesection and Lower Body Negative Pressure. Aerospace Med., vol. 38, no. 3, Mar. 1967, pp. 243-247.

Musgrave, F. Story; Zechman, Fred W.; and Mains, Richard C.: Changes in Total Leg Volume During Lower Body Negative Pressure. Aerospace Med., vol. 40, no. 7, July 1969, pp. 602-606.

Musgrave, F. Story; Zechman, Fred W.; and Mains, Richard C.: Comparison of the Effects of 70° Tilt and Several Levels of Lower Body Negative Pressure on Heart Rate and Blood Pressure in Man. Aerospace Med., vol. 42, no. 10, Oct. 1971, pp. 1065-1069.

NASA, MSC: Mercury Project Summary, Including Results of the Fourth Manned Orbital Flight. NASA SP-45, 1963.

NASA, MSC: Gemini Summary Conference. NASA SP-138, 1967.

NASA, MSC: Gemini Blood Pressure Signal Conditioner. NASA SP-5054, 1968, pp. 29-30.

Samueloff, Shlomo L.; Browse, Norman L.; and Shepherd, John T.: Response of Capacity Vessels in Human Limbs to Head-up Tilt and Suction on Lower Body. J. Appl. Physiol., vol. 21, no. 1, Jan. 1966, pp. 47-54.

Stevens, Paul M.: Cardiovascular Dynamics During Orthostasis and the Influence of Intravascular Instrumentation. Am. J. Cardiol., vol. 17, Feb. 1966, pp. 211-218.

Stevens, Paul M.; and Lamb, Lawrence E.: Effects of Lower Body Negative Pressure on the Cardiovascular System. Am. J. Cardiol., vol. 16, Oct. 1965, pp. 506-515.

Stevens, Paul M.; Miller, Perry B.; Gilbert, Charles A.; Lynch, Theodore N.; Johnson, Robert L.; and Lamb, Lawrence E.: Influence of Long-Term Lower Body Negative Pressure on the Circulatory Function of Man During Prolonged Bed Rest. Aerospace Med., vol. 37, no. 4, Apr. 1966a, pp. 357-367.

Stevens, Paul M.; Miller, Perry B.; Lynch, Theodore N.; Gilbert, Charles A.; Johnson, Robert L.; and Lamb, Lawrence, E.: Effects of Lower Body Negative Pressure on Physiologic Changes Due to Four Weeks of Hyperoxic Bed Rest. Aerospace Med., vol. 37, no. 5, May 1966b, pp. 466-474.

Vogt, Fred B.; and Johnson, Philip C.: Effectiveness of Extremity Cuffs or Leotards in Preventing or Controlling the Cardiovascular Deconditioning of Bed Rest. Aerospace Med., vol. 38, no. 7, July 1967, pp. 702-707.

Wolthuis, Roger A.; Hoffler, G.W.; and Johnson, R.L.: Lower Body Negative Pressure as an Assay Technique for Orthostatic Tolerance: Part I. The Individual Response to a Constant Level (-40 mm Hg) of LBNP. Aerospace Med., vol. 41, no. 1, Jan. 1970, pp. 29-35.

Wolthuis, Roger A.; Hoffler, G.W.; and Johnson, R.L.: Lower Body Negative Pressure as an Assay Technique for Orthostatic Tolerance: Part II. A Comparison of the Individual Response to Incremental vs. Constant Levels of LBNP. Aerospace Med., vol. 41, no. 4, Apr. 1970, pp. 419-424.

Wolthuis, Roger A.; Hoffler, G.W.; and Baker, Joseph T.: Improved Waist Seal Design for Use With Lower Body Negative Pressure (LBNP) Devices. Aerospace Med., vol. 42, no. 4, Apr. 1971, pp. 461-462.

CHAPTER 5
EXERCISE RESPONSE

by

J.A. Rummel, Ph.D.
C.F. Sawin, Ph.D.
E.L. Michel, M.S.

Lyndon B. Johnson Space Center

Introduction

Inherent in the successful completion of the Apollo Program was the necessity for the lunar surface crewmen to engage in long and strenuous periods of extravehicular activity (EVA). Even though reduced gravity was expected to make some tasks less arduous, reduced suit mobility and a complex timeline indicated that metabolic activity would exceed resting levels for extended periods of time. Because the type and extent of physiological dysfunction that could result from habitability in a zero-g environment had not been established, appropriate physiological tests were performed within Apollo Program constraints to ascertain whether the physiological response of the crewmen to exercise was altered as a result of space flight.

Early planning for the Apollo Program had provided that some indication of these factors would be measured in flight; however, the Apollo spacecraft fire and the resultant program redirection eliminated this capability. The next approach was to conduct only preflight and postflight exercise response studies and to assume that these findings would document any changes of cardiopulmonary status resulting from space flight. Obviously, with such an endeavor, there were circumstances that could not be experimentally controlled. First, the readaptation process would be expected to begin immediately after reentry into the Earth's gravitational field and to introduce or modify responses that might have been measured in null gravity. Additionally, required crew recovery procedures presented perturbations which precluded a well controlled experimental design; the crewmen spent variable amounts of time in a hyperthermal spacecraft while it was in the water; orbital mechanics constraints dictated recovery times which precluded assurance that postflight testing would be accomplished in the same circadian time frame in which preflight testing was performed. The influence of these conditions and that of other physical and emotional stresses could not be isolated from the response attributed to zero-g exposures. However, not attempting to provide information relating physiological responses to exercise stress would have been an unsuitable alternative for maintaining management of the medical aspect of the Apollo Program.

This section contains the preflight and postflight exercise findings. Preliminary results were summarized previously (Berry, 1969; Berry, 1970; Rummel et al., 1973).

Methods

From the many methods that have been used to conduct exercise stress tests (Bruce et al., 1965; Bruce et al., 1969; Blackburn et al., 1970; Rochmis & Blackburn, 1971; Taylor et al., 1969), the bicycle ergometer and a graded stress protocol were selected for the Apollo Program. The selection of a bicycle ergometer as the stress device (Rummel et al., 1973) was influenced mainly by the fact that it had been chosen for the Skylab exercise program. The bicycle ergometer was the only device capable of enabling quantitation of the work level and of providing a basis for experimental evaluation inflight. The Apollo experience provided a data pool and background information for the Skylab inflight exercise response testing.

A graded exercise test permitted a progressive evaluation of physiological control system response and provided a better understanding of safe stress limits. Heart rate was used for determining stress levels (Maxfield & Brouha, 1963; Burger, 1969). By maintaining the same heart rate levels before and after flight, the same relative cardiovascular stresses were imposed.

Although the exact duration of each stress level was adjusted slightly (one to two minutes) for the late Apollo missions to accomplish additional measurements, the graded stress protocol comprised exercise levels of 120, 140, and 160 beats per minute, corresponding to light, medium, and heavy work, respectively, for each individual. For the Apollo 9 and 10 missions, a stress level of 180 beats per minute was also accomplished. The entire test protocol was conducted three times within a 30-day period before lift-off. Postflight tests were conducted on recovery day, as well as 24 to 36 hours after recovery.

During each test, workload, heart rate, blood pressure, and respiratory gas exchange (oxygen consumption, carbon dioxide production, and minute volume) measurements were made. For the Apollo 15 to 17 missions, cardiac output measurements were obtained by the single-breath technique (Kim et al., 1966). Arteriovenous oxygen differences were calculated from the measured oxygen consumption and cardiac output.

Figure 1 shows an exercising control subject at the Kennedy Space Center launch facilities. This same equipment was packed and moved to the recovery ship for postflight testing.

Each preflight test was treated separately, and a mean value (Rummel et al., 1973) was computed for each subject for each mission with the crewman serving as his own control. A preflight mean and variance estimate for all Apollo crewmen was then computed, and a similar statistic was computed for the separate postflight examinations. Statistical evaluations were made by means of standard t-test criteria. Although three members of the medical operations team were tested in the same time sequence in which the crewmembers were tested, these subjects essentially served as instrumentation controls.

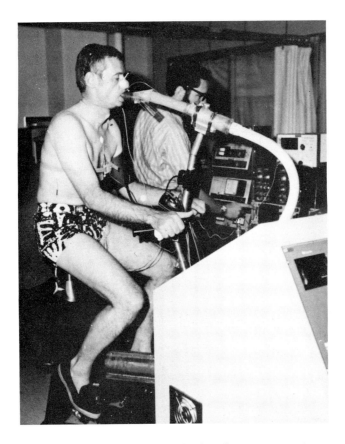

Figure 1. Control subject engaged in bicycle ergometry testing.

Results

The applicable data for each test on each crewman are given in table 1. Because these data were voluminous, only summaries and statistical considerations are presented. Testing, as noted earlier, was conducted both preflight and postflight. Test protocols were divided into three basic categories: prestress, exercise stress, and poststress.

Prestress Data

Significant changes in the sitting heart rate were observed immediately after flight; the mean difference was an approximate 16 beats per minute increase. This variable was not significantly elevated by the second postflight test (R+1). The only other significant changes observed were a slight increase in minute volume on the day of recovery and on R+1, and an increase in the resting respiratory gas exchange ratio on R+1.

Table 1

Physiological Measurements Made Before, During, and After Exercise Stress

Variable	Preflight			Day of Recovery				Day After Recovery			
	Mean	Standard Deviation	Number of Observations	Mean	Standard Deviation	Probability Level	Number of Observations	Mean	Standard Deviation	Probability Level	Number of Observations
Prestress Period											
Sitting heart rate beats/min	73.6	9.6	31	89.8	17.3	<0.001	27	79.3	13	NS	24
O_2 consumption l/min STPD	.279	.064	25	.291	.087	NS	20	.294	.097	NS	17
CO_2 production l/min STPD	.232	.052	12	.279	.062	NS	9	.271	.051	NS	9
Minute volume l/min BTPS	8.07	1.26	16	9.79	2.74	<0.05	11	10.0	2.57	<0.02	12
Respiratory exchange ratio	.85	.08	13	.88	.11	NS	9	.93	.08	<0.05	9
Systolic blood pressure (mm Hg)*	117	10.2	28	111	11.1	NS	24	117	9.0	NS	24
Diastolic blood pressure (mm Hg)*	78	6.3	28	79	5.8	NS	24	78	7.5	NS	24
Stress Period											
O_2 consumption l/min STPD at a heart rate of:											
120 beats/min	1.54	0.33	31	1.19	0.38	< 0.001	24	1.49	0.32	NS	21
140 beats/min	2.00	0.36	31	1.63	0.35	< 0.001	24	1.94	0.36	NS	21
160 beats/min	2.50	0.42	31	2.06	0.38	< 0.001	24	2.41	0.45	NS	21
180 beats/min **	2.98	0.50	31	2.52	0.43	< 0.001	24	2.85	0.56	NS	21

*1 mm Hg = 133.3224 N/m²

** Six individuals actually tested to this level — others extrapolated

NS = Not significant

STPD = Standard temperature and pressure, dry

BTPS = Body temperature and pressure, saturated

Table 1 (Continued)

Physiological Measurements Made Before, During, and After Exercise Stress

Variable	Preflight			Day of Recovery				Day After Recovery			
	Mean	Standard Deviation	Number of Observations	Mean	Standard Deviation	Probability Level	Number of Observations	Mean	Standard Deviation	Probability Level	Number of Observations
O_2 consumption l/min STPD at a workload of: 900 kpm/min	1.94	0.20	31	1.90	0.29	NS	23	2.09	0.33	<0.05	23
O_2 consumption l/min/kg STPD at a heart rate of: 160 beats/min	33.1	5.6	31	28.2	6.0	<0.005	27	32.9	6.3	NS	22
180 beats/min	39.5	6.6	31	34.6	6.8	<0.01	27	39.3	7.7	NS	24
Systolic blood pressure (mm Hg)* at a heart rate of: 160 beats/min	206	22.7	31	184	30.5	<0.005	27	201	28.6	NS	27
Systolic blood pressure (mm Hg)* at 15 l/min cardiac output	170	18.0	09	173	35.8	NS	09	180	32.7	NS	09
Diastolic blood pressure (mm Hg)* at a heart rate of: 160 beats/min	089	9.5	31	080	11.8	<0.005	27	084	19.2	NS	27
Mean arterial pressure (mm Hg)* at 15 l/min cardiac output	111	15.0	09	109	17.5	NS	09	114	18.2	NS	09
Minute volume (l/min BTPS) at an O_2 consumption of 2.0 l/min STPD	52.4	7.7	31	54.7	8.8	NS	24	54.3	8.6	NS	22

*1 mm Hg = 133.3224 N/m²

Table 1 (Continued)

Physiological Measurements Made Before, During, and After Exercise Stress

Variable	Preflight			Day of Recovery				Day After Recovery			
	Mean	Standard Deviation	Number of Observations	Mean	Standard Deviation	Probability Level	Number of Observations	Mean	Standard Deviation	Probability Level	Number of Observations
Stress Period (Continued)											
Cardiac output (l/min) at a heart rate of: 160 beats/min	23.2	5.5	09	14.7	3.9	<0.001	09	21.6	4.8	NS	09
Arteriovenous O$_2$ difference, volumes percent, at a heart rate of: 160 beats/min	14.4	1.6	07	13.6	1.4	NS	07	12.5	2.9	NS	07
Arteriovenous O$_2$ difference, volumes percent, at an O$_2$ consumption of 2.0 l/min STPD	11.6	1.9	09	12.9	2.2	NS	08	13.1	2.7	NS	07
Poststress Period											
Heart rate beats/min	121.9	12.0	26	128.7	13.0	NS	18	122.3	11.9	NS	13

Exercise Stress Data

Several significant changes for this period were noted after flight. The relationship between heart rate and oxygen consumption (O_2 pulse) was significantly altered at all heart rate levels, whether evaluated on an absolute basis (liters per minute) or corrected for body weight (liters per minute per kilogram). There were no significant changes in the oxygen required for a given workload immediately after flight, although a small increase was noted during the R+1 examination.

Both the systolic and diastolic blood pressures attained at a given heart rate level were significantly decreased immediately after flight but returned to normal by R+1. There were no significant changes in the relationship between blood pressure and levels of oxygen consumption or cardiac output.

The interrelationships of respiratory parameters (O_2 consumption per minute volume and O_2 consumption per CO_2 production) indicated no significant changes immediately after flight. Results of the R+1 examination indicated that minute volume increased minimally.

A statistically significant decrease of large magnitude (−36 percent), was noted after flight in the cardiac output at a heart rate of 160 beats per minute. This variable had returned to preflight levels by the time of R+1 examination.

Poststress Data

Only heart rate data collected during the second minute of recovery are presented. None of the measured variables changed significantly after the flight.

Discussion

The basic physiological processes involved in the response to increased metabolic activity are shown in figure 2. This discussion is an attempt to put available data into perspective with these principles. Those parameters that are measured or indirectly calculated are also indicated in the figure.

The external work in Apollo exercise stress testing always consisted of bicycle ergometer pedal resistance of a known level. Because respiratory gas exchange was measured, changes in mechanical efficiency or the amount of oxygen required for a given work level could be evaluated. A workload of 150 watts was selected for evaluation because this level of stress was attained by all Apollo astronauts during exercise testing. The preflight and immediate postflight mean oxygen consumption values were almost identical, an indication that there had been no basic change in mechanical efficiency. Utilizing the average resting oxygen consumption rate of 0.279 liter per minute, the mechanical efficiency is calculated to be approximately 26 percent. Other investigators have reported efficiencies of 30 percent (Whipp, 1970), 21 percent (Wasserman et al., 1967), 20 percent (Henry & DeMoor, 1950), 24 percent (Davies & Musgrove, 1971), 23 percent (Christensen et al., 1960), and 24 percent (Åstrand & Rodahl, 1970). Thus, the mechanical efficiency measured on the Apollo crewmen agrees with other bicycle ergometer studies.

The efficiency of respiratory gas exchange required to support the metabolic activity of the tissues was evaluated by studying the oxygen consumption/minute volume

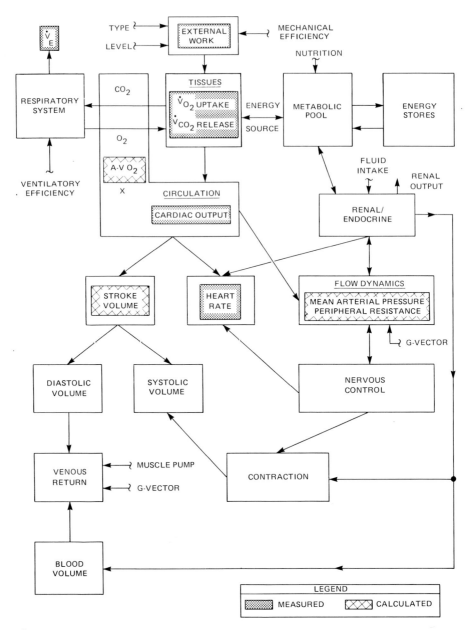

$\dot{V}_E$ = pulmonary rate

$\dot{V}_{O_2}$ = O_2 utilization rate

$\dot{V}_{CO_2}$ = carbon dioxide production rate

A-V O_2 = arteriovenous O_2 difference

Figure 2. Physiological mechanisms associated with increased metabolic activity.

relationship, which has been called the ventilatory equivalent for oxygen. At a rate of two liters per minute oxygen consumption, no significant change in the resulting minute volume was observed. The value of 2.62 liters minute volume per 100 cm^3 of oxygen consumption agrees with previously reported values of 2.7 (Higgs et al., 1967), approximately 2.5 (Hermansen & Saltin, 1969), and 2.2 to 2.5 liters (Cunningham, 1963). Cunningham (1963) reviewed fourteen studies in which this relationship was evaluated.

The circulatory responses required to support increased metabolic activity are striking and involve a complex system of varying physical properties and feedback control loops. Oxygen consumption requirements are equal to the cardiac output times the arteriovenous oxygen difference (A-V O_2). Although the relationship between oxygen consumption and cardiac output (and thus a change in A-V O_2 difference) appeared to change in some individuals, the overall means for the nine subjects indicated no significant changes (table 1). The absolute preflight values for cardiac output are approximately 20 to 25 percent greater than previously reported (Åstrand et al., 1964; Ekblom et al., 1968; Hermansen, 1970; Gilbert & Auchincloss, 1971) for this level of exercise. However, an evaluation of cardiac output/heart rate relationships indicated highly significant decreases in stroke volume immediately after flight. This decrease had returned to normal at the R+1 examination. These interrelationships explain the significant reduction in oxygen pulse (O_2 consumption/heart rate relationship) immediately after flight. The reduced cardiac output for the same heart rate may be responsible for the significant reduction in systolic and diastolic blood pressure immediately after flight.

The mechanism responsible for the reduced stroke volume is unknown and cannot be evaluated from the available data. The possible alternatives are a decrease in the systolic volume caused by myocardial contraction changes or a decrease in diastolic volume caused by decreased venous return. Changes in the latter could be caused by changes in the circulating blood volume, by redistribution of blood volume to the lower extremities, or by both of these mechanisms.

Based on the above physiological responses to exercise measured after space flight, it can be assumed that there was no significant change in mechanical or respiratory efficiency. Heart rate was significantly elevated for the same oxygen consumption; when coupled with a reduced stroke volume, increased heart rate maintained the same cardiac output/oxygen consumption relationship. The decreased cardiac output for the same heart rate could explain the observed reduced pressure in the systemic arteries. However, two points need to be considered. First, this general statistical response is different in some individuals, and the possibility of separate or different mechanisms operating in these separate cases should be recognized. For instance, some crewmen appeared to have had changes in peripheral resistance. Thus, each individual must be evaluated on the basis of his own particular response. Second, these responses were measured after recovery in a temporal and physical environment that was not controlled with sufficient precision to enable definition of the physiological response directly associated with the zero-g exposures.

These studies were extremely beneficial in assuring the success of the Apollo Program and have provided alternative hypotheses for inflight study during the Skylab missions.

References

Åstrand, Per-Olof: Aerobic Work Capacity During Maximal Performance Under Various Conditions. Supplement I to Circulation Research, Vols. XX and XXI, March 1967.

Åstrand, P.; Cuddy, T.E.; Saltin, B.; and Stenberg, J.: Cardiac Output During Submaximal and Maximal Work. J. Appl. Physiol., vol. 19, no. 2, 1964, pp. 268-274.

Åstrand, Per-Olof; and Rodahl, Kaare: Textbook of Work Physiology. McGraw-Hill Book Company (New York), 1970.

Berry, Charles A.: Preliminary Clinical Report of the Medical Aspects of Apollos VII and VIII. Aerospace Med., vol. 40, 1969, pp. 245-254.

Berry, Charles A.: Summary of Medical Experience in the Apollo 7 Through 11 Manned Space Flights. Aerospace Med., vol. 41, 1970, pp. 500-519.

Blackburn, H.; Winckler, G.; Vilandre, J.; Hodgson, J.; and Taylor, H.L.: Exercise Tests. Medicine and Sport, Vol. 4: Physical Activity and Aging. Karger (Basel/New York), 1970, pp. 28-36.

Bruce, R.A.; Rowell, L.B.; Blackmon, J.R.; and Doan, A.: Cardiovascular Function Tests. Heart Bulletin, vol. 14, 1965, pp. 9-14.

Bruce, R.A.; and McDonough, J.R.: Stress Testing in Screening for Cardiovascular Disease. Bull. N.Y. Acad. Med., vol. 45, no. 12, December 1969, pp. 1288-1305.

Burger, G.C.E.: Heart Rate and the Concept of Circulatory Load. Ergonomics, vol. 12, no. 6, 1969, pp. 857-864.

Christensen, E.H.; Hedman, R.; and Holmdahl, I.: The Influence of Rest Pauses on Mechanical Efficiency. Acta Physiol. Scand., vol. 48, 1960, pp. 443-447.

Cunningham, D.J.C.: Breathing in Exercise. Brit. Med. Bull., vol. 19, no. 1, 1963, pp. 25-30.

Davies, C.T.M.; and Musgrove, J.: The Aerobic and Anaerobic Components of Work During Submaximal Exercise on a Bicycle Ergometer. Ergonomics, vol. 14, no. 2, 1971, pp. 257-263.

Ekblom, B.; Åstrand, P.; Saltin, B.; Stenberg, J.; and Wallstrom, B.: Effect of Training on Circulatory Response to Exercise. J. Appl. Physiol., vol. 24, no. 4, 1968, pp. 518-528.

Gilbert, R.; and Auchincloss, J.H., Jr.: Comparison of Cardiovascular Responses to Steady- and Unsteady-State Exercise. J. Appl. Physiol., vol. 30, no. 3, 1971, pp. 388-393.

Henry, F.M.; and DeMoor, Janice: Metabolic Efficiency of Exercise in Relation to Work Load at Constant Speed. J. Appl. Physiol., vol. 2, no. 9, 1950, pp. 481-487.

Hermansen, Lars; Ekblom, Bjorn; and Saltin, Bengt: Cardiac Output During Submaximal and Maximal Treadmill and Bicycle Exercise. J. Appl. Physiol., vol. 29, no. 1, 1970, pp. 82-86.

Hermansen, Lars; and Saltin, Bengt: Oxygen Uptake During Maximal Treadmill and Bicycle Exercise. J. Appl. Physiol., vol. 26, no. 1, 1969, pp. 31-37.

Higgs, B.E.; Clode, M.; McHardy, G.J.R.; Jones, N.L.; and Campbell, E.J.M.: Changes in Ventilation, Gas Exchange and Circulation During Exercise in Normal Subjects. Clin. Sci., vol. 32, 1967, pp. 329-337.

Kim, T.S.; Rahn, H.; and Farhi, L.E.: Estimation of True Venous and Arterial P_{CO_2} by Gas Analysis of a Single-Breath. J. Appl. Physiol., vol. 21, 1966, pp. 1338-1344.

Maxfield, Mary E.; and Brouha, Lucien: Validity of Heart Rate as an Indicator of Cardiac Strain. J. Appl. Physiol., vol. 18, no. 6, 1963, pp. 1099-1104.

Rochmis, Paul; and Blackburn, H.: Exercise Tests: A Survey of Procedures, Safety, and Litigation Experience in Approximately 170 000 Tests. JAMA, vol. 217, no. 8, 1971, pp. 1061-1066.

Rummel, J.A.; Michel, E.L.; and Berry, C.A.: Physiological Response to Exercise After Space Flight — Apollo 7 to Apollo 11. Aerospace Med., vol. 44, no. 3, 1973, pp. 235-238.

Taylor, H.L.; Wang, Yang; Rowell, L.; and Blomqvist, G.: The Standardization and Interpretation of Submaximal and Maximal Tests of Working Capacity. Pediatrics, vol. 32, no. 10, 1963, pp. 703-722.

Taylor, H.L.; Haskell, W.; Fox, S.M., III; and Blackburn, H.: Exercise Tests: A Summary of Procedures and Concepts of Stress Testing for Cardiovascular Diagnosis and Function Evaluation. Measurement in Exercise Electrocardiography. Ernst Simmonson Conference, part 4, H. Blackburn, ed., Charles C. Thomas (Springfield, Illinois), 1969, pp. 259-305.

Wasserman, Karlman; Van Kessel, Antonius L.; and Burton, George, G.: Interaction of Physiological Mechanisms During Exercise. J. Appl. Physiol., vol. 22, no. 1, 1967, pp. 71-85.

Whipp, Brian J.; Seard, Charles; and Wasserman, Karlman: Oxygen Deficit-Oxygen Debt Relationships and Efficiency of Anaerobic Work. J. Appl. Physiol., vol. 28, no. 4, 1970, pp. 452-456.

CHAPTER 6
NUTRITIONAL STUDIES

by

Paul C. Rambaut, Sc.D.[*]
Malcolm C. Smith, Jr., D.V.M.
Harry O. Wheeler, Ph.D.

Lyndon B. Johnson Space Center

Introduction

The importance of nutrition in the adaptation of man to weightlessness was recognized long before the first Apollo flight. Nutrition remained a primary concern despite the fact that early projections of difficulties in swallowing, defecating, and urinating in weightlessness had proved unfounded. By the conclusion of the Gemini Program, space life scientists had noted several subtle changes with possible nutritional etiology.

Changes in musculoskeletal function appeared to be significant among these findings (Rambaut et al., 1973; Vogel et al., 1974). Prior to the first manned space flight, it had been suspected that the musculoskeletal system would be particularly susceptible to prolonged withdrawal of gravitational stress. Astronauts were subjected to a nullified gravitational field while they were confined in a vehicle in which mobility and physical activity were restricted. These conditions singly, or in combination, were expected to cause deterioration of bones and muscles.

The control studies by Deitrick, Whedon, and Shorr (1948) of the immobilization of four young, healthy men for as long as seven weeks clearly demonstrated that immobilization in body casts led to marked increases in urinary calcium. These levels more than doubled in five weeks and were accompanied by negative calcium balances as well as by related changes in nitrogen and phosphorus metabolism. In addition, a decrease in the mass and strength of the muscles of the lower extremities occurred, and deterioration in circulatory reflexes to gravity resulted within one week.

Other studies with immobilized subjects indicated that the clinical disorders most likely to be encountered during prolonged space flight are primarily a consequence of an imbalance between bone formation and resorption. As a result of these conditions, there is a loss of skeletal mass, which could eventually lead to hypercalcemia, hypercalciuria, osteoporosis, and possibly nephrolithiasis (Issekutz et al., 1966).

---

[*]Now with Bureau of Food, Food and Drug Administration.

Since the most meticulous work has disclosed that the greatest loss of calcium during bed rest is a result of increased urinary excretion, studies in which only urine calcium was measured are pertinent. The total evidence indicates that a one to two percent per month loss of body calcium is a reasonable prediction for persons in a weightless environment (Hattner & McMillan, 1968).

With the advent of space flight, additional studies have been performed on the effects of simulated weightlessness on skeletal metabolism. Graybiel and co-workers (1961) found there was no increase in urinary calcium excretion after one week of almost continuous water immersion. Negative balances of small magnitude and changes in bone density of the calcaneus during bed rest are indicated by Vogt and co-workers (1965).

The role of simulated altitude in modifying the metabolic effect of bed rest has been investigated (Lynch et al., 1967). In a study of 22 healthy men, four weeks of bed rest at ground-level atmospheric pressure conditions resulted in expected increases in urinary and fecal calcium and in urinary nitrogen, phosphorus, sodium, and chloride. In similar metabolic studies performed with another 22 subjects at bed rest at simulated altitudes of 3000 and 3700 meters, urinary calcium losses were significantly less as the altitude increased (Lynch et al., 1967). Urinary losses of phosphorus, nitrogen, sodium, and chloride were less at a simulated altitude of 3700 meters than they were during bed rest studies at ground level. Results of these studies indicate that diminished atmospheric pressure, or perhaps a decreased partial pressure of oxygen or a change in pH, may have a preventive effect on mineral loss from the skeleton. Limited data available from inflight studies tend to support the use of immobilization as a terrestrial model to simulate alterations in calcium metabolism during space flight. During the 14-day Gemini 7 flight, loss of calcium occurred in one of the two astronauts, and the changes in phosphorus and nitrogen balance also indicated a loss of muscle mass (Lutwak et al., 1969; Reid et al., 1968).

As evidenced from bed rest studies lasting from 30 to 36 weeks, mineral losses are likely to continue unabated during prolonged space flight. In balance studies (Vogel & Friedman, 1970; Donaldson et al., 1970), calcium losses from the skeleton during bed rest averaged 0.5 percent of the total body calcium per month. In the same subjects, tenfold greater rates of localized loss from the central portion of the calcaneus were detected by gamma-ray-transmission scanning.

Inflight weight losses were experienced throughout Project Mercury, Gemini, and the Apollo missions. Such weight losses were attributed, in part, to losses in body water. Since weight was not regained completely in the 24-hour period immediately postflight, it was probable that tissue had also been lost. What part of these losses was brought about by insufficient caloric intakes was unknown.

Speculation on the theoretical energy requirements of man during space flight began before the United States Project Mercury and the Soviet Vostok flights. At one time, it had seemed logical to assume that activity in a weightless environment would require less energy than at one g because work associated with counteracting the force of gravity would be eliminated. However, caloric requirements are affected by numerous variables including age, physical and mental activity, stress, body size and composition, together with relative humidity, radiation, pressure, and environmental temperature. During the

Apollo missions, therefore, the question of inflight caloric requirements was explored in much greater depth.

Metabolic changes in addition to those associated with an inadequate intake of energy were also elucidated during the Gemini Program. The possibility remained that space flight conditions would exert exaggerated demands on the micronutrients and would thus lead to some marginal deficiency state. It is believed that Soviet nutritionists provided their crewmen with elevated quantities of water-soluble vitamins, and that they had observed increased destruction of the B vitamins under conditions of prolonged low frequency vibration of test subjects. These observations were not confirmed during the Gemini Program. However, because alterations were seen in red cell mass and plasma volume, the vitamin E content of the diet in the presence of the hyperoxic Gemini spacecraft atmosphere was questioned (Fischer et al., 1969).

The development of future space food systems necessitated an accurate knowledge of inflight human nutrition requirements. Food systems having minimum weight and minimum volume are required for space flight (Heidelbaugh et al., 1973). For this reason, the Apollo foods were generally dehydrated and formulated to occupy little volume. The nutritional consequence of these measures was a matter of continuing interest in the Apollo Program.

Approach

Food Analysis

With very few exceptions, all foods used during the Apollo Program were analyzed for nitrogen, fat, carbohydrate, crude fiber, calcium, phosphorus, iron, sodium, potassium, and magnesium content. Some composite Apollo menus were analyzed for water- and fat-soluble vitamins. It was not always feasible to analyze the same lot of food that was actually used during the mission, and the variation in analytical values from one lot to another and from one item to another must be considered when the intake data are reviewed.

Dietetics

The menus used by the Apollo astronauts were formulated from flight-qualified Apollo foods in combinations that complied with the personal preferences of the crewmen and that met the Recommended Daily Dietary Allowances (NAS, NRC, 1968). The menus were primarily composed of dehydrated foods that could be reconstituted before eating. The foods were consumed in a prearranged sequence but could be supplemented by a variety of additional items that were packaged in an individually accessible form.

Nutrient Intake Measurements

The quantity of individual nutrients consumed during all Apollo missions is presented in table 1 as a composite estimate derived from numerous measurements. The crewmen were provided with prepackaged meals that were normally consumed in a numbered sequence. Foods omitted or incompletely consumed were logged. During the Apollo 16 and 17 missions only, these deviations from programmed menus were reported to flight controllers in real time. Snack items consumed that were not in the programmed prepackaged menus were also recorded in the flight logs. On all Apollo flights, most food residue and unopened food packages were returned; the residue was weighed only to provide more precise information on inflight food consumption and to verify inflight logging procedures. For the Apollo 16 and 17 missions, nutrient intake information was obtained for 72 hours before flight and for approximately 48 hours after flight.

Table 1

Average Nutrient Intake During Apollo Missions

Mission Number	Mission Duration, Days	Nutrient, gm			
		Protein	Fat	Carbohydrate	Fiber
7	10	84	69	269	—
8	6	64	40	229	—
9	10	77	53	257	—
10	8	51	31	211	—
11	10	81	64	279	—
12	10	64	47	264	3.9
13	7	58	49	234	—
14	8	83	75	286	—
15	11	112	99	370	7.8
16	11	73	61	272	4.9
17	12	91	86	285	4.8
Average, all Apollo missions		76	61	269	5.4

For the Apollo 17 mission, a five-day metabolic balance study was performed approximately two months before the mission by using the flight menus and collecting urine and fecal wastes. Low residue diets were generally used commencing three days before each Apollo flight in order to reduce fecal mass and frequency during the first few days of flight.

Fecal Measurements

Fecal samples were returned from all Apollo flights and analyzed for a variety of constituents either by nuclear activation analysis or by wet chemistry techniques.

Metabolic Balance

Analysis of blood obtained postflight on early Apollo missions, together with certain endocrinological and electrocardiographic changes in Apollo 15, made it desirable to measure urine volume and bring back samples of urine on Apollo 16. During this mission, it was also possible to continue to return fecal samples and to continue to measure nutrient intake. Sufficient data were therefore available to conduct a partial metabolic study.

For a more detailed metabolic balance study in conjunction with Apollo 17, accurate measurements of fluid intake and output were performed approximately two months before the mission. A five-day food compatibility/metabolic study was performed in which the three Apollo 17 prime and backup crewmembers consumed their flight foods, and metabolic collections were performed. The study was designed to obtain baseline data on the excretory levels of electrolytes and nitrogen in response to the Apollo 17 flight menus. The crewmembers consumed the flight menu foods for five complete days. During the last three days of this test, complete urine and fecal collections were made.

Beginning 64 hours before Apollo 17 lift-off and continuing throughout the mission until 44 hours following recovery, all food and fluid intake was measured. For the Lunar Module Pilot, these collections continued until suit donning; for the Commander and the Command Module Pilot, collection continued until approximately 12 hours before lift-off. All urine was collected, measured, sampled, and returned for analysis. Urine was collected before and after flight in 12-hour pools. Complete stool collections were performed.

All deviations from programmed food intake were logged and reported. All foods were consumed according to preset menus arranged in four-day cycles. Every food item used during the flight was derived from a lot of food that had been analyzed for the constituents to be measured. Inflight water consumption was measured by use of the Skylab beverage dispenser. During the preflight and postflight periods, conventional meals were prepared in duplicate for each astronaut. One duplicate of each meal was analyzed in addition to the residue from the other duplicates to measure intake and output.

Apollo 17 inflight urine samples were collected by means of a biomedical urine sampling system (BUSS). Each BUSS consisted of a large pooling bag, which could accommodate as much as four liters of urine collected during a day, and a sampling bag, which could accommodate as much as 120 cc. The BUSS was charged with 30 mg of lithium chloride. The lithium chloride concentration in the sample bag was used as a means of determining total urine volume. Each BUSS also contained boric acid to effect stabilization of certain organic constituents.

The inflight urine collection periods began with suit doffing at approximately 00:07:00 ground elapsed time (GET). The collection periods were the times between scheduled effluent dumps and were approximately 24 hours each. During undocked flight of the Command Module, urine was collected only from the Command Module Pilot. During periods in which the crewmen were suited, urine was collected in the urine collection and transfer assembly and subsequently dumped overboard without sampling. However, urine collected in the Commander and Command Module Pilot assemblies during the Command Module extravehicular activities (255:00:00 to 260:00:00 GET) was also returned. For the Apollo 17 mission, the periods during which urine was not collected are as follows:

1. Commander and Command Module Pilot – lift-off to suit doffing (00:00:00 to 00:07:00 GET)

2. Command Module Pilot – Lunar Module activation and lunar descent (108:00:00 to 114:30:00 GET)

3. Command Module Pilot – rendezvous (187:00:00 to 195:00:00 GET)

4. Commander and Lunar Module Pilot – Lunar Module activation, lunar descent,
    lunar surface operations and rendezvous (107:00:00 to 208:00:00 GET)

Urine collected from the Commander and the Command Module Pilot from rendezvous
to the beginning of the first collection period after rendezvous (approximately 197:00:00
to 208:00:00 GET) was also dumped directly overboard.

Each BUSS was marked with the name of the crewmember and the ground elapsed
time of collection. Following each collection period, the urine pool was thoroughly
mixed before a sample was taken. The urine samples represented a 24-hour void and were
subsequently analyzed for electrolytes, nitrogen, and creatine.

All fecal samples collected from each crewmember for the following periods were
returned: beginning 64 hours before lift-off, during the mission, and for 44 hours after
the flight. Inflight fecal samples were chemically preserved for storage in the spacecraft.

Body Volume Measurements

For the Apollo 16 crewmembers, a measurement of body volume was made by
stereophotogrammetry, using a special computer program, three times before the flight
and three times after the flight (Peterson & Herron, 1971). Body density was calculated
from body volume and weight. Density was used to calculate the percentage of fat by
means of the following formula.

$$\frac{495}{\text{body density}} - 450 = \text{percent fat}$$

Changes in calculated lean body mass and total body fat were converted into caloric
equivalents by means of standard values of 37.6 kJ/gm[*] for fat and 16.7 kJ/gm for protein.

Total body water was measured by means of potassium-42 dilution (Johnson et al.,
1974). Lean body mass was calculated as follows.

$$\text{LBM} = \frac{\text{total body water}}{0.73}$$

$$\text{body weight} - \text{LBM} = \text{total body fat}$$

Findings

The nutritional composition of the typical Apollo inflight diet is given in table 2. This
diet, which is characteristically high in protein and carbohydrate and low in residue and
fat, was not necessarily consumed by all astronauts in its entirety.

---

[*]1 Joule = .239 calorie.

Table 2

Nutritional Composition of Typical Apollo Diet

Nutrient	Percent of Dry Weight
Protein	18
Fat	17
Total carbohydrate	61
Fiber	1.0
Minerals	3.0

A typical Apollo diet was analyzed for vitamins, and results were compared with Recommended Daily Dietary Allowances (NAS, NRC, 1968). The data indicate the Apollo diet provided an excess of some vitamins (A, E, C, B_{12}, B_6, and riboflavin) and marginal amounts of others (nicotinate, pantothenate, thiamine, and folic acid).

The average intake of protein, fat, and carbohydrate for the Apollo 7 through 17 crewmen is given in table 3. Fiber intake measurements are given for the Apollo 12, 15, 16, and 17 missions.

The quantity of energy supplied by dehydrated food for the Apollo 15 to 17 missions is given in table 4. The average energy intake of each Apollo crewmember is given in table 5. These energy values were calculated from the composition of the food consumed. Average energy intakes expressed on the basis of body weight are given in table 6. For comparison, the average energy intake of selected Apollo crewmembers during a mission and on the ground is given in table 7.

The average intakes of calcium, phosphorus, sodium, and potassium for each Apollo crewman are given in table 8. Diets for the Apollo 16 and 17 missions were fortified with potassium gluconate. The contribution of supplementary potassium gluconate to the total intake for the Apollo 15, 16, and 17 crewmen is given in table 9.

Inflight fecal samples were analyzed for inorganic constituents using nuclear activation analyses and wet chemistry techniques. The findings were summarized by Brodzinsky and co-workers (1971). Inflight fecal samples were also analyzed for total fat, fatty acids, and conjugated and unconjugated bile acids (tables 10 and 11). Data on fat absorption in flight (Apollo 16 and 17) are given in table 12.

Apollo 16 Metabolic Study

The input and output of various elements, particularly potassium, were carefully examined in the Apollo 16 balance study and a detailed assessment of energy metabolism was made (Johnson et al., 1974). The average daily inflight potassium intake for the Commander was 113.6 milliequivalents. During the mission, potassium was lost by the fecal route at a rate of approximately 6.4 mEq/day, whereas approximately 18.8 mEq/day were lost before the flight and 20.5 mEq/day after the flight. During the mission, absorbed potassium levels were 107.2 mEq, whereas preflight and postflight levels were 94.8 and 77.6 mEq, respectively. During the extravehicular and lunar surface periods, the Commander consumed a maximum of 152.4 mEq daily.

Table 3

Nutrient Intake During Apollo Missions

Mission Number	Mission Duration, Days	Crewman	Nutrient, gm			
			Protein	Fat	Carbohydrate	Fiber
7	10	CDR	81	72	259	—
		CMP	96	78	280	—
		LMP	74	56	268	—
8	6	CDR	59	39	231	—
		CMP	80	49	240	—
		LMP	52	33	217	—
9	10	CDR	86	60	280	—
		CMP	78	53	240	—
		LMP	66	47	252	—
10	8	CDR	58	34	213	—
		CMP	46	30	213	—
		LMP	49	30	208	—
11	10	CDR	79	65	290	—
		CMP	71	54	224	—
		LMP	94	73	322	—
12	10	CDR	70	50	263	4.6
		CMP	65	49	249	3.9
		LMP	57	42	280	3.3
13	7	CDR	59	50	239	—
		CMP	57	47	235	—
		LMP	57	49	228	—
14	8	CDR	90	76	309	—
		CMP	79	61	230	—
		LMP	81	89	319	—
15	11	CDR	126	115	356	8.2
		CMP	109	94	334	7.9
		LMP	100	89	421	2.2
16	11	CDR	88	73	319	6.2
		CMP	79	60	295	5.3
		LMP	52	50	203	3.1
17	12	CDR	88	68	248	3.9
		CMP	87	87	293	5.3
		LMP	98	104	314	5.3

Table 4

Energy Supplied by Dehydrated Food

(Values in percent of total Joules consumed)

Apollo Mission Number	Crewman		
	CDR	CMP	LMP
15	57.7	63.9	57.3
16	57.7	59.4	62.4
17	43.0	46.9	44.2

Table 5

Average Energy Intake During Apollo Missions

[Values in kJ/day (kcal/day)]

Apollo Mission Number	Crewmen		
	CDR	CMP	LMP
7	8235 (1970)	8945 (2140)	7524 (1800)
8	6186 (1480)	7064 (1690)	5601 (1340)
9	8026 (1920)	7190 (1720)	6855 (1640)
10	5643 (1350)	5267 (1260)	5225 (1250)
11	8527 (2040)	6855 (1640)	9530 (2280)
12	7315 (1750)	6981 (1670)	7064 (1690)
13	6604 (1580)	6437 (1540)	6354 (1520)
14	9656 (2310)	7190 (1720)	9739 (2330)
15	12 134 (2903)	10 456 (2492)	10 751 (2572)
16	10 044 (2403)	6542 (1565)	9890 (2366)
17	7545 (1805)	9547 (2284)	8389 (2007)

The average daily inflight potassium intake for the Lunar Module Pilot was 114.7 mEq, compared with an average daily preflight intake of 110.5 mEq and an average daily postflight intake of 97.5 mEq. During the preflight, inflight, and postflight phases, the average daily fecal losses were 33.5, 11.1, and 31.0 mEq, respectively. The absorbed daily potassium levels for preflight, inflight, and postflight phases were 77.0, 103.6, and 66.5 mEq, respectively. Although these levels were less than the recommended levels of 150 mEq per day, they were adequate for ground-based requirements. A peak level of 148 mEq per day was consumed by the Lunar Module Pilot during lunar· surface activities.

Table 6

Apollo Inflight Energy Intake Based on Body Weight
[Values in kJ/kg/day (kcal/kg/day)]

Apollo Mission Number	Crewmen		
	CDR	CMP	LMP
7	93.7 (22.4)	128.8 (30.8)	106.7 (25.5)
8	80.8 (19.3)	92.0 (22.0)	84.5 (20.2)
9	109.9 (26.3)	97.0 (23.2)	92.5 (22.1)
10	71.1 (17.0)	68.7 (16.4)	66.1 (15.8)
11	108.7 (26.0)	90.8 (21.7)	122.2 (29.2)
12	109.9 (26.3)	99.1 (23.7)	101.1 (24.2)
13	84.1 (20.1)	71.9 (17.2)	89.8 (21.5)
14	123.4 (29.5)	95.8 (22.9)	117.2 (28.0)
15	149.7 (35.8)	141.8 (33.9)	145.2 (34.7)
16	125.5 (30.0)	104.6 (25.0)	135.4 (32.4)
17	93.7 (22.4)	123.8 (29.6)	110.5 (26.4)

Table 7

Comparison of Apollo Inflight and
Ground-Based Average Energy Intake
[Values in kJ/kg (kcal/kg)]

Mission Number	Crewman	Ground-Based Intake *	Inflight Intake **
9	LMP	151.4 (36.2)	92.5 (22.1)
12	CDR	157.3 (37.6)	109.9 (26.3)
	LMP	147.3 (35.2)	101.3 (24.2)
16	CDR	184.1 (44.0)	125.4 (30.0)
	CMP	150.9 (36.1)	104.5 (25.0)
	LMP	176.8 (42.3)	135.6 (32.4)
17	CDR	129.6 (31.0)	93.7 (22.4)
	CMP	163.9 (39.2)	123.8 (29.6)
	LMP	130.8 (31.3)	110.5 (26.4)

 * Mean value is 154.7 ± 18.4 kJ/kg (37.0 ± 4.4 kcal/kg)
**Mean value is 110.8 ± 13.8 kJ/kg (26.5 ± 3.3 kcal/kg)

For the Command Module Pilot, average daily preflight, inflight, and postflight dietary potassium intakes were 94.3, 79.9, and 82.4 mEq, respectively. Fecal samples for the same periods indicated that potassium levels were 27.6, 6.3, and 26.2 mEq, respectively. Available daily preflight, inflight, and postflight potassium levels were, therefore, 66.7, 73.6, and 56.2 mEq, respectively.

Table 8

Inflight Intake of Calcium, Phosphorus, Sodium, and Potassium
(Values in milligrams)

Apollo Mission Number	Crewman											
	Commander				Command Module Pilot				Lunar Module Pilot			
	Calcium	Phosphorus	Sodium	Potassium	Calcium	Phosphorus	Sodium	Potassium	Calcium	Phosphorus	Sodium	Potassium
7	644	1060	3810	1879	938	1125	4000	1958	925	841	3480	1336
8	427	847	3170	1229	479	983	3980	1571	366	760	2730	986
9	562	1146	4000	1677	489	1073	3770	1708	494	892	3410	1386
10	836	814	2970	1463	808	746	2290	1376	854	701	2670	1182
11	1036	1050	2770	1751	851	901	2060	1441	1114	1225	3220	2061
12	1095	1090	3580	1835	1022	1028	3240	1685	1291	965	3290	1484
13	870	780	3630	2036	871	720	3480	1942	786	716	3350	1964
14	802	1308	4870	2485	809	1109	3780	2147	843	1304	4750	2576
15	810	1914	6529	3554	748	1624	5274	2720	790	1636	5131	2923
16	811	1696	3860	4432	470	1074	2743	3345	683	1500	3547	4208
17	655	1376	3657	2847	692	1563	4324	3627	659	1447	3611	3237

Table 9

Potassium Intake

(Values in milliequivalents)

Apollo Mission Number	Crewman	Total Potassium Intake	Supplementary Potassium as K-gluconate
15	CDR	91.1	0
	CMP	69.7	0
	LMP	74.9	0
16	CDR	114.2	23
	CMP	81.8	26
	LMP	106.9	26
17	CDR	77.2	10
	CMP	88.5	18
	LMP	98.1	19

Input and output data on sodium, chloride, and calcium levels for the Apollo 16 crewmembers are summarized in table 13.

In the analysis of the balance study performed for the Apollo 17 mission, inflight metabolic data were compared with those obtained during the five-day control study conducted approximately two months prior to flight. Rigorous intake and output measurements were accomplished immediately before the flight and after the flight to detect gross changes; however, the duration of these periods was not sufficient to establish reliable metabolic baselines.

For the Apollo 17 Command Module Pilot, water consumption from all sources was considerably lower during the flight than during the control balance study (table 14). Inflight urine outputs were also proportionately lower for all three crewmembers than those established during the control study. When the conditions of temperature and humidity that prevailed during the flight are considered, it is estimated that in insensible water loss of 900 to 1200 cc/day occurred. This loss was equivalent to the preflight loss. Total body water measurements also did not support the tendency toward negative water balance (see Section III, Chapter 2, Clinical Biochemistry).

Based on numbers adjusted for equilibrium during the control phase and insensible losses, all three crewmembers were in negative calcium balance during the inflight period (table 14). The negative balance was particularly pronounced for the Command Module Pilot. For two of the crewmembers, the negative calcium balance persisted after the flight. All crewmembers had exhibited a pronounced positive balance during the five-day control period study possibly because the flight diets contained a higher calcium level than did the customary daily intake of these crewmembers (table 14). As can be expected from the negative calcium balance, phosphorus balance was generally negative during the flight.

All three crewmembers demonstrated a sustained negative nitrogen balance during the flight (table 14). Occasional negative nitrogen balances of small magnitude were also detected before the flight. Diminished nitrogen retention is supportive evidence for the

Table 10

Analysis of Fecal Samples Based on Dry Weight

(Values are averages ± standard deviation)

Test	Apollo Mission Number							
	7	8	9	11	12	13	14	15
Moisture, percent	6.78 ± 1.11	5.99 ± 1.53	6.31 ± 0.794	7.72 ± 5.42	6.67 ± 0.778	7.53 ± 1.32	9.56 ± 0.933	4.94 ± 1.73
Nitrogen, percent	4.05 ± 0.44	5.87 ± 0.394	5.70 ± 0.85	5.76 ± 1.42	4.94 ± 0.570	5.34 ± 0.778	4.45 ± 0.428	5.50 ± 0.14
Protein, percent	25.3 ± 2.71	38.46 ± 3.13	35.61 ± 5.30	36.70 ± 9.92	30.90 ± 3.56	33.39 ± 4.86	27.79 ± 2.66	34.38 ± 0.87
Total lipids, percent	12.9 ± 5.40	11.74 ± 4.46	12.64 ± 4.25	15.14 ± 0.509	17.75 ± 4.54	15.26 ± 3.92	23.76 ± 5.91	12.9 ± 3.25
Crude fiber percent	7.57 ± 2.47	5.22 ± 1.42	21.81 ± 4.46	7.06 ± 1.79	13.20 ± 7.46	14.05 ± 5.42	14.44 ± 6.08	5.97 ± 0.75
Energy value, *kcal/100 gm	533.68 ± 27.46	530.8 ± 42.7	523.58 ± 38.03	519.15 ± 20.55	501.33 ± 33.9	547.17 ± 55.43	521.8 ± 42.3	573.40 ± 20.78
Potassium, mg/100 gm	1435.57 ± 357.07	1571.6 ± 239.1	1724.1 ± 516.0	1318.35 ± 503.17	1377.5 ± 352.05	1967.8 ± 284.8	1524.5 ± 448.5	1884.7 ± 557.6
Nickel, mg/100 gm	4.21 ± 2.08	2.70 ± 1.48	18.27 ± 10.10	3.37 ± 0.948	10.58 ± 0	4.60 ± 2.88	— ± —	9.70 ± 6.94

*1 kcal = 4.184 kJ

Table 11

Fatty Acid Analysis of Fecal Samples Based on Total Fat

(Values are percentage of total fat ± standard deviation)

	C12	C14	C16	C18	C18:1	C18:2	C18:3	C2X
Apollo 7	0.60 ± 0.18	0.88 ± 0.51	24.84 ± 7.28	32.63 ± 11.84	30.8 ± 10.07	5.01 ± 3.79	—	14.22 ± 11.34
Apollo 8	1.00 ± .52	1.70 ± .99	24.34 ± 8.11	22.85 ± 6.30	32.72 ± 3.80	7.95 ± 5.35	—	12.20 ± 3.26
Apollo 9	1.50 ± 1.22	2.76 ± 1.14	31.07 ± 7.70	38.02 ± 4.67	22.10 ± 6.41	2.88 ± 2.66	—	5.01
Apollo 11	1.10 ± .18	2.24 ± .30	21.44 ± 1.56	24.72 ± 13.04	16.10 ± 1.27	2.55 ± 1.27	—	16.81 ± 5.52
Apollo 12	1.70 ± 1.19	4.44 ± 1.99	30.36 ± 7.25	33.99 ± 8.68	17.06 ± 6.31	2.05 ± 1.96	0.58	—
Apollo 13	1.38 ± 1.58	1.48 ± .72	19.8 ± 5.63	37.92 ± 11.66	32.84 ± 12.65	4.94 ± 3.10	0.858 ± 0.316	—
Apollo 14	1.34 ± .81	1.78 ± 1.41	17.06 ± 5.96	30.44 ± 17.81	25.00 ± 9.75	5.85 ± 9.34	.82 ± .01	5.70 ± 4.74
Apollo 15	1.44 ± .78	16.28 ± 1.94	20.81 ± 6.00	49.32 ± 2.28	10.56 ± 8.80	2.11	1.05	—

general musculoskeletal deterioration noted on previous flights and during ground-based hypokinetic simulations of flight-type conditions.

Table 12

Analysis of Fat Absorbed

Measurement	Sample Number					
	1	2	3	4	5	6
Apollo 16 mission						
Food, gm/day	135	73	100	50	98	60
Feces, gm/day	10.28	2.33	7.84	4.99	7.61	1.21
Fat absorbed, percent	92	97	92	90	92	98
Apollo 17 mission						
Food, gm/day	114	68	87	104	73	87
Feces, gm/day	6.03	.86	1.63	2.10	1.87	1.83
Fat absorbed, percent	95	99	98	98	97	98

Sodium intakes during the flight were all less than 250 mEq/day. Intake and output measurements for sodium indicated positive balances for this element during the flight for all three crewmembers (table 14). However, sodium output in sweat was not measured and this route of excretion could have accounted for all the apparent "positive balance" and even have resulted in a slight negative balance for sodium. Sodium balance was positive during the flight for all three crewmembers (table 15) if insensible losses are neglected.

In compliance with previous recommendations based on observed inflight potassium deficits, inflight potassium intakes were maintained above normal ground-based intakes (73 to 97 mEq/day) (table 15). Potassium retention during the flight was significantly less than that established during the control study. A summary of overall metabolic balance for Apollo 17 crewmembers with all numbers adjusted to reflect equilibrium during the control period is presented in table 15.

Anthropometric Measurements

A summary of body weight changes based on the mean of the weights on 30, 15, and 5 days before lift-off compared to those obtained immediately after recovery is presented in table 16. The weight changes during the 24-hour period immediately following recovery are also given.

Body volume was measured before and after the Apollo 16 mission by stereophotogrammetry. An analysis of densitometric data is presented in table 17.

Table 13

Intake and Absorption Data — Apollo 16

Commander

Day	Item	Water (gm)	kcal	Protein (gm)	Fat (gm)	CHO (gm)	Crude Fiber (gm)	Ash (gm)	Ca (mg)	P (mg)	Na (mEq)	K (mEq)	Mg (mg)	Cl (mEq)
F-3	Total intake	3645	3989	147.7	200.8	366.1	0	22.88	1033	2270	222.3	128.0	473	130.1
	Feces	54	108	6.7	1.7	7.3	.86	2.10	269	298	4.4	8.7	127	.3
F-2	Total intake	3442	3217	134.6	126.8	391.5	0	21.95	1130	1924	183.9	126.2	424	123.5
	Feces	123	351	15.8	12.5	22.4	3.25	5.40	919	851	3.6	25.3	364	1.3
F-1	Total intake	2631	2402	103.5	92.9	265.7	0	14.24	580	1677	121.5	86.4	226	60.1
	Feces	76	276	16.8	9.3	12.5	2.17	5.39	945	803	20.9	22.5	342	.6
F+0	Total intake	1229	2047	79.9	115.3	166.0	1.69	11.74	561	1285	158.7	73.7	184	106.5
	Feces	36	78	5.2	2.4	4.1	.44	1.70	340	249	.7	7.4	120	.009
F+1	Total intake	2448	2421	81.8	84.2	412.4	8.98	19.3	882	1622	183.5	129.9	262	187.3
	Feces	82	321	16.1	11.3	15.9	3.00	8.4	1095	945	35.1	27.4	401	3.3
F+2	Total intake	1750	1627	74.8	55.6	221.8	2.70	16.1	564	1106	184.7	77.5	140	148.5
	Feces	—	—	—	—	—	—	—	—	—	—	—	—	—
F+3	Total intake	1629	2586	105.6	73.3	412.5	7.18	19.1	791	2002	207.9	129.4	242	168.9
	Feces	—	—	—	—	—	—	—	—	—	—	—	—	—
F+4	Total intake	1846	2059	61.5	61.0	338.5	6.06	19.0	938	1144	175.2	152.4	192	121.1
	Feces	—	—	—	—	—	—	—	—	—	—	—	—	—
F+5	Total intake	2029	2007	91.5	48.1	322.9	5.86	19.9	990	1624	123.0	81.9	252	103.7
	Feces	—	—	—	—	—	—	—	—	—	—	—	—	—
F+6	Total intake	1869	2425	92.4	59.4	400.9	5.84	20.8	962	1481	219.9	147.0	276	186.3
	Feces	—	—	—	—	—	—	—	—	—	—	—	—	—
F+7	Total intake	1907	2302	69.3	62.4	414.8	4.07	16.3	1037	1513	141.1	124.0	216	80.5
	Feces	—	—	—	—	—	—	—	—	—	—	—	—	—
F+8	Total intake	1437	2405	96.9	103.3	269.8	6.00	19.9	1055	1683	253.5	133.1	272	169.5
	Feces	10	*	1.18	1.9	1.5	.22	1.3	97	66	16.6	1.8	21	*
F+9	Total intake	1216	1432	71.4	36.5	240.6	6.99	14.7	516	1072	130.0	101.1	197	167.2
	Feces	—	—	—	—	—	—	—	—	—	—	—	—	—

*Insufficient sample.

Table 13 (Continued)

Intake and Absorption Data – Apollo 16

Commander (Continued)

Day	Item	Water (gm)	kcal	Protein (gm)	Fat (gm)	CHO (gm)	Crude Fiber (gm)	Ash (gm)	Ca (mg)	P (mg)	Na (mEq)	K (mEq)	Mg (mg)	Cl (mEq)
F+10	Total intake	2301	2363	121.8	105.4	268.0	5.54	25.8	563	1472	253.3	100.0	209	200.5
	Feces	88	268	17.7	6.8	16.2	2.35	8.5	1927	1193	18.2	29.6	333	2.3
R+0	Total intake	2432	1816	71.5	76.6	200.3	0	12.19	728	1268	97.6	93.0	242	54.2
	Feces	59	145	8.9	4.4	9.0	1.42	3.36	654	456	1.3	15.7	167	.4
R+1	Total intake	2895	2744	97.9	92.3	388.2	0	13.80	755	1293	120.1	117.6	214	83.6
	Feces	156	329	22.4	4.9	22.5	5.85	7.95	1221	1039	5.5	45.9	374	1.1
R+2	Total intake	1655	1101	48.1	58.8	95.4	0	8.93	314	881	91.7	83.4	143	61.0
	Feces	*	*	*	*	*	.54	*	*	*	*	*	*	*

Lunar Module Pilot

Day	Item	Water (gm)	kcal	Protein (gm)	Fat (gm)	CHO (gm)	Crude Fiber (gm)	Ash (gm)	Ca (mg)	P (mg)	Na (mEq)	K (mEq)	Mg (mg)	Cl (mEq)
F-3	Total intake	4050	3369	120.7	114.0	352.5	0	18.20	811	1872	179.6	119.6	391	132.1
	Feces	—	—	—	—	—	—	—	—	—	—	—	—	—
F-2	Total intake	4285	3375	128.7	93.1	396.2	0	16.66	734	1743	147.2	113.3	362	117.3
	Feces	59	179	11.3	4.2	9.6	1.18	4.80	653	747	11.3	20.2	369	.7
F-1	Total intake	3348	2929	118.5	76.5	305.7	0	14.74	515	1914	130.2	98.5	353	83.2
	Feces	162	435	31.9	14.1	29.0	3.25	16.10	2121	1896	5.1	54.7	1008	3.4
F+0	Total intake	1808	2233	69.7	111.4	252.2	.67	11.32	669	1300	125.6	91.5	176	82.1
	Feces	71	*	10.8	5.3	9.2	1.54	4.07	653	601	1.8	19.0	320	.8
F+1	Total intake	2365	1980	64.4	56.6	328.9	4.29	16.7	596	1136	169.5	110.2	197	210.2
	Feces	87	306	17.2	10.2	14.5	1.92	6.5	931	70	4.4	29.9	443	1.8
F+2	Total intake	1794	1588	59.4	51.1	244.0	2.92	13.4	507	938	140.7	83.7	136	167.3
	Feces	—	—	—	—	—	—	—	—	—	—	—	—	—
F+3	Total intake	1484	1904	112.0	55.2	274.0	6.04	18.9	513	1627	209.3	129.5	227	190.7
	Feces	—	—	—	—	—	—	—	—	—	—	—	—	—
F+4	Total intake	2059	1986	49.0	44.4	406.5	5.67	17.0	862	923	161.9	145.8	172	138.0
	Feces	—	—	—	—	—	—	—	—	—	—	—	—	—

* Insufficient sample.

Table 13 (Continued)

Intake and Absorption Data – Apollo 16

Lunar Module Pilot (Continued)

Day	Item	Water (gm)	kcal	Protein (gm)	Fat (gm)	CHO (gm)	Crude Fiber (gm)	Ash (gm)	Ca (mg)	P (mg)	Na (mEq)	K (mEq)	Mg (mg)	Cl (mEq)
F+5	Total intake	1968	1615	89.6	40.0	250.2	5.19	17.86	885	1354	102.3	76.9	232	96.0
	Feces	—	—	—	—	—	—	—	—	—	—	—	—	—
F+6	Total intake	1995	2369	16.4	63.9	383.7	7.35	19.96	876	1607	192.1	148.6	283	150.4
	Feces	—	—	—	—	—	—	—	—	—	—	—	—	—
F+7	Total intake	1756	2034	64.0	51.1	332.5	3.32	13.20	989	1329	133.4	114.2	175	81.2
	Feces	—	—	—	—	—	—	—	—	—	—	—	—	—
F+8	Total intake	1783	2133	93.0	75.2	295.6	5.10	18.03	932	1582	187.5	126.4	268	180.0
	Feces	177	390	29.4	8.9	16.3	3.88	16.71	2191	1607	6.0	45.9	367	2.5
F+9	Total intake	1126	1388	70.4	36.1	232.6	7.22	14.0	532	1027	127.6	142.3	177.3	168.1
	Feces	—	—	—	—	—	—	—	—	—	—	—	—	—
F+10	Total intake	1645	1679	70.4	71.7	213.7	2.73	17.93	389	1114	153.5	93.3	177	178.0
	Feces	54	319	15.9	13.6	14.0	1.97	6.55	681	495	51.3	27.5	187	5.9
R+0	Total intake	2298	2585	74.1	97.7	347.4	0	11.30	568	1147	129.3	87.8	165	85.2
	Feces	394	913	49.9	33.1	57.1	13.26	19.70	2636	2953	79.4	93.0	684	6.6
R+1	Total intake	3175	3373	125.1	108.2	482.5	0	16.67	851	1705	166.0	120.1	264	100.8
	Feces	—	—	—	—	—	—	—	—	—	—	—	—	—
R+2	Total intake	2246	2436	71.9	111.3	292.3	0	13.01	487	1245	142.7	84.7	185	98.3
	Feces	—	—	—	—	—	—	—	—	—	—	—	—	—
	Command Module Pilot													
F-3	Total intake	2141	2202	76.0	113.3	202.9	0	13.63	566	1141	130.1	98.0	305	101.5
	Feces	130	293	19.2	9.4	21.2	3.90	6.46	925	866	8.9	29.6	414	1.0
F-2	Total intake	2610	1855	77.6	93.5	136.2	0	11.55	410	1004	100.3	94.3	322	90.1
	Feces	29	(a)	7.8	4.2	10.0	.75	3.30	514	(a)	1.6	14.2	219	.6

*Insufficient sample.

Table 13 (Continued)

Intake and Absorption Data – Apollo 16

Command Module Pilot (Continued)

Day	Item	Water (gm)	kcal	Protein (gm)	Fat (gm)	CHO (gm)	Crude Fiber (gm)	Ash (gm)	Ca (mg)	P (mg)	Na (mEq)	K (mEq)	Mg (mg)	Cl (mEq)
F-1	Total intake	2356	2338	78.2	82.2	303.9	0	12.10	434	1208	127.4	90.6	224	94.5
	Feces	99	329	22.3	9.3	12.6	1.89	7.00	1185	977	2.0	34.1	471	1.0
F+0	Total intake	1753	2057	48.2	105.8	221.4	1.30	11.92	630	1046	167.7	91.1	175	109.1
	Feces*	–	–	–	–	–	–	–	–	–	–	–	–	–
F+1	Total intake	1292	1394	30.0	58.0	201.3	3.38	11.7	382	681	136.7	79.1	110	194.0
	Feces	37	115	4.8	3.4	7.3	1.26	2.3	345	*	5.7	10.9	131	.7
F+2	Total intake	1227	1052	48.0	31.5	147.8	1.54	10.71	306	658	130.7	53.5	90	107.2
	Feces	–	–	–	–	–	–	–	–	–	–	–	–	–
F+3	Total intake	1432	1706	83.2	46.3	267.5	4.41	12.5	614	1389	123.9	95.0	159	100.8
	Feces	–	–	–	–	–	–	–	–	–	–	–	–	–
F+4	Total intake	1086	1115	25.1	24.5	200.9	1.68	5.70	400	495	55.2	45.4	97	41.0
	Feces	32	110	4.9	2.3	7.6	1.52	2.21	382	309	2.0	11.3	126	.4
F+5	Total intake	1476	1348	82.2	44.4	175.5	2.61	13.3	425	1216	124.2	82.6	165	85.7
	Feces	–	–	–	–	–	–	–	–	–	–	–	–	–
F+6	Total intake	1089	1165	24.0	57.3	151.0	2.16	11.3	228	546	68.5	75.9	128	38.5
	Feces	–	–	–	–	–	–	–	–	–	–	–	–	–
F+7	Total intake	1475	1437	48.6	24.7	233.8	2.29	10.0	856	995	99.4	91.7	118	52.5
	Feces	144	343	21.9	7.5	20.8	2.52	10.0	1612	1352	28.3	47.2	416	2.6
F+8	Total intake	1186	1263	31.2	55.1	177.3	4.22	11.0	340	613	88.9	81.1	142	75.5
	Feces	–	–	–	–	–	–	–	–	–	–	–	–	–
F+9	Total intake	1048	919	41.7	20.1	156.6	3.12	9.9	251	640	85.1	73.3	139	105.0
	Feces	–	–	–	–	–	–	–	–	–	–	–	–	–
F+10	Total intake	1526	2037	103.2	90.7	224.7	2.94	17.7	714	1551	215.6	110.4	219	136.3
	Feces	–	–	–	–	–	–	–	–	–	–	–	–	–

*Insufficient sample.

Table 13 (Continued)

Intake and Absorption Data — Apollo 16

Command Module Pilot (Continued)

Day	Item	Water (gm)	kcal	Protein (gm)	Fat (gm)	CHO (gm)	Crude Fiber (gm)	Ash (gm)	Ca (mg)	P (mg)	Na (mEq)	K (mEq)	Mg (mg)	Cl (mEq)
R+0	Total intake	2387	2084	58.3	94.8	250.1	0	10.75	474	1016	108.3	73.1	194	73.8
	Feces	—	—	—	—	—	—	—	—	—	—	—	—	—
R+1	Total intake	2712	2474	83.8	112.6	289.0	0	13.76	670	1173	121.2	87.0	271	93.3
	Feces	190	428	26.2	7.6	26.8	3.32	9.87	1678	1365	8.3	53.5	477	2.1
R+2	Total intake	1927	2022	64.1	101.0	216.2	0	11.93	488	1012	126.2	87.0	215	92.5
	Feces	62	214	13.4	3.7	13.0	1.36	4.67	791	655	1.8	25.2	234	.8

Table 14

Balance of Water, Calcium, Phosphorus, Nitrogen, and Sodium
During the Apollo 17 Mission

Parameter	Control Measurement			Inflight Measurement		
	CDR	CMP	LMP	CDR	CMP	LMP
Water						
Intake, ml	2666	3734	2268	2143	2705	2270
Urine, ml	1750	2516	1279	1120	1518	992
Feces, ml	63	146	73	68	142	116
Water absorbed, ml	853	1072	916	955	1045	1162
Water absorbed, cc/kg body weight	10.6	13.9	12.1	11.8	13.5	15.3
Calcium						
Intake, mg	673	811	622	675	704	643
Urine, mg	98	204	118	117	182	89
Feces, mg	257	247	269	540	721	591
Calcium absorbed, mg	318	360	235	18	−199	− 37
Phosphorus						
Intake, mg	1603	1883	1544	1430	1646	1438
Urine, mg	1139	1056	1087	1267	1561	1253
Feces, mg	239	227	281	280	592	510
Phosphorus, absorbed, mg	225	600	176	−117	−507	−325
Nitrogen						
Intake, N/day/gm	17.6	17.9	15.9	13.2	16.5	13.7
Urine, N/day/gm	14.0	13.3	16.7	15.7	16.4	15.0
Feces, N/day/gm	2.1	2.2	1.5	1.4	1.9	2.1
Nitrogen absorbed, N/day/gm	1.1	2.4	− 2.3	− 3.9	− 1.8	− 3.4
Sodium						
Intake, mEq	216	209	185	168	205	163
Urine, mEq	149	139	192	143	164	135
Feces, mEq	2	5	3	17	26	7
Sodium absorbed, mEq	65	65	−10	8	15	21
Potassium						
Intake, mEq	99	117	95	73	81	97
Urine, mEq	75	81	82	76	75	89
Feces, mEq	4	7	5	12	13	16
Potassium absorbed, mEq	20	29	8	− 15	− 7	− 8

Table 15

Twelve-Day Totals for Apollo 17 Metabolic Balance

Parameter	Crewman		
	CDR	CMP	LMP
Water, ml	1224	− 324	2952
Sodium, mEq	− 684	− 600	+ 372
Potassium, mEq	− 420	− 444	− 180
Calcium, mg	−3600	−11 028	−3264
Phosphorus, mg	−4104	−13 284	−6012
Nitrogen, gm	− 60	− 101	− 13
Protein (N x 6.25), gm	− 375	− 631	− 75
Mass, kg *	− 4.56	− 2.68	− 3.06
Mass, kg **	.25	− 1.50	− 2.50

* Measurement made on day of recovery.
** Measurement made 24 hours after recovery.

Discussion

Most of the Apollo crewmembers did not eat all the food available. Among the reasons for reduced appetite were decreased hunger, a feeling of fullness in the abdomen, nausea (Berry & Homick, 1973), and preoccupation with the critical mission tasks. Dislike of the food and inadequate rest during the mission were minor problems (Berry, 1970). The evidence suggests that either weightlessness or some other aspect of the mission environment caused the crewmen to restrict their food intake below quantities available and below quantities necessary to maintain body weight.

A reasonable estimate of the energy requirement during a flight can be obtained by correlating careful measurements of food intake with losses or gains in body tissue. The data reveal a mean energy intake of 7854 ± 1735 kJ/day for astronauts during the Apollo missions. If this intake is compared to the NAS, NRC Recommended Daily Dietary Allowance of about 12 000 kJ/day, it is apparent that an average energy deficit was incurred by each Apollo astronaut.

To quantitate the metabolic energy demands throughout the mission and to help define body composition changes, efforts were made during the Apollo 16 mission to control nutrient intake at a constant level throughout the preflight, inflight, and postflight periods. It was believed that stabilizing dietary intake would afford maximum opportunity for detecting body composition changes caused by adaptation to weightlessness.

The mean loss in body weight between the day of the preflight total body water determination and the day of recovery was 3.9 kg. Measurements of total body water loss by tritiated water dilution indicated a mean decrease of 1.77 liters.

Table 16

Total Weight Changes During and Following the Apollo Missions
(Values in kilograms)

Mission Number	Crewman		
	Commander	Command Module Pilot	Lunar Module Pilot
Weight losses during mission			
7	−2.29	−2.86	−2.86
8	−3.77	−2.41	−3.77
9	−3.41	−3.77	−4.90
10	−3.04	−4.45	−5.49
11	−4.09	−3.50	−2.86
12	− .82	−3.54	−6.36
13	−4.54	−5.04	−3.04
14	−1.73	−5.90	−3.00
15	−2.18	−1.54	−3.59
16	−4.81	−4.04	−2.63
17	−4.56	−2.68	−3.06
Weight gains during first 24 hours following each mission			
7	.75	3.50	4.00
8	2.75	.75	.50
9	2.75	8.50	4.25
10	2.25	1.75	1.50
11	6.00	−	4.00
12	2.00	4.00	3.00
13	−	−	−
14	1.00	7.00	1.00
15	−	−	−
16	2.50	3.00	2.50
17	.25	−1.50	−2.50

Total 17

Apollo 16

Densitometric Data Uncorrected for Lung Volume

	CDR	CMP	LMP
Preflight Weight (kg)	78.822	62.514	72.480
Volume (l)	75.499	62.136	73.199
Density (kg/l)	1.044	1.006	.990
Postflight Weight (kg)	75.425	59.343	70.442
Volume (l)	74.859	57.854	71.399
Density (kg/l)	1.008	1.026	.987

When body water loss was converted into lean body mass lost, it was determined that the three crewmembers lost fat in addition to lean body mass because the lean body mass loss does not equal the recorded weight loss. The daily caloric expenditure of the Apollo 16 crewmen can be calculated from the known caloric value of metabolized fat (37.6 kJ/gm and of lean body mass (16.7 kJ/gm). For the three crewmembers, the mean daily caloric expenditure was 17 347 kJ.

Changes in total body potassium measured both by radioactive (potassium 42) dilution and by balance techniques did not reveal a significant loss of lean body mass, an indication that a fat and fluid loss occurred rather than a lean body mass loss. If only body fat were lost, the energy requirement for the three Apollo 16 crewmen would be 21 556, 12 043, and 14 291 kJ/day, with a mean of 15 963 kJ (Johnson et al., 1970).

In an alternate method of summarizing the data, each crewman's body mass loss was calculated from the differences between his mean body weight obtained 30, 15, and 5 days before flight and his weight immediately after flight.

Total body water lost was defined as the mass regained by each astronaut during the 24-hour period following recovery. In this instance, it was assumed that the mean weight loss that was not due to either water or protein loss was due to loss of fat. By this method, a larger loss in body fat was calculated to have occurred in all crewmembers.

Because of difficulties in controlling the respiratory cycle during body volume measurement (Peterson & Herron, 1971), the calculated changes in body composition included the effect of respiration as a random variable; thus, the data have too large a variance for calculation of individual changes in body fat.

During the Apollo 17 mission, a complete collection of urine and feces samples was added to a record of dietary intake so that metabolic balance measurements could be made. By using the results of this study, the energy balance of each crewmember during the Apollo 17 mission was estimated. Each crewmember decreased his intramission energy intake. During the mission, this intake decreased from a mean of 141.3 kJ/kg body weight to 109.1 kJ/kg and represented a 23 percent decrease in the caloric intake of the crewmen. This decrease would result in a net mean deficit in caloric intake of 30 129 kJ throughout the mission (Johnson et al., 1974).

The mean weight loss of the Apollo 17 crewmen was 3.3 kg. Nitrogen balance data reveal a loss of approximately 1 kg of protein, and the remaining loss can be attributed to fat. A mean caloric deficit of approximately 104 500 kJ is, therefore, assumed to have occurred (Johnson et al., 1974; Leach et al., 1974).

Body tissue losses were first calculated for each astronaut by averaging successive body weights obtained before the mission and subtracting the body weights measured 24 hours after recovery (Rambaut et al., 1973). It had been assumed that any decrease in body mass between the preflight weight and the weight recorded 24 hours after recovery represented water lost. An average of 1.5 kg weight was not regained during this 24-hour period. If this loss was composed entirely of fat, it would represent an additional inflight expenditure of approximately 5643 kJ/day. Commencing with Apollo 16, food and fluid intake, urinary and fecal output, and total body water were measured for each crewman before, during, and after the flight. From these measurements were derived estimates of protein loss, lean body mass, and total body fat. Body volume was estimated by stereophotogrammetry, and body density was calculated. From all these data, it became apparent that crewmembers had lost fat in addition to losing lean body mass.

Losses of musculoskeletal constituents (Rambaut et al., 1973; Vogel et al., 1974) and a variety of fluid and electrolyte anomalies have been detected by biochemical investigations associated with the Gemini, Apollo, Voskhod, and Soyuz flights. The electrolyte anomalies were particularly pronounced during the Apollo 15 mission and may have been associated with inflight cardiac arrhythmias and postflight changes in exercise performance and cardiovascular responses.

Certain therapeutic measures including the elevation of dietary potassium intake were partly responsible for the lack of significant metabolic disturbances following the Apollo 16 mission. Similar elevations in dietary potassium were effected for the Apollo 17 crewmembers.

The negative nitrogen and potassium balances that were observed during the Apollo 17 mission are indicative of a loss in the body mass.

Summary

Apollo nutrient intakes have been characteristically hypocaloric. Estimates of body composition changes from metabolic balance data, from preflight and postflight weights and volumes, and from total body water and potassium provide no evidence for diminished caloric requirements during a flight.

As observed during the Gemini Program and during periods of bed rest, measurements of bone density and metabolic balance confirm a tendency toward loss of skeletal tissue in weightlessness.

No evidence exists that any inflight metabolic anomaly, including hypokalemia, was induced by marginal or deficient nutrient intakes. In general, the Apollo crewmen were well nourished and exhibited normal gastroenterological functions, although appetite was somewhat diminished and the organoleptic response to food was somewhat modified during flight.

References

Berry, C.A.: Summary of Medical Experience in the Apollo 7 Through 11 Manned Space Flights. Aerospace Med., vol. 41, 1970, pp. 500-519.

Berry, C.A.; and Homick, G.L.: Findings of American Astronauts Bearing on the Issue of Artificial Gravity for Future Manned Space Vehicles. Aerospace Med., vol. 44, 1973, pp. 163-168.

Brodzinsky, R.L.; Rancitelli, L.A.; Huller, W.A.; and Dewey, L.S.: Calcium, Potassium and Iron Loss by Apollo 7, 8, 9, 10, and 11 Astronauts. Aerospace Med., vol. 42, 1971, pp. 621-626.

Dietrick, J.E.; Whedon, G.D.; and Shorr, E.: Effects of Immobilization Upon Various Metabolic and Physiologic Functions of Normal Man. Am. J. of Med., vol. 4, no. 3, 1948.

Donaldson, C.L.; Hulley, S.D.; Vogel, J.M.; Hattner, R.S.; Bayers, J.H.; and McMillan, D.E.: Effect of Prolonged Bed Rest on Bone Mineral. Metabolism, vol. 19, 1970, pp. 1071-1084.

Fischer, C.L.; Johnson, P.C.; and Berry, C.A.: Red Blood Cell Mass and Plasma Volume Changes in Manned Space Flight. JAMA vol. 200, 1969, pp. 579-583.

Graybiel, A; and Clark, B.: Symptoms Resulting from Prolonged Immersion in Water: The Problem of Zero G Asthemia. Aerospace Med., vol. 32, 1961, pp. 181-196.

Hattner, R.S.; and McMillan, D.E.: The Influence of Weightlessness Upon the Skeleton. Aerospace Med., vol. 39, 1968, pp. 849-855.

Heidelbaugh, N.D.; Smith, M.C.; and Rambaut, P.C.: Food Safety in NASA Nutrition Programs. J. Am. Vet. Med. Assn., vol. 163, 1973, pp. 1065-1070.

Issekutz, B.; Blizzard, J.; and Birkhead, N.C.: Effect of Prolonged Bedrest on Urinary Calcium Output. J. Appl. Physiol., vol. 21, 1966, p. 1013.

Johnson, P.C.; Leach, C.S.; and Rambaut, P.C.: Estimates of Fluid and Energy Balances of Apollo 17. J. of Aerospace Med., vol. 44, 1970, pp. 1227-1230.

Johnson, P.C.; Rambaut, P.C.; and Leach, C.S.: Apollo 16 Bioenergetic Considerations. Nutrition and Metabolism, vol. 16, 1974, pp. 119-126.

Leach, C.S.; Rambaut, P.C.; and Johnson, P.C.: Adrenal Cortical Responses of the Apollo 17 Crewmembers. Aerospace Med., vol. 45, 1974, pp. 529-534.

Lutwak, L.; Whedon, G.D.; LaChance, P.A.; Reid, J.M.; and Lipscomb, H.S.: Mineral, Electrolyte, and Nitrogen Balance Studies of the Gemini VII 14-Day Orbital Space Flight. J. Clin. Endocrinol. and Metabolism, vol. 29, 1969, pp. 1140-1156.

Lynch, T.N.; Jensen, R.L.; Stevens, P.M.; Johnson, R.L.; and Lamb, L.E.: Metabolic Effects of Prolonged Bed Rest: Their Modification by Simulated Altitude. Aerospace Med., vol. 38, 1967, pp. 10-20.

NAS, NRC: Recommended Dietary Allowances. Seventh revised ed. National Academy of Sciences, National Research Council, Food and Nutrition Board, Publication 1964 (Washington, D.C.), 1968.

Peterson, C.R.; and Herron, R.E.: Stereophotogrammetry Applied to Physical Medicine and Rehabilitation. Sou. Med. J., vol. 64, 1971, pp. 281-284.

Rambaut, P.C.; Heidelbaugh, N.D.; and Smith, M.C.: Calcium and Phosphorus Mobilization in Man During Weightless Flight Activities. Report 25 (Research and Development Associates for Military Food and Packaging Systems, Inc.), 1973, pp. 1-7.

Rambaut, P.C.; Heidelbaugh, N.D.; Reid, J.M.; and Smith, M.C.: Caloric Balance During Simulated and Actual Space Flight. Aerospace Med., vol. 44, 1973, pp. 1264-1269.

Reid, J.M.; Lutwak, L.; and Whedon, G.D.: Dietary Control in the Metabolic Studies of the Gemini VII Space Flight. J. Am. Dietet., A., vol. 53, 1968, pp. 342-347.

Vogel, J.M.; and Friedman, R.J.: Mineral Content Changes in the Os Calcis, Ulna, and Radius Induced by Prolonged Bedrest. In: Bone Mineral Conference, CONF-700515, USAEC (Chicago), May 22-23, 1970, pp. 408-423.

Vogel, J.M.; Rambaut, P.C.; and Smith, M.C.: Bone Mineral Measurements from Apollo Experiment M-078. NASA TMX-58110, Jan. 1974.

Vogt, F.B.; Mack, P.B.; Beasley, W.G.; Spencer, W.A.; Cardus, D.; and Valbonna, C.: The Effect of Bedrest on Various Parameters of Physiological Function. NASA CR-182, 1965.

CHAPTER 7
SKELETAL RESPONSE

by

Paul C. Rambaut, Sc.D.[*]
Malcolm C. Smith, Jr., D.V.M.

Lyndon B. Johnson Space Center

Pauline Beery Mack, Ph.D[†]

**Texas Womens' University
Denton, Texas**

John M. Vogel, M.D.

**U.S. Public Health Service Hospital
San Francisco, California**

Introduction

Derangements of bone mineral metabolism can be considered to be one of the major threats to the health of crewmen on prolonged missions.

The integrity of bone and the maintenance of a skeleton capable of resisting the stresses of everyday life are functions of several factors (Hattner & McMillan, 1968):

1. The pulling forces that are exerted on bone by its attached muscles.

2. The forces that are exerted along the longitudinal axis of the skeletal system by gravity.

3. The piezoelectric forces.

4. The hydrostatic forces that permit the proper flow of blood with its nutrient materials to, and the waste products from, the bone.

This complex set of stimuli is balanced to provide a bone structure capable, by its chemical composition as well as by its architectural deployment of these materials, of supporting the organism and resisting the forces against which the organism must function. Bone is a living organ that is continuously remodeling itself. When mechanical forces applied to the skeleton during normal activity in a one-g environment are removed, bone mineral is lost because bone resorption is allowed to outstrip bone formation. This factor represents a danger not only because of the risk of fracture in demineralized bones, but also because the associated increased urinary calcium excretion might lead to the formation of kidney stones.

---

[*]Now with Bureau of Foods, Food and Drug Administration.
[†]Deceased.

Early radiographic densitometric studies in Gemini by Mack and co-workers (1967) revealed significant bone mineral losses in the os calcis, radius, and phalanges of crewmen who were exposed to varying short periods of weightlessness. Because the degree of loss appeared excessive for such short periods of weightlessness, further evaluation of the data led to a lower estimate of loss (Vose, 1974).

It is necessary, however, to view the Gemini and early Apollo results with an appreciation of the problems inherent in the measurement techniques used in Gemini 4, 5, and 7, and Apollo 7 and 8. X-ray densitometry — with its attendant problems of a polychromatic energy beam, film characteristic changes, film development variables, and ultimate translation of film density to digital analysis — has many sources of error. Many of the problems associated with the radiographic technique are amplified when measurements are to be made at a variety of locations with wide differences in temperature, humidity, power sources, and equipment, as was the case with the earlier studies.

A photon absorptiometric technique (Witt et al., 1970; Vogel & Anderson, 1972) that does not suffer from these problems was investigated by applying it to a series of bed rest studies (Donaldson et al., 1970; Hulley et al., 1971; Hantman et al., 1973). The results showed the technique to be suitable for the measurement of later Apollo crews (Rambaut et al., 1972). Apollo 14 was to include postflight quarantine, and neither the X-ray densitometric nor photon absorptiometric techniques had previously been adapted to these conditions. Because the crew was to be isolated preflight and quarantined postflight, a device had to be designed that was compact, required minimal storage area, was adaptable to measuring mineral in representative upper and lower extremity bones, and was sufficiently portable for use preflight at the Lyndon B. Johnson Space Center and the John F. Kennedy Space Center, and postflight in the Mobile Quarantine Facility aboard the recovery carrier and in the quarantine area of the Lunar Receiving Laboratory (LRL) at JSC. Because no changes were seen, the procedure was not applied to Apollo 17 crewmen.

Methods and Materials

The rectilinear bone mineral scanner designed and built for the Apollo missions was compact, easily disassembled, and had the capacity for operation in two configurations: heel scanning (figure 1) and arm scanning (figure 2). The unit consisted of a scanning yoke, an apparatus for moving the yoke, and devices for positioning the limb to be scanned.

The scanning yoke held a collimated source and collimated detector 13 cm apart with the apertures aligned in direct opposition. The source contained 1480×10^{10} disintegrations/second (400-millicurie) iodine-125 and was shielded, except for a 3 mm-diameter collimator output hole. The detector was a sodium iodide scintillator mounted in a housing collimated to 3 mm. The limb to be scanned was placed between the source and detector. The yoke was attached to a movable ram by means of a special mounting stud that allowed for two different mounting configurations [figures 1(a) and 2(a)].

Rectilinear scanning was accomplished by moving the yoke sequentially in two directions. First, a traverse of the ram into and out of its housing constituted a row during which data were collected (X-axis). Second, a movement by the Y-axis unit at the completion of each row constituted an increment during which no data were collected.

The beam of radiation was oriented parallel to the Z-axis. The conversion of the scanner from one configuration to the other required a 90° rotation of the frame with respect to the base and a 90° rotation of the yoke with respect to its mounting stud.

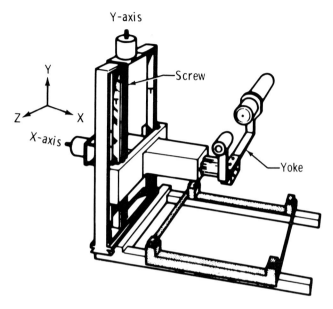

(a) Diagram of heel scanner

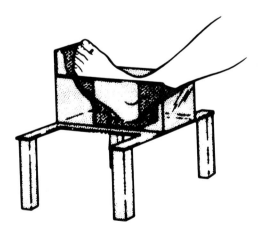

(b) Diagram showing heel mounted
and ready for scanning

Figure 1. Heel scanner.

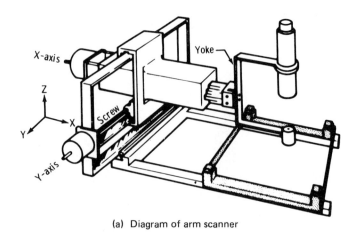

(a) Diagram of arm scanner

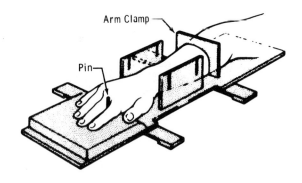

(b) Diagram showing arm mounted
and ready for scanning

Figure 2. Arm scanner.

A row of data collected during the X-axis traverse contained 256 points, each point representing an interval of 0.397 mm for a total row width of 10.16 cm. After the completion of each row, the ram and yoke were moved by 3.0 mm increments along the Y-axis. (This length is standard for Y-axis increments.) A full scan was completed when 16 rows of data or 4096 data points had been collected.

The devices that held the limbs stable and in position for scanning consisted of two interchangeable tables on a common base that slid on the scanner legs for positioning. The base was locked into position by locking thumbscrews.

All scans were made of the left os calcis, with the heel resting in a foot mold mounted in a plastic box on a table [figure 1(b)]. The plastic foot mold was fashioned from an impression of each subject's foot made before the study. The box was filled with water to provide a constant tissue-equivalent path length. The scan was started at a point determined from an initial radiograph to include the entire central os calcis in 16 parallel rows, each spaced 3 mm apart (figure 3).

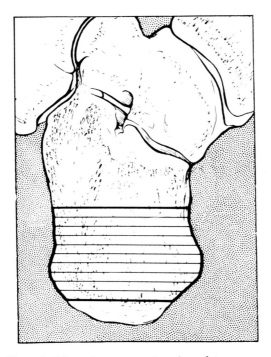

Figure 3. Schematic representation of os calcis scan rows.

During arm scanning, the arm lay horizontally between two plastic vertical uprights on the arm table top [figure 2(b)]. Pegs in a movable handrest positioned and held the arm with the ulnar styloid opposite a reference point in the upright. To maintain a constant tissue-equivalent path length, the arm was surrounded by Superstuff (Oil Center Research, Lafayette, Louisiana) and covered with a thin sheet of plastic. Sixteen rows were scanned at 3-mm intervals beginning 2 cm proximal to the level of the ulnar styloid.

Bone scans using the photon absorptiometry technique were made for the crews of Apollo 14, 15, and 16 approximately one month, two weeks, and one week before flight. Four postflight measurements were made for each crew. No bone studies were performed on the crews of Apollo 9 through 13. During the postflight period of Apollo 14, because of the space restrictions in the Mobile Quarantine Facility and the isolation restrictions of the Lunar Receiving Laboratory, only a single scanner could be deployed in each of these areas. For this reason, arm and heel scans were performed separately using the same scanner in each of the two configurations. The scanner setup was performed by the Flight Surgeon. The data acquisition electronics were located outside of the quarantine area with passthrough cable connectors installed previously in the bulkhead of the Mobile Quarantine Facility and the wall of the crewmen's communication and visiting area of the Lunar Receiving Laboratory. On the two subsequent missions, arm and heel studies were performed simultaneously both preflight and postflight, because quarantine was no longer required.

Results

In general, no mineral losses were observed in the os calcis, radius, and ulna during the 10-day Apollo 14 flight (tables 1, 2, and 3). The Lunar Module Pilot (LMP) had a change of mineral in the central os calcis of +3.5 percent when immediate preflight and postflight measures were compared, in contrast to the -0.7 percent for the Commander (CDR), and +1.5 percent for the Command Module Pilot (CMP). The preflight measurements varied from +0.8 to -1.1 percent of mean baseline for all three crewmembers. In contrast, there was a greater variation in the three controls of +1.8 to -2.8 percent. Postflight measurements for control subjects 1, 2, and 3 were +2.9, -3.1, and -1.0 percent of mean baseline.

Table 1

Apollo 14 Left Os Calcis Mineral Content Change
(Percent change from mean baseline[*])

Time	Crewmen			Control Subjects		
(Days)	CDR	LMP	CMP	1	2	3
F − 26	+0.7	+0.2	+0.2	−1.8	+0.6	+1.0
F − 15	−1.1	− .3	+ .8	+1.5	−1.5	−2.8
F − 6	+ .3	+ .2	+1.0	+ .3	+ .9	+1.8
R − 8	−	−	−	− .5	+ .9	−
R − 2	−	−	−	.0	−	−
R + 10**	− .4	+3.7	+ .5	−	−	−
R + 30**	−	+3.3	−	−	−	−
R + 6	−2.6	+5.9	+ .2	+2.9	−	−
R + 16	−1.0	+4.8	+1.2	.0	−	−
R + 18	−	−	−	−	−3.1	−1.0

[*]Based on hydroxyapatite equivalency in mg/cm^2: mean value for nine rows scanned.
**Hours.

The radius measurements postflight ranged within the values obtained preflight (table 2). When immediate preflight values were compared to postflight values, there were -0.7, +2.2, and -0.3 percent changes for the CDR, LMP, and CMP, respectively.

The ulna mineral content was somewhat more variable, but postflight values were essentially within the preflight range (table 3). When immediate preflight and postflight values were compared, there were -3.6, -2.9, and -5.2 percent changes for the CDR, LMP, and CMP. These changes appear to be large; however, there was a ±2.5 to 3.0 percent variation preflight for the CDR and LMP and a -7.2 to +5.7 percent variation for the CMP. This latter variation appears to be instrumental rather than real.

Table 2

Apollo 14 Right Radius Mineral Content Change
(Percent change from mean baseline*)

Time	Crewmen			Control Subjects		
(Days)	CDR	LMP	CMP**	1	2	3
F − 26	−0.7	−3.5	−5.3(−−)	−1.6	−1.5	−3.9
F − 15	+ .1	+4.1	+3.5(+ .8)	+ .3	+ .1	+1.1
F − 6	+ .6	− .7	+1.8(− .8)	+1.3	+1.0	+2.8
R − 6	−	−	−	− .6	+ .5	−
R + 1	− .1	+1.5	+1.5(−1.1)	−	−	−
R + 6	− .4	+1.4	+3.5(+ .9)	+2.3	−	−
R + 16	+ .3	+3.4	+3.3(+ .7)	+1.8	−	−
R + 18	−	−	−	−	+2.2	+4.7

*Based on corrected computer unit values.
**Percent values in parenthesis based on only 2 baseline values; the first being omitted.

Table 3

Apollo 14 Right Ulna Mineral Content Change
(Percent change from mean baseline*)

Time	Crewmen			Control Subjects		
(Days)	CDR	LMP	CMP**	1	2	3
F − 26	−2.1	−0.1	−7.2(−−)	−1.5	−1.5	−0.1
F − 15	+ .1	−2.5	+1.5(−2.0)	+1.8	− .9	+1.1
F − 6	+2.0	+2.6	+5.7(+2.0)	− .3	+2.3	− .9
R − 6	−	−	−	−1.0	+3.4	−
R + 1	−1.6	− .3	***	−	−	−
R + 6	+3.0	−2.7	+ .3(−3.2)	+1.1	−	−
R + 16	− .3	0	− .5(−3.8)	−2.0	−	−
R + 18	−	−	−	−	− .5	−2.0

*Based on corrected computer unit values.
**Percent values in parenthesis based on only two baseline values; the first being omitted.
***No match in ulna width. Data not valid.

A significant increase in fat was observed on the plantar side of the os calcis. Changes were seen in all crewmen immediately postflight. The most significant change was in the CMP's measurement at ten hours after recovery (R+10). There was a 34 percent increase in fat equivalence when compared to the immediate preflight measurement. This increase would have resulted in a 4.3 percent overestimation of bone mineral if the soft tissue contribution had not been measured. In contrast, the CDR had an 8.4 percent increase and the LMP an 8.1 percent increase with a potential 2.2 to 2.5 percent overestimation in mineral.

As with the Apollo 14 crew, no mineral losses were observed during the 11-day Apollo 16 flight. The left os calcis mineral values immediately postflight were +1.2, +0.4, and +0.4 percent of mean baseline for the CDR, CMP, and LMP, respectively (table 4). The four controls measured on the day before recovery were -0.6, +1.5, +2.5, and -0.3 percent of mean baseline. Therefore, no changes can be attributed to the flight.

Table 4

Apollo 16 Left Os Calcis Mineral Content Change
(Percent change from mean baseline)

Time (Days)	Crewmen			Control Subjects			
	CDR	CMP	LMP	1	2	3	4
F − 30	−0.4	−0.5	+1.0	−0.1	+2.3	−0.8	+1.9
F − 15	− .1	+ .1	− .9	+1.4	− .5	+1.7	−1.2
F − 5	+ .5	− .3	− .2	−1.3	−1.8	−1.0	− .7
R − 2	−	−	−	+ .4	− .3	0	− .1
R − 1	−	−	−	− .6	+1.5	+2.5	− .3
R + 4 to 7*	+1.2	+ .4	+ .4	−	−	−	−
R + 24*	−1.0	−1.5	+1.4	−	−	−	−
R + 3	− .4	−2.5	− .8	− .7	− .2	+ .5	−1.1
R + 7	−	−1.4	−	+2.4	+1.6	+2.4	+ .3

*Hours

The distal radius mineral measurements immediately postflight were +1.0, +2.1, and +1.5 percent of mean baseline for the CDR, CMP, and LMP, respectively (table 5). The four controls were +0.1, +0.1, +0.5, and 0.0 percent of mean baseline on the day before recovery. These values are within the ±2 percent accuracy of the technique, and no radius mineral losses can therefore be attributed to the flight. The distal right ulna values immediately postflight were -2.2, -3.5, and -3.3 percent of mean baseline for the CDR, CMP, and LMP, respectively (table 6). Similar values (-2.8, -2.9, -0.5, and -2.7 percent) were observed in the controls on the day before recovery. It is, therefore, reasonable to conclude that there were no significant changes from preflight in the Apollo 16 crew.

The Apollo 15 data differed somewhat from that obtained on Apollo 14 and 16 in that two crewmen lost mineral from the left central os calcis during this mission (table 7).

When compared with the mean baseline values, there were -6.6, -7.3, and -0.5 percent changes in the CDR, CMP, and LMP, respectively. The changes for control subjects 1, 2, and 3 were +0.3, -0.2, and -2.8 percent, respectively. The CDR regained his mineral more rapidly than the CMP, and both were near baseline values by the end of two weeks. The magnitude of these losses must be evaluated in terms of the variability in the controls observed during the postflight period. Taken in this context, the losses exhibited by the CDR and CMP could more likely reflect losses of about 5 to 6 percent.

Table 5

Apollo 16 Right Radius Mineral Content Change
(Percent change from mean baseline)

Time (Days)	Crewmen			Control Subjects			
	CDR	CMP	LMP	1	2	3	4
F − 30	+0.3	+0.2	+1.6	−0.2	−0.2	+0.8	+2.7
F − 15	+ .1	+1.2	− .3	+ .3	0	+ .3	− .7
F − 5	− .4	−1.4	−1.3	− .1	+ .3	−1.1	−2.0
R − 2	−	−	−	− .5	−1.6	−1.6	+ .1
R − 1	−	−	−	+ .1	+ .1	+ .5	0
R + 4 to 7*	+1.0	+2.1	+1.5	−	−	−	−
R + 24*	− .9	+2.0	−1.4	−	−	−	−
R + 3	+1.0	− .9	− .2	+1.0	−1.0	−1.2	+1.3
R + 7	−	+1.1	−	+ .5	−1.2	+ .6	− .3

*Hours

There were essentially no changes in radius mineral during flight, namely -1.1, -2.3, and -1.0 percent for the CDR, CMP, and LMP, respectively (table 8). Changes for control subjects 1, 2, and 3 were -1.6, -0.9, and +0.1 percent, respectively. Also, the crew's ulna mineral changes were not significant when compared with the control subjects (table 9). Immediate postflight values differed from the mean preflight by -1.4, -3.6, and -1.8 percent for the CDR, CMP, and LMP, respectively. Changes for control subjects 1, 2, and 3 were +0.6, +0.1, and -2.2 percent, respectively. The -3.6 percent mineral change in the CMP may be significant, but he was +1.4 percent of the mean baseline the following day. As noted in the Apollo 14 and 16 crews, there is a greater variation in the ulnar mineral determinations, the cause of which is unknown.

Whereas there were signficant changes in the soft tissue composition in the CMP of Apollo 14, there were no significant changes in any of the Apollo 15 or 16 crewmembers.

Table 6

Apollo 16 Right Ulna Mineral Content Change
(Percent change from mean baseline)

Time	Crewmen			Control Subjects			
(Days)	CDR	CMP	LMP	1	2	3	4
F − 30	−1.3	+0.4	+1.2	+0.8	+0.4	+0.5	+2.5
F − 15	+ .1	− .5	+1.6	− .4	− .5	+1.0	−2.1
F − 5	+1.2	+ .2	−2.8	− .4	+ .1	−1.4	− .4
R − 2	−	−	−	−3.2	−5.2	+1.7	− .8
R − 1	−	−	−	−2.8	−2.9	− .5	−2.7
R+4 to 7*	−2.2	−3.5	−3.3	−	−	−	−
R + 24*	−1.1	+1.5	+1.7	−	−	−	−
R + 3	−1.0	+ .3	−4.7	+1.1	− .6	+1.8	+2.6
R + 7	−	−1.8	−	+ .6	−1.4	+3.2	+2.5

*Hours

Table 7

Apollo 15 Left Os Calcis Mineral Content Change
(Percent change from mean baseline*)

Time	Crewmen			Control Subjects		
(Days)	CDR	CMP	LMP	1	2	3
F − 27	+0.1	−0.9	+0.1	−0.7	−1.7	0
F − 13	− .2	+ .4	− .2	+ .6	+2.0	+ .3
F − 5	+ .1	+ .5	+ .1	+ .1	− .3	− .3
R − 2	−	−	−	−2.2	−1.1	−1.0
R + 0	−6.6	−7.3	− .5	−	−	−
R + 1	−3.1	−5.7	−1.0	+ .3	− .2	−2.8
R + 5	−2.4	−3.5	− .08	−1.7	−1.3	−2.4
R + 14	−1.4	−1.7	−	−	+2.0	+ .5

*Based on mg/cm^2 of hydroxyapatite in nine rows of the central os calcis.

Discussion

The purpose of this study was to determine the effect of weightlessness on bone during prolonged space exploration. Ground-based studies designed to mimic the altered physiologic state were used to construct a time-effect curve. Bed rest, which most closely models the weightless state at least as far as the musculoskeletal system is concerned, has served as an experimental model to assess the bone mineral changes observed during bed rest periods of up to 36 weeks, and to determine what remedial measures might be used to stem the tide of bone mineral loss. The loss of bone mineral in the bedridden patient has long been recognized. Contrary to previous reports, total recovery does occur (Donaldson et al., 1970). Because of the combined effects of immobility and weightlessness, losses of bone mineral in flight were expected to be, if anything, more severe than were seen in bed rest.

Table 8

Apollo 15 Right Radius Mineral Content Change
(Percent change from mean baseline[*])

Time	Crewmen			Control Subjects		
(Days)	CDR	CMP	LMP	1	2	3
F − 27	+0.4	+0.7	+0.2	+0.9	+2.5	+1.7
F − 13	+ .8	− .3	+ .1	−1.0	−1.7	0
F − 5	−1.1	− .4	− .3	0	− .8	−1.7
R + 2	−	−	−	−3.5	−4.0	−1.1
R − 0	−1.1	−2.3	−1.0	−	−	−
R + 1	−4.7	−2.6	−3.3	−1.6	− .9	+ .1
R + 5	− .1	− .6	+1.6	−2.5	− .5	−1.3
R + 14	+ .1	− .3	−	−	−1.3	−2.5

[*]Based on gm/cm of bone mineral as derived by Cameron.

Table 9

Apollo 15 Right Ulna Mineral Content Change
(Percent change from mean baseline[*])

Time	Crewmen			Control Subjects		
(Days)	CDR	CMP	LMP	1	2	3
F − 27	+0.6	+0.4	+0.5	+1.3	+2.1	+3.7
F − 13	− .8	+ .1	−2.1	+2.4	− .7	−3.2
F − 5	+ .3	− .5	+1.7	−3.8	−1.3	− .4
R − 2	−	−	−	−1.3	−2.8	−1.2
R + 0	−1.4	−3.6	−1.8	−	−	−
R + 1	0	+1.4	+2.1	+ .6	+ .1	−2.2
R + 5	+ .9	+ .5	−2.1	−3.3	−5.0	+ .4
R + 14	0	+1.4	−	−	−1.0	+ .7

[*]Based on gm/cm of bone mineral as derived by Cameron.

The early reports of significant bone mineral losses in the five- to fourteen-day Gemini and Apollo flights served to emphasize the need for correlating the bed-rest-induced mineral losses with those observed during varying periods of weightlessness. Time-effect curves for both situations needed to be established so that better estimates could be obtained on the risk of prolonged space flight as translated from the ground-based bed rest studies.

Using a gamma photon absorptiometric technique, a time-effect curve was constructed for the bed rest state. The following conclusions were derived:

1. Periods of up to 36 weeks of bed rest can account for a 40 percent mineral loss from the central os calcis (Donaldson et al., 1970). This bone is highly trabecular, as well as weight bearing. In contrast, the ulna and the radius (primarily cortical and non-weight-bearing bones) failed to exhibit mineral losses during periods of up to 30 weeks of bed rest (Vogel et al., 1974). It is acknowledged that the muscular forces may not have been reduced in the case of the radius and that the hydrostatic forces may not have been sufficiently altered to result in a breakdown in homeostasis.

2. The amount of initial mineral content in the os calcis can influence the rate of mineral loss (Vogel et al., 1974). In a study of 19 subjects on 17 to 36 weeks of bed rest, two groups of subjects emerged: those who exhibited a high mineral content at the onset and eventually lost the least mineral both in percent and in quantity, and those who exhibited a low mineral content at the onset and lost at a greater rate than the other group.

3. The rate of mineral loss in general, but not in all cases, was greatest during the second 12 weeks of bed rest and the least after the 24th week.

4. The mean rate of mineral loss in the os calcis was approximately 5 percent per month, in contrast to a whole body calcium loss of 0.5 percent per month (Donaldson et al., 1970). Therefore, the os calcis is not representative of all the bones in the body, and weight-bearing bones are more inclined to lose mineral in the recumbent state than the non-weight-bearing bones.

5. The rate of mineral regain after reambulation follows a pattern roughly similar to that of the loss; that is, if the maximal loss took 24 weeks, regain to baseline also took approximately 24 weeks.

6. Little or no os calcis mineral loss was observed in less than 21 days of bed rest and often was not observed until after 15 weeks (table 10).

From these data, a predictive model was established for the bed rest situation. In this model, the ratio of initial mineral content to the initial 24-hour urinary hydroxyproline excretion is related to observed losses (Lockwood et al., 1972). The greater this ratio, the slower and smaller the losses and, conversely, the smaller the ratio, the faster and greater the losses. The accurate measurement of baseline 24-hour urinary hydroxyproline excretion is, therefore, an essential requirement for this prediction term.

Because of the limited available data, no time-response curve could be established for the weightless state. It appears, however, that the time-response curve obtained from the bed rest studies may be more prolonged with respect to the time of onset of demineralization than is observed in true weightlessness (Donaldson et al., 1970; Hulley et al., 1971; Hantman et al., 1973). Yet, this does not appear to be true for all crewmen; in particular, the Apollo 14 and 16 crewmen and the LMP of Apollo 15 had no mineral losses in the os calcis in 10 to 21 days.

Table 10

Left Os Calcis Mineral Content Changes During Bed Rest
(19 subjects – 29 measurements)

Days of Bed Rest	Subject	Percent of Baseline	Days of Bed Rest	Subject	Percent of Baseline
7	G.F.	+2.1	23	A.D.	−4.5
7	B.L.	− .6	24	R.B.	+ .8
7	R.W.	0	24	J.F.	−2.4
8	T.A.	−1.5	24	D.M.	− .6
8	A.K.	−1.4	24	M.H.*	+1.0
9	R.G.	−1.2	25	F.C.	+ .2
10	M.H.	− .8	25	J.C.	−1.9
14	J.G.	−2.3	25	W.R	+2.1
16	F.K.	− .5	28	G.M.	+1.2
17	F.B.	0	30	F.B.*	+ .4
17	R.R.	+ .5	30	J.G.*	−2.5
21	G.F.*	− .2	30	R.R.*	−1.3
21	B.L.*	−5.1	31	R.G.*	−3.2
22	T.A.*	+3.3	31	F.K.*	−4.1
22	A.K.*	−2.6			

*Os calcis mineral change was measured twice for particular subject.

Repetitive studies of normal ambulatory males carried out over six to eight months exhibited a 0.9 to 1.5 percent standard deviation from the mean in repetitive measurements performed every two to three weeks (table 11). Furthermore, control subjects 1 and 2 studied during the Apollo 14, 15, and 16 missions had maximal variations from their mean values of -2.7 to +2.1 percent for control subject 1 and -2.4 to +2.1 percent for control subject 2 (table 11). Therefore, it seems reasonable that not only did the six Apollo 14 and 16 crewmen and the LMP of Apollo 15 fail to lose calcaneal mineral (table 12), but that the 2.9 and 2.8 percent losses for the Gemini 7 crewmen, 2.1 and 3.0 percent losses for the CDR and CMP of Apollo 8 and 0.8 and 2.3 percent gains for the LMP and CMP of Apollo 7 could also represent minimal or no losses from this bone (table 13).

These data must be contrasted to the 7.8 and 10.3 percent losses in Gemini 4, 15.1 and 8.9 percent losses in Gemini 5, 7.0 percent loss for the LMP on Apollo 8, 5.4 percent

Table 11

Bone Mineral Content of Left Os Calcis

Control Subject	Date	Mineral Content, mg/cm^2	Mean ± Standard Deviation in —	
			mg/cm^2	Percent
Apollo 14				
1	Jan. 4, 1971	493.74		
	Jan. 15, 1971	483.29		
	Jan. 24, 1971	495.37	488.70 ± 8.8	1.8
	Feb. 2, 1971	495.39		
	Feb. 27, 1971	475.69		
2	Jan. 4, 1971	634.68		
	Jan. 15, 1971	610.30		
	Jan. 24, 1971	639.77	625.63 ± 11.71	1.9
	Feb. 18, 1971	621.27		
	Feb. 27, 1971	622.12		
Apollo 15				
1	June 27, 1971	476.45		
	July 13, 1971	493.93		
	July 20, 1971	482.95		
	Aug. 5, 1971	478.88	483.89 ± 7.1	1.5
	Aug. 9, 1971	483.61		
	Aug. 12, 1971	478.12		
	Aug. 19, 1971	493.86		
2	June 27, 1971	632.03		
	July 12, 1971	633.73		
	July 19, 1971	630.16		
	Aug. 5, 1971	625.81	626.17 ± 8.3	1.3
	Aug. 9, 1971	614.26		
	Aug. 12, 1971	616.69		
	Aug. 20, 1971	635.17		
Apollo 16				
1	Mar. 16, 1972	486.49		
	Mar. 30, 1972	493.58		
	Apr. 9, 1972	480.22		
	Apr. 25, 1972	488.29	487.74 ± 6.4	1.3
	Apr. 26, 1972	483.82		
	Apr. 30, 1972	483.36		
	May 4, 1972	498.59		
2	Mar. 16, 1972	631.03		
	Mar. 30, 1972	611.61		
	Apr. 9, 1972	614.42		
	Apr. 25, 1972	618.43	617.90 ± 6.7	1.1
	Apr. 26, 1972	616.96		
	Apr. 30, 1972	611.95		
	May 4, 1972	620.87		

loss for the CDR on Apollo 7 (table 13), and the reported losses of 6.6 and 7.3 percent for the CDR and CMP of Apollo 15 (table 12). The 6.7 and 7.3 percent mineral losses for the 12-day mission (Apollo 15) are in line with losses observed during the 18-day Soyuz 9 mission where there was no interlude of lunar gravity (1/6 g) (Biriukov & Krasnykh, 1970).

Table 12

Bone Mineral Changes During Apollo 14, 15, and 16
(Photon absorptiometric technique, percent change)
from mean baseline)

Mission	CDR	LMP	CMP
Central Left Os Calcis			
Apollo 14	−0.4	−3.7	+0.5
Apollo 15	−6.6	− .5	−7.3
Apollo 16	+1.2	+ .4	− .4
Distal Right Radius			
Apollo 14	−0.1	+1.5	+1.5
Apollo 15	−1.1	−1.0	−2.3
Apollo 16	+1.0	+1.5	+2.1
Distal Right Ulna			
Apollo 14	−1.6	−0.3	+0.3[*]
Apollo 15	−1.4	−1.8	−3.6
Apollo 16	−2.2	−3.3	−3.5

[*]R + 1 measurement

Losses of this magnitude did not occur in bed rest subjects until after the tenth week; very little significant change was evident until the fourth to sixth week of bed rest. This appears to be similar to the comparisons made by Biriukov and Krasnykh (1970) who considered the Soyuz 9 flight to be similar to their 62- to 70-day bed rest confinement. Krasnykh's studies of 70- to 73-day bed rest subjects (1969) resulted in an observed average loss of 11.1 percent in five subjects, without total recovery occurring after 20 to 40 days of reambulation. This observation appears to be similar to the authors' studies where an average loss of 10.5 percent was observed in eight subjects after ten weeks of bed rest, with recovery after reambulation requiring a time approximately equivalent to the duration of bed rest.

Clearly, there are no known experimental differences to account for all of these observations. Only in Apollo 14, 15, and 16 were there exposures to 1/6 g for short periods of time. Of the six crewmen who experienced such an exposure, only the CDR of Apollo 15 had mineral losses in the os calcis, and he experienced a more rapid recovery than the CMP who had no such exposure. Yet, the CMP for Apollo 14 and 16 did not experience any mineral losses. Of the nine crewmen studied, the CDR and CMP of Apollo 15 had the greatest baseline mineral content; that is, 706.2 and 704.7 mg/cm^2, respectively, while the LMP had 576.3 mg/cm^2. The Apollo 14 crew had 562.0, 520.4, and 673.1 mg/cm^2, and the Apollo 16 crew had 606.3, 601.4, and 532.6 mg/cm^2. The losses experienced during Apollo 15 are at variance with the bed rest observations.

Table 13

Gemini 4, 5, and 7 and Apollo 7 and 8
Bone Mineral Changes During Flight

Mission	CP* (percent)	P** (percent)	CDR (percent)	LMP (percent)	CMP (percent)
		Central Os Calcis			
Gemini 4	− 7.8	−10.3			
Gemini 5	−15.1	− 8.9			
Gemini 7	− 2.9	− 2.8			
Apollo 7			−5.4	+ 0.8	+ 2.3
Apollo 8			−2.1	− 7.0	− 3.0
		Distal Radius			
Gemini 5	−25.3	−22.3			
Apollo 7			−3.3	+ 3.4	− 3.6
Apollo 8			−8.8	−11.1	−11.4
		Distal Ulna			
Apollo 7			−3.0	+ 2.1	− 3.4
Apollo 8			−6.4	−12.4	−16.2

*Command Pilot
**Pilot

The level of dietary calcium and phosphorus appears to have some effect on the rate of mineral loss in bed rest subjects (Mack & LaChance, 1967). Some initial protective effect is observed when supplemental calcium and phosphorus are administered (Hantman et al., 1973). In examining the data available, the calcium intake could be considered low only in the case of the crews of Gemini 4 and 5, the crew of Apollo 8, the CDR of Apollo 7, and the CMP of Apollo 16; all others had an excess of 700 mg of calcium in their diet (table 14). Additional exercise could have been a factor during Gemini 7 and the Apollo missions as well as on Soyuz 9. Nevertheless, at this time, no clear-cut pattern can be developed from the data available.

The results of the later Apollo studies contrast most sharply with the previously reported flight mineral data in Gemini and Apollo in the case of the radius and ulna. In none of these missions were there any significant losses in either of these bones for any of the crewmen or controls. In these studies, the most distal area of the ulna and radius, where the two bones are distinctly separated, was measured. This is the more trabecular area of these bones. As shown in table 13, there were variations in Apollo 7 of -3.3, +3.4, and -3.6 percent for the radius and -3.0, +2.1, and -3.4 percent for the ulna. These data are not particularly different from the data of -0.1, +1.5, and +1.5 percent for the radius and -1.6, -0.3, and +0.3 percent for the ulna on Apollo 14; 0.0, -0.7, and -1.9 percent for the radius and -1.7, -3.5, and -3.1 percent for the ulna on Apollo 15; and +1.0, +1.5, and +2.1 percent for the radius and -2.2, -3.3, and -3.5 percent for the ulna on Apollo 16 (table 14). In contrast, the reported values for Gemini 5 were -25.3 and -22.3 percent for the radius with no data available for the ulna, and those for Apollo 8 were -8.8, -11.1, and -11.4 percent for the radius and -6.4, -12.4, and -16.2 percent for the ulna. Data for these two bones have not been reported for Soyuz 9, and, to date, no data have been reported for Soyuz 11.

Table 14
Bone Mineral Change Related to Calcium Intake

Mission	Crewmen	Calcium (mg)	Os Calcis (percent)	Radius (percent)	Ulna (percent)
Gemini 4	CP	679	− 7.8	−	−
	P	739	−10.3	−	−
Gemini 5	CP	373	−15.1	−25.3	−
	P	333	− 8.9	−22.3	−
Gemini 7	CP	945	− 2.9	−	−
	P	921	− 2.8	−	−
Apollo 7	CDR	644	− 5.4	− 3.3	− 3.0
	LMP	925	+ .7	+ 3.4	+ 2.1
	CMP	938	+ 2.3	−	−
Apollo 8	CDR	427	− 2.1	− 8.8	− 6.4
	LMP	366	− 7.0	−11.1	−12.4
	CMP	479	− 2.9	−11.4	−16.2
Apollo 14	CDR	802	− 0.4	− 0.1	− 1.6
	LMP	843	+ 3.7	+ 1.5	− .3
	CMP	809	+ .5	+ 1.5	+ .3*
Apollo 15	CDR	857	− 6.7	0	− 1.7
	LMP	778	− .6	− .7	− 3.5
	CMP	725	− 7.8	− 1.9	− 3.1
Apollo 16	CDR	805	+ 1.2	+ 1.0	− 2.2
	LMP	705	+ .4	+ 1.5	− 3.3
	CMP	468	+ .4	+ 2.1	− 3.5

*R + 1 measurement

It is not possible at this time to attempt any correlations on these conflicting data. Clearly, Gemini 7 and Apollo 7 had the greatest similarity to the Apollo 14, 15, and 16 results and Gemini 4 and 5 and Apollo 8 had the least. Based on the bed rest experience, one would not have expected significant losses from the upper extremity bones. The differences between the photon absorptiometric and X-ray densitometric techniques can account partly for these differences. The accuracy of the radiographic technique has been considered to approach 10 percent, whereas the photon absorptiometric technique can claim a 2 percent accuracy (Cameron et al., 1969). It would appear that the forces generally applied to the upper extremity bones are still applied during flight, although they are significantly reduced. In contrast, except for the lunar excursion periods, compression forces, most vital to the integrity of the os calcis, are completely removed from that bone.

Reliable calcium balance data for these missions are not available. During Gemini 7 when a metabolic balance technique was used, the net calcium balance was distinctly less positive for both crewmen (Lutwak et al., 1969). The mean urinary calcium increased during the second week by 23 percent for the Command Pilot (CP) and 9 percent for the Pilot (P), the latter not being significant. However, the changes in calcium balance were appreciable. In addition to weightlessness, investigators speculate that high oxygen atmosphere, low pressure, exercise, and dietary protein reduction were factors that contributed in varying degrees to the calcium balance changes in these two crewmen. The greater negativity of the CP was supported by a slightly greater mineral loss in the hand phalanx 4-2 (-6.55 percent compared to -3.82 percent) and distal talus (-7.06 percent compared to -4.0 percent) but not by the os calcis (-2.9 percent compared to -2.8 percent), capitate (-4.31 percent compared to -9.3 percent), or the hand phalanx 5-2 (-6.78 percent compared to -7.83 percent) (tables 13 and 15).

The CDR on Apollo 8 is estimated to have had a 1.01 gm/day mass balance deficit, and the average for all three crewmen on Apollo 7 was a 0.59 gm/day deficit (Brodzinski, 1971). These data are based on the examination of fecal calcium only, and are only approximate because the fecal calcium excretion was assumed to be a constant 80 percent of the daily total. This value has been shown to vary between 69.4 and 91.6 percent. In bed rest studies (Donaldson et al., 1970; Hulley et al., 1971; Hantman et al., 1973), the calcium balance became negative almost immediately and reached a peak in the fifth to eighth week with a range of about 250 ± 200 mg/day (two standard deviations) (Hantman et al., 1973). These Apollo data reflect a greater negative balance that might account for an earlier onset of the mineral loss.

Other bones were studied by X-ray densitometry, and the results obtained are listed in table 15 for completeness. No specific pattern can be ascribed to these results on the basis of duration of weightlessness, calcium intake (table 14), or physical activity. The crew of Gemini 5 appears to have had the greatest losses in all of the bones studied.

Conclusions

It is concluded that loss of mineral from bone incident to periods of weightlessness is comparable to that observed in bed rest subjects but that the magnitude is not severe. If these losses were allowed to continue unabated for a prolonged period of time, the consequences might be more serious because the losses are probably not confined to the bones described. Because of either biological variability between subjects or factors not yet identified, not all crewmen were similarly affected during the ten- to twelve-day missions. These studies can be used to construct a time-effect curve that can be compared with the bed rest data, thus permitting a reasonable degree of prediction for longer space missions.

Table 15

Mineral Changes in Other Bones Studied
by X-Ray Densitometry

Mission	Bone	CP (percent)	P (percent)	CDR (percent)	CMP (percent)	LMP (percent)
Gemini 7	Distal talus	− 7.06	− 4.00			
	Capitate	− 4.31	− 9.30			
	Phalanx 4-2	− 6.55	− 3.82			
	Phalanx 5-2	− 6.78	− 7.83			
Gemini 5	Distal talus	−13.24	− 9.87			
	Capitate	−17.10	−16.80			
	Phalanx 4-2	− 9.86	−11.80			
	Phalanx 5-2	−23.20	−16.98			
Gemini 4	Distal talus	−10.69	−12.61			
	Capitate	− 4.48	−17.64			
	Phalanx 4-2	− 4.19	− 8.65			
	Phalanx 5-2	−11.85	− 6.24			
Apollo 7	Central talus			−3.6	+ 1.8	+2.9
	Phalanx 4-2			−9.3	+ 2.0	−6.5
	Capitate			−4.1	+ 3.3	−3.4
Apollo 8	Central talus			−2.6	− 2.8	−3.2
	Phalanx 4-2			−2.2	− 2.4	+4.8
	Capitate			−9.6	−12.1	−6.7
Soyuz 9	Phalanx II	−	− 4.1			
	Phalanx III	− 5.0	− 5.0			
	Phalanx IV	− 3.1	− 4.3			
	Phalanx V	− 4.7	− 8.9			

References

Biriukov, E.N.; and Krasnykh, I.G.: Changes in the Optical Density of Bone Tissue and in the Calcium Metabolism of the Astronauts. A.G. Nikovaev and V.I. Sevastianov, Moscow, Kosmicheskaia Biologiia i Meditsina, vol. 4, Nov.-Dec. 1970, pp. 42-45.

Brodzinski, R.L.; Rancitelli, L.A.; Haller, W.A.; and Dewey, L.S.: Calcium, Potassium, and Iron Loss by Apollo VII, VIII, IX, X, and XI Astronauts. Aerospace Med., vol. 42, no. 6, June 1971, pp. 621-626.

Cameron, John R.; Jurist, John M.; Sorenson, James A.; and Mazess, Richard B.: New Methods of Skeletal Status Evaluation in Space Flight. Aerospace Med., vol. 40, no. 10, Oct. 1969, pp. 1119-1122.

Donaldson, Charles L.; Hulley, Stephen B.; Vogel, John M.; Hattner, Robert S.; Bayers, J.H.; and McMillan, D.G.: Effect of Prolonged Bed Rest on Bone Mineral. Metab., vol. 19, no. 12, 1970, pp. 1071-1084.

Hantman, D.A.; Vogel, J.M.; Donaldson, C.L.; Friedman, R.J.; Goldsmith, R.S.; and Hulley, S.B.: Attempts to Prevent Disuse Osteoporosis by Treatment with Calcitonin, Longitudinal Compression and Supplementary Calcium and Phosphate. J. Clin. Endocrinol. Metab., vol. 36, no. 12, 1973, pp. 29-42.

Hattner, R.S.; and McMillan, D.E.: Influence of Weightlessness Upon the Skeleton: A Review. Aerospace Med., vol. 39, no. 8, Aug. 1968, pp. 849-855.

Heuck, F.; and Schmidt, E.: Die quantitative bestimmung des mineralgehaltes des knochen aus dem Rontgenbild. Fortschr. Roentgenstr., vol. 93, 1960, pp. 523-554.

Hulley, Stephen B.; Vogel, John M.; Donaldson, Charles L.; Bayers, Jon H.; Friedman, Ronald J.; and Rosen, Sheldon N.: Effect of Supplemental Oral Phosphate on the Bone Mineral Changes During Prolonged Bed Rest. J. Clin. Inv., vol. 50, no. 12, 1971, pp. 2506-2518.

Krasnykh, I.G.: Mineral Saturation of Bone Tissue Under Conditions of Prolonged Hypodynamia. NASA TT F-639, 1969.

Lockwood, D.R.; Lammert, J.E.; Vogel, J.M.; and Hulley, S.B.: Bone Mineral Loss During Bed Rest. Proceedings of the Clinical Aspects of Metabolic Bone Disease, Excerpta Medica Foundation (Amsterdam), 1972, pp. 148-151.

Lutwak, Leo; Whedon, G. Donald; LaChance, Paul A.; Reid, Jeanne M.; and Lipscomb, Harry S.: Mineral, Electrolyte and Nitrogen Balance Studies of the Gemini-VII Fourteen-Day Orbital Space Flight. J. Clin. Endocrinol. Metab., vol. 29, Sept. 1969, pp. 1140-1156.

Mack, Pauline B.; LaChance, Paul A.; Vose, George P.; and Vogt, Fred B.: Bone Demineralization of Foot and Hand of Gemini-Titan IV, V and VII Astronauts During Orbital Flight. Am. J. Roentgenology, Radium Therapy, and Nuclear Medicine, vol. 100, no. 3, 1967, pp. 503-511.

Mack, Pauline B.; and LaChance, Paul A.: Effects of Recumbency and Space Flight on Bone Density. Am. J. Clin. Nutr., vol. 20, no. 11, 1967, pp. 1194-1205.

Rambaut, Paul C.; Deitlein, Lawrence F.; Vogel, John M.; and Smith, Malcolm C., Jr.: Comparative Study of Two Direct Methods of Bone Mineral Measurement. Aerospace Med., vol. 43, no. 6, June 1972, pp. 646-650.

Vogel, John M.; and Anderson, Jerome T.: Rectilinear Transmission Scanning of Irregular Bones for Quantification of Mineral Content. J. Nucl. Med., vol. 13, no. 1, 1972, pp. 13-18.

Vogel, J.M.; Rambaut, P.C.; and Smith, M.C.: Bone Mineral Measurement from Apollo Experiment M078, NASA TMX-58110, 1974.

Vose, G.P.: Review of Roentgenographic Bone Demineralization Studies of the Gemini Space Flights. Am. J. Roentgenology, Radium Therapy and Nuclear Medicine, vol. 121, 1974, pp. 1-4.

Witt, R.M.; Mazess, R.B.; and Cameron, J.R.: Standardization of Bone Mineral Measurements. Proceedings of Bone Measurement Conference, Atomic Energy Commission Conference 700515, 1970, pp. 303-307.

CHAPTER 8
APOLLO FLIGHT CREW VESTIBULAR ASSESSMENT

by

J.L. Homick, Ph.D.
Lyndon B. Johnson Space Center

Earl. F. Miller, II, Ph.D.
Naval Aerospace Medical Research Laboratory

Introduction

The human vestibular system consists of two types of specialized sensory receptors located in the inner ear. The semicircular canals are structured to respond primarily to angular accelerations of the head. The otolith organs, closely related to the canals both anatomically and functionally, are highly sensitive to linear accelerations and to changes in the direction of gravity acting on the head. These two receptor mechanisms together provide sensory information essential to the perception of body position and movement.

Results of physiological and anatomical studies have shown that afferent fibers from these receptors project to a number of areas of the brain and the spinal cord and can interact with or influence neural activity in those areas. Thus, the reticular system, the autonomic nervous system, the eye muscles, and the voluntary skeletal muscles can be affected either directly or indirectly by vestibular activity. In laboratory and field investigations, it has been well documented that excessive stimulation of the vestibular receptors can lead to a variety of behavioral and physiological disturbances ranging from decreased alertness, voluntary restriction of physical activity, oculomotor impairment, nausea and, in extreme cases, vomiting. Discrepancies among visual, vestibular, and tactile-kinesthetic spatial perceptions can lead to stressful sensory conflict, which can also cause disturbances ranging from disorientation to nausea and vomiting.

Because a highly unusual gravito-inertial stimulus environment is present in space flight, concern was expressed early in the United States manned space flight program about vestibular problems that might occur during flight, particularly motion sickness. For this reason, antimotion-sickness drugs were carried onboard the first manned Mercury spacecraft. The drugs provided were Tigan and Marezine, in both oral and injectable forms. However, no symptoms occurred and neither of these drugs was required. The early Mercury crewmen were also instructed to perform head movements cautiously and to reach to different areas in the spacecraft. Again, no problems were reported.

Like the Mercury flight series, the Gemini flights, including those involving extravehicular activity, were free of significant vestibular problems. Results of quantitative preflight, inflight, and postflight tests performed during the Gemini 5 and 7 missions indicated that lifting the gravitational load from the otolith organs did not result in any disturbance of the integrative processes of the central nervous system that might have influenced the crewmen's spatial orientation. Also, there were no significant differences between preflight and postflight measurements of ocular counterrolling (Graybiel et al., 1967). A phenomenon that occurred during the Gemini Program, and that has been reported routinely by American flight crews since that time, was a feeling of "fullness of the head" upon entering weightlessness. Some astronauts described this sensation as a feeling of "hanging upside down." As a result, the idea was quickly adopted that these men had experienced an inversion illusion or a spatial disorientation. On the basis of better descriptions from the crewmen involved, the investigators are reasonably certain that this phenomenon was not an inversion illusion, but the result of a redistribution of extravascular and intravascular fluids.

The Apollo Program included several significant changes from Project Mercury and the Gemini Program in the type of vehicle and the type of mission being flown. The Apollo Command Module (CM) had a considerably larger habitable volume than had either the Gemini or the Mercury spacecraft. Therefore, for the first time in the American space program, crewmen were able to move about freely within the spacecraft. Beginning with the Apollo 9 flight, the CM and the Lunar Module (LM) were docked in flight, and crewmen were able to move back and forth between two vehicles for the first time. Beginning with the Apollo 11 flight, the first lunar landing, crewmen made transitions from zero g in flight to activity in one-sixth g on the lunar surface and back to zero g. With these changes, particularly the greater mobility permitted by the larger volume of the CM and the LM, the first serious vestibular problems became evident. The purpose of this report is to present and discuss all available information on vestibular system function during the Apollo series of space flights.

Methods

Qualitative Assessment Procedures

With one exception that is described in a following section, no systematic program to assess quantitatively the effects of space flight on crew vestibular function was pursued during the Apollo flight series. A major portion of the understanding of vestibular problems encountered during space flight is based, therefore, on qualitative information derived from a variety of sources. An attempt has been made to compile detailed motion experience histories for each astronaut in the Apollo flight series. These histories indicate whether or not an individual astronaut has ever experienced motion sickness in automobiles, in boats, during zero-g parabolic flight maneuvers, or during spacecraft egress exercises. In addition, heavy emphasis has been placed on subjective reporting by individual astronauts on the type and the magnitude of vestibular disturbances experienced during and following their missions.

Special Preflight and Postflight Laboratory Measurements

Because of the need to obtain more definitive information on the effects of exposure to the space flight environment on the vestibular system, procedures were implemented to perform preflight and postflight vestibular tests on the Apollo 16 and 17 crewmen. To accomplish a reasonably comprehensive evaluation of vestibular function, two types of tests were performed. Postural equilibrium tests were selected as a means of providing an assessment of a behavioral skill that is not only of practical importance, but also sensitive to altered vestibular inputs that may result from prolonged exposure to weightlessness. The second test used, caloric irrigation, complemented the tests of balance by monitoring for changes in semicircular canal activity as a possible cause of postmission dysequilibrium.

Postural equilibrium was tested by using a modified and shortened version of a standard laboratory method (Graybiel & Fregly, 1966). Each crewman was fitted with military-type shoes for this test, both preflight and postflight, to rule out differences in footwear as a variable in intersubject and intrasubject comparisons. Rails of four widths (1.90, 3.17, 4.45, and 5.72 cm) plus the floor provided the foot support for the standing crewman. A tape 10.16 cm wide and 68.5 cm long served as a foot-guide alinement for the floor portion of the test. Time, the performance measure of balance, began when the crewman, standing on the prescribed support with his feet in a tandem heel-to-toe arrangement, folded his arms. His eyes remained open in the first test series. In the second series, the time measurement was initiated after the crewman attained a balanced position and closed his eyes. Several practice trials were allowed on representative rails until the crewman demonstrated full knowledge of the test procedure and reasonable confidence in his approach to this balancing task.

The initial rail width for testing with eyes open was 3.17 cm. Three test trials with a maximum duration of 50 seconds each were given. If the time limit was reached in the first two trials, a third was not performed, and a perfect score of 100 seconds (100 percent of the required task) was recorded for the initial support width. If the crewman failed to obtain a perfect score, the two largest time values for the three trials were summed to obtain the final score. The choice of the second width depended on the individual's performance on the initial support width. If his score was greater than or equal to 80 percent, the next smaller support width was used; if less than 80 percent, the next larger was used. Testing on a third support width was required when both of the two prior width scores fell either below or above the 80 percent level. The testing with eyes closed followed the same procedure, except that a larger rail support (5.72 cm) was used initially. The eyes-closed test was executed in very dim laboratory light to initiate dark-adaptation of the crewman in preparation for the caloric test.

Electrodes for recording nystagmic eye movements were attached before the postural equilibrium test. After cleaning the appropriate skin areas with 95 percent isopropyl alcohol, silver chloride (Beckman) electrodes were placed at the outer canthus of each eye and the reference electrode was placed in the center of the forehead. A Tracor RN-243 electronystagmograph system was used throughout the caloric test to record corneoretinal potential changes. Electronystagmographic calibration of eye movements in degrees per centimeter was obtained with the crewman sitting in an upright position and fixating on two alternately flashing red lights placed at a distance from the center of eye rotation, providing a separation of 20° of arc. Eye movement calibration and all subsequent caloric testing were done in a dark room. The crewman then was reclined in a fixed Tracor torsion swing chair so that his head was approximately 60° from upright, and the line from his outer canthus to the tragus of the ear was vertical. Baseline measurements then were made for at least 40 seconds to determine the presence of spontaneous nystagmus. Two separate water baths were maintained at temperatures that ensured irrigating temperatures of 308.65°K (35.5°C) and 307.15°K (34.0°C) by a heater-mixer element. These temperatures were very accurately sensed by thermistors located near the exit nozzles of the irrigating syringes, and were maintained between tests by a continuous recirculation of water.

Calorization of each crewman proceeded according to the following schedule: right ear (RE), 308.65°K; left ear (LE), 308.65°K; RE, 307.15°K; and LE, 307.15°K. In each case, 155 to 160 cm^3 of water were directed onto the tympanic membrane for a period of 40 seconds. To maintain mental alertness, the crewman silently solved arithmetic problems throughout certain specified periods during the response period.

Following irrigation of each ear at 308.65°K and a period of continuous recording that indicated the disappearance of all nystagmic response, an additional period (140 seconds) of rest was instituted; this rest period was increased to 260 seconds following the 307.15°K temperature irrigation. After all caloric testing, eye movement calibrations again were made in accordance with the pretest procedure.

Preflight data were collected on the Apollo 16 prime and backup crewmen at 30 days before launch (F − 30). Postflight data were collected on all three prime crewmen three days following recovery (R + 3); two of the crewmen were tested again at R + 7. Preflight data on the Apollo 17 prime and backup crewmen were obtained at F − 30 and at F − 15. No postflight data were collected on any of the Apollo 17 crewmen.

Results

Inflight Disturbances

Motion sickness histories of individual Apollo crewmen, as well as motion sickness symptoms and vestibular related illusions experienced by Apollo crewmen during space flight, are summarized in table 1. All three Apollo 7 crewmen had positive motion sickness histories. During their mission, however, none of these crewmen − including the Lunar Module Pilot (LMP), who performed purposeful spinning and tumbling maneuvers in the Command Module − experienced any symptoms of motion sickness. While donning his space suit, the Apollo 7 LMP did experience a brief tumbling illusion once, as indicated in table 1. All three Apollo 8 astronauts had some history of motion sickness. During flight, soon after leaving their couches, all three crewmen experienced nausea apparently as a result of rapid body movements. For the Commander (CDR), these symptoms progressively worsened; and, shortly after waking from his first sleep period, he vomited. In this particular case, the severe symptoms experienced were in part caused by gastroenteritis. The antimotion-sickness drug, Marezine, was ineffective for the CDR, but it did alleviate the stomach awareness and nausea experienced by the other two crewmen.

Table 1

Illusions and Motion Sickness Symptoms Experienced by Apollo Astronauts

		Motion Sickness History			Illusions/Motion Sickness Symptoms in Space Flight			
Flight	Crewman	In Land, Air and Sea Vehicles	In Zero G Parabola	In Spacecraft Egress or Egress Training	Tumbling Illusions	Stomach Awareness	Nausea	Vomiting
7	CDR	X						
	CMP*	X	X	X	X			
	LMP*	X		X				
8	CDR	X	X			X	X	
	CMP	X	X	X		X	X	X**
	LMP*	X	X			X		
9.	CDR				X			
	CMP			X		X	X	
	LMP*	X	X	X		X		X
10	CDR	X						
	CMP	X						
	LMP	X	X			X		
11	CDR	X		X				
	CMP	X	X	X				
	LMP	X	X					
12	CDR	X						
	CMP			X				
	LMP*							

Table 1 (Continued)

Illusions and Motion Sickness Symptoms Experienced by Apollo Astronauts

Flight	Crewman	Motion Sickness History			Illusions/Motion Sickness Symptoms in Space Flight			
		In Land, Air and Sea Vehicles	In Zero G Parabola	In Spacecraft Egress or Egress Training	Tumbling Illusions	Stomach Awareness	Nausea	Vomiting
13	CDR	X	X	X				
	CMP*					X	X	
	LMP*					X		X
14	CDR	X						
	CMP*							
	LMP*	X						
15	CDR			X	X			
	CMP*							
	LMP*		X			X		
16	CDR	X						
	CMP*	X	X					
	LMP*	X	X					
17	CDR	X	X			X		
	CMP*	X	X					
	LMP*	X	X			X		

(Modified and updated from Berry and Homick, 1973).

*No prior space flight experience.

**Concomitant illness.

The first clear episode of a severe vestibular related motion sickness problem occurred during the Apollo 9 mission. Because this incident is unique, a detailed account is given. The crewman involved, the LMP, had fewer flying hours than the average astronaut and a definite history of motion sickness. Also, he was making his first space flight. Because he was concerned about his previous history, he took one 50-mg Marezine tablet three hours before lift-off and another one 1-1/2 hours after orbital insertion. Upon rising from the couch later on the first day, he observed that when he turned his head rapidly, he experienced mild dizziness. The dizziness did not seem to interfere with his performance, and he was able to control it by executing all movements slowly and by turning at the waist instead of turning his head. He did not experience any nausea with the dizziness that was produced by head movements.

Shortly after donning his pressure suit for transfer from the CM to the LM at approximately 40:00 ground elapsed time, the Apollo 9 LMP vomited suddenly. The characteristic prodromal symptoms of motion sickness were not experienced. He was, however, able to retain the vomitus in his mouth long enough to use a disposal bag effectively. In the postflight medical debriefing, he could not recall whether he felt nauseated after vomiting or whether he experienced some relief. About four hours later, he vomited again after he had transferred to the LM. Again, the vomiting was sudden and was not preceded by much warning. Aspiration of the vomitus did not occur on either occasion. Just before vomiting the second time, he had been closing circuit breakers and cycling switches located in different areas of the cabin. Such activities require considerable movement within the LM. Immediately following the second episode of vomiting, he felt much better and noted a marked improvement in his ability to move around freely. The only residual symptom was a loss of appetite and an aversion to the odor of certain foods. Until the sixth day of the mission, he subsisted exclusively on liquids and freeze-dehydrated fruits (Apollo 9 Mission Report, 1969).

Because of great concern about the inflight problems of the Apollo 9 LMP, a decision was made to perform comprehensive vestibular tests on him at the Naval Aerospace Medical Institute, Pensacola, Florida. Functional tests of the labyrinth included audiometry, measurements of semicircular canal sensitivity (caloric irrigation and oculogyral illusion), ocular counterrolling, and ataxia/postural equilibrium. Provocative tests included the "dial test" (performance of head and arm movements in the slow rotating room), a coriolis motion sickness test (performance of programmed head movements while rotating in a chair), an off-vertical rotation test, and a cineramic motion picture.

On the basis of these tests, it was concluded that the Apollo 9 LMP had normal function of the vestibular apparatus. The provocative tests, including parabolic flight test data, indicated that he had no greater than average susceptibility to motion sickness. Furthermore, he showed an ability to adapt or to gain increased tolerance with repeated exposures to provocative stimuli.

As a result of the Apollo 9 vestibular problem, increased attention was given to developing techniques for predicting and preventing any such future occurrences. Insufficient time prevented individual crewmen from engaging in any special preflight vestibular adaptation activities. However, on the basis of research performed using the slow rotating room at the Naval Aerospace Medical Institute, it was determined that vestibular adaptation to the weightless environment might progress more rapidly if the crewmen executed planned head movements very early during their flights. Also, the antimotion-sickness drug was changed from Marezine to a combination of scopolamine and Dexedrine.

During the first day of the Apollo 10 flight, the LMP executed the recommended head movements in an attempt to hasten vestibular adaptation. The head movements quickly induced stomach awareness and nausea, and he was compelled to stop. He tried these head movements again on the second day and again had to stop after one minute because of the rapid onset of symptoms. After the second day of flight, he apparently had adapted and experienced no further difficulties. On the seventh day of the mission, he experimented with the head movements again and was able to perform them for five minutes before symptoms began to appear. No other Apollo 10 crewman experienced any inflight symptomatology.

Although several of the Apollo 11 and Apollo 12 astronauts had positive motion sickness histories, none of these crewmen reported any difficulties either during weightless flight or on the lunar surface. The complete absence of vestibular problems during lunar surface activity throughout the Apollo Program has proved significant. Before the Apollo 11 mission, many predictions had been made regarding possible disorientation and postural stability problems that might occur on the lunar surface.

Very early in the Apollo 13 flight, vestibular problems were experienced by two of the crewmen, including the LMP, who vomited on the second day. All available information indicated that both of these crewmen had negative motion sickness histories. The CDR, who had a definite history of motion sickness, experienced no vestibular symptomatology during this flight. Although comprehensive historical data are not available for the Apollo 14 flight crew, at least two of the crewmen had some past experience with motion sickness. This history was especially true of the CDR, who, several years before the Apollo 14 flight, underwent successful corrective surgery for Ménière's disease. No crewman encountered vestibular difficulties during the Apollo 14 mission.

Complete historical data are not available for the Apollo 15 flight crew; however, at least two of the crewmen had some minimal past experience with motion sickness. During the flight, the CDR and the Command Module Pilot (CMP) had no illusions or symptoms. The LMP reported, however, that he experienced a sensation of impending vestibular difficulties and therefore limited his motions during the first several days of the flight. This condition cleared, and he had no subsequent problems during lunar extravehicular activity and return to Earth. Following splashdown and recovery, however, he developed some unusual symptoms that probably were partly vestibular in origin. He reported a feeling of dizziness or lightheadedness that persisted for seven days following recovery. This condition was not accompanied by any type of gastrointestinal disturbance. Locomotion was not impaired, nor was any tinnitus reported. In addition, he commented on a 30° head-down, tilted sensation experienced when supine. This sensation was most apparent during periods of "twilight" sleep and persisted even when he turned onto his side. The tilted sensation was not present when he was fully awake, regardless of postural position. This condition gradually lessened; the degree of tilt appeared to decline and disappeared entirely after the fifth postrecovery day. At about the same time that his symptoms disappeared, he was subjected to several different clinical vestibular tests, which were conducted by an otolaryngologist. The tests included a standard Hallpike (measurement of the amount of nystagmus produced by alternate irrigation of the right and left ear canals with warm or cold water), positional nystagmus, postrotary nystagmus, and standard audiometry. The crewman's responses on all of the tests were normal.

All Apollo 16 and Apollo 17 crewmen had positive motion sickness histories. However, only the Apollo 17 CDR and LMP experienced inflight disturbances. In both of these cases, the symptoms were mild and disappeared after the third day of flight.

An overall summary of Apollo motion sickness findings is presented in table 2. Eleven of the 33 individuals who have flown on Apollo flights have experienced apparent vestibular difficulties. Of these eleven, nine had positive motion sickness histories. Conversely, 18 of 27 individuals with positive histories had no inflight symptomatology. Six of the eleven crewmen with inflight problems experienced minor symptoms, two experienced moderate symptoms, and three had severe symptomatology. As previously stated, it is questionable whether the vomiting experienced by one of these latter individuals was vestibular in origin or due primarily to gastroenteritis. Six (40 percent) of the 15 individuals making their first space flight developed inflight symptoms. Of the 18 veteran pilots, only five (approximately 28 percent) experienced symptoms.

Table 2

Apollo Motion Sickness General Summary

Category	Number of Crewmen
Motion Sickness (MS) History and Inflight MS	
Total Apollo crewmen	33
Positive MS history	27
Positive MS history with inflight MS	9
Positive MS history with no inflight MS	18
Negative MS history	6
Negative MS history with inflight MS	2
Negative MS history with no inflight MS	4
Total crewmen with inflight MS	11
Severity of Inflight Symptoms	
Occurrences of mild MS (stomach awareness)	6
Occurrences of moderate MS (stomach awareness, nausea)	2
Occurrences of severe MS (stomach awareness, nausea, vomiting)	3
Previous Space Flight Experience	
Inexperienced crewmen (first space flight)	15
Inexperienced crewmen with inflight MS	6
Veteran crewmen (one or more space flights)	18
Veteran crewmen with inflight MS	5

Special Laboratory Measurements

Because no postflight tests were performed on the Apollo 17 flight crew, complete laboratory data for the Apollo 16 crewmen only are described.

Test results showing the ability of each Apollo 16 crewman to balance on rails of various widths are presented in figure 1. Preflight findings for all three crewmen are within the range of performance typically exhibited by young, healthy, pilot-type subjects. Examination of figure 1 indicates that during the first (R + 3) and second (R + 7) postflight test periods, postural equilibrium with eyes open was nearly identical to preflight performance for all crewmen. The CDR actually demonstrated a slight progressive improvement on this task with time. At R + 3, however, the CDR and the CMP exhibited a marked decrease in postural stability when deprived of all visual sensory cues. When these two individuals were tested again at R + 7, there was a definite improvement in postural stability with eyes closed compared to their R + 3 performance. The CMP bettered his preflight, eyes-closed scores, whereas the performance of the CDR was approximately midway between his two previous scores.

The principal characteristics of the spontaneous nystagmus — as well as the lag, the maximum velocity, the maximum frequency, and the duration of nystagmus elicited from each Apollo 16 crewman in response to the two irrigation temperatures — are summarized in table 3. Lag is defined as the time between the onset of irrigation and the first measurable nystagmus. Maximum velocity was obtained by selecting the ten-second epoch of a given record that contained the greatest preponderance of high-velocity, slow-phase nystagmus, and by calculating the average slow-phase velocity value for that epoch. Maximum frequency was obtained similarly. The duration of nystagmus is the interval between onset and complete cessation of nystagmus.

In general, the preflight responses indicate that all crewmen possess normally functioning canals bilaterally. The nystagmus produced was always in the expected direction. Spontaneous nystagmus was present in all three Apollo 16 crewmen, but no meaningful trends were observed with this parameter. Also, all of the crewmen exhibited an asymmetry or labyrinthine preponderance which, with the exception of a slight reversal in the CMP at R + 7, remained unchanged.

To facilitate more discernible intersubject and intrasubject comparisons, the primary parameters of lag, maximum velocity, maximum frequency, and duration of nystagmus are plotted in the form of bar graphs for each Apollo 16 crewman at each irrigating temperature in figures 2 to 4. Right and left ear data are shown separately in each figure. Examination of figure 2 indicates that during the first test period (R + 3), the nystagmic responses of the LMP were very similar to his preflight responses, particularly at 308.65°K. The tendency toward shorter lag times, higher velocities and frequencies, and longer durations of nystagmus with the more stressful water temperature (307.15°K) is also quite apparent in these data, as is the consistent right-greater-than-left response asymmetry. Because no postflight changes were detected with either postural equilibrium or caloric irrigation procedures, the Apollo 16 LMP was not tested further. Changes in the CDR's responses to caloric irrigation at R + 3 are readily observable in figure 3. With two exceptions that occurred with the 307.15°K stimulus, all of the R + 3 response parameters are elevated compared to the F − 30 baseline. When tested again four days

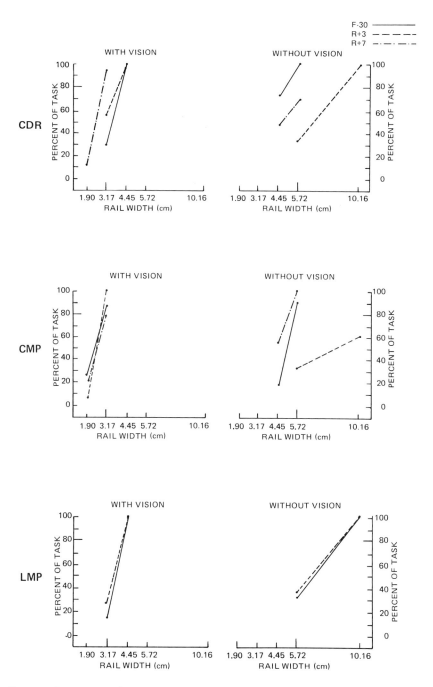

Figure 1. Pre- and postflight postural equilibrium scores for the Apollo 16 CDR, CMP, and LMP. Performance with eyes open and eyes closed, expressed as percent of task, is plotted as a function of rail width.

Table 3

Apollo 16 Pre- and Postflight Caloric Irrigation Results

Crewman	Temperature °K (°C)	Ear	Nystagmus Direction			Lag (sec)			Avg. Velocity (°/sec)			Max. Velocity (°/sec)			Max. Frequency (beats/sec)			Duration (sec)			Total Beats (40 sec)			R/L* Asymmetry (Percent)		
			F-30	R+3	R+7	F-30	R+3	R+7	F-30	R+3	R+7	F-30	R+3	R+7	F-30	R+3	R+7	F-30	R+3	R+7	F-30	R+3	R+7	F-30	R+3	R+7
CDR	SN**	—	R	—	—	—	—	—	1.5	2.2	2.3	—	—	—	—	—	—	—	—	—	9	9	10	—	37.0 (L>R)	33.0 (L>R)	37.2 (L>R)
	308.65 (35.5)	R	R	R	R	27.0	48.9	42.7	—	—	—	2.6	4.1	3.4	0.4	1.0	0.6	151	178	115	—	—	—	—	—	—
	308.65 (35.5)	L	L	L	L	32.3	33.3	35.5	—	—	—	6.1	10.7	7.2	0.6	0.8	0.7	173	234	199	—	—	—	—	—	—
	307.15 (34.0)	R	R	R	R	34.6	36.3	53.0	—	—	—	4.7	9.2	4.7	0.3	0.8	0.5	179	170	164	—	—	—	—	—	—
	307.15 (34.0)	L	L	L	L	22.4	43.0	29.4	—	—	—	9.8	15.7	10.5	1.5	0.5	1.4	192	244	194	—	—	—	—	—	—
LMP	SN	—	L	—	—	—	—	—	0.3	0.8	—	—	—	—	—	—	—	—	—	—	5	17	—	—	33.4 (R>L)	38.0 (R>L)	—
	308.65 (35.5)	R	R	R	—	25.0	18.4	—	—	—	—	6.1	5.9	—	1.0	1.2	—	265	189	—	—	—	—	—	—	—
	308.65 (35.5)	L	L	L	—	41.6	35.2	—	—	—	—	2.2	2.5	—	0.6	0.8	—	148	134	—	—	—	—	—	—	—
	307.15 (34.0)	R	R	R	—	17.2	19.0	—	—	—	—	12.3	11.5	—	1.5	1.9	—	262	203	—	—	—	—	—	—	—
	307.15 (34.0)	L	L	L	—	24.8	22.2	—	—	—	—	7.0	5.3	—	1.5	0.8	—	159	188	—	—	—	—	—	—	—
CMP	SN	—	R	—	—	—	—	—	2.0	2.1	0	—	—	—	—	—	—	—	—	—	12	7	0	—	33.2 (L>R)	6.0 (L>R)	6.6 (R>L)
	308.65 (35.5)	R	R	R	R	43.5	78.2	72.9	—	—	—	2.1	2.8	3.5	0.4	0.7	0.3	149	130	122	—	—	—	—	—	—
	308.65 (35.5)	L	L	L	L	42.0	66.0	38.9	—	—	—	6.9	5.9	5.1	0.8	1.0	0.4	192	114	129	—	—	—	—	—	—
	307.15 (34.0)	R	R	R	R	30.2	40.0	67.9	—	—	—	8.6	9.0	11.0	0.6	0.8	1.3	186	215	110	—	—	—	—	—	—
	307.15 (34.0)	L	L	L	R	31.2	55.9	69.0	—	—	—	14.4	7.4	7.6	1.0	0.7	0.8	177	201	130	—	—	—	—	—	—

*R = Right; L = Left.

**Spontaneous nystagmus.

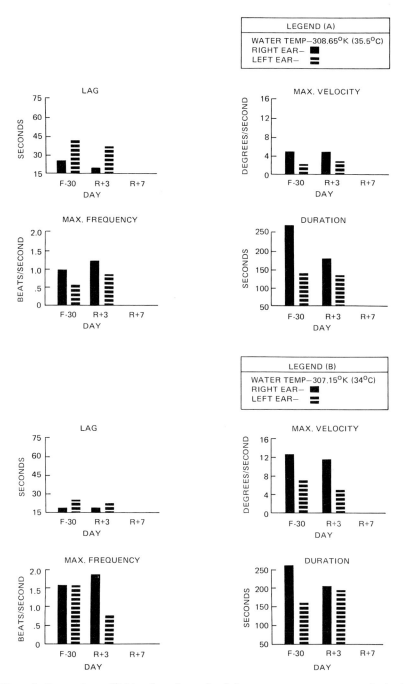

Figure 2. Pre- and postflight values for each of four nystagmus parameters obtained from the Apollo 16 LMP. Responses to irrigation with water temperatures of 308.65°K and 307.15°K are shown in (A) and (B) respectively.

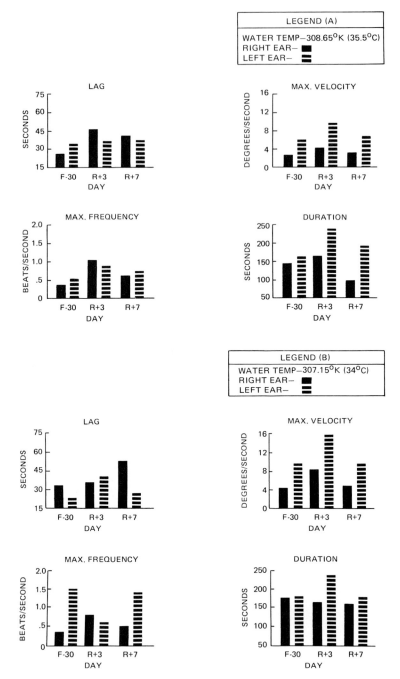

Figure 3. Pre- and postflight values for each of four nystagmus parameters obtained from the Apollo 16 CDR. Responses to irrigation with water temperatures of 308.65°K and 307.15°K are shown in (A) and (B) respectively.

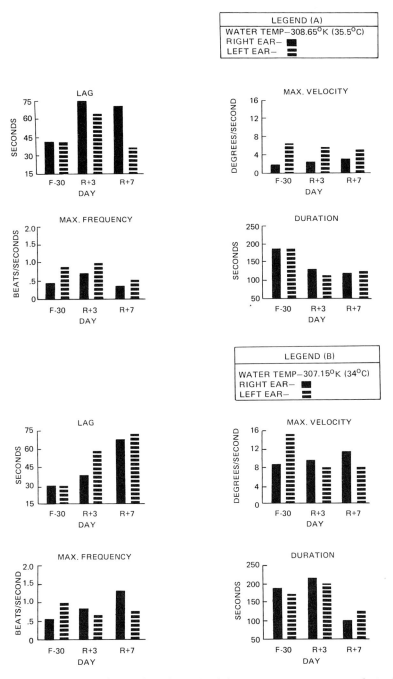

Figure 4. Pre- and postflight values for each of four nystagmus parameters obtained from the Apollo 16 CMP. Responses to irrigation with water temperatures of 308.65°K and 307.15°K are shown in (A) and (B) respectively.

later, the CDR's nystagmic responses had essentially returned to preflight values. Figure 4 indicates that, although a few parameters were elevated at R + 3 compared to F − 30 and R + 7, the data for the CMP are scattered and no overall trends are apparent. Left/right asymmetry, which is pronounced in the first two crewmen, is not well defined in this individual.

Although no provocative tests were administered, a motion experience questionnaire completed before flight by each crewman indicated that all had low susceptibility to motion sickness under one-g conditions. As stated previously, none of the Apollo 16 crewmen reported experiencing any symptoms of motion sickness during the flight.

Discussion and Implications

Apollo 16 Special Study

In evaluating the results of the Apollo 16 special study, the type of tests that were used and the manner in which they were performed should be considered. Postural equilibrium with eyes open served as a control condition for the eyes-closed portion of the test. Whereas none of the crewmen at any time showed appreciable change in postural stability with eyes open, a performance change was noted in two crewmen (CDR and CMP) when they were deprived of visual cues, and were required to balance solely on the basis of vestibular and proprioceptive sensory cues. This finding suggests that subtle alterations in these nonvisual sensory modalities were present at R + 3. The fact that the eyes-open scores did not change suggests that visual cues compensated for the relative decrease in performance observed in the eyes-closed task. This finding is not unusual. When minor changes occur in the vestibular system, they often can be overridden by vision, which normally dominates human spatial orientation (Howard & Templeton, 1966). It can reasonably be assumed that the relative improvement seen in these two individuals at R + 7 represented a return to normal of the sensory mechanisms involved.

It is also recognized that the postural stability test employed in this study is primarily a behavioral task and, as such, is subject to learning effects. Examination of the data indicates that a slight amount of learning may have occurred. The only clear evidence, however, is in the case of the CDR on the eyes-open portion of the test. Even if a learning effect was present, it could only have biased the postflight performance in a positive direction, and it is clear that a decline in eyes-closed performance occurred in two of the crewmen at R + 3. The significant improvement in eyes-closed postural stability observed in these two crewmen at R + 7 undoubtedly is more representative of a return to normal function of the sensory systems involved than of a simple learning effect.

An alert mental state is conducive to the elicitation of nystagmus (Guedry, 1965). Apparently as a result of an understandable emotional letdown following their mission, the crewmen exhibited some difficulty in maintaining an alert mental state during the caloric test at R + 3. This condition should have tended to suppress nystagmus; however, the CDR did show a very clear elevation in nystagmic activity at R + 3, indicative of a labyrinthine hypersensitivity. The somewhat erratic nystagmic activity observed in the CMP is also suggestive of unstable postflight vestibular function.

The finding of both decreased postural stability and increased nystagmic activity in the same two crewmen at R + 3 corresponds well to a study reported previously by

Fregly and Graybiel (1970). Using procedures very similar to those employed in this study, these investigators found a high positive correlation between tests of ataxia and caloric irrigation. The majority of their subjects who performed poorly on the ataxia tests, particularly with eyes closed, also yielded abnormal responses to caloric stimulation.

On the basis of the data, a tentative conclusion is that the postflight responses observed in two of the Apollo 16 crewmen reflected changes in vestibular function brought about by exposure to the conditions encountered during their mission. Because of the limitations inherent in this study, it is not possible to generalize from these data or to identify causal factors with any degree of certainty. Although lack of a gravitational stimulus was probably the most important environmental factor, other physiological stressful events such as launch, entry, and recovery activities may have contributed to the observed changes.

Overall Assessment of Apollo Series

The lack of quantitative preflight, inflight, and postflight vestibular data on individual crewmen renders a valid assessment of the Apollo findings difficult. However, certain tentative conclusions can be made:

1. Increased mobility, and thus increased head movements as afforded by the larger volume of the Apollo CM/LM, resulted in a higher incidence of vestibular disturbances in the Apollo Program than in previous programs.

2. In most cases in which symptoms did occur, they were mild to moderate and could be controlled by limiting head movements the first few days in flight.

3. Adaptation of the vestibular receptors to the weightless environment apparently occurred within the first several days of flight for most individuals. However, on the basis of these Apollo data alone, one can only speculate whether or not adaptive processes will lead to complications of a different nature during long duration missions.

4. Extravehicular activity in one-sixth g on the lunar surface resulted in no disorientation or vestibular disturbances. Apparently, one-sixth g is an adequate stimulus for the otolith organs to provide sensory information regarding gravitational upright and, hence, maintenance of posture.

5. With one important exception on the Apollo 15 mission, no crewmen experienced pronounced vestibular disturbances after returning from space flight. This finding suggests that adaptive processes that occur during weightless space flight missions of up to two weeks in duration do not render the vestibular system significantly hyposensitive or hypersensitive following sudden return to a one-g environment. Again, on the basis of these data alone, one can only speculate whether or not this condition will be true following very long exposure to zero g.

6. Whether or not an individual is likely to develop inflight vestibular problems cannot be predicted reliably from his previous history of motion sickness. However, astronauts making their first space flight appear to be slightly more susceptible to the development of inflight symptoms than are experienced astronauts.

The results of followup studies on two individuals who demonstrated the most significant inflight and postflight vestibular problems have already been discussed. However, further comment about one of these cases is warranted.

The severe motion sickness of the LMP during the Apollo 9 flight, and the subsequent negative findings during laboratory tests, underscore a very important problem in understanding vestibular function in weightlessness. Parabolic flight research has shown that it is very difficult to predict an individual's vestibular responses in zero g on the basis of his responses in one g. An individual may have normal vestibular responses on the ground and show markedly greater or lesser susceptibility to vestibular stimulation in weightlessness (Miller et al., 1969). The Apollo 9 LMP may well be one of these unique individuals who become more sensitive.

One of the most obvious implications of the Apollo flight crew vestibular evaluation is a need for more inflight as well as preflight and postflight vestibular information on the astronaut population. Only by examining with quantitative methods the men who actually fly in space can a thorough understanding of the effects of weightless space flight on vestibular function be attained. Without such information, reliably predicting possible vestibular problems for individual crewmen will be difficult. One positive step toward achieving this desired goal will be available through the Skylab human vestibular function experiment.

References

Berry, Charles A.; and Homick, Jerry L.: Findings on American Astronauts Bearing on the Issue of Artificial Gravity for Future Manned Space Vehicles. Aerospace Med., vol. 44, no. 2, Feb. 1973, pp. 163-168.

Fregly, A.R.; and Graybiel, A.: Labyrinthine Defects as Shown by Ataxia and Caloric Tests. Acta Oto-Laryngol., Stockholm, vol. 69, Mar. 1970, pp. 216-222.

Graybiel, A.; et al.: Vestibular Experiments in Gemini Flights V and VIII. Aerospace Med., vol. 38, no. 4, Apr. 1967, pp. 360-370.

Graybiel, A.; and Fregly, A.R.: A New Quantitative Ataxia Test Battery. Acta Oto-Laryngol., Stockholm, vol. 61, Apr. 1966, pp. 292-312.

Guedry, F.E., Jr.: Psychophysiological Studies of Vestibular Function. Contributions to Sensory Physiology. Vol. I. Academic Press, 1965.

Howard, I.P.; and Templeton, W.B.: Human Spatial Orientation. John Wiley and Sons, 1966.

Miller, E.G.; Graybiel, A.; Kellogg, R.S.; and O'Donnel, R.D.: Motion Sickness Susceptibility Under Weightless and Hypergravity Conditions Generated by Parabolic Flight. Aerospace Med., vol. 40, no. 8, Aug. 1969, pp. 862-868.

National Aeronautics and Space Administration: Apollo 9 Mission Report. MSC-PA-R-69-2. Prepared by Mission Evaluation Team, Manned Spacecraft Center, Houston, Texas, May 1969.

Inflight Experiments

Travel outside Earth's atmosphere can expose a spacecraft and its occupants to potentially dangerous regions of radiation. Four experiments flown aboard later Apollo missions were designed to assess the degree to which exposure to cosmic ray particle radiation might present a hazard to astronauts. Interest centered around high-energy galactic cosmic radiation (HZE particles). In the single experiment in which man was the experimental animal, attempts were made to relate reports of light flashes "seen" by astronauts to HZE events. Other experiments studied the effects of this type of radiation on plant and animal tissue.

CHAPTER 1

BIOSTACK—A STUDY OF THE BIOLOGICAL EFFECTS
OF HZE GALACTIC COSMIC RADIATION

by

Professor Horst Bücker

University of Frankfurt, Federal Republic of Germany

Introduction

The high atomic number—high energy particle component (HZE particles) of galactic cosmic radiation was discovered in 1948 and radiobiologists soon became concerned as to the effect this new type of ionizing radiation might have upon living systems exposed to it. Soon after discovery of the HZE particles, Tobias in 1952 predicted that a visual light flash sensation could be experienced by individuals exposed to these particles. There followed direct experimental evidence of the character and effectiveness of HZE particles. Chase (1954) describes graying of hair in balloon-borne black mice; Eugster (1955) demonstrated cellular death by single hits of heavy ions on *Artemia Salina* eggs; and similar effects were reported by Brustad (1961) on maize embryos. Brain injury studies were attempted by Yagoda and co-workers (1963) and by Haymaker and co-workers (1970) in balloon-borne mice and monkeys, respectively.

Very high local concentration of absorbed energy produced by an HZE particle can cause serious biological effects upon an organism since complete cells can be damaged or destroyed. The ultimate consequence of such damage is dependent upon the organism's ability to repair or replace the affected cell. The destruction of cells in the central nervous system is of serious concern since these cells cannot regenerate.

Although the potential hazards to living systems from the heavy nucleii component of galactic cosmic radiation was recognized, very little active research was conducted until the crews of Apollo 11 and subsequent Apollo missions reported experiencing a visual light flash phenomenon. The primary reason for the inactivity in this field was an inability to generate particles with comparable charge and energy with existing accelerators. The light flashes experienced by the astronauts provided an increased impetus for radiobiological experimentation by direct exposure to the HZE particles in space. Exposure to HZE particles during a spaceflight mission offers several unique advantages, principally, exposure to the primary spectra modified only by the interactions in the relatively lightly shielded space vehicle. Balloon-borne exposures were

343

limited to a spectrum significantly modified by the shielding of the remaining atmosphere and by the geomagnetic field.

The Biostack experiment was designed to study the effect of individual heavy nucleii of the cosmic radiation environment upon biological systems during actual space flight. Since there were no means by which the Biostack experiment could be insulated from other spaceflight factors, such as null gravity, the experiment must be considered one of studying the combined effects of cosmic radiation and other spaceflight factors.

The objectives of the Biostack experiments were to study, in a direct manner, the biological effects of individual heavy nucleii with high energy loss (HZE); to obtain as much information as possible on the mechanisms of biological damage by HZE particles; to measure the charge and energy spectra of cosmic radiation within the Apollo Command Module; and to provide data to allow an estimate of the hazard to man from space radiation.

It was of great importance to place this experiment on the last two Apollo flights, since both were lunar missions. Apollo 16 and 17 would leave the Earth's magnetic field and enter a region of space where the galactic cosmic ray flux was modulated only by the solar magnetic field. Very little is known concerning the radiation environment outside the geomagnetic field, and HZE particles are of special interest. At the time of Apollo 16 HZE particles were not available on Earth, and only a limited capability to generate them has been achieved since the completion of the Apollo lunar missions.

Accomplishment of these objectives of the Biostack experiment required considerable ingenuity. The experiment design had to meet several criteria in order to take advantage of the two remaining flight opportunities. The design had to be simple enough to be implemented and qualified for spaceflight in a relative short time. The package had to be compact, lightweight, and require minimal changes in the spacecraft to enable stowage. Most importantly, the experiment design could not draw power from the spacecraft or impact the astronauts' activities.

Procedures

The objectives of the experiment and the constraints imposed upon it were met by a design that allowed the study of the combined action of individual heavy nucleii of cosmic radiation and spaceflight factors in biological systems in a state of rest. Detailed information on the particle incidence, energy loss, and spectra were essential information to be obtained. The Biostack experiment package contained a series of monolayers of selected biological objects fixed in position and interleaved with physical track detectors (figure 1). This arrangement permitted evaluation of individual tracks, and allowed identification of each penetrating particle and determination of its relationship to possible effects on biological matter in its path.

The execution of the experiment had two major thrusts; identification and quantitation of the influence of HZE particles on biological systems at the molecular, cellular and organismic levels; and the localization of individual HZE particles and the quantitation of the physical and dosimetric parameters of the particles.

A very sophisticated method must be used to localize precisely the trajectory of a particle relative to the biological objects and to correlate the physical data of the particle relative to the observed biological effects along its path. Special methods were developed for this purpose (Bücker et al., 1973) in the Biostack experiment. Biological specimens and physical track detectors were selected to achieve the optimum return of information.

The biological systems had to meet the following criteria: (1) the organisms had to survive the period of experimental exposure in the dormant state and yet be viable for the subsequent phases of the experiment; (2) they had to comprise a variety of species to allow evaluation of radiation effects at different levels of biological organization; (3) they had to vary in radiation sensitivity (based on previous radiobiological experimentation with X-ray and other radiations); and (4) based again on previous work, be representative of genetic or somatic radiation damage mechanisms. The biological organisms investigated in the experiment and the responsible investigators are shown in table 1. The radiation effects subsequently studied were changes in cellular and organismic growth, damage to cellular components and induction of mutations leading to genetic changes of biological significance.

Figure 1. The Biostack experiment package: left, external view of container;
right, stack of biological objects in monolayers and physical detectors.

Incident radiation was measured by several different track detectors and an integrating lithium fluoride thermoluminescence dosimeter. The detectors and responsible investigators are listed in table 2. These detectors complemented one another in their recording characteristics of HZE-particles as well as in the localization of the biological region hit.

Special methods were developed for optimal localizing of the point of penetration in the biological layer. The accuracy in determining this penetration point reached $\pm 1\ \mu$m. Therefore, in the case of the animal eggs and seeds, which all exceeded $50\ \mu$m in diameter, even the hit region inside the biological organisms could be detected. For these objects, a sufficiently high accuracy was obtained with all three types of detectors. In the case of the bacterial spores, however, which were $1.5\ \mu$m in diameter, several spores usually covered the determined target area, each with a different probability of sustaining a hit.

Table 1

Biological Experiments in the Biostack

Biological System		Investigator	Organization
Monocellular	Spores of Bacillus subtilis	G. Horneck	University of Frankfurt, Germany
	Cysts of Colpoda cucullus	H. Planel, J. P. Soleilhavoup	University of Toulouse, France
Plant	Seeds of Arabidopsis thaliana	E. Reinholz	MPI für Biophysik Frankfurt, Germany
	Radiculae of Vicia faba	W. Scheuermann	T. University of Hannover, Germany
Animal	Eggs of Artemia salina	W. Rüther, E. H. Graul H. Planel, J. P. Soleilhavoup	University of Marburg, Germany University of Toulouse, France
	Eggs of Tribolium castaneum Eggs of Carausius Morosus	W. Rüther	University of Marburg, Germany

For determination of the target area inside the spore layer, plastic detectors of cellulose nitrate (CN) were used. The CN sheet was in fixed contact with the biological layer. This contact was maintained during flight, during postflight etching and track measurements, and during growth studies. Protection of the biological layer against the toxic etching solution resulted in only one etch cone on the side of the CN sheet which was not covered with biological specimens. The trajectory of an HZE particle in the biological layer had to be extrapolated from this etch cone. With silver chloride (AgCl) crystals, on the other hand, the biological layer was not exposed to toxic agents during the development of the particle track images. The nuclear emulsion, attached to some of the biological layers, received the pattern of biological objects by weak optical illumination, during postflight disassembly. The hit biological objects were identified directly from the developed emulsion, which showed the HZE particle track together with faint images of the biological objects and a coordinate grid. Beside identification of the biological area hit, evaluation of the track detectors resulted in extensive information on the flux and angular incidence of the cosmic ray particles, on their absorption by the wall of the spacecraft and the Biostack material, and on the spectral distribution of their charge, energy, and energy loss.

The influence of the factors attendant to space flight (high gravity vectors, null gravity, vibration, and temperature) were assessed by detailed controls made in parallel with the Biostack experiment. For each space flight experiment, four identical Biostacks were built. In each case, three units were delivered to NASA: one prime flight unit, one backup, in case of damage to the prime flight unit, and one ground control to remain in Houston. One laboratory control unit was kept in Frankfurt. Since the primary flight unit was flown in both missions and a backup unit served as ground control, the two

Table 2

Radiation Detectors in the Biostack Experiment

Cosmic Radiation Component	Detector	Range of Information on Z and LET	Threshold	Tissue Equivalence	Background Noise	Investigators	Organization
Ions	Nuclear Emulsion K2, K5 Plastics	Very broad	No	No	High	R. Kaiser, J. P. Massué, R. Pfohl	LPC — CRN Strasbourg, France
	Cellulose Nitrate, Poly- carbonate	Medium	Yes	Yes	Low	W. Enge, O. C. Allkofer, K. Bartholomä, R. Beaujean, W. Heinrich, K. Fukui	University of Kiel, Germany
	AgCl-Crystals Illuminated	Broad	Yes	No	Medium to Low	E. V. Benton	University of San Francisco
γ-Rays, X-Rays, Protons	LiF Thermo- luminescence Dosimeter	Integrating Dosimeter				E. Schopper, G. Henig, J. U. Schott	University of Frankfurt, Germany
						H. Francois, G. Portal	CEA, Paris, France

remaining units were available for further investigation. For Biostack I (Apollo 16), a balloon flight at Fort Churchill, Canada, was conducted with one of the remaining units, while the other served as the relevant control. For Biostack II (Apollo 17), one of the remaining units was irradiated at the University of California at Berkeley at the Bevatron with carbon and oxygen ions. The other was subjected to vibration, acceleration, and shock at the Centre National d'Etudes Spatiales (CNES) in Toulouse, France.

Results

The Biostack I experiment was launched with Apollo 16 on April 16, 1972. Splashdown into the Pacific was on April 28. The total mission time was 266 hours. The temperature in the Command Module during the mission ranged between 290°K and 296°K (17°C and 23°C) and the limits of 287°K and 301°K (14°C and 28°C) were never exceeded. The flight data of the Apollo 17 mission, with which the Biostack II was flown, were quite similar to those of Apollo 16. The total mission time of Apollo 17 was 304 hours. In both missions, the Biostack experiment was placed in the R-1 compartment of the Apollo Command Module. Its position relative to the wall of Command Module is shown in figure 2.

The approximate absorption in the four different layers of the wall of the Command Module was about 2.4 gm/cm^2. The bottom of the Biostack container was aluminum 3.00 mm thick with absorption 0.84 gm/cm^2. Since the software of the Biostack itself absorbed radiation, there was a decrease of radiation from outside to inside. Figure 3 shows some data of the physical evaluation of Biostack I as a function of absorption. From this it is evident that the flux of efficient HZE particles behind an absorption screen of 20 gm/cm^2 is still half of the total flux encountered in the mission of Apollo 16. This datum demonstrates the difficulty of shielding the crew of a space vehicle against the HZE particles encountered in deep space.

In each Biostack experiment, several thousand biological objects were hit by an HZE particle. Their response to an HZE particle stopping within the object (an ender) or passing through was studied in detail. The result was a broad spectrum of HZE-particle induced effects in biological matter. This spectrum of biological effects can be categorized as processes (1) insensitive to a hit; (2) moderately sensitive to a hit; and (3) highly sensitive to a hit by an HZE particle.

Insensitive Processes

In bacterial spores and plant seeds, germination was found to be highly resistant to an HZE particle hit. During germination, the bacterial spores, *Bacillus subtilis*, initially phase bright, became dark. This was probably the result of a change in the refractive index, caused by excretion of dry matter, slight swelling, and redistribution of water within the spore. This process has proved to be highly radiation resistant. Irradiation with X-rays of doses approximately 400 krad, which reduced the surviving fraction of colony formers to about 10^{-4}, did not influence the germination process. Much higher doses, approximately 2000 krad are necessary to induce "pseudogermination," which is correlated with an increased permeability of the cell wall. The germinating fraction of the spores hit was more than 90 percent in the Biostack I experiment and reached nearly 100 percent in the

Biostack II experiment. This fraction did not differ significantly from that of the controls, indicating a high resistance to HZE-particle bombardment. Pseudogermination was not observed on the spores hit. Likewise, the *Arabidopsis thaliana* seeds hit germinated with the same frequency and rate as the controls.

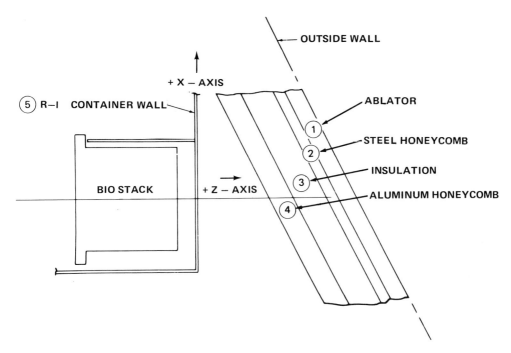

Figure 2. Schematic of stowage and effective shielding
of the Biostack experiments in the Apollo Command Module.

① ablator, 1.78 cm thick		absorption 0.914 gm/cm^2
② steel honeycomb, 0.2 mm thick		absorption 0.319 gm/cm^2
③ insulation, 3.175 cm thick		absorption 0.305 gm/cm^2
④ aluminum honeycomb, 0.5 mm thick		absorption 0.139 gm/cm^2
⑤ wall of R1 container, assumed as aluminum, 2.5 mm thick		absorption 0.692 gm/cm^2
	Total	absorption 2.369 gm/cm^2

The growth of *Vicia faba radiculae* also did not differ significantly from that of the controls. It is likely that the surrounding intact cells replaced the destroyed cells, if any destruction occurred. Even cytological investigations dealing with achromasia of the nuclear material or repairability of damages in the nuclear DNA did not reveal any remarkable influence of HZE particles.

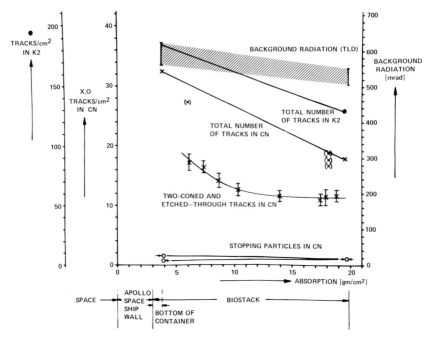

Figure 3. Data from physical detectors in Biostack I,
Apollo 16, as a function of absorption.

Moderately Sensitive Processes

The developmental stages, following the germination process, proved to be more sensitive to a hit of an HZE particle. During spore outgrowth, the spore cases rupture and the embryo vegetative cell emerges, to develop into the fully grown vegetative cell. A reduction was noted in the outgrowth of the *Bacillus subtilis* spores hit in Biostack I. After radiation with X-rays, the outgrowing fraction decreased with irradiation dose. A dose of 350 krad produced a surviving fraction of 37 percent of outgrowing cells. Only 45 percent of the spores hit were able to grow out compared to a 72 percent outgrowth of the flight control. The spores that did not grow out simultaneously with the flight control never resumed their development during incubation.

The frequency of multicaulous *Arabidopsis thaliana* plants grown from hit seeds was remarkably increased. This anomaly was not observed in the ground controls and was very rarely observed in the flight controls. Thus it is assumed that the multicaulous forms were developed from seeds, in which cells of the vegetative cone had been destroyed by a penetrating HZE particle.

Only 55 percent of the *Artemia salina* eggs hit were able to pass the first developmental stage, the emergence. During this process, the egg shell cracks open and the nauplius larva emerges, still enclosed in the egg membrane. In most of the eggs hit, no development at all was detected. Clearing the egg shell with antiformin revealed an undeveloped gastrula.

Highly Sensitive Processes

The animal eggs were most sensitive to HZE-particle hits. Whereas irradiation of *Artemia salina* eggs with gamma-rays, neutrons, electrons, and even helium ions (Z=2) resulted in a sigmoidal dose effect curve regarding development to a swimming larva, irradiation with oxygen ions of 160 MeV resulted in a exponential curve. It is assumed that the passage of one single HZE particle may damage a cellular area large enough to disturb embryogenesis. Only ten percent of the *Artemia salina* eggs hit developed to a swimming larvae, compared to 90 percent of the ground controls and 45 percent of the non-hit flight controls. The larvae derived from hit eggs had a high mortality. Only a few reached maturity, and none was completely normal in further growth and behavior. They never reached the normal 12-mm length and pair mating was reached retardedly. Time until deposition of eggs took twice as long as in the case of ground controls. The number of broods varied from none to two and the number of descendants in the F1 generation was reduced. Malformations increased by a factor of ten. Shortened extremities or abnormal thorax or abdomen were most frequently noted.

These results show that HZE-particle induced damage in cells of the encysted blastula may be manifest in the gastrula stage, or even in later steps of development of the larva or the adult. This indicates an inability of intact cells to replace the function of destroyed cells.

Similar effects were found during development of hit *Tribolium castaneum* eggs. Hatching frequency was significantly lowered, and, during the first two days after hatching, a high mortality was observed. The frequency of abnormalities was increased from 2.5 percent in controls to 48 percent in the experimental organisms. The most frequent malformations were curved abdomina, fused segments of the abdomen or the antennae, and split or shortened elytra.

Likewise, the hatching of hit *Caurausius morosus* eggs was significantly reduced. Many of the larvae died during the first two weeks after hatching. Curved abdomina and fused segments or shortened legs were the main abnormalities observed in the descendants of the eggs hit. The frequency of malformations was increased from 1.5 to 23 percent.

Discussion

The physical characteristics of the HZE particles are important in regard to biological efficiency. The integral distribution function of the relative energy loss (REL) was obtained from analysis of the plastic detectors of Biostack I. The REL spectrum agrees satisfactorily with that obtained in the MEED experiment (Benton & Henke, 1973 and Section IV, Chapter 3 of this book), which was stowed within the Command Module for nearly the entire mission. However, the personal radiation detectors of the lunar surface crewmen recorded higher fluxes (Benton & Henke, 1972).

In the biological studies of Biostack, special attention was placed on the effects of HZE particles of very high energy. Therefore, it was agreed to restrict the studies of relative energy loss to hits above a threshold of $1.8 \text{ GeV/cm}^2\text{gm}$. For each particle that hit biological materials, the REL in the biological layer was determined. In cellulose nitrate detectors, the length of a single etch cone gave the REL of the particle at that point in its path. In hit spores, REL values of 3.1 GeV/cm^{2}gm were determined.

The charge of the HZE particle is another physical characteristic of interest. The charge of each particle that hit was estimated from the relation of the cone length L and the residual range R (figure 4). In the *Bacillus subtilis* spore hit evaluation, charges ranged from $Z \geqslant 12$ to $Z \geqslant 24$.

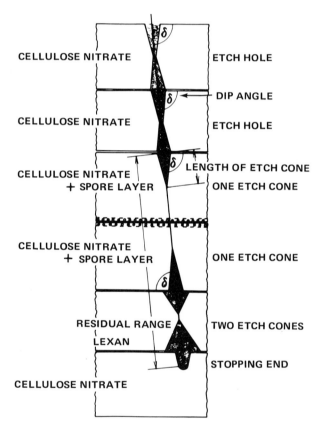

Figure 4. Schematic representation of track of a stopping HZE particle; from *Bacillus subtilis* unit.

All particles that reached the Biostack penetrated the 3 gm/cm^2 shielding of the spacecraft wall. A mean flux of approximately 0.1 particles/cm^2-hr of $Z \geqslant 4$ was found for Biostack I and II. The flux diminished remarkably from outside to the inside of the Biostack due to absorption of the Biostack material itself, approximately 16 gm/cm^2.

Space flight conditions complicated the radiobiological research of HZE-particle effects. Launch vibration, weightlessness, and ground exposure to cosmic background radiation were the principal factors acting on the biological material. Therefore, specimens flown but not hit were taken as flight controls, in addition to control groups.

Summary and Conclusions

The *Bacillus subtilis* spores were shown not to be influenced by the space flight environment. Germination and outgrowth of the flight controls agreed with that of the ground controls, also the rate of cellular elongation was not different. Likewise, there was no difference in the kinetics of germination of *Arabidopsis thaliana* flight control and ground control seeds. Slight damage, however, was observed in the *Artemia* flight control eggs. The percentage of emergence and hatching was reduced in comparison with the ground controls. Those flight control individuals, those able to hatch, afterwards developed completely in accordance with the ground controls. This slight damage of the flight controls has been assumed to be caused either by vibrational stress or by cosmic background radiation.

The concept of the Biostack experiment made it possible for the first time to examine the relationship between cosmic ray HZE particles and their biological effects. Emphasis should be placed on the fact that the dose causing the biological effects during the Apollo space flights was less than 35 millirem. This dose is much lower than the yearly permissible dose for man on Earth, according to the recommendations of the International Commission on Radiation Protection. At the present time, the question concerning the significance of human HZE-particle exposures in long-duration space flights cannot be answered satisfactorily. Further biophysical experiments will be necessary to establish the upper limit of HZE-particle fluence that can be tolerated inside spacecraft on long-duration missions.

The data of the Biostack I and II experiments confirm the assumption that HZE particle-induced damage might become manifest if a significant number of nonreplaceable cells are destroyed. In manned space flight, the prime candidate in this connection is the central nervous system, which consists of highly differentiated nonreplaceable cells. The question arises as to how many cells might be destroyed by each hit compared to the number of cells that form a functional unit. It is likely that a large number of HZE-particle hits to the same area of the brain would be required to destroy that particular function and that the HZE-particle radiation environment poses no major threat to manned space activities that may be undertaken in the foreseeable future.

References

Benton, E.V.; and Henke, R.P.: The High Energy Multicharged Particle Exposure of the Microbial Ecology Evaluation Device Onboard Apollo 16 Spacecraft. In, Proceedings of the Microbial Response to Space Environment Symposium, G.R. Taylor, ed. NASA TM X-58103, 1973, pp. 179-189.

Benton, E.V.; and Henke, R.P.: Heavy Cosmic Ray Exposure of Apollo 16 Astronauts. USF-TR-72-20, 1972.

Brustad, T.: Molecular and Cellular Effects of Fast Charge Particles. Radiation Research, vol. 15, 1961, p. 139.

Bücker, H.; et al.: Life Sciences and Space Research XI. In, Proceedings of the 16th Plenary Meeting of COSPAR (Konstanz, Germany), May 23 - June 6, 1973.

Chase, H.B.: Cutaneous Effects of Primary Cosmic Radiation. Journal of Aviation Medicine, vol. 25, 1954, p. 388.

Eugster, J.: Weltraumstrahlung. Bern, Switzerland: Medizinsuhen Verlag Hans Huber, 1955.

Haymaker, W.; Bailey, O.T.; Benton, E.V.; Vogel, F.S.; and Zeman, W., in collaboration with others: Brain Study in Balloon-Borne Monkeys Exposed to Cosmic Rays. Aerospace Medicine, vol. 41, 1970, p. 989.

Tobias, C.A.: Radiation Hazards in High Altitude Aviation. Journal of Aviation Medicine, vol. 23, 1952, p. 345.

Yagoda, H.; et al.: Brain Studies of Mice Exposed to Cosmic Rays in the Stratosphere and Report of Nuclear Emulsion Monitoring in Four Balloon Flights from Bemidji, Minnesota, July - August 1960. Military Medicine, vol. 28, 1963, p. 655.

CHAPTER 2
APOLLO LIGHT FLASH INVESTIGATIONS

by

W. Zachary Osborne, Ph.D.
Lawrence S. Pinsky, Ph.D.

University of Houston
Houston, Texas

J. Vernon Bailey

Lyndon B. Johnson Space Center

Introduction

Crewmembers of the Apollo 11 mission were the first astronauts to describe an unusual visual phenomenon associated with space flight. During transearth coast, both the Commander and the Lunar Module Pilot reported seeing faint spots or flashes of light when the cabin was dark and they had become dark-adapted. It is believed that these light flashes result from high energy, heavy cosmic rays penetrating the Command Module structure and the crewmembers' eyes. These particles are thought to be capable of producing visual sensations through interaction with the retina, either by direct deposition of ionization energy in the retina or through creation of visible light via the Cerenkov effect.

Crewmembers of Apollo 12 and 13 were questioned concerning this phenomenon during postmission debriefings. All reported the ability to "see" the flashes with relative ease when the spacecraft was dark with their eyes either open or shut. The Apollo 12 Commander stated that "There were big bright ones all over," and added that he had not seen anything similar during his two Earth-orbital Gemini missions. The Commander of the Apollo 13 mission also observed these flashes but could not remember seeing them during his earlier Apollo 8 mission.

The fact that the light flashes could be seen with eyes either open or closed suggests that the flash effect is produced by cosmic radiation penetrating the optical nervous system at some point. The fact that dark adaptation is necessary reinforces the view that the phenomenon is connected with the retina rather than with a direct stimulation of the optic nerve, since the biochemical changes associated with dark adaptation are localized in the retinal tissue.

Light Flash Observation Periods

The debriefing reports of crewmembers on the Apollo 11, 12, and 13 missions led to the establishment of dedicated observing sessions on all subsequent Apollo flights. Three separate one-hour sessions were programmed for Apollo 15 and two one-hour sessions for Apollo 16 and 17. Simple blindfolds, designed to avoid corneal pressure, were used to obtain and maintain a state of complete dark adaptation during the observing session. Crewmembers' comments and descriptions of each event were radioed to tracking stations and simultaneously recorded on tape in the spacecraft.

The flashes were generally described as white or colorless. The only exception was the report by the Apollo 14 Lunar Module Pilot who described a flash as "blue with a white cast, like a blue diamond." Three basic types of flashes were reported. The most prevalent was the "spot" or "starlike" flash, which also has been referred to as a "super nova." Sixty-six percent of the flashes were of this variety, described by the Apollo 15 Commander as resembling a photographic flashbulb that has been flashed across a dark arena, several hundred feet from the observer. The Apollo 14 LMP described the flash as being less clear than he had anticipated. "There still seemed to be at least two flashes, maybe a bright flash followed an instant later by a more subdued flash, or perhaps a halo-like effect - there does not seem to be a set pattern in each case. Sometimes it is a very clear single flash; at other times it seems to be followed by a halo. Sometimes it seems followed by an adjacent flash." On occasion, stars were reported in pairs, either both in the same eye or one star in each eye.

The type of flash described as a "streak" was the second most abundant, occurring about 25 percent of the time. Some streaks were described as sharp lines, while others appeared to be diffuse. Still others were reported as dashed lines, with the most common version consisting of two principal segments with a gap in the middle. All streaks had a sense of movement, appearing to be "going from left to right" or "coming straight at me." It has been hypothesized that these streaks were caused by particles with trajectories approximately tangent to the retina, and their apparent motion was due to either eye movement or the shape of the streak.

The final type of flash was referred to as a "cloud" and occurred in eight percent of the cases. Clouds were flashes with no discernible shape and always appeared in the peripheral visual field. The Apollo 14 Command Module Pilot described the clouds as resembling a lightning discharge when viewed from behind terrestrial clouds in the distance. Some of the cloud flashes were so large as to appear to fill the entire periphery, while leaving the central visual field dark.

The number of events of each type seen by each observer in individual one-hour sessions is shown in table 1. This table also presents the elapsed time in minutes from the start of dark adaptation to the observation of the first event for sessions where that time is known. This elapsed time, that is until the first flash was seen, averages to 19.3 minutes, compared with an average event rate after dark adaptation of one event every 2.9 minutes.

Analyses of the elapsed time between events for a particular observer, and between events for any observer, both indicate that the events seen during each one-hour session were randomly distributed in time. Further, there does not appear to be a significant preference for one eye or the other, either for a single event or for all events taken together.

Table 1

Summary of Light Flash Events Observed During Apollo Dedicated Sessions
(The tapes containing detailed descriptions of events observed
on the Apollo 15 translunar coast were lost during playback to the ground.)

Phase of Flight	Crewman	Length of Session (min)	Time to First Event (min)	Number of Events				
				Total	Streak	Star	Cloud	Mixture
Apollo 14								
TEC	CMP	47	29	12	2	8	1	1
	LMP	47	17	22	5	13	3	1
	CDR	47	18	14	3	8	1	2
Apollo 15								
TLC	CMP	60	10	22	—	—	—	—
	LMP	60	9	12	—	—	—	—
	CDR	60	10	25	—	—	—	—
LO	LMP	60	10	12	6	5	0	1
TEC	CMP	60	30	8	2	5	0	1
	LMP	60	26	9	3	5	0	1
	CDR	60	17	6	0	6	0	0
Apollo 16								
TLC	LMP	60	†	47	7	36	2	2
	CDR	60	†	22	6	14	1	1
TEC	CMP	60		0	0	0	0	0
	LMP	60	‡	21§	1‖	4‖	2‖	1‖
	CDR	60	21	8	1‖	0	0	0
Apollo 17								
TLC	CMP	60	15	17	5	10	1	1
	CDR	60*	39*	11	6	4	1	0
TEC	CMP	60						
	LMP	60						
	CDR	60						

*A high phosphene level was reported during the first half of the session. †The crew were already dark-adapted and seeing flashes when the time session began. ‡The first seven flashes were not reported in real time; the elapsed time to the first event is not available but is probably about 15 minutes. §The total includes those not reported in real time. ‖Complete event descriptions were not available.

LO	=	Lunar orbit	CDR	=	Commander
CMP	=	Command Module Pilot	TEC	=	Transearth coast
LMP	=	Lunar Module Pilot	TLC	=	Translunar coast

It can be noted in table 1 that no results are presented for the Command Module Pilot of the Apollo 16 mission. He was the only Apollo crewmember briefed to look for the phenomenon who failed to see it. He volunteered the information that he considers his night vision to be poor.

An interesting feature of the light flash phenomenon is shown in table 2. The data presented indicates the mean time between events after dark adaptation for each observer, and the average value for all observers for each session. Session averages were computed by weighting the individual values according to the corresponding dark-adapted observing times. It can be seen from the table that the average time between events was longer during transearth coast (TEC) (returning from the moon) observation periods than during translunar coast (TLC) sessions. TEC dark adaptation times (time to witness the first flash) also were considerably longer than those found during TLC sessions. In addition, most crewmembers commented that the flashes seemed not only less frequent during the TEC sessions but also much less brilliant. The most dramatic example of this difference occurred on Apollo 17, when all crewmen reported that no events were seen during the entire one-hour transearth coast session. During a similar translunar coast session, the two observing crewmen reported a total of 28 events.

Table 2

Mean Time Between Events After Dark Adaptation Times. No observing session was scheduled for the Apollo 14 translunar coast. No events were reported in the Apollo 17 transearth coast session. (See legend to Table 1 for abbreviations.)

Flight	Crewman	Translunar Coast Sessions		Transearth Coast Sessions	
		Mean Time Between Events (min)	Dark Adaptation Time (min)	Mean Time Between Events (min)	Dark Adaptation Time (min)
Apollo 14	CMP			1.64	29
	LMP			1.43	17
	CDR			2.23	18
	Average			1.71	21.3
Apollo 15	CMP	2.38	10	4.29	30
	LMP	4.64	9	4.25	26
	CDR	2.08	10	8.60	17
	Average	3.05	9.7	6.01	24.3
Apollo 16	LMP	1.28	–	2.50	–
	CDR	2.73	–	5.57	21
	Average	2.00	–	3.85	21.0
Apollo 17	CMP	2.81	15.0*	–	–
	CDR	2.10	–	–	–
	Average	2.59	15.0	–	–
All sessions combined		2.58	11.0†	2.91	22.6§

*Dark adaptation time available for the CMP only.   †Averaged over four observers.   § Averaged over seven observers.

A number of possible mechanisms were examined in an attempt to explain the decrease in flash events during TEC observing sessions. These included physical factors such as geomagnetic shielding effects from the Earth's magnetosheath tail, a relative difference in spacecraft shielding, and possible flux modulation due to solar activity. None of these mechanisms offered an adequate explanation. Crewmember variables such as fatigue or some visual impairment also were investigated. All crewmembers reported feeling well rested and alert for the TEC sessions and no basis was found to ascribe this phenomenon to a physiological change. It was suggested by the Apollo 16 Command Module Pilot that the extremely bright albedo light from the lunar surface as viewed from lunar orbit may have been sufficient to produce residual effects such as dark adaptation impairment for the TEC duration. This suggestion is currently being investigated independently. The anomaly remains as an apparently real effect for which no unique explanation has as yet been demonstrated.

Monte Carlo Simulations

A Monte Carlo simulation of the exposure of an astronaut to cosmic radiation during a mission was accomplished as a means of gaining additional insight into the light flash observations. The Monte Carlo calculation was done by tracing the fate of each of a large number of cosmic ray particles through the spacecraft-observer system to assess its effectiveness in causing a light flash. Physical variables used in this simulation included the charge, energy, and direction of motion of particles, as chosen from established cosmic ray charge and energy distributions and a random direction distribution. Also taken into account, as appropriate, were (1) solar modulation of the primary cosmic ray energy spectrum; (2) effects of the Earth's magnetic field, including specific dependence of cutoff rigidity upon particle momentum direction; and (3) shadowing of the primary cosmic rays by the Earth. Detailed models of spacecraft shielding presented to the cosmic ray beam also were included.

Physiological parameters used in the simulation were: (1) thickness of the sensitive region of the retina; (2) minimum projection of the sensitive region track segment on a plane tangent to the surface of the retina; and (3) minimum energy loss rate for the ionizing particles in the sensitive region. A water phantom was used as being a reasonable approximation of the geometry of the observer. Accumulated experience indicates that observer sensitivity to light flashes can vary by a factor of two; therefore it was not deemed necessary to incorporate the best available model of the human anatomy. Physiological parameters were adjusted, within boundaries dictated by light flash data obtained in accelerator experiments and by physical measurements of the retina, in order to achieve agreement between observed and predicted flash rates. This was done with and without the inclusion of Cerenkov radiation. Table 3 shows the values used for visual system parameters in the simulation and presents the predicted Monte Carlo flash rates.

The Monte Carlo calculations also resulted in predicted charge and energy spectra at the retina for particles believed to cause light flashes. The predicted charge spectrum is shown in table 4, which also includes the primary cosmic ray charge spectrum to facilitate comparisons. Inspection of the Apollo predictions shown in table 4 reveals that almost all of the Apollo light flashes probably were caused by particles with $Z \geqslant 12$, even though only approximately 25 percent of the $Z \geqslant 6$ primary cosmic rays have $Z \geqslant 12$. This can be understood by an inspection of table 5, which contains a summary of the predicted energy spectra for the effective particles. Only at very low energies (0 to 200 MeV/nucleon), that is near the end of their range, do members of the C and O group have an energy deposition rate large enough for them to cause light flashes.

Table 3

Monte Carlo Simulation Parameters
and Flash Rate Comparisons

Visual System Parameters	
Effective retina thickness	50 μm
Minimum projected track length inside retina with energy loss rate greater than minimum value	40 μm
Minimum energy loss rate 370 MeV cm^2/gm or 37 keV/μ in water	
Apollo Flash Rates	
Maximum observed rate	0.8/min
TLC average rate	0.4/min
Monte Carlo rate without Cerenkov	0.7/min
Monte Carlo rate with Cerenkov	1.0/min

Table 4

Predicted Relative Fluxes at the Retina
for Particles Believed to Cause Flash Response

Z	Primary Cosmic Radiation	Apollo	
		Monte Carlo No Cerenkov	Monte Carlo With Cerenkov
6– 8	.693	.150	.115
9	.025	.029	.022
10	.036	.036	.123
11	.043	.063	.134
12	.074	.100	.131
13–14	.043	.183	.140
15–21	.038	.226	.173
22–28	.047	.213	.163

Table 5

Predicted Relative Energy Spectra of Effective Particles
at the Retina for Apollo

Energy Interval MeV/Nucleon	Primary CR	Charge Interval							
		No Cerenkov Radiation				With Cerenkov Radiation			
		6-8	9-14	15-21	22-28	6-8	9-14	15-21	22-28
0- 200	.05	1.0	.27	.05	.07	1.0	.11	.05	.07
200- 400	.11		.53	.08	.08		.21	.08	.08
400- 600	.11		.20	.09	.08		.10	.10	.09
600-1000	.18			.19	.13		.14	.18	.13
>1000	.55			.59	.64		.44	.59	.63

Finally, the Monte Carlo calculations were used to predict the number of $Z \geqslant 6$ and $Z \geqslant 12$ particles which should have passed through an observer's eyes during the Apollo 17 mission. This simulation predicts that, during the 60 minutes of an Apollo 17 observing session, a total of approximately 640 $Z \geqslant 6$ primary cosmic rays (and spallation secondaries) would pass through the eyes, as would approximately 130 $Z \geqslant 12$ particles.

ALFMED Experiment

A system was developed for the Apollo 16 and 17 missions to obtain, for the first time, a direct physical record of incident cosmic ray particles which would allow correlation with crewmembers' reports of light flashes. The measurement system is known as the Apollo Light Flash Moving Emulsion Detector (ALFMED).

The ALFMED was an electromechanical helmet-like device that supported cosmic radiation-sensitive emulsions around the head of the test subject (figures 1 to 3). A direct physical record was provided of cosmic ray particles that passed through the emulsion plates and, in turn, through the head of the subject. The ALFMED contained two sets of glass plates coated on both sides with nuclear emulsion and supported in a protective framework. One set of plates was fixed in position within the headset and surrounded the front and sides of the head. A second similar set of plates was located exterior and parallel to the inner fixed plates and could be translated at a constant rate (10μ/sec) with respect to the fixed plates, thereby providing a time resolution for events to within one second. The total translation time available was 60 minutes, after which the moving plates could be returned to the original or reference orientation.

The postflight analysis of the ALFMED plates proceeded through the following steps:

1. *Location scan* – The fixed plate was placed on a special microscope stage containing the moving plate and positioned in the reference orientation (i.e., the relative orientation of the plates during stowage). The fixed plate was then scanned for tracks directed toward at least one eye, and the counterpart of each such track was sought in the moving plate. The absence of an aligned counterpart indicated that the track was a candidate (i.e., a track that originated while the plates were moving).

Figure 1. Exterior view of Apollo light flash moving emulsion detector (ALFMED)
with outer cover removed.

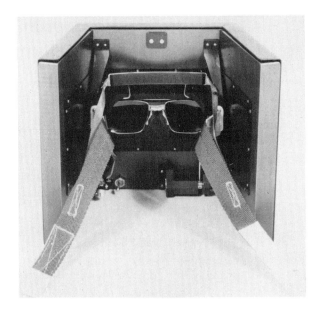

Figure 2. Interior view of ALFMED device.

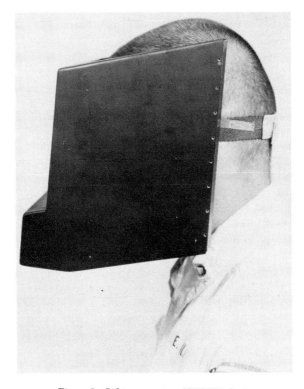

Figure 3. Subject wearing ALFMED device.

2. *Trajectory measurement* — The direction of the track was measured, and the subsequent trajectory through the head was predicted.

3. *Translation scan* — For all the candidate events located in the first step, a scan of the moving plate along the line of translation was made to locate the counterpart track. A measurement of the translation distance for each event was also made, yielding the time of occurrence of the event.

4. *Correlation with observations* — The list of events was compared with the observations reported by the crewmen in an attempt to determine if cosmic rays did in fact cause the phenomenon; if there was an apparent charge, energy, or linear energy transfer (LET) threshold; or if some particular event types correlated with certain particle types (e.g., streaks caused by tracks tangent to the retina, etc.).

5. *Charge and energy measurement* — Particles passing through the emulsion (Eastman Kodak NTB-3) left latent images which were developed in the same fashion as the latent images on normal photographic film due to exposure to light. Some of the secondary electrons (δ-rays) produced by the passage of the particle through the emulsion have sufficient range to leave small tracks of their own. A detailed analysis of the density

of these secondary tracks over the entire available track length in the emulsion could yield charge measurements with an uncertainty of $Z = \pm 1$. For kinetic energies/nucleon in the interval 50 MeV/nuc$< E \leqslant$ 300 MeV/nuc, the analysis could also yield a measurement of the kinetic energy.

Apollo 16 and Apollo 17 ALFMED Results

The ALFMED film plates for the Apollo 16 mission were processed immediately following the flight and examined extensively at that time. The ALFMED fixed plates used for the flight had 200 μm-thick emulsion on both surfaces while the moving plates had 50 μm-thick emulsions. Thus the total emulsion thickness was approximately 500 μm. This, coupled with the extremely high particle flux experienced during the Apollo 16 mission (the highest for any of the Apollo missions), made it quite difficult to scan the plates as originally planned. It was therefore decided that, due to the delays involved, it would be advantageous to proceed with the Apollo 17 analysis first. Experience gained during Apollo 17 analysis procedures then might be used to improve Apollo 16 analysis techniques.

As a result of the difficulties in scanning the Apollo 16 plates, the Apollo 17 plates were flown with 50 μm-thick layers on both sides, giving a total emulsion thickness of 200 μm. This greatly improved track detectability.

Analysis of the Apollo 17 plates yielded a total of 2360 individual tracks with directions that appeared approximately correct for passage through the eye of the astronaut. Of these tracks, 483 did not initially appear to have positional counterparts in the moving plates. These particles were all considered candidates for events which occurred during the period of observation and while the moving plates were displaced from their reference orientation.

Of the 483 tracks, 229 were in the front plate. Detailed trajectory measurements on the 229 front plate candidates revealed that 65 of that number passed through one eye or the other (or both). (Since the front plate was scanned first in each analysis step, the efficiencies for the various steps were probably somewhat less than those for the side plates.) Upon careful inspection, 50 of the 65 eye-directed tracks were found to have alined counterparts in the moving plate for the reference orientation, thereby reducing the front-plate sample to 15 genuine candidates.

The Monte Carlo calculations predict that one should expect approximately 30 $Z \geqslant 12$ candidate tracks in the front plate which originated during the translation period. The current number of 15 candidates indicates that most probably the first-scan efficiency for such tracks is roughly 50 percent. We consider it unlikely that any $Z \leqslant 8$ events are included in this first-scan sample, but experience leads us to believe that a rescan will result in a considerably improved efficiency, especially for the smaller charges.

Two of the 15 genuine candidates were found to coincide, to within five sconds, with reported flash observations. It is anticipated that after final measurements are made, the coincidences can be determined to accuracies of one or two seconds.

The first coincidence is with the fifth light flash reported, and occurred some 1465 seconds after the plate translation began. It was described as "just a spot" in the left eye. The candidate particle traversed the left side of the left eye, moving upward and slightly to the right, and passed almost tangent to the retina. Detailed charge and energy measurements have not yet been completed; however, the particle was almost certainly heavier than oxygen.

The second coincidence is with the eleventh event reported, and it occurred after 2368 seconds of plate translation. The light flash was described as a glow, "about one eighth of an inch in diameter", and appeared to be three-fourths of the way out from the center to the edge of the visual field at about 10:00 o'clock in the right eye.

The second candidate trajectory passed through the right side of the right eye, heading from the front left to the right rear, and slightly upward. A rough estimate of its location as it would appear to the observer places it in the periphery at approximately the proper distance, but at 8:30 or 9:00 o'clock, rather than at 10:00 o'clock as reported. Eye movement at the time of observation might account for this minor discrepancy. This particle is also most probably heavier than oxygen.

Summary and Conclusions

In summary, available results are consistent with expectations based upon geometrical considerations and upon the Monte Carlo calculations. First, evidence shows that, at least in part, the flashes seen by astronauts are correlated with charged particles traversing the retina. Further, since the flux of these particles is sufficient to explain the entire phenomenon, it is likely that all of the flashes originate in this manner. From our sample of two coincidences, we find no contradiction with the ability of the observer to discern in which eye the event occurred. Finally, the ALFMED technique has been demonstrated to be effective as a procedure for study of the light flash phenomenon.

References

Benson, R.E.; and Pinsky, L.S.: Biomedical Experiments: Part C. Visual Light Flash Phenomenon. In Apollo 16 Preliminary Science Report. NASA SP-315, 1972.

Pinsky, L.S.; Osborne, W. Z.; and Bailey, J.V.: Visual Light Flash Phenomenon. In Apollo 17 Preliminary Science Report. NASA SP-330, 1973.

Pinsky, L.S.; Osborne, W.Z.; Bailey, J.V.; Benson, R.E.; and Thompson, L.F.: Light Flashes Observed by Astronauts on Apollo 11 through Apollo 17. Science, vol. 183, 1974, pp. 957-959.

CHAPTER 3
THE APOLLO 16 MICROBIAL RESPONSE
TO SPACE ENVIRONMENT EXPERIMENT

by

Gerald R. Taylor, Ph.D.

Lyndon B. Johnson Space Center

Introduction

Microorganisms have been subjected to a large variety of space flight conditions on many United States and Soviet missions including Sputnik 4–6, Vostok 1–6, Voskhod 1 and 2, Cosmos 110, Nerv 1, Discoverer 18, Gemini 9, 10, and 13, Agena 8, and Biosatellite 2. This considerable number of flights carried a large array of viruses, bacteria, and fungi which were exposed to many different space flight conditions.

Most of these past studies were concerned with establishing the now accepted principle that microbes can survive in the harsh space environment. However, during the conduct of these viability studies certain anomalies were noticed which suggested that the survival of some microbes was enhanced, whereas others were adversely affected by the space environment. For example, aqueous suspensions of spores from members of the genus *Streptomyces* (*Actinomyces* in the Soviet Union) demonstrated quite different results following exposure to space flight conditions aboard the third, fourth, and fifth Soviet satellites (Glembotskiy et al., 1962). The space flight conditions reportedly

The author wishes to acknowledge the contributions of the following persons, without whom the many segments of this experiment could not have been completed. T.K. Mattingly, III, C. Chassay, J.V. Bailey, and R.C. Simmonds of the Johnson Space Center; A.M. Heimpel of the U.S. Department of Agriculture, Beltsville, Maryland; B.G. Foster and D.O. Lovett of Texas A&M University, College Station, Texas; J. Spizizen and J.E. Isherwood of Scripps Clinic and Research Foundation, LaJolla, California; H. Bücker, G. Horneck, and H. Wollenhaupt of the University of Frankfurt, Germany; P.A. Volz, Y.C. Hsu, D.E. Jerger, J.L. Hiser, and J.M. Veselenak of Eastern Michigan University, Ypsilanti, Michigan; E.V. Benton of the University of San Francisco, California; R.A. English and R.D. Brown of the Kelsey-Seybold Clinic, Houston, Texas; R.T. Wrenn, W.L. Ellis, R.A. Long, M.B. Parson, C. Carmichael, and J. Lindsay of Northrop Services, Inc., Houston, Texas.

Special thanks is given to the Biological Sciences Section of Northrop Services, Inc., Houston, Texas, in grateful appreciation for technical assistance provided to this study. Appreciation is also expressed to Aerojet Medical and Biological Systems, El Monte, California, for design and fabrication of the experiment hardware.

increased the incidence of spore germinations of Strain 2577 of S. *erythreus* by about six times that of the ground controls, whereas the viability of Strain 8594 decreased sharply. These examples are typical of past survival studies where results are quite evenly divided among those which report synergism, antagonism, or no relationship at all between space flight and microbial viability (de Serres, 1969; Glembotskiy et al., 1962; Kovyazin et al., 1962; Lorenz, 1968; Mattoni, 1968; & Parfenov, 1967). Many previous studies were hindered by technical constraints, mission anomalies, or the inability to provide meaningful controls. As a result, and in spite of the best effort of the investigators, equivocal results were often produced. One of the objectives of the present experiment was to take advantage of the considerable array of past experimentation, overcome as many equivocating obstacles as possible, and help to establish a meaningful relationship between space flight and the viability of several different microbial systems.

A few of the more recent United States and Soviet microbiology studies have investigated the effect of space flight on other parameters in addition to viability. Generally, these studies have involved genetic changes, and as with the survival studies, they have produced variable results (Antipov, 1967; Antipov et al., 1969; de Serres, 1969; de Serres & Webber, 1968; de Serres et al., 1969; Jenkins, 1968; Mattoni, 1968; Parfenov, 1967; & Zhukov-Verezhnikov et al., 1963). However, the combined results of these studies suggest the possibility that the conditions of space flight influence microbial genetic alterations (Townes, 1970). The "Microbial Response to Space Environment" experiment was designed to evaluate this effect as well as to determine the survivability of microorganism species.

General Experiment Design

From the multitude of microbial species and challenge systems available, the experiment system outlined in table 1 was established. This experiment system comprised a variety of species, each of which may be considered to be a model system for evaluation of some medically important activity. Investigators were invited to study those phenomena within their area of expertise, and to conduct critical investigations in their own laboratories. This method allowed a large number of individual studies to be conducted in a coordinated manner, and permitted a variety of species to be housed within a single piece of flight hardware. Each investigator selected a test system which was nonpathogenic to man (to avoid possible contamination of the crew), was well characterized relative to the phenomenon to be studied, lent itself well to simple and rapid screening tests, and was compatible with the unique environment of the flight hardware.

In order to allow for dose-response studies and comparative investigations, certain variables were provided within the flight hardware. Microbes could either be suspended in 50 microliters of fluid or could be dried on a suitable carrier. Some of the microbes were exposed to the vacuum of space whereas others were retained at one atmosphere. As detailed genetic studies required exposure to a mutagenic source, provisions were made to expose test systems to the full light of space or to components of the solar ultraviolet spectrum at peak wavelengths of 254 nm, 280 nm, and 300 nm. An optical filtering system was provided to control the total radiant energy reaching exposed test systems from a minimum of 4×10^1 ergs cm^{-2} to a maximum of 8×10^8 ergs cm^{-2}. The use of ambient solar radiant energy as the mutagen necessitated close monitoring of this factor. Photographic emulsion and a modification of the potassium ferrioxalate system of Wrighton and Witz (1972) were used to record the amount of radiant energy which actually reached selected test systems (table 2). The possible mutagenic activity of galactic radiation necessitated the inclusion of lithium fluoride thermoluminescent dosimeters and a package of passive nuclear track detectors capable of recording high-energy multicharged particles (table 2).

Table 1
Biological Components

Phenomenon Studied	Assay System	Microorganism	Investigator
Lipolytic α toxin production	Lytic zone on agar		R. T. Wrenn, W. L. Ellis Northrop Services, Inc. Houston, Texas
Deforming β toxin production	*Sarcina flava* and house fly	*Bacillus thuringiensis*	G. R. Taylor, R. C. Simmonds NASA Manned Spacecraft Center Houston, Texas
Fatal δ toxin production	Silk worm and crystal assay		A. M. Heimpel U. S. Dept. of Agriculture Beltsville, Maryland
Infectivity	Mouse	*Nematospiroides dubius*	R. A. Long, W. L. Ellis Northrop Services, Inc. Houston, Texas G. R. Taylor NASA Manned Spacecraft Center Houston, Texas
Hemorrhagic factor production	Guinea pig and hemoglobin	*Aeromonas proteolytica*	B. G. Foster, D. O. Lovett Texas A. & M. University College Station, Texas
Hemolytic enzyme production	Human erythrocytes		
Genome alteration	Spore production	*Bacillus subtilis* spores, strains HA 101 HA 101 (59) F	J. Spizizen, J. E. Isherwood Scripps Clinic and Research Foundation La Jolla, California
UV and vacuum sensitivity	Colony formation	*Bacillus subtilis* spores, strain 168	H. Bücker, G. Horneck, H. Wollenhaupt University of Frankfurt, Germany
Bacteria phage infectivity	Host lysis	*Escherichia coli* (T-7 phage)	J. Spizizen, J. E. Isherwood Scripps Clinic and Research Foundation La Jolla, California
Cellulolytic activity	Cloth fibers	*Chaetomium globosum*	P. A. Volz, Y. C. Hsu, D. E. Jerger J. L. Hiser, J. M. Veselenak Eastern Michigan University Ypsilanti, Michigan
Animal tissue invasion	Human hair	*Trichophyton terrestre*	
Drug sensitivity	Antibiotic sensitivity in agar	*Rhodotorula rubra Saccharomyces cerivisiae*	

Table 2

Dosimetry Components

Measurement	Monitor Used	Assay Systems	Investigator
High-energy multicharged particles	Passive nuclear track detectors	Lexan Cellulose nitrate Photographic emulsion Silver chloride	E. V. Benton University of San Francisco San Francisco, California
Ultraviolet light	Passive dosimeters	Potassium ferrioxalate actinometry Photographic emulsion	M. B. Parson, R. A. Long, W. Ellis Northrop Services, Inc. Houston, Texas G. R. Taylor NASA Manned Spacecraft Center Houston, Texas
Penetration of galactic irradiation	Thermo- luminescent dosimeters	Lithium fluoride	J. V. Bailey NASA Manned Spacecraft Center Houston, Texas R. A. English, R. D. Brown Kelsey-Seybold Clinic Houston, Texas

These latter studies were conducted in a manner that allowed for direct correlation with similar readings obtained from the BIOSTACK experiment, the Apollo crew personnel radiation dosimeters, and the Apollo Light Flash Moving Emulsion Detector (ALFMED), all of which were used in the Apollo 16 Command Module.

Description of the Flight Hardware

Each biological test sample, containing 10^2 to 10^6 living cells as appropriate, was housed in a chamber (cuvette) 5 mm on a side, composed of Kel-f plastic with a quartz window (figure 1). There were three types of these chambers, one of which was designed to contain 50 microliters of fluid. This type possessed, on the side opposite the quartz window, a fill port which was sealed with Shelwax 500 after filling with the test solution. The cuvette body was designed to have a seven-degree internal slope to prevent possible shadowing of the organisms.

The other two cuvette types were both designed to retain biological test systems which had been deposited on Millipore filter chips with a mean pore size of 0.45 microns. The only difference between these latter two types was that one was vented to the outside, thus allowing for exposure of the contents to the vacuum of space (figure 1).

All loaded cuvettes which were to be exposed to UV irradiation were placed beneath neutral density filters which were situated under bandpass filters. This optical filter combination respectively controlled the amount and the wavelength of light reaching the microbial systems (figure 2). Cuvettes and optical filters were placed in trays (figure 3) which were mounted in a hardware case which measured 11.4 x 11.4 x 24.5 cm. The flight hardware (figure 4), designated the Microbial Ecology Evaluation Device (MEED), contained 798 cuvettes with biological test systems, 140 neutral density filters, 28 bandpass filters, eight recording thermometers, one high-energy multicharged particle dosimeter, 64 potassium ferrioxalate actinometry cuvettes, 44 photographic film cuvettes, and 18 thermoluminescent dosimetry cuvettes. The flight hardware was placed within a stowage bag which helped absorb the launch vibrations and provided additional thermal insulation. The bag was made from nonflammable Beta cloth and nonflammable Fluorel sponge foam.

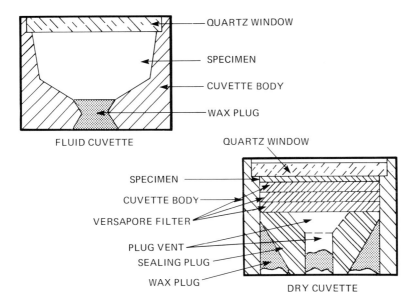

Figure 1. Biological test sample cuvette design.

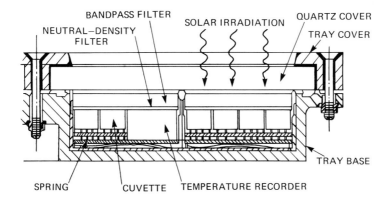

Figure 2. Optical filter configuration.

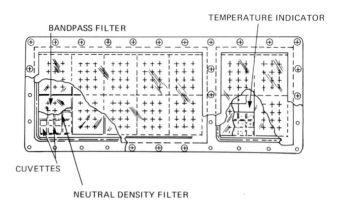

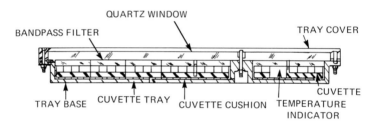

Figure 3. Details of MEED tray interior.

Deployment of the Microbial Ecology Evaluation Device

During the extravehicular activity phase of the Apollo 16 transearth coast, the MEED hardware was removed from its protective stowage bag while in the crew compartment and affixed to the distal end of the television boom which was then attached to the handle of the opened hatch door (figure 4). The procedure of deploying the MEED hardware by an Apollo 16 astronaut is shown in figure 5.

A small attitude adjustment of the Command Module was required to place the appropriate surface of the MEED directly perpendicular to the rays of the sun. This was indicated by a solar positioning device incorporated into the exterior surface of the MEED. After attaining the proper attitude, the MEED was opened so that the biological test systems and actinometers were exposed to the direct rays of the sun. After exactly ten minutes of such exposure the device was closed, removed from the television boom, and replaced in its protective bag for transport back to the Johnson Space Center.

Design of Individual Test Systems

Aeromonas proteolytica

This microorganism was selected for studying the effects of solar irradiation and space flight conditions on the production of extracellular enzymes because it produces an

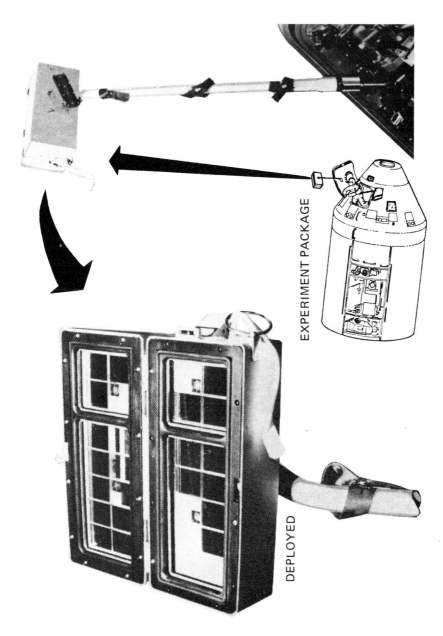

EXPERIMENT PACKAGE

DEPLOYED

Figure 4.   Hardware for the Microbial Ecology Evaluation Device.

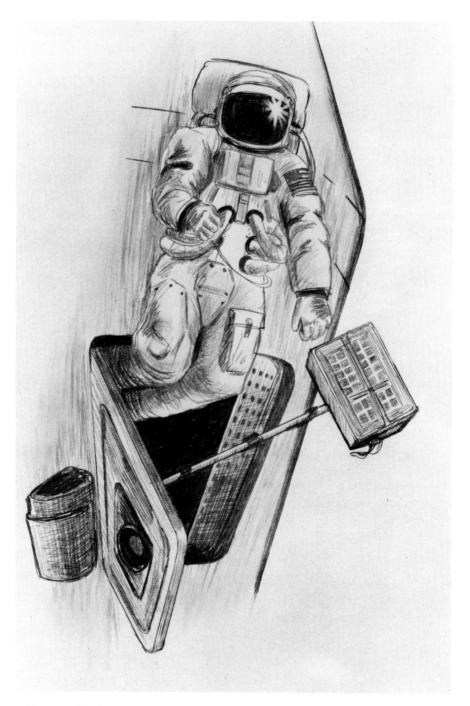

Figure 5. Artist's conception of inflight deployment of MEED hardware by an astronaut.

endopeptidase which can cause intracutaneous hemorrhage and necrosis in laboratory animals (Foster, 1972), and a hemolysin which is elaborated into the culture fluid and has the ability to hemolyse human erythrocytes (Foster, 1972). This microbe was retained in fluid suspensions and exposed to solar ultraviolet irradiation at peak wavelengths of 254 nm, 280 nm, and 300 nm. In addition to survival evaluations, cells recovered from the flight hardware were quantitatively tested for alterations in toxin production. Postflight analysis of retrieved cells indicated that there was no significant difference between the survival rates of inflight and ground-based control.

Bacillus subtilis

Different strains of this species were evaluated by two different groups as indicated in table 1. Spores of this species are generally highly resistant to harsh environments and were therefore expected to yield a high return of viable cells for detailed genetic analyses.

The manner in which spores of Strain 168 survive when exposed to one or more factors of space has been critically studied in simulation experiments (Horneck et al., 1971) as well as in the BIOSTACK experiment which was flown on Apollo 16 and 17. For the present study, spores were exposed to space vacuum and solar ultraviolet irradiation at a peak wavelength of 254 nm to determine the influence of these space factors on their survival evaluated in terms of colony-forming ability. The combined action of space vacuum and solar ultraviolet irradiation at a peak wavelength of 254 nm resulted in greater loss of viability than was observed in ground-based studies. Space vacuum alone did not cause a decrease in survival of predried spores, indicating that air-dried spores may survive exposure to space vacuum if shielded against solar irradiation. The additional environmental factors of space flight did not measurably influence the viability and irradiation response of spores of Strain 168.

Another investigative group exposed *Bacillus subtilis* spores of Strains HA 101 and HA 101 (59) F to the space flight environment both in aqueous suspensions and in dry layers, as outlined in table 1. These strains require three specific amino acids for growth which are used as identification and mutation detection markers. In addition, Strain HA 101 (59) F is defective in the ability to repair radiation damage (Gass et al., 1971), and is therefore highly susceptible to the damaging effects of ultraviolet irradiation. Generally, the lethal effects of irradiation at peak wavelengths of 254 and 280 nm were greater for dried spores than for those exposed to distilled water. Additionally, the repair-defective strain was more sensitive at both wavelengths of UV irradiation. As expected, survival rates for space flight-exposed spores did not differ significantly from analogous aliquots in the ground control units. Detailed genetic analyses are being performed to determine if any mutational effects of space flight were obtained.

Bacillus thuringiensis var. *thuringiensis*

This microorganism, which has widely been used as a biological insecticide, was selected for inclusion in this experiment because it produces three toxins which are active against biological systems and lends itself well to both rapid screening and critical *in vivo* analyses. The toxins include a lipolytic a-exotoxin which in some ways resembles the

Phospholipase C produced by *Clostridium perfringens,* a deforming β-exotoxin which is a nucleotide that is heat stable and kills insects at time of molt or pupation, and a crystalline δ-endotoxin which is a proteinaceous factor that destroys the midgut cells in many Lepidopterans, causing gut paralysis and eventual death (Heimpel, 1967).

As with the *B. subtilis* tested, there was no significant difference between the mean of *B. thuringiensis* survivors from the ground control, flight control, and vibration control units. Also, there was no significant difference between the means of survivors for any of the groups exposed to solar ultraviolet light in space. There was a significant difference (p<0.01) in the survival rate of those groups exposed to full sunlight in space when compared with the nonirradiated control groups. This indicates that the space-flown spores of this species were resistant to the levels of ultraviolet irradiation encountered in the test, but were sensitive to the full light of the sun. This follows previously established patterns obtained from ground-based studies (Cantwell & Franklin, 1966) and is not considered anomalous behavior.

Phage T7 for *Escherichia coli*

Survival studies of the T-7 bacteriophage of *Escherichia coli* were included in an attempt to relate the present experiment to the space flight-mediated effects reported by Soviet investigators for *E. coli* phages which were flown on numerous manned flights (Antipov, 1967; Hotchin, 1968; Lorenz, 1968; and Zhukov-Verezhnikov, 1968). Rather than the T-1 or K-12 (λ) phage commonly used in Soviet space flight studies, the simpler and more stable T-7 phage was chosen for this study in hopes that it would be more resistant to the rigors of space flight and therefore prove to be a better UV test subject. Postflight survival evaluations support this hypothesis because large losses in the non-UV exposed flight subjects (as compared to the ground controls) are not indicated. The lethal effect of inflight solar ultraviolet irradiation at a peak wavelength of 254 nm was considerably higher than ground-based controls which were exposed to the same levels of irradiation; however, the characteristic shape of the dose response curve was similar to the curve of the ground control data.

Nematospiroides dubius

This nematode was chosen for study largely because it is a complex multicellular organism which has been successfully cultured *in vitro* from the egg to the third stage infective larvae (Weinstein et al., 1969), is pathogenic to laboratory mice but not to humans, and is quite insensitive to the special holding conditions of the flight hardware.

A total of 2×10^5 ergs cm^{-2} of solar inflight ultraviolet irradiation at a peak wavelength of 254 nm was sufficient to completely inhibit ultimate infection in the murine host and subsequent maturity to adult worms. Therefore, the survival of space flight irradiated larvae was too low for further comparative studies.

Comparison of nonirradiated flight and ground control subjects revealed no differences in survival, infectivity in mice, formation of adults, or subsequent egg productions. There was, however, a significant decrease in egg viability within the group of adults which descended from flight control larvae that were exposed to the space flight environment (excluding vacuum) but received no solar ultraviolet irradiation. This was an important observation since this control group was not purposefully exposed to any experimental stresses and was simply a "passenger" on the space flight.

Mycological Studies

Four different species of fungi (two filamentous fungi and two yeasts) were incorporated within the experiment package. Each of these species was carefully selected by the investigator (table 1) so that exhaustive postflight studies of medically important activities could be performed and compared to suitable ground-based controls.

Trichophyton terrestre was selected because it has the ability to attack human hair under laboratory conditions and has not been shown to be naturally infectious. The other filamentous fungus, *Chaetomium globosum*, was of special interest because of the cellulolytic activity it has demonstrated on cloth fibers, such as those which compose portions of the flight garments of the astronauts (Volz & Jerger, 1973). The two yeasts, *Rhodotorula rubra* and *Saccharomyces cerevisiae*, were included because they lend themselves well to drug sensitivity studies and other quantitative evaluations having medical importance. Analysis of postflight data indicate that in no case was there a significant difference between survival rates of static ground controls and other ground control aliquots which were subjected to simulated launch vibration. There were slight differences between survival rates of these two control series and the inflight controls (not irradiated) of three of the test species. The survival of flown *C. globosum*, *R. rubra*, and *S. cerevisiae* was slightly lower than corresponding ground controls. In addition, aliquots of *T. terrestre* and *S. cerevisiae* demonstrated some sensitivity to inflight solar ultraviolet irradiation when measured in terms of a loss of cell viability.

During the viability studies, selected isolates were recovered for ongoing postflight investigations. These additional studies include evaluations of hyphal growth dynamics and possible alterations in the chromosomal configuration of different filamentous phenotypes. The nutrient requirements and drug sensitivity of returned phenotypes are also being investigated for comparison with ground control values. Additionally, isolates of *T. terrestre* are being examined for changes in the ability to decompose human hair *in vitro*.

Ultraviolet Dosimetry

Two methods were employed to monitor the actual radiant energy penetrating selected optical components of the flight hardware. One of these methods involved Kodak High Resolution Film (Estar Thick Base) SO-343 which had been purged of oxygen and sensitized with dry nitrogen gas to decrease the rate of latent-image fading. This system was reliable over a range of 4×10^1 to 5.2×10^2 ergs cm^{-2} total energy with a peak wavelength of 254 nm. Postflight analyses indicated that the dosimeters received at least as much energy as had been expected from calculations based on data from the NASA established Solar Spectral Irradiance Standard (Thekaekara, 1971). The photographic film monitoring method proved to be a useful tool for measuring small amounts of UV irradiation in space.

Solar irradiation within the range of 4×10^4 ergs cm^{-2} to 4×10^5 ergs cm^{-2} was monitored by an adaptation of the Potassium Ferrioxalate Actinometry System described by Wrighton and Witz (1972). Data collected from analysis of the contents of flight control and ground control cuvettes indicate that neither the simulated launch vibration nor the total space flight exerted a detectable change in preirradiated control systems. The ferrioxalate monitoring system, therefore, was shown to have the stability required for successful measurements made within the flight hardware. Analysis of inflight irradiated actinometry systems verified that the optical filter components of the Microbial Ecology Evaluation Device performed in a manner which allowed for critical evaluation of exposed biological test systems.

High Energy-Multicharged Particle Dosimetry

It was impossible, in the design of the flight hardware, to protect test systems from galactic irradiation. Therefore this factor had to be measured in order to better understand any observed biological effects. Data were obtained with two separate systems.

One set of measurements was obtained by strategically distributing 76 extruded thermoluminescent dosimeters composed of lithium fluoride wafers throughout the flight hardware. This distribution was used to allow dose determinations for each tier, for each of the six sides, and for the central volume of the closed assembly. Statistical analysis of the resulting data indicates that the various areas within the MEED received extremely uniform irradiation from the ionizing irradiation components of the space environment. Therefore, it is valid to omit this factor as a variable when comparing inflight test systems. The mean dose of all MEED thermoluminescent dosimeters (TLD) was 0.48 ± 0.02 rad with a range of 0.44 to 0.51 rad. Doses to crewmembers (from crew passive TLD measurements) were reported as ranging from 0.48 to 0.54 rad, with a mean of 0.51 ± 0.02 rad. The dose of 0.48 ± 0.02 rad represents a total absorption of 48 $\pm$ ergs of ionizing energy per gram of biological material within the MEED. This value was applicable to all samples within the flight hardware, including flight controls and UV irradiated samples.

The other set of galactic irradiation measurements was conducted in response to current concern for the effect of high energy-multicharged (HZE) particles on biological systems. A 2.5 x 3.8 cm container was provided within the flight hardware and ground control units to house four different types of dosimeters capable of recording these entities. Lexan dosimeters, identical to those employed in the crew personnel passive dosimeters, were used so that direct correlation could be made. Cellulose nitrate (CN) dosimeters were included in the MEED as well as in the Apollo Light Flash Moving Emulsion Detector (ALFMED) which was flown on Apollo 16, again allowing for direct comparisons. The other two detectors, Ilford G5 and silver chloride, were flown only in the MEED, but were of considerable value in establishing the HZE particle environment experienced by the flight hardware.

Both the Lexan and the cellulose nitrate (CN) detectors revealed track fluences (track cm^{-2}) of the HZE particles. Since the CN detector is more sensitive, it showed track fluences substantially higher than those found in Lexan. The sensitivity of the two detectors is such that the CN records particles with a Z (atomic number) greater than six, while Lexan records particles with a Z greater than ten. Comparison of Lexan and CN track fluences found in the MEED flight hardware showed them to be somewhat lower than those found in either the ALFMED or the passive personnel dosimeters. These observations, along with the depressed TLD values presented above, imply that the MEED flight hardware had a somewhat greater average shielding as compared with either the ALFMED or the personnel passive detectors. Likewise, these data are slightly lower than those obtained from the TLD and CN detectors employed in the BIOSTACK flight hardware, which was stowed in the Command Module in an area of minimal shielding to ambient cosmic radiation.

Summary and Conclusions

This experiment system was designed to evaluate the effect of a particular space flight on the survival rate of nine different species. Although a reasonable variety of organisms (viruses, yeasts, filamentous fungi, bacteria, and an invertebrate) were tested under several different conditions, no statistically valid differences could be detected in the survival of flight samples when compared to corresponding ground-based controls. In general, these evaluations were based on multiple observations of from ten to thirty replicates of up to one million cells each. While the results of this experiment conflict with those of certain other space flight investigations, as noted in the Introduction, it must be observed that the conditions of a particular space flight cannot be exactly duplicated, and therefore results from different flights are not directly comparable.

References

Antipov, V.V.: Biological Studies Aboard the Spacecraft "Vostok" and "Voskhod." Vol. 6 of Problems of Space Biology, N.M. Sisakyan, ed., Nauka Press (Moscow), 1967, pp. 67-83.

Antipov, V.V.; Delone, N.L.; Nikitin, M.D.; Parfyonov, G.P.; and Saxonov, P.P.: Some Results of Radiobiological Studies Performed on Cosmos-110 Biosatellite. Vol. 7 of Life Sciences and Space Research, W. Vishniac and F.G. Favorite, eds., North-Holland Publishing Co. (Amsterdam), 1969, pp. 207-209.

Cantwell, G.E.; and Franklin, B.A.: Inactivation by Irradiation of Spores of Bacillus thuringiensis var. thuringiensis. J. Invert. Pathol., vol. 8, 1966, pp. 256-258.

de Serres, F.J.: Effects of Radiation During Space Flight on Microorganisms and Plants on the Biosatellite and Gemini XI Missions. Vol. 7 of Life Sciences and Space Research, W. Vishniac and F.G. Favorite, eds., North-Holland Publishing Co. (Amsterdam), 1969, pp. 62-66.

de Serres, F.J.; and Webber, B.B.: The Combined Effect of Weightlessness and Radiation on Inactivation and Mutation – Induction in Neurospora crassa During the Biosatellite II Mission. Bioscience, vol. 18, 1968, pp. 590-595.

de Serres, F.J.; Miller, I.R.; Smith, D.B.; Kondo, S.; and Bender, M.A.: The Gemini XI S-4 Spaceflight Radiation Inter-action Experiment II. Analysis of Survival Levels and Forward-Mutation Frequencies in Neurospora crassa. Radiation Res., vol. 39, 1969, pp. 436-444.

Foster, B.G.: Toxic Properties of Aeromonas proteolytica. In Abstract of Annual Meeting of American Society for Microbiology, 1972, p. 110.

Gass, K.B.; Hill, T.C.; Goulian, M.; Strauss, B.S.; and Cozzarelli, N.R.: Altered Deoxyribonucleic Acid Polymerase Activity in a Methyl Methanesulfonate-Sensitive Mutant of Bacillus subtilis. J. Bact., vol. 108, 1971, pp. 364-374.

Glembotskiy, Ya. L.; Prokof'yeva-Belgovskaya, A.A.; Skamina, Z.B.; and Khvostova, V.V.: Influence of Spaceflight Factors on Heredity and Development in Actinomycetes and Higher-Order Plants. Vol. 1 of Problems of Space Biology, N.M. Sisakyan, ed., USSR Academy of Sciences Publishing House (Moscow), 1962, pp. 259-271.

Heimpel, A.M.: A Critical Review of *Bacillus thuringiensis* var. *thuringiensis* Berliner and Other Crystalliferous Bacteria. Annual Rev. of Entomology, vol. 12, 1967, pp. 287-332.

Horneck, G.; Bücker, H.; and Wollenhaupt, H.: Survival of Bacterial Spores Under Some Simulated Lunar Surface Conditions. In Vol. 9 of Life Sciences and Space Research, Akademie-Verlag (Berlin), 1971, pp. 119-124.

Hotchin, J.: The Microbiology of Space. J. of the British Interplanetary Society, vol. 21, 1968, pp. 122-130.

Jenkins, D.W.: U.S.S.R. and U.S. Biosciences. Bioscience, vol. 18, 1968, pp. 543-549.

Kovyazin, N.V.; Lukin, A.A.; and Parfenov, G.P.: The Effect of Space Flight Factors of the Satellite "Vostok-2" on Haploid and Diploid Yeasts. In Vol. 2 of Problems in Space Biology, N.M. Sisakyan and V.I. Yazdovskiy, eds., 1962, pp. 156-160.

Lorenz, P.R.: Survival of Microorganisms in Space. Space Life Sciences, vol. 1, 1968, pp. 118-130.

Mattoni, R.H.T.: Space Flight Effects and Gamma Radiation Interaction on Growth and Induction of Lysogenic Bacteria. Bioscience, vol. 18, 1968, pp. 602-608.

Parfenov, G.P.: Genetic Investigations in Outer Space. Cosmic Research, vol. 5, 1967, pp. 121-133.

Taylor, G.R.; Chassay, C.E.; Ellis, W.C.; Foster, B.G.; Volz, P.A.; Spizizen, J.; Bücker, H.; Wrenn, R.T.; Simmonds, R.C.; Long, R.A.; Parson, M.B.; Benton, E.V.; Bailey, J.V.; Wooley, B.C.; and Heimpel, A.M.: Microbial Response to Space Environment. In Apollo 16 Preliminary Science Report. NASA SP-315, 1972, pp. 27-11 through 27-17.

Taylor, G.R.; Spizizen, J.; Foster, B.G.; Volz, P.A.; Bücker, H.; Simmonds, R.C.; Heimpel, A.M.; and Benton, E.V.: A Descriptive Analysis of the Apollo 16 Microbial Response to Space Environment Experiment. Bioscience, vol. 24, 1974, pp. 505-511.

Thekaekara, M.P.: Solar Electromagnetic Radiation. NASA SP-8005, 1971, pp. 13-15.

Townes, C.H.: Infectious Disease in Manned Spaceflight – Probabilities and Countermeasures. Space Science Board of the National Academy of Sciences (Washington, D.C.), 1970, p. 86.

Volz, P.A.; and Jerger, D.E.: Fungal Growth on Fabrics Selected for Space Flight. Amer. Fabrics, vol. 98, 1973, p. 75.

Weinstein, P.P.; Newton, W.L.; Sawyer, T.K.; and Sommerville, R.T.: *Nematospiroides dubius*: Development and Passage in the Germfree Mouse, and a Comparative Study of the Free-Living Stages in Germfree Feces and Conventional Cultures. Trans. Amer. Microsc. Soc., vol. 88, 1969, pp. 95-117.

Wrighton, M.; and Witz, S.: Stability of Fe (II) in Ferrioxalate Solutions. Mol. Photochem., vol. 3, 1972, pp. 387-394.

Zhukov-Verezhnikov, N.N.; Mayskiy, I.N.; Yazdovskiy, V.I.; and Pekhov, A.P.: Evaluating the Biological Effectiveness of Space Flight Factors by Means of the Lysogenic Bacteria *E. coli* K-12 (λ). Aviation and Space Medicine, V.V. Parin, ed., Akademiya Meditsinskikh Nauk (Moscow), 1963, pp. 158-160.

Zhukov-Verezhnikov, N.N.; Rybakov, N.I.; Kozlov, V.A.; Saksonov, P.P.; Dubrov, N.N.; Antipov, V.V.; Podoplelov, I.I.; and Parfenov, G.P.: Results of Microbiological and Cytological Investigations Conducted During the Flights of "Vostok" Type Vehicles. In Vol. 4 of Problems in Space Biology, N.M. Sisakyan, ed., USSR Academy of Sciences Publishing House (Moscow), 1968, pp. 252-259.

CHAPTER 4

THE APOLLO 17 POCKET MOUSE EXPERIMENT (BIOCORE)[*]

by

Webb Haymaker, M.D.
Bonne C. Look
NASA Ames Research Center

Eugene V. Benton, Ph.D.
University of San Francisco

Richard C. Simmonds, D.V.M.
NASA Ames Research Center

Introduction

Travel outside the protective atmosphere of Earth can expose a spacecraft and its occupants to potentially dangerous regions of radiation. Missions conducted to date, including those of Apollo, have been fortunate since radiation doses received by astronauts have been low and of no clinical significance. However, as space missions increase in duration and move beyond the moon, the danger from radiation will become more serious.

---

[*]A full report of this experiment (BIOCORE M 212: Biological Cosmic Ray Experiment) is given in the April 1975, Special Issue of Aerospace Medicine. The present paper represents an amplification of Paper I of the report. Permission for use of that paper was granted by Aerospace Medicine.

The authors wish to express their thanks to the following individuals for their support and participation in the BIOCORE experiment: *Pathology Group:* O.T. Bailey, H.R. Brashear, R.L. Dennis, J.T. Ellis, L.R. Eversole, R.O. Greep, G.A. Harrison, W.S. Hartroft, L.C. Johnson, L.M. Kraft, C.C. Lushbaugh, J. Miquel, M.L. Moss, D.E. Philpott, E.A. Porta, T. Samorajski, G. Shklar, A. Takahashi, T.V. Talmadge, F.S. Vogel, and W. Zeman. *Biology Group:* A.R. Behnke, Jr., K.R. Brizzee, L.C. Erway, T. Laird, C. Leach, H.A. Leon, R.G. Lindberg, P. Pearson, J.M. Ordy, K. Suri, J.W. Tremor, D.B. Webster, and D.L. Winter. *Engineering Group:* W.F. Barrows, F.L. Cota, J.A. D'Urso, E.G. Park, Jr., G.H. Shillinger, C.E. Turnbill, and H.A. Zabower. *Physics Group:* E.V. Benton and M.R. Cruty. *Biotechnology Group:* W.W. Ashley, R.M. Binnard, S. Black, W. Cooper, R.L. Corbett, W.A. Dunlap, G.L. Humason, G. Klein, B. Lloyd, M. McTigue, Jr., W.T. Platt, J. Smith, V. Teas, and T. Tilbury. *Support Group:* P.F. Beales, R.K. Clayton, M. Heflin, J.R. Larey, D.Leaffer, and J.F. Saunders. The team acknowledges the invaluable management support and encouragement of H. Mark, H.P. Klein, and J. Billingham.

In order to gain a better understanding of radiation hazards, the Biocore Experiment was flown on Apollo 17. This experiment attempted to assess the degree to which exposure to cosmic ray particle radiation might present a risk to astronauts. In this study, five pocket mice, with plastic dosimeters implanted beneath the scalp, were flown in a sealed canister. The objective was to determine whether microscopically visible lesions, attributable to particle radiation, could be found in brain, eye, and other tissues in these animals.

Particular interest in the effects of particle radiation on tissue arises from the markedly different character of high energy (HZE) particle radiation as compared with that of electromagnetic (E-M) radiation (X-rays, γ–rays). The energy deposition (dosage) in E–M irradiation *decreases* exponentially with penetration depth into the target. In contrast, the energy deposition by a particle can *increase* as the particle penetrates the target and decelerates, the maximum energy loss per unit path length (LET: linear energy transfer) occurring near the stopping point (Bragg peak) (figure 1). Most of the energy deposition from particle radiation occurs in a very narrow cylinder around the trajectory, within which there is intense ionization of the target's atoms. While the concept of dosage is not strictly meaningful in assessing the radiobiological effects of HZE particle radiation, perspective on the potential destructive character is obtained by noting that the "dosage" (energy deposition per gram) in the immediate vicinity of the particle trajectory can be on the order of megarads or higher.

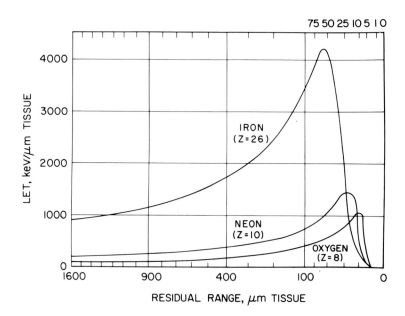

Figure 1. LET as function of residual range (distance to the stopping point) for three species of heavy atomic nuclei. Not only is the maximum LET much larger for the heaviest particle (iron) shown, but also the range of the very high LET values (arbitrarily > 1000 KeV/μm) increases rapidly as nuclear charge (Z) increases.

For a given incident energy, a charged particle will penetrate a target to a relatively well-defined depth that is a function of the particle's charge. Collaterally, the LET of a particle at any point along its trajectory is a function of the particle's charge and distance from the stopping point. In the present experiment, use was made of this last property, that is, measurement of the LET, where the LET of each HZE particle was determined from measurements on the particle's track in the subscalp detector. Charge and distance to the particle's stopping point were calculated from the detector data.

Plan of the Experiment

The primary objective of this experiment was to determine whether a specific portion of the high Z — high energy (HZE) galactic cosmic ray particle spectrum, especially particles with $Z \geqslant 6$, can produce microscopically visible injury of the brain and eye. Pocket mice (*Perognathus longimembris*) obtained from the California desert were selected as the biological target (figure 2). Five of these mice were flown on Apollo 17. Not only the brain and eyes, but also many other tissues of these animals were studied for evidence of cosmic ray particle damage.

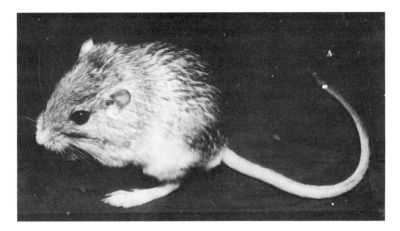

Figure 2. The Little Pocket Mouse, *Perognathus Longimembris*.

In order to correlate any observed tissue damage in the heads of the flight mice with the passage of HZE cosmic ray particles, it was necessary to record the trajectories of as many of the particles passing through the heads during the flight as possible. To monitor the primary targets — the brain and, to some extent, the eyes — a particle detector composed of four layers of plastic (two of Lexan polycarbonate and two of cellulose nitrate), sealed into a unit and coated with Paralene C for protection against tissue fixatives, was developed. The dosimeter, designed to cover the entire brain from the olfactory bulbs anteriorly to the cerebellum posteriorly, was mounted on a Silastic elastomer platform, the underside of which was contoured to the skull (figure 3). The assembly was implanted beneath the mouse scalp, where scalp tension fixed its position with respect to the skull. No deleterious effects in the mice due to the presence of the subscalp assembly were observed, even several months after implantation.

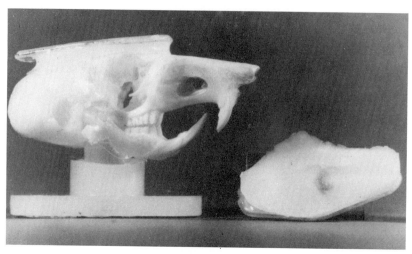

Figure 3. Monitor assembly on skull of pocket mouse. At right is an assembly viewed from below; the Silastic elastomer is molded to fit the skull.

Flight Experiment Preparation

To house the five mice during the Apollo mission, a closed, self-sustaining system was developed in which potassium superoxide (KO_2) served as the oxygen source and as the carbon dioxide absorber. The system was perfected to the point that the well-being of the mice over their projected 13-day flight would be reasonably assured. The major problem was to house the mice and the KO_2 in a canister 35.6 cm long and 17.8 cm in diameter (14 in. and 7 in.), in such a manner that the mice could feed and move about despite the tendency to free float. A water supply system was unnecessary since the mice produce water metabolically from their food. Each mouse was housed in a metal tube having a diameter [2.54 cm (1 in.)] slightly larger than the mouse that would allow it to turn about. Each tube ran the full length of the canister. The KO_2 tube of a larger diameter, centrally located, ran the full length of the canister (figure 4).

There was concern whether the mice would experience excess fatigue from negotiating in the weightless state and lose their appetite. To explore this possibility, 14-day clinostat tests were carried out. The mice together with their seeds, housed in plastic boxes, were rotated at 1/4 RPM. During the revolutions of the boxes, cascading seeds inundated the mice, and when they could no longer stay on top of the seeds, the mice would become torpid and roll with the seeds. At intervals, the mice became active again and ate. It was expected that the cylindrical shape and small bore of the tubes in the flight canister would minimize tumbling in the zero-g environment, that the mice would not have difficulty in moving about within their tubes, and that they would be able to consume an adequate number of seeds to survive.

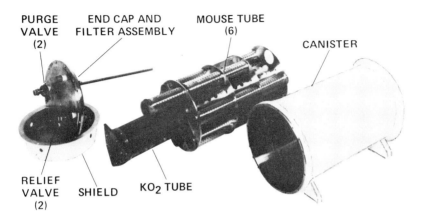

Figure 4. Components of flight package, partially assembled. The KO_2 tube and the mouse tubes can be removed from the supporting spool for cleaning and for reloading the KO_2. The purge tube attached to the end cap carries the oxygen to the closed end of the canister to assure ample purging of the air in the canister during experiment startup.

Four aspects of the environment within the canister needed to be investigated in order to determine whether the mice would be taking the trip under survivable conditions: the oxygen partial pressure, the carbon dioxide partial pressure, the temperature, and the relative humidity.

During the many tests (about 60) that were performed under ambient temperature conditions approximating those of the Apollo flight, the oxygen partial pressure within the canister frequently rose to as high as 83×10^3 N/m^2 (12 psi), and occasionally higher. Consequently, a separate study was conducted in which 28 mice were individually exposed in an environmental chamber to oxygen at a partial pressure of 83×10^3 N/m^2, at $297^{\circ}K$ ($24^{\circ}C$), and to a relative humidity of 20 percent over a period of seven days. All survived the test.

The KOH generated by the interaction of KO_2 and respiratory H_2O appeared to be an ample absorbent, but nonetheless the tolerance of the mice to carbon dioxide buildup needed to be determined. To this end, six mice were sealed in a chamber in which the initial oxygen partial pressure was 33×10^3 N/m^2 (4.8 psi). The mice withstood an atmosphere in which the partial pressure of carbon dioxide rose to 19×10^3 N/m^2 (2.8 psi), while the oxygen partial pressure fell to $13 \times 10^3 N/m^2$ (1.87 psi) in a four-hour test.

The other aspects of the canister environment requiring investigation were (1) temperature, and (2) relative humidity (R.H.). Too high a temperature would be prejudicial to the animals' well-being and potentiate the toxic effects of oxygen. Too low a relative humidity would dehydrate both the animals and the seeds.

Prior studies determined that pocket mice in a sea-level atmosphere can easily tolerate an ambient temperature of 308°K (35°C) for one month. A calculated temperature profile anticipated a temperature of 300°K (27°C) during part of the flight (figure 5), and was the cause of some concern, since free convection does not occur in zero g, and the heat generated by the KO_2 and by the mice in the canister would have to be dissipated by conduction and radiation. Accordingly, the heat dissipated from the canister, including heat loss at the canister–Command Module interfaces, was investigated through studies conducted on the canister in a vacuum environment. It was established that heat dissipation at the interfaces would probably maintain the temperature in the mouse tubes at no higher than 301°K (28°C).

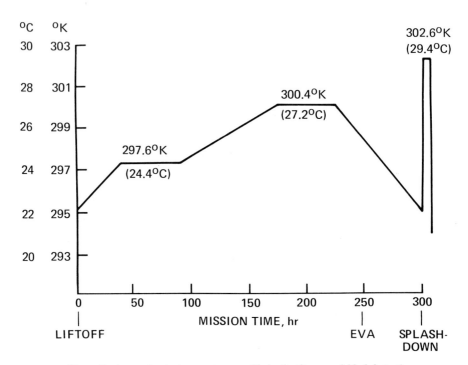

Figure 5. Approximate temperature profile in the Command Module in the region where the canister was to be located, as calculated for the Apollo 17 flight.

The effects of the combined temperature-oxygen pressure stress were investigated next. Eighteen mice (while in canisters) were exposed to an oxygen partial pressure of 83×10^3 N/m^2 (12 psi) in a room with a temperature of 305°K (32°C). The relative humidity was maintained at 22 percent during the test. Six additional mice were exposed to the same temperature, but in a sea-level atmosphere, to serve as test controls. All of these mice had undergone earlier oxygen tolerance testing. Most of the heavier mice survived the test in satisfactory condition, while four of the lighter mice and one heavy mouse (weighing 10 gm) died; all control mice in heat alone survived, indicating that relatively heavy mice (mice weighing 9.5 gm or more) were the animals of choice.

The problem of relative humidity (R.H.) as it affected the pocket mice was considered. In an open-system, oxygen flow-through experiment, with an oxygen partial pressure of 28×10^3 to 34×10^3 N/m^2 (4 to 5 psi) and ambient temperature of 302°K (29°C), it was shown that the mice could withstand a relative humidity of 90 to 100 percent over a period of five days. Furthermore, in test runs in which the R.H. was rather low — 23.4 percent R.H. or lower — the animals survived in apparent good condition despite a loss in weight.

From the results of these and other studies it was evident that the pocket mouse is exceptionally hardy and can survive wide variations in its environment. Moreover, histological studies performed on many mice subjected to testing in canister oxygen environments revealed no change in the brains or eyes of the animals, and relatively little change in the lungs.

The primary criteria in the selection of the mice to be carried on Apollo 17 were weight (9.5 gm or more), the general state and behavior, condition of the scalp over the dosimeter, the presence or absence of nasal discharge, the appearance of the pelage, and the activity of the animal and its housekeeping habits.

Test Procedures

Of the animals used as the major controls for the flight animals, some were non-experimental controls, while others had been subjected to KO_2 oxygen tests as controls against the oxygen partial pressures anticipated in the canister during flight. But the most appropriate controls for the flight animals were the five mice taken to NASA Kennedy Space Center (KSC) a few days prior to launch. Two canisters were loaded with five mice each at KSC; one was chosen to fly, and the other to serve as flight backup. The flight backup canister was flown back to NASA Ames Research Center (ARC), where the mice were subjected to all stresses anticipated for the flight mice that could be carried out on the ground. They were perfused with fixing fluid on the same day (December 19) as the flight animals. Four of these mice were used as flight controls.

A week or two prior to the time of anticipated spacecraft splashdown, 12 control animals were perfused at the University of Hawaii in Honolulu (during the time the engineers and pathologists were stationed there to process the flight animals in the event of a mission abort), and an additional 17 animals were perfused at Pago Pago. Four of the latter served as flight controls. The others were used as controls for subsequent histological studies.

Two flight acceptance tests were run to qualify the hardware for flight. The two tests were run concurrently (November 5 through 22, 1972). In these tests as well as in preparation for flight, the initial step after the animals had been sealed in the canisters was to flush the canisters with 100 percent oxygen for 15 or 25 minutes, a procedure that left little residual nitrogen in the canisters. In the acceptance tests, the oxygen partial pressure fell to a minimum of 17×10^3 N/m^2 (2.4 psi) and rose steadily thereafter. On day 15, the pressure reached peaks of 81×10^3 and 84×10^3 N/m^2 (11.7 and 12.2 psi), but fell to about 34×10^3 N/m^2 (5 psi) at the start of the simulated EVA maneuver. Figure 6 shows the test profile.

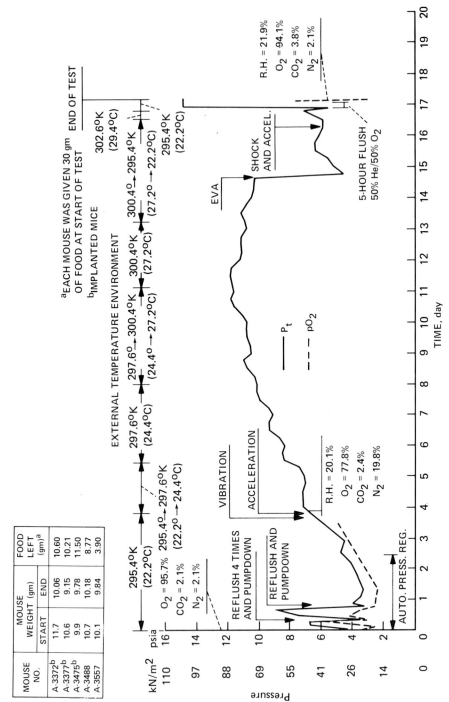

Figure 6. KO₂ Expt. No. 64, an acceptance test of the S/N 05 hardware. The tube containing the KO₂ was of stainless steel. A total of 520 gm of 40% catalyzed/60% noncatalyzed KO₂ mixture was used.

Flight Backup Test Carried Out Concurrently With the Apollo Flight

The initial pumpdown period of this test lasted 37 minutes. The minimum oxygen partial pressure reached during autoregulation was 17×10^3 N/m^2 (2.5 psi). About 12 hours after the launch of Apollo 17, the package was flown from the Kennedy Space Center to the Ames Research Center, causing a gap of 20 hours in the pressure data for the time period starting from preparation for transport of the animal package at the Kennedy Space Center until its installation in a test chamber at the Ames Research Center. During those 20 hours the total pressure rose from 37×10^3 to 64×10^3 N/m^2 (5.4 to 9.3 psia). All five animals survived the test in excellent condition.

The flight backup canister experienced the same ambient temperature except during the flight from the Kennedy Space Center to the Ames Research Center. The flight backup and two other control canisters were flushed with a mixture of 50 percent helium/50 percent oxygen toward the end of the test period, a procedure to be carried out on the flight canister following splashdown. Moreover, the mice in all three canisters were subjected to certain other stressful situations that were expected to be imposed on them aboard Apollo 17: vibration following Apollo lift-off, launch acceleration with a peak of 5 G soon after lift-off and a second peak of 2.5 G at second stage burnout, peaks of 6.8 G and 4 G during reentry of the spacecraft into the atmosphere, and 37 G on splashdown. These were test levels; the values were in excess of those anticipated on the flight of Apollo 17. The mice tolerated the vibration and the G stresses without apparent ill effects.

The data on the experiment package flown on Apollo 17 are given in figure 7. The animals were placed in the canister on December 2, 1972. The initial pumpdown was performed in 36 minutes. The minimum oxygen partial pressure reached during autoregulation was 19×10^3 N/m^2 (2.8 psi). The Apollo was launched on December 7. In the extravehicular activity (EVA) preparation during the flight, the Command Module (CM) was emptied of its atmosphere and exposed to the vacuum of space in about eight minutes, and the EVA was accomplished in about one hour. Hence, the rapidity of the decompression of the mice in the CM (to 34×10^3 N/m^2, 5 psia) can be assumed to have been approximately the same for the mice in the two flight acceptance canisters on the ground and for the mice in the flight backup canisters as well. It can also be assumed that the pressure in the flight canister rose slowly after the EVA maneuver. The rate of recompression of the CM had no effect on the pressure in the flight. Splashdown in the Pacific occurred on December 19, with the package received on the recovery ship on day 13 of the flight (day 17 from the time the animals had been placed in the canister), where it was flushed with He/O$_2$ gas mixture. The flushing was continued during transport by plane to Pago Pago.

Upon arrival at Pago Pago the flight package was taken to a laboratory at the Lyndon B. Johnson Tropical Medical Center. On opening the canister about seven hours after splashdown, four of the five mice were found alive, while the fifth (A-3352) was dead. Two of the surviving mice (A-3305 and A-3356) were active and in excellent condition when released from their tubes into a container for observation. The other two surviving mice (A-3326 and A-3400), when first examined, were docile and hunched up, as though exhausted or arousing from torpor. They moved forward only a few steps when prodded.

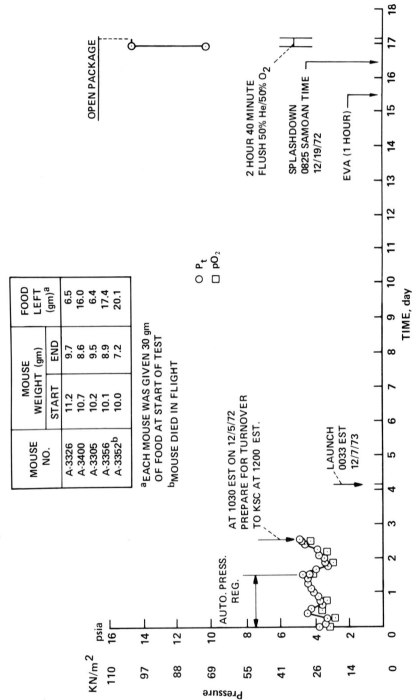

Figure 7. Data on the Apollo 17 flight package (S/N 03). The tube containing KO_2 was of stainless steel. A mixture of 40% catalyzed/60% noncatalyzed KO_2 was used.

A-3326, the female of the group and the most subdued, was uncoordinated on walking and would fall to one side or the other when it attempted to sit up on its hind quarters. Later, on histological examination, it was found that severe hemorrhage had occurred into its middle ear cavities during the flight. This could easily have accounted for the incoordination.

After all the animals had been examined and their weights recorded, the four live animals were anesthetized with Metofane and perfused with a fixing fluid, FAM (FAM: formaldehyde, 1 part; acetic acid, 1 part; methyl alcohol, 8 parts). The perfusion was carried out via the heart by means of a Harvard apparatus. The brain of the mouse (A-3352) that did not survive the flight was fixed by introducing FAM into the subarachnoid space via the orbits.

Upon completion of the perfusion procedures, the heads of all the animals were immersed in FAM. The next morning (after about 12 hours' fixation) the heads were transferred to 70 percent methyl alcohol.

Processing of Tissues for Histological Study,
Establishment of Cosmic Ray Particle Trajectories

Back at NASA Ames Research Center three days after autopsy of the animals at Pago Pago, the first step was to place the head of the animal that died during the flight (A-3352) in a standardized aluminum box, and to secure the head by means of ear bars, a jaw bar, and a nose clamp. The box was then secured on a rotatable stage attached to the platform of a stereotaxic apparatus. Then the scalp was turned back and the position of the dosimeter (with the head still in the box) established by photographs, and the degree of tilt with respect to the stereotaxic apparatus platform established by means of a laser beam. The dosimeter was then removed for analysis at the University of San Francisco. About three weeks later, the same protocol was followed for the other four mice and, in addition, X-rays of the heads in various planes were taken to establish more clearly the position and degree of tilt of the dosimeters.

The five heads, still in the aluminum boxes and immersed in 70 percent methyl alcohol, were transported to Duke University for further processing. The heads were removed from the boxes and each was decalcified. The heads were then returned to their boxes, and alined in exactly the same position as before. The next step was to dehydrate the heads by passing them through alcohols and xylol according to standard methods. Then one end of each box — that near the occiput — was removed and replaced by a microtome chuck, whereupon the boxes were filled with low melting point paraffin. The heads were serially sectioned in the coronal plane, from anterior to posterior, at ten millimicrons. The total number of sections per head came to approximately 1600, of which about 1200 included the brain. All the sections were stained by the PAS-hematoxylin method.

In order to locate the paths of cosmic ray particles through the heads of the flight mice, it was necessary that a procedure be devised whereby the trajectory of each cosmic ray particle registered in the subscalp dosimeters would be extrapolated into and be identifiable in the heads of control mice. Before this procedure could be initiated the dosimeters needed to be analyzed to determine cosmic ray particle trajectories. A total of 80 heavy particle tracks were found in the five dosimeters. The head of each mouse to be used as a control for a flight mouse was placed in a fixed position in a standardized aluminum box, in the manner just described for the flight mice. The box was then secured on a rotatable stage situated on the platform of a sterotaxic apparatus. Through a painstaking procedure, a manila paper "dosimeter," identical in size and shape to the flight dosimeters, was placed on the head of each mouse in precisely the same position and at the same degree of tilt as had been recorded for each of the flight mice. Fine drills were then directed through the control head by means of the arm of the stereotaxic apparatus, the drills being introduced along the trajectory (within the limits of experimental accuracy) of each of the cosmic ray particles that had penetrated the dosimeter of a flight mouse. Where numerous tracks (up to 20) were found in the subscalp dosimeter of a single flight mouse, the heads of as many as four mice were "tracked," with four to five tracks per head to serve as controls for that flight mouse (figure 8); the number of "tracked" control heads totaled 17. The heads of these animals were carried to Duke University, where they were processed and serially sectioned in the same manner as for the flight mice.

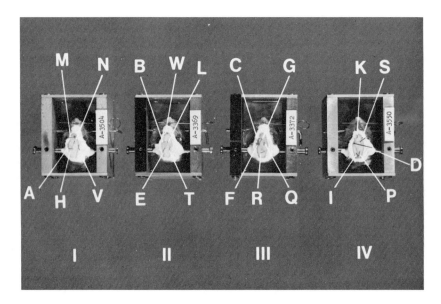

Figure 8. "Tracked" control heads (A-3504, 3369, 3372, and 3550) for flight mouse A-3400, showing drill in place for each trajectory.

The significance of this tracking procedure was that the pathologists could check any lesion found in the brain of a flight animal against the location of the drill tracks in the control brains. If congruity was found between a lesion in a histological section of a flight mouse and a drill core in the corresponding control histological section, and if the lesion was consistent with current concepts of what a cosmic ray-induced lesion should look like — that is linear, or columnar or even spherical — there would be a high probability that the lesion was produced by the cosmic ray particle.

In the meanwhile, the body tissues of the flight mice and many control mice were being processed for study at numerous institutions in the United States as well as at NASA Ames Research Center.

Results of Analysis of the Subscalp Dosimeters

For the 80 cosmic ray particles recorded in the five subscalp dosimeters (table 1), the energy loss by the particles per millimicron of dosimeter traversed (LET) ranged from 0.16 to 0.5 MeV/μm, with only a few of the particles in the very heavy charge group (Z > 20). The relatively narrow charge and LET spectra of the registered particles are attributable (1) to attenuation of the frequency of the very high Z component of the free space cosmic ray flux by the shielding of the Apollo spacecraft and of the flight package itself, and (2) to the fact that any high LET particle detector is more likely to register a cosmic ray particle in the high LET (< 0.1 MeV/μm) range than in the very high LET range ($\geqslant$ 0.1 MeV/ μm), since a much smaller portion of the trajectory lies in the very high LET range.

Another set of data listed in table 1 relates to particle thindown direction. Only five of eighty particles were determined with high certainty to have penetrated the dosimeter prior to entering the head, while 41 particles may have passed through the head prior to reaching the dosimeter. The thindown direction of the remaining 32 particles* was not determinable, although statistically, approximately one-half should have thinned down in the direction of the head after traversing the dosimeter. Obviously, particles would have a lower LET in tissue than recorded in the dosimeter if they penetrated the head before reaching the dosimeter. The reverse would be true for the five particles coursing downward into the head after having penetrated the dosimeter; table 2 gives the characteristics of these particles. Two of these particles were classed as in the medium charge group (Z = 6 to 9), and three as in the heavy (Z $\geqslant$ 10) category. LETs in the dosimeter for these five particles ranged from 0.24 to 0.32 MeV/μm. The residual range (distance to the stopping point from the dosimeter) computed for each of the particles is cited in the table. Of the 80 particles recorded in the subscalp dosimeters, these five particles were of paramount interest to the pathologists because their stopping points were calculated to be within or near the brain.

Among the cosmic ray particles whose thindown direction was not determinable were the ten particles of highest charge. These were grouped together as heavy (Z $\geqslant$ 10) and very heavy (Z > 20) (H-VH) because of uncertainty as to which of the two charge groups they belonged. All had an LET equal to or greater than 0.5 MeV/μm at the level of the dosimeter, and their stopping points were more than 1.2 mm beyond the level of the dosimeters. Brain, eyes and other head tissues in areas traversed by these ten particles were given particular attention in the search for lesions because of their heaviness and LET.

A further point to be made with reference to the monitoring system was that the dosimeters could be expected to record on the average about 50 percent of the cosmic

---

*This adds up to 78 particles. Two of the particles thought to have traversed the head were found on microscope examination of serial head sections not to have done so.

Table 1

Characteristics of 80 Cosmic Ray Particles
Recorded in the Subscalp Dosimeters of the Five Flight Mice

Mouse No.	No. of Tracks	LET (MeV/μm)	Charge Group*					Residual Range (mm)	Thindown Direction†		
			L	M	H	VH	H-VH		Down§	Up	Not Determinable
A-3326	13	0.16 – 0.30	0	11	2	0	—	> 0.6 – 2.6	1	9	3
A-3400	17	0.16 – 0.24	0	15	2	0	—	≫ 0.6 – 3.6	2	11	4
A-3305	18	0.16 – 0.27	1	9	8	0	—	> 0.6 – 24	0	10	8
A-3356	17	0.17 – 0.37	0	9	7	1	—	> 0.5 – 26.5	3	9	5
A-3352	5	0.20 – 0.27	0	1	4	0	—	1.1 – 16	1	2	2
H-VH particles for all 5 mice	10	≳ 0.5	—	—	—	—	10	> 1.2	—	—	10

* Light particle, Z 3-5; medium, Z 6-9; heavy Z ⩾ 10; very heavy ⩾ 20.
† Direction: down, through dosimeter into the head; up, through the head before reaching the dosimeter.
§ On microscopic examination, the number of particles was corrected from 7 to 5 particles.

Table 2

Data on the Characteristics of Five Cosmic Ray Particles
Which Penetrated the Dosimeter Prior to Reaching the Head

Flight Animal	Control Head "Tracked"	Track Designation	Charge Group*	LET (MeV/μm)	Residual Range (mm)	Head Structures Penetrated
A-3400	A-3372	C	M	0.24	⩾ 0.6	Left cerebral cortex, hippocampal formation, cerebellum, middle ear cavity
A-3400	A-3369	E	M	0.24	⩾ 0.6	Left eye, including retina
A-3356	A-3571	G	H	0.32	2.2	Right olfactory bulb, frontal lobe, caudate, putamen, pallidum, int. capsule, optic tract, hippocampal formation, cerebral cortex, bony labyrinth, middle ear cavity
A-3356	A-3554	T	M	0.26	⩾ 0.6	Left olfactory bulb, nasal cavity
A-3352	A-3359	B	H	0.27	3.4	Left frontal lobe, optic nerve, nasopharynx, roof of mouth

*M, medium charge group (Z 6-9); H, high charge group (Z ⩾ 10).

ray particle flux through the mouse brain, since particles incident on the mouse came from all directions and the mice were not restrained. As a consequence, some particles could have passed through or terminated in or near the brain without having been registered in the dosimeters. Thus the pathologists were faced with the possibility of observing cosmic ray particle-induced lesions in the brain and other target tissues without the presence of corresponding tracks in the dosimeters.

The pocket mouse heads were exposed to far broader Z and LET spectra of particles than the 80 HZE particles indicated in table 1. However, only the HZE particles, which were registered, were the particles of interest in the present experiment.

The tissues traversed by some of the cosmic ray particles are indicated in table 2. Analysis revealed that one or more head structures of the five flight mice were traversed by particles; the scalp by 76 particles; the eye by 5; the nasal cavity by 15; the middle ear cavity by 23; and the brain by 59 particles (olfactory bulb, 14; cerebellum, 12; hippocampal formation, 11; and hypothalamus, 3).

Body Tissues

Study of the body tissues of the four flight animals that survived the flight revealed no changes that could be regarded as due to cosmic particle radiation. Some pertinent observations, however, emerged from the studies. The increased oxygen partial pressure to which the flight animals and control test animals had been exposed depressed erythropoiesis in the bone marrow. The increased oxygen partial pressure did not induce changes in periodontal or other oral tissues. The lungs appeared relatively resistant to oxygen intoxication, attributable in part to the inclusion of nitrogen with the oxygen. Mild pneumonitis was observed in all four flight backup mice, but not in the flight mice. The liver in one flight mouse (A-3305) contained large focal areas of hepatocellular necrosis of undertermined etiology, while those of the other flight mice and the four flight backup mice were normal or virtually normal.

The kidneys of the flight mice were unremarkable. The juxtaglomerular apparatus could not be evaluated because the fixing fluid (FAM) had dissolved the granules from its cells. Assessment of the adrenal cortex according to the method used revealed no significant alterations. A study of certain nuclei of the hypothalamus and of the cell population of the pituitary gland and, to some extent, the adrenal cortex revealed minor enlargement of neuronal nuclei in the supraoptic nucleus as the sole positive finding. This suggested an antidiuretic hormone response.

The thyroid appeared normal in all mice in which it was examined, including the thyroid of three of the flight animals. The same was true for the parathyroids. Soft-tissue calcifications were found in a number of the mice — flight mice and controls alike — and thus the possibility exists that this might be attributable to parathyroid hyperactivity.

Heart muscle showed no ostensible change in any of the animals. Histological changes in skeletal muscle of the flight animals were minimal and were found to occur in the control animals with comparable frequency. This was with the exception of *Sarcocystis* infestation. *Sarcocystis* were not found in any of the flight mice, but they were present in three of the five flight backup mice.

Tissues with continuously replicating cells were given special attention. The lack of abnormalities in bone marrow in the flight mice except for reduced erythropoiesis has already been mentioned. In the upper small intestine of the flight mice the mitoses in the crypts of Lieberkühn were normal in appearance. The gonads also showed no differences ascribable to the Apollo 17 mission. In two of the three surviving male flight mice (but not in the third) spermatogenesis was advanced to the same degree as in ground control mice at the same season.

Olfactory Mucosa

There was another tissue composed of continuously replicating cells, the olfactory epithelium, which was severely damaged in the four surviving flight animals and to a lesser degree in the animal that died. The respiratory epithelium in all these animals was, by contrast, unaltered. The need to assess the changes in the olfactory epithelium in some detail became evident when it was found that the nasal epithelium of the 17 major control animals, of which four were flight backup animals, was entirely free from change.

There were two kinds of pathological change in the olfactory epithelium. One was characterized by disorganization of much of the epithelium, in the sense that the thickness of the layer and the number of its constituent cells varied from area to area in a given strip of olfactory epithelium. The other consisted of multifocal severe lesions originating either in the disarrayed epithelium just mentioned or in intact epithelium. Intermediate stages between these two types of change were sometimes encountered.

The lesions were in various stages of evolution ranging from acute, in which a few cells or masses of cells were being sloughed from the epithelium, to "old," in which newly proliferated cells had replaced the sloughed cells. The acute lesions elicited a conspicuous polymorphonuclear leukocytic response. The proportion of lesions classified as recent, of intermediate duration, and old, was roughly the same in each of the four mice; nor did the lesions vary perceptibly in character from mouse to mouse. Obviously the lesions had been caused throughout the 17-day stay of the mice in the flight canister or throughout the 13 days of flight. The presence of aggregates of polymorphonuclear leukocytes in the tunica submucosa was the chief finding in the olfactory mucosa of the mouse that died during the flight.

The lesions in the olfactory epithelium had virtually the same spatial distribution in the epithelium in all these mice. However, their size and configuration in a given animal varied considerably. Most astonishing was their number: at least 51 to 90 lesions per animal. By comparison, the number of high-energy cosmic ray particles $Z \geqslant 6$ traversing the nasal mucosa was calculated to total ten to fourteen particles per animal. Thus, the number of lesions in the olfactory mucosa was at least four to nine times the calculated number of cosmic ray particles $Z \geqslant 6$ that impinged on the mucosa. To determine whether concurrence existed between lesions and cosmic ray particle trajectories, the paths of particles through the nasal cavity were established by tracing the tracks of drills that had been inserted through the heads of the 17 major control mice in the trajectory of each of the particles. A total of 15 particles recorded in the dosimeters were found to have traversed the nasal cavity in the five flight animals (figure 9). Concurrence was usually observed, but since the lesions, which were frequently multifocal and usually relatively large, were also found more or less precisely in the same location in the olfactory mucosa of the contralateral nasal cavity (which presumably had not been intersected by a cosmic ray particle), implication of the cosmic ray particles under consideration as solely instrumental in lesion production could not be justified.

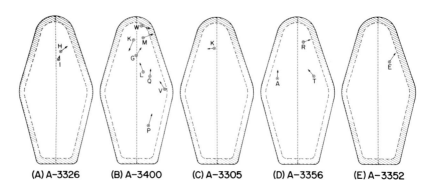

(A) A-3326   (B) A-3400   (C) A-3305   (D) A-3356   (E) A-3352

Figure 9. Subscalp dosimeters of the five flight mice, showing the sites at which they were intercepted by cosmic ray particles that penetrated the nasal cavities. The letters are designations of the individual particles. The arrows indicate roughly the projected direction of the particle trajectory through the nasal cavity.

In view of the intensity of olfactory epithelial involvement, the question arose whether the vomeronasal organ was also affected. Examination revealed that the neuroepithelium in two of the four surviving flight mice exhibited alterations analogous to the disarray observed in the olfactory epithelium of the flight mice. In one of these animals the disarray was present in the *left* vomeronasal organ, yet in the "tracked" control animal the drill that had been used intersected the *right* vomeronasal organ. Hence in this animal there was no concurrence between the cosmic ray particle trajectory and the damaged neurosensory cells.

A number of possible causes of damage of the olfactory and vomeronasal epithelium were considered: systemic or regional infection; inhaled particulate material (seed dust); byproducts from the KO_2 bed reaching the mice in aerosol or particulate form; gas contaminants originating in the flight package which the animals breathed; volatile substances from the dead mouse reaching the live mice; weightlessness; and cosmic ray particle radiation. Where feasible, studies were conducted in an effort to rule in or rule out some of these potentially causative factors. No definitive conclusions were reached as to the cause of the lesions. One point, however, was evident: whatever the cause, it had to be operative only in the space environment, for the olfactory epithelium in the flight backup animals and the other animals that were used as major flight controls was unaffected. Another point was that if the pathological changes in the olfactory epithelium were cosmic ray particle-induced, then the entire spectrum of cosmic particle radiation (including protons, etc.) would have to be operative, not solely the particles that were recordable in the subscalp dosimeters; and furthermore, it would be necessary that the olfactory mucosa be particularly radiosensitive. Data in support of these possibilities are not available.

Ear

The status of the finer structure of the inner ear could not be assessed in any of the animals because the perfusion technique used (FAM introduced through the heart) did not provide adequate fixation. Suffice it to say that no changes attributable to factors operative in the space environment were observed.

In all of the flight animals as well as in all of the flight backup animals, hemorrhagic materials were found in the middle ear cavity bilaterally. In the animal that died during flight (A-3352), massive hemorrhage, which was fairly fresh, was found in the middle ear cavity bilaterally. In regard to the four live animals, there was an indication that their condition on recovery after the flight was related to the degree of hemorrhagic materials in their middle ear cavities. Mouse A-3305 was in the best condition when examined: no hemorrhage was found, the only blood constituent in air cells being proteinaceous material, the latter signifying that an alteration in capillary permeability had occurred, not capillary rupture. Mouse A-3326 (the female of the group) was in the worst condition: hemorrhage in its middle ear cavities was severe. Mouse A-3400 was groggy on initial examination: hemorrhage of recent origin was encountered. Mouse A-3356 was in excellent condition: the hemorrhage, which was of moderate degree, had largely been resorbed by the time the mouse was observed.

The occurrence of hemorrhage in the flight and flight backup animals was not unexpected because much the same was noted with considerable frequency during preflight KO_2 test runs, presumably as the result of pressure excursions in the canisters in which the mice were housed. The question thus arose: in the space environment would the hemorrhagic materials in the middle ear cavities and the cellular reactions thereto differ from those occurring in the control animals?

In serial sections from the flight mice and flight backup mice, a wide diversity of hemorrhagic materials was found in air cells of the middle ear cavities. To establish a frame of reference whereby possible differences in the reaction of air cell contents to factors in the space environment could be assessed, it was decided that the incidence of polymorphonuclear leukocytes in the hemorrhagic materials (blood clots, plasma, proteinaceous material) would be the sole variable to be taken into account in the evaluation. The results were surprising: air cells that contained proteinaceous material or plasma carried a significantly higher incidence in the flight animals than in the flight backup animals and, moreover, polymorphonuclear leukocytes were encountered in the proteinacous material — sometimes in great number — in the flight animals but not in the flight backup animals. Moreover, leukocyte attraction to resorbing blood clots seemed greatest in the flight animals.

Factors peculiar to the space environment were taken into consideration as instrumental in the greater exudation of blood components into air cells of the flight mice and the greater degree of leukotaxis. No basis was found on which to invoke weightlessness as causative. Analysis of the subscalp dosimeters revealed that 23 cosmic ray particles registered in the dosimeters had traversed the middle ear cavities of the four mice that survived the flight. Concurrence between particle trajectories and aggregates of polymorphonuclear leukocytes in air cells was sometimes observed, but the incidence of the leukocytes along the particle trajectories was no greater than in adjacent air cells

presumed not to have been traversed by cosmic ray particles. Hence some further inquiry
was needed.

Ambient atmospheric pressure and air pressure within the middle ear cavities in the
pocket mouse are normally kept equalized by means of Eustachian tubes that connect the
nasopharynx with these cavities, in much the same way as in the human. It may
reasonably be assumed that some factor related to this exchange in the flight animals was
different than in the flight backup animals. One outstanding difference in the two groups
was the presence of severe lesions in the olfactory mucosa in the flight animals but not in
the flight backup animals. This difference may provide the key if it could be assumed that
some airborne noxious agent caused not only the olfactory mucosal lesions but also the
increased exudation and greater leukotaxis in the middle ear cavities of the flight animals.
This could, if the assumption is valid, have been brought about (1) directly upon passage
of the agent through the Eustachian tubes, or (2) indirectly through a local effect on the
Eustachian tubes that would decrease their patency. The operation of either mechanism
could have resulted in greater capillary injury in air cell linings in the flight animals than
in the backup animals. However, since no noxious agent within the flight canister was
identified as the cause of the lesions in the olfactory mucosa, the actual cause of the
greater response in the middle ear cavity remains as open to explanation as was the case
for the olfactory mucosal lesions. The presence of exudate in the nasopharynx might have
been a factor in Eustachian tube obstruction in some of the flight animals.

Scalp

The scalps of the flight animals (except that of the mouse that died during flight)
were obtained for study at the time that the subscalp dosimeters were removed for
analysis. Chronic inflammatory changes attributable to the presence of the dosimeters
were observed in all of these scalps. In addition, a total of 13 tiny lesions were found in the
epidermis or in hair follicles in three of the flight animals. (In the fourth animal, scarring
of the scalp owing to the presence of the dosimeter was too extensive to allow
evaluation.) The lesions were characterized by necrosis of epithelial cells, both in the
epidermis and the hair follicles, in focal areas measuring up to 100 μm across. In ten of
the thirteen lesions, polymorphonuclear leukocytes were present in varying numbers in
the dermis and subcutaneous connective tissue in a columnar distribution extending
downward from the sites of the necrotic epidermal cells (scalp thickness, 0.15 to
0.2 mm). It was evident that all the lesions were incurred during the course of the flight
inasmuch as leukocyte lifetime in tissues is no more than about five days.

The question was posed whether the epidermal lesions had resulted from scalp
contusion during the flight, with the exudation of acute inflammatory cells in the dermis
a secondary reactive phenomenon, or whether cosmic ray particles, in traversing the scalp,
had in themselves created the lesions. Comparison was made with the scalps of two
control animals. In one of the controls (A-3329), in which a dosimeter had been
implanted for approximately the same period of time as for the flight animals, the scalp
contained two superficial focal epidermal lesions but no polymorphonuclear leukocytes
in the dermis or subcutaneous connective tissue. This was in addition to larger areas in the
scalp in which chronic reactive changes of moderate degree were observed. The scalp of

the second control animal (A-3494), under which a dosimeter had not been implanted, was free from epidermal-dermal lesions.

If the scalp lesions were indeed attributable to cosmic ray particle "hits," then one would have anticipated that lesions having the same characteristics would be present in the skin of flight animals in areas that had not been subjected to dosimeter implantation. Accordingly, an area of skin from the back of a flight mouse was serially sectioned, then studied. Examination revealed two tiny focal lesions in the epidermis. Beneath one of these lesions the dermis contained a few mononuclear cells and polymorphonuclear leukocytes. A single striated muscle fiber deep to the other epidermal lesion was focally necrotic, and occasional polymorphonuclear leukocytes were found in its vicinity. Moreover, the area contained a few lipid-filled macrophages. In an examination of hundreds of other fields in other sections from the area of skin obtained from this animal no such cells were observed.

Comparison of the 13 lesion sites in the three scalps with the sites of the 76 particle trajectories in the subscalp dosimeters revealed only one possible coincidence between a lesion and a registered particle trajectory. The particle in question ($Z > 10$) passed initially through the mouse head, had an LET of $220 \, \text{KeV}/\mu m$ as it traversed the dosimeter, and stopped in the scalp. Although there was only this one possible coincidence between particle trajectory and lesion, there remains the possibility that some of the lesions were produced by unregistered particles, that is particles with $Z < 6$ and LET $\lesssim 150 \, \text{KeV}/\mu m$. If these lower LET particles were radiobiologically effective, one would have expected that the registered particles would have induced damage. The issue as to whether the focal lesions observed in the scalp of the four flight mice, and in the skin of the back in one of the flight mice, were produced by cosmic ray particles remains unresolved.

Eyes

Both eyes of two of the mice that survived the flight and one eye each of the other two surviving mice were retained in situ and serially sectioned along with the head and examined under the light microscope. After animal perfusion (at Pago Pago), the other two eyes of these flight animals were removed, placed in glutaraldehyde, and subsequently studied by phase contrast and by electron microscopy. One eye of the dead flight mouse was retained in situ, whereas the other was not available for study.

Five cosmic ray particles had trajectories that intersected the eyes of the four surviving mice. They were shown to have traversed the retina at varying distances from the optic nerve head. Four of the particles ($Z = 6$ to 9 for three of them, and $Z \geqslant 10$ for the fourth) went through the head before reaching the subscalp dosimeter, while the thindown direction of the fifth ($Z \geqslant 10$) was not determinable. On the average, the particle LET in the retina was $\lesssim 200 \, \text{KeV}/\mu m$. No retinal lesions were observed in the flight animals.

Calvarium, Brain, Meninges

Preliminary to examining the brain sections of the flight and the flight backup animals, a study was made of the calvaria and related tissues in the region where the monitor assemblies (dosimeters and their supporting platforms) had been implanted. The objective was to determine whether alterations occurring in these tissues could have created artifacts in the underlying brain tissue. Reference is made to erosion of the very thin calvarium (0.1 mm in thickness) which might allow invasion by an infective agent or in some manner interfere with meningeal blood supply.

Histological examination showed that each of the monitor assemblies had become surrounded by a thin fibrous tissue capsule, in and around which was a mild chronic inflammatory reaction with rare polymorphonuclear leukocytes. Giant cell reaction was surprisingly slight. There was marked atrophy of the calvarium under the monitor assemblies. Fibrosis of the dura mater was slight and was confined to a few small areas. The leptomeninges were virtually unaltered. These findings indicated that tissue reactions to the dosimeters would introduce no complicating factors in the analysis of the brains.

Mitoses in the dentate gyrus of the hippocampal formation were approximately one-third as frequent in the flight mice, and occurred about one-half as often in the flight backup mice as in non-experimental control animals. The significance of these findings is not clear, but it is suggested that the cause may be found in the internal environment of the flight and backup canisters, possibly the oxygen partial pressure. Otherwise no pathological changes were observed in the brain tissue of the flight animals or in the meninges. Special attention was given the meninges in the regions where columns of leukocytes were observed in the overlying scalps. No leukocytes were found in the meninges in these regions. If cosmic ray particles were the cause of the scalp lesions, a difference in vulnerability could be postulated: for mesodermal tissue (scalp), high vulnerability to particle radiation; for neuroectodermal tissue (meninges), low vulnerability.

Summary and Conclusions

Although detailed studies were performed in an effort to answer the question whether HZE cosmic ray particles are injurious to brain tissue, it should be appreciated that the lack of demonstrable lesions by no means negates this possibility. The lack of lesions or an inflammatory reaction that could be attributed to cosmic ray particle "hits" needs to be evaluated in light of certain limiting factors relative to the recording of particles in the subscalp dosimeters and of the LETs of the particles themselves. A total of 80 particles were registered in the dosimeters of the five mice, nine of which did not pass through the head. Among these 71 particles, only five were known to have had a downward trajectory through the dosimeter, with thindown of the particles within or in the vicinity of the head (table 1). Of the 32 particles of undeterminable thindown direction, ten of which were in the heavy to very heavy charge group (table 2), roughly half must be considered to have also passed through the brain prior to being registered in the dosimeters. Thus, most of the particles had a higher LET in the dosimeter than in the brain. Owing to the attenuation of the very high LET components of the cosmic ray particle flux by the Apollo 17 spacecraft and by the animal package shielding, most of the particles that penetrated the brain were in the lower portion of the high LET range (0.16 to 0.2 MeV/μm), and of medium to heavy charge. Most of the particles of prime interest biologically – those with a very high Z (iron group) and an LET in the MeV/μm range – did not reach the mice.

In summary, the lesions in the scalp can be taken as circumstantial evidence of vulnerability to radiation from cosmic ray particles, but this issue remains unresolved. Also remaining undetermined is the causation of the damage of the olfactory epithelium and the factor responsible for the greater exudation and the greater leukotaxis in the middle ear cavities, as well as the reasons for the difference in frequencies of mitoses encountered in the dentate gyrus of the hippocampal formation in experimental and control groups of animals. The absence of demonstrable lesions in the brain leaves unresolved the degree of vulnerability of brain tissue to this source of radiation. Obviously, substantially less shielded exposures to cosmic ray particles are needed if the effects (or the lack of effects) of the particles on brain tissue and other target structures are to be established.

Quarantine

The lunar quarantine program was designed to ensure that return of lunar material represented no threat to the public health, to agriculture, or to other living resources. It established definitely that no life exists on the moon. The crews of the three lunar quarantine missions, Apollo 11, 12, and 14, experienced no health problems as a result of their exposure to lunar samples. Plants and animals also showed no adverse effects. Stringent quarantine was terminated after Apollo 14, but lunar samples continued to be protected to guarantee that scientists would receive uncontaminated materials for study.

CHAPTER 1
THE LUNAR QUARANTINE PROGRAM

by

Richard S. Johnston
John A. Mason
Bennie C. Wooley, Ph.D.[*]
Gary W. McCollum
Bernard J. Mieszkuc

Lyndon B. Johnson Space Center

Introduction

In 1963, a special subcommittee of the Space Science Board of the National Academy of Sciences was convened to consider the general problem of handling material and personnel returned from flights to the moon. The subcommittee recommended that NASA establish a quarantine program to ensure that the Earth and its ecology would be protected from any possible hazard associated with the return of lunar material.

The development of the requirements, the philosophy, and the guidelines which resulted in the Apollo quarantine program were the joint responsibility of NASA and a newly-formed Interagency Committee on Back-Contamination (ICBC). Those federal agencies responsible for protecting public health, agriculture, and other living and natural resources had representatives on the ICBC. Included on the Committee were members of the National Academy of Sciences and representatives from the U.S. Public Health Service, U.S. Department of Agriculture, and U.S. Department of Interior.

The charter of the Committee defined its purpose as follows:

1. To protect the public's health, agriculture, and other living resources.

2. To protect the integrity of the lunar samples and the scientific experiments.

3. To ensure that the operational aspects of the program were least compromised.

An interagency agreement, which served as a basis for the development of the quarantine program, was developed and approved. Implementation of the program

---

[*]Currently with Becton, Dickinson, and Company, Rutherford, N.J.

was the responsibility of NASA. The Committee served only as an advisory body to review and approve plans proposed by NASA.

The quarantine objectives of the Apollo Program included biological containment of the crewmen, lunar samples, and other lunar-exposed material until released from quarantine, and biological assessment of the returned lunar materials to ensure that safe release could be effected.

The Apollo Back-Contamination Program was divided into three phases (figure 1). The first phase was concerned with procedures to be followed by the crewmen while inflight to eliminate the return of lunar-surface contaminants in the Command Module (CM). The second phase included spacecraft and crew recovery and the provisions for isolation and transport of the crewmen, spacecraft, and lunar samples to the Lyndon B. Johnson Space Center (JSC). The third phase encompassed the quarantine operations in the Lunar Receiving Laboratory (LRL).

In order to meet the ICBC requirements, NASA began to plan special quarantine facilities, equipment, and operational procedures. The facilities and procedures made necessary by the quarantine program were often well beyond the state of the art. Quarantine represented a major impact on the Apollo Program. It meant that the crew, the Command Module, and the lunar material had to be isolated from the moment of arrival back on Earth.

Specific physical science and biomedical requirements for the collection, return, and examination of lunar samples were formulated. Whereas the primary concern of the physical science advisory groups was to ensure that procedures and equipment were developed that would minimize the possibility of the contamination of the lunar samples by terrestrial organic and inorganic material, the primary concern of the biomedical advisory groups was to ensure that equipment and procedures were developed that would minimize the possibility of introducing the lunar material into the biosphere. Although the possibility of discovering an existing life system was considered remote, it could not be ignored. Consequently, appropriate quarantine precautions were required for both the crewmen and the lunar samples.

Program Description

Quarantine Requirements

By observation of plant and animal diseases, it was determined that most terrestrial disease agents were capable of invading a host and causing evident disease symptoms within 21 days after exposure of the host. Most disease agents capable of causing epidemic or rapidly spreading diseases were sufficiently virulent to be transmitted in less than 21 days. The ICBC decided that a crew quarantine period of at least 21 days should be required after each Apollo mission.

Intensive medical examinations of the flight crewmembers during quarantine determined if any medical problems existed as a result of exposure to lunar material. The returned lunar samples and equipment were evaluated to ensure that release of these items to an investigation team did not represent a hazard. To

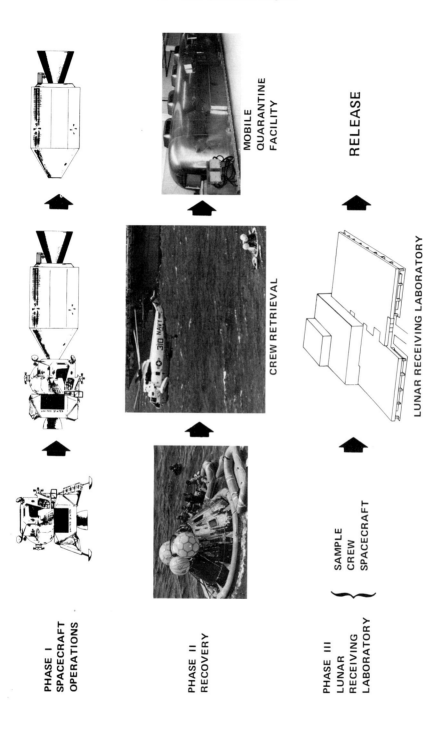

PHASE I
SPACECRAFT
OPERATIONS

PHASE II
RECOVERY

CREW RETRIEVAL

MOBILE
QUARANTINE
FACILITY

RELEASE

PHASE III
LUNAR
RECEIVING
LABORATORY

SAMPLE
CREW
SPACECRAFT

LUNAR RECEIVING LABORATORY

Figure 1. Apollo Back-Contamination Program.

accomplish this and other functions, the Lunar Receiving Laboratory was constructed at the Johnson Space Center to serve in the following manner:

1. As a quarantine facility for returning Apollo crewmembers, spacecraft, equipment, and lunar samples.

2. As an isolation facility where specific biomedical evaluations of the lunar samples could be performed to determine whether the samples contained any hazardous replicating microorganisms.

3. As an isolation facility where time-critical physical science investigations could be performed. (Time-critical investigations were those for which data would be lost or seriously degraded if the experiments were not initiated during the quarantine period.)

4. As a facility for lunar sample preparation and distribution to outside principal investigators for detailed scientific analyses.

Quarantine Assumptions and Guidelines

The coordination of the multidisciplinary, and often contradictory, requirements presented a unique series of problems, many of them associated with the hypothetical nature of an unknown lunar hazard. If precise scientific and technical decisions were to be made, basic assumptions and guidelines had to be followed. Those established for development of the Lunar Quarantine Program (LQP) were as follows:

1. The existence of hazardous, replicating microorganisms on the moon would be assumed.

2. The preservation of human life should take precedence over the maintenance of quarantine.

3. Biological containment requirements should be based on the most stringent means used for containment of infectious terrestrial agents.

4. The sterilization requirement should be based on methods needed for the destruction of the most resistant terrestrial forms.

5. Hazard detection procedures should be based on an alteration of the ecology and classical pathogenicity.

6. The extent of the biological test protocol would be limited to facilities approved by the Congress, to well-defined systems, and to biological systems of known ecological importance.

Together, guidelines 1 and 2 provided the basis for the Lunar Quarantine Program; that is, although the probability that life existed on the moon was extremely low, the risk was sufficiently high that a quarantine program was justified. However, this risk was not considered great enough to permit an otherwise avoidable injury and/or loss of human life just to maintain the integrity of the program.

Many critical decisions, especially those involving emergency procedures, could not have been made without the establishment of the second guideline. Typical examples were emergency procedures for escape of crewmembers should the Command Module begin to sink after splashdown, and emergency exit procedures should a major fire occur in the LRL living quarters for quarantined personnel. The third guideline became the basic criterion for the design and operation of the required containment systems. Again, the dilemma was that procedures and equipment had to be designed, fabricated, and operated to contain microbial agents that were assumed to exist on the moon and about which no characteristics were known. It was decided that the biological containment requirements should be based on the most stringent means used at that time to contain infectious terrestrial agents. The fourth guideline established that sterilization requirements should be based on the method needed for destruction of the most resistant terrestrial life forms. Terrestrial spore-forming microorganisms were used as models in providing design criteria for equipment and guidelines for sterilization procedures.

The fifth guideline concerned the detection of hazards assumed to be present. The term "hazard" had to be defined before a method of detection could be developed. Procedures were limited to those capable of detecting an agent that would exhibit classical pathogenicity to some terrestrial life form or that could establish itself in a terrestrial environment and thereby alter the ecology. This guideline limited the search to the detection of replicating microorganisms. Parameters such as toxicity were eliminated; even if the lunar samples were highly toxic, the toxicity characteristics would be self-limiting and non-propagating.

The sixth guideline dealt with methods to be used for the detection of replicating microorganisms that could cause disease or establish and replicate themselves in some terrestrial environment. The guidelines made a first level of decision possible in that the efforts of the biological test program were directed toward the specific detection of hazards to the biosphere. Because the program was focused on hazards to the terrestrial environment, only terrestrial environmental conditions were acceptable as test systems.

Three limitations were set for the biological test protocols in support of the quarantine program. Test systems for which little or no baseline or background information was available were not considered. Systems of known ecological importance were stressed. Lastly, the size of the facility and the scope of activities were determined for planning purposes.

The period of quarantine for spacecraft, crew, and lunar samples was considered to have begun as soon as the Apollo crewmen left the moon. Isolation was accomplished by containing men and equipment first in the Mobile Quarantine Facility (MQF) located on the hangar deck of the recovery ship, and, later, the Lunar Receiving Laboratory at the Johnson Space Center. A crew surgeon and recovery engineer joined the crew in the MQF and remained with them throughout the period of quarantine.

Boxes containing samples of lunar rocks and soil from early missions were opened at JSC in a unique vacuum chamber. The chamber was designed to ensure sample sterility and to provide a method for preliminary examination without compromising sample integrity by exposure to air. The vacuum simulated lunar pressure.

The quarantine program was carried out with minimal breaks. There were a few instances in the LRL operations when technicians had to be quarantined because of leaks in vacuum chamber gloves while personnel were handling the lunar material or when similar faults in the other protective devices occurred. These instances were infrequent. In no instance was the biological containment of the crewmen, lunar samples, and/or any other exposed material compromised.

Equipment and Facilities

Equipment

Spacecraft Equipment. The Apollo spacecraft carried equipment specifically to maintain cleanliness and to reduce the quantity of lunar dust in the spacecraft environment. This equipment included vacuum brushes, lunar equipment stowage bags, and other items to maintain spacecraft cleanliness.

Recovery Equipment. A Mobile Quarantine Facility (MQF) was designed and fabricated to house and transport the Apollo crewmen from the recovery ship to the Lunar Receiving Laboratory. The MQF was equipped to house six people for a period of ten days and provided a lounge, galley, and sleeping and toilet facilities. It was powered through several systems to interface with various ships, aircraft, and transportation vehicles. Quarantine was assured in the MQF through the maintenance of negative internal pressure and by filtration of effluent air.

Waste water from washing and showers was chemically treated and stored in special containers. Body wastes (urine and feces) were stored in special tanks in the Mobile Quarantine Facility. Items were passed in or out through a submersible transfer lock. The MQF could be serviced with utilities (power, communications, alarm system) from shipboard, aircraft, and/or trucks. Redundant power systems and fans assured maintenance of a negative pressure. Specially packaged and controlled meals could be passed into the facility to be prepared in a microwave oven. Medical equipment was also provided for use in immediate postlanding crew examinations and tests.

Biological isolation garments were used in Apollo 11 to isolate the crew from the Earth's environment and from contact with recovery personnel. These garments were constructed from a fabric which effectively isolated microorganisms from the crewman's body. The garment was donned in the spacecraft before the helicopter hoist operation and was worn until the crew entered the MQF aboard the primary recovery ship. The suit was fabricated of nylon. A respirator was worn with the garment. It featured an air-inlet flapper valve and high efficiency air-outlet filter to biologically filter expired gas. The Apollo 11 crew used a heavier biological isolation garment, but this was discarded as an unnecessary precaution after the initial lunar landing flight. On later missions, a lightweight overgarment was used when transferring from the Command Module to the MQF.

Special containers were fabricated for return of the medical and lunar samples, films, and data tapes from the recovery area to the LRL.

Lunar Receiving Laboratory

The final phase of the Apollo back-contamination program was completed in the JSC Lunar Receiving Laboratory (figures 2 and 3). The LRL, housed in Building 37 at JSC, covers 7700 m² (83 000 ft²) of floor space and includes several distinct areas. These are: the Crew Reception Area (CRA), Vacuum Laboratory, Sample Laboratories (Physical and Bio-Science), and an administrative and support area. Special building systems were employed to maintain airflow into sample-handling areas and the Crew Reception Area to sterilize liquid waste and to incinerate contaminated air from the primary containment systems.

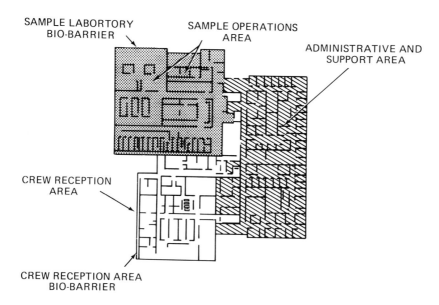

Figure 2. Functional area floor plan.

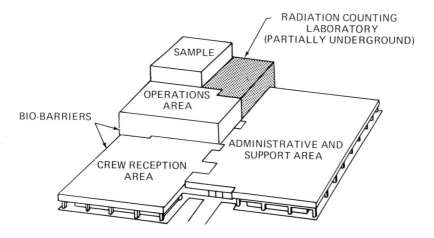

Figure 3. Perspective view of functional areas.

Biological containment in the Lunar Receiving Laboratory relied on a primary and secondary barrier system. The primary biological barrier consisted of the vacuum complex and Class III biological cabinets. A secondary barrier was maintained in the Crew Reception Area and the sample laboratory by maintaining the areas at negative pressure with respect to the atmospheric pressure external to the building. Within these two barriers the postmission work on returned lunar samples was performed. The design and operational features for the primary and secondary barriers are described below.

The need for a central facility to carry out the foregoing functions was identified early in 1964. A series of studies preceded the construction of the building, which began in July 1966. The test system equipment was developed and installed during the period from mid-1966 until approximately September 1968.

The Lunar Receiving Laboratory was built to meet the most stringent biological containment requirements of the U.S. Army Biological Laboratories, Fort Detrick. This was a unique facility in many respects. It contained a vacuum chamber which permitted scientists to manipulate and examine lunar samples without breaking the vacuum or risking contamination of the samples or themselves. It had a low-level radiation counting facility and could safely accommodate a large variety of biological specimens.

Primary Biological Barrier.

The Vacuum Complex. The vacuum complex was the area in which sample containers were opened and processing of the lunar material was initiated. This system was sterilized before return of the containers to ensure lunar samples would not be contaminated with terrestrial microorganisms. All materials entering the vacuum complex after premission sterilization were sterilized using peracetic acid. All items leaving the complex during the quarantine period were either placed in vacuum-tight containers, the exteriors of which were sterilized with peracetic acid, or were directly sterilized with the acid. Effluent gases from the vacuum chamber pumps were passed through absolute biological filters, incinerated, and filtered again prior to venting to the outside environment. All lunar samples left the vacuum complex in sterilized vacuum-tight containers. The containers were placed in sealed plastic bags for handling within the sample laboratory.

Biological Cabinets. Biological and physical/chemical testing of the lunar samples was performed within biological cabinets. These cabinets were gastight enclosures through which all manipulations were performed using neoprene gloves. Air or nitrogen entered the cabinets through absolute biological filters, was incinerated, and was filtered again before being vented to the outside. All material entering the cabinets was sterilized. The cabinets were operated at a pressure negative with respect to the laboratory to ensure that any leak that developed would be directed into the cabinets rather than into the laboratory.

Secondary Biological Barrier. The rooms in which the cabinets were housed were also maintained at a pressure negative with respect to the adjacent corridors. This guaranteed that any escaping lunar material would be contained. The secondary biological barrier which surrounded the sample laboratory included facility systems and operational procedures. Tight building construction was used and all penetrations were sealed. The sample laboratory had a single-pass air conditioning supply and exhaust system which maintained the area at a pressure negative with respect to the outside air. Inlet air was filtered, and air exited through absolute biological filters. All liquid waste coming from the sample laboratory area was sterilized with steam before being transported to the JSC sewage treatment plant. All solid materials including waste, clothing, and trash were sterilized. The sample laboratory area received supplies during quarantine operations through ultraviolet-lighted airlocks.

Procedures

Lunar and Command Module Operations

The Apollo crewmembers represented the prime source of contamination to the lunar surface. Three other sources of contamination were: (1) waste products such as feces, urine, and residual food; (2) viable terrestrial microorganisms released during Lunar Module depressurization; and (3) microorganisms present in the LM waste water system. Procedures were defined to eliminate massive contamination of the lunar surface from these three sources. Of the three, waste products were the chief source of potential contamination. To minimize the thrust required for lift-off from the lunar surface, waste products had to be removed from the ascent stage of the LM. All waste products were stored in the equipment bays of the descent stage. Even if the storage bags had leaked or the integrity of the containers had been violated, microbial contamination would have been contained within the descent stage of the LM and not deposited on the lunar surface.

The primary quarantine-related concern in collecting lunar samples was to minimize their contamination with viable terrestrial microorganisms. Such contamination would have complicated interpretation of biological findings. Lunar samples were collected with sterile tools and returned to the Lunar Receiving Laboratory in a sterile environment. The types of materials used for fabricating tools and other items that came in contact with lunar material were severely limited by the physical scientific contamination requirements and by weight restrictions. A high-temperature bakeout under vacuum conditions was considered the best method for removing volatile terrestrial contaminants from the hardware. This treatment, at a sufficient temperature for a sufficient period of time, also satisfied the sterilization requirements for the hardware.

The procedures and the hardware necessary for the stowage of collected lunar samples were considered next. Because the lunar material had existed for millions of years in an almost perfect vacuum, the physical scientists decided that the lunar samples should be transported to Earth under environmental conditions as near to those on the moon as technically feasible. This decision necessitated the design and fabrication of a pressure vessel that could be filled with lunar samples and sealed on the lunar surface, and in which the internal environment could be maintained throughout the sample transfer from the lunar surface to the LRL. Because the pressure vessel had to be an ultraclean, gastight container, no additional requirements were necessary in terms of quarantine control.

The Lunar Module was designed to include a bacterial filter system to prevent contamination of the lunar surface when the cabin atmosphere was released at the start of lunar exploration. Before reentering the LM, the crewmen brushed any lunar surface dust or dirt from their space suits. They scraped their feet on the LM footpad and kicked the LM ladder while ascending to dislodge any particles on their boots.

After cabin repressurization, the LM was launched from the lunar surface and docked with the Command Module. The CM tunnel was pressurized and checks made to ensure that an adequate pressurized seal had been made. The crewmen then vacuumed the Lunar Module, their space suits, and the lunar surface equipment. To prevent dust particles from being transferred from the Lunar Module atmosphere to the Command Module, provisions were made to ensure a positive CM pressure relative to the LM.

The Apollo Lunar and Command Modules had separate environmental control systems that removed dirt particles continually from the spacecraft atmosphere. In normal operation, the environmental control-space suit systems were used to condition the cabin atmosphere. Cabin gas was drawn into the system, and, as it passed through the lithium hydroxide canister, nearly all dirt particles were filtered from the atmosphere. This cleansing action reduced the amount of airborne lunar dust in the LM at the time of docking with the Command Module. The 63-hour operation of the CM environmental control system had the capability to virtually remove all lunar dust from the atmosphere which had been transferred from the Lunar Module during docked operations.

The vacuuming system allowed material as small as 0.3 micron to be trapped in the lithium hydroxide canisters. Visible liquids were removed by the liquid dump system. The crewmen used towels to wipe surfaces clean of liquids and/or dirt particles. The three suit hoses were located at random positions around the spacecraft for positive ventilation and cabin atmosphere filtration.

Recovery

The general requirements of the recovery quarantine operation were as follows:

1. *Crew Safety.* To provide a safe method for the retrieval and return of crew and spacecraft.

2. *Biological Isolation.* To provide isolation during the recovery operation and during the movement of the crew and equipment from the recovery area to the LRL.

3. *Sustenance Provisioning.* To provide eating, sleeping, and hygienic facilities for the crew and technical personnel during the return phase.

4. *Medical and Debriefing Provisioning.* To provide some limited medical facilities and interfaces during the recovery and transportation phases.

5. *Transportation.* To provide suitable hardware for the transportation of the crew, CM, and hardware by ship, aircraft, and truck.

The quarantine phase of the recovery operation began as soon as the Command Module had been located and the flotation collar installed by swimmers. The swimmers were instructed to withdraw upwind from the immediate vicinity of the Command Module after installing the collar. An additional swimmer, dressed in a protective garment, was then delivered by helicopter to the raft attached to the flotation collar on the spacecraft. The spacecraft hatch was opened momentarily and three protective garments and masks were passed to the crew.

After the crewmen had donned the garments in the spacecraft, they closed the postlanding ventilation system valves. The hatch was then opened and they egressed into the raft which contained a decontaminant solution. The hatch was closed immediately after egress, and the swimmer who had provided the crew with their garments and masks sponged them off with a solution of organic iodine, an antibacterial agent. The spacecraft hatch was also washed down with the solution (figure 4).

Figure 4. Apollo Crewmen in biological isolation garments
egressing their spacecraft.

The Command Module crew was retrieved by helicopter and delivered to the aircraft carrier. The helicopter was then towed to the immediate vicinity of the Mobile Quarantine Facility where the crew left the helicopter and immediately entered the Mobile Quarantine Facility. Following crew egress, the swimmer decontaminated the Command Module, the collar, the raft, and his own protective garment with an antibacterial agent. When the Command Module exterior had been decontaminated, all decontamination equipment and the liferafts used by the Apollo crewmen were sunk at sea.

The Command Module was retrieved by the ship, towed to the immediate vicinity of the MQF, and coupled to it with a plastic tunnel. The recovery engineer from the MQF entered the Command Module via the tunnel, removed samples and data, and completed Command Module shutdown procedures. The Command Module hatch was resealed and remained sealed until it was placed in the Lunar Receiving Laboratory in Houston.

The biomedical samples and lunar sample containers, film, data, etc., from the CM were packaged and decontaminated for return to the Johnson Space Center. The Mobile Quarantine Facility with the astronauts, one crew surgeon, and one recovery engineer was transported by the recovery ship to Hawaii where it was placed aboard an aircraft for the flight to Houston. In Houston, the MQF was taken to the Johnson Space Center and coupled to the Lunar Receiving Laboratory for transfer of crew, associated personnel, and equipment. The MQF was then sealed and placed in quarantine as authorized.

The Command Module was also subjected to reaction control system decontamination and pyro-safing in Hawaii. The CM was then transported to the Johnson Space Center where it arrived approximately five days after the astronauts.

Quarantine of Personnel

The final phase of the Apollo back-contamination program was completed in the Lunar Receiving Laboratory. The sequential flow of crewmen, spacecraft, and lunar samples is shown in figure 5. The crewmen and spacecraft were quarantined for a minimum of 21 days and were released after the completion of certain prescribed tests. The lunar sample was quarantined for a period of 50 to 80 days, depending on the results of extensive biological tests. In addition to the three Apollo crewmembers, other personnel quarantined in the LRL were two crew surgeons, a recovery engineer, medical laboratory technicians, cooks, and stewards.

During the quarantine period, the crew and their immediate contacts underwent daily medical examinations. Basic observations consisted of recording oral temperature and pulse rate, and a brief interview by the crew surgeon. Biological specimens were obtained from the crew on the twelfth and eighteenth days after lunar departure, and the crew underwent another complete physical examination on the twenty-first day. Selected microbiologic and immunologic examinations were also conducted at several points in the quarantine. The purpose of the latter examinations was to provide diagnostic information in the event of clinical illness.

Provisions were made to treat routine illness and minor injuries within the Crew Reception Area. Equipment and a small working pharmacy were available. Serious illness and injury were also to be treated onsite so far as possible. But, had any of the Apollo crewmen or support personnel become critically ill or injured, the quarantine would have been broken and the individual transported to the nearest appropriate medical facility.

In the event of a serious crew illness, a quarantine Medical Advisory Panel was available for consultation. This panel consisted of experts in various aspects of infectious disease empowered to provide diagnostic information pertinent to any release recommendation.

Release recommendations for the crew and support staff were developed by the medical staff. The medical status of both the crew and the support personnel exposed to the crew and/or to the lunar mission equipment was taken into consideration. Technically, release of the Apollo crews might have been delayed because of illness among the support staff. This, however, never occurred.

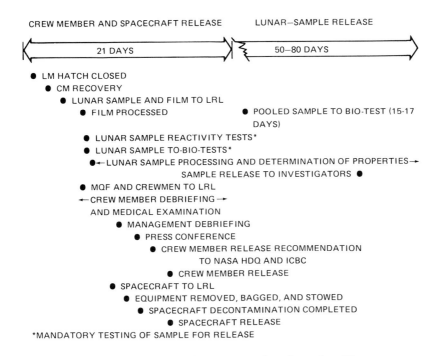

CREW MEMBER AND SPACECRAFT RELEASE   LUNAR–SAMPLE RELEASE

21 DAYS   50–80 DAYS

● LM HATCH CLOSED
  ● CM RECOVERY
    ● LUNAR SAMPLE AND FILM TO LRL
      ● FILM PROCESSED   ● POOLED SAMPLE TO BIO-TEST (15-17
                                      DAYS)
     ● LUNAR SAMPLE REACTIVITY TESTS*
     ● LUNAR SAMPLE TO-BIO-TESTS*
     ●←LUNAR SAMPLE PROCESSING AND DETERMINATION OF PROPERTIES→
                    SAMPLE RELEASE TO INVESTIGATORS ●
  ● MQF AND CREWMEN TO LRL
  ←CREW MEMBER DEBRIEFING →
    AND MEDICAL EXAMINATION
           ● MANAGEMENT DEBRIEFING
             ● PRESS CONFERENCE
               ● CREW MEMBER RELEASE RECOMMENDATION
                   TO NASA HDQ AND ICBC
                 ● CREW MEMBER RELEASE
  ● SPACECRAFT TO LRL
      ● EQUIPMENT REMOVED, BAGGED, AND STOWED
        ● SPACECRAFT DECONTAMINATION COMPLETED
           ● SPACECRAFT RELEASE
*MANDATORY TESTING OF SAMPLE FOR RELEASE

Figure 5. Apollo Back-Contamination flow chart, phase III.

To safeguard the health of LRL personnel, every worker was subjected to extensive medical examinations before each Apollo lunar mission. Because of the potential hazard of working with lunar material, a requirement was established that pregnant employees, all persons taking medication, and those requiring medical aids such as crutches, braces, or hearing aids would not be permitted to enter the secondary biological barrier. In addition, serum pools were collected from each individual who might be exposed to lunar material. The stored samples would serve as a baseline for analysis of any medical complications that might arise in the years following the exposure.

The quarantine program was in effect for the crews of Apollo 11, 12, and 14. Procedures differed very little for the three flights. The quarantine of the Apollo 11 crew was uneventful. No signs or symptoms of infectious disease related to lunar exposure became apparent in any of the crewmen or support staff. No microorganisms attributable to an extraterrestrial source were recovered from the crewmen or the spacecraft. Release of crew, equipment, and lunar samples took place on schedule.

No variations of the quarantine procedure occurred during recovery and return of the Apollo 12 crew. However, the biological isolation garments used for Apollo 11 were not used for Apollo 12 or 14 since they proved to be uncomfortably hot during recovery operations. They were replaced with lightweight coveralls and biological masks which filtered exhaled air. No significant trends were noted in any biochemical, immunological, or hematological parameters in either the flight crew or support personnel.

The only change in quarantine procedures for the Apollo 14 mission was the use of two MQFs and two helicopter transfers of the crew and support personnel. This procedure was implemented to return the crew to the Lunar Receiving Laboratory five days earlier than on the previous lunar landing missions. No signs of illness or significant trends related to lunar material exposure were reported, and again, release took place on schedule.

Quarantine of the Spacecraft

There was no plan to decontaminate the spacecraft unless anomalies occurred during a mission that might have indicated the need for an early spacecraft release. Provisions were made, however, for spacecraft decontamination, if required. Before installing the biological barrier (door panels) on the CM, the exterior was photographed, and preparations were made for connecting the decontamination equipment. These activities were performed by non-quarantined personnel, who did not deal with "contaminated" systems. These persons then left the room in which the spacecraft was located and biological barriers were installed.

The spacecraft room contained all equipment required for decontamination of the Command Module. There were also communications and closed circuit television for monitoring and supporting cleanup and decontamination activities. Personnel from the Crew Reception Area were trained to open the Command Module hatch and remove the double-bag stowed equipment, including lithium hydroxide canisters, fecal bags, food bags, and space suits. The individual working inside the CM doffed shoe covers upon egress. All persons then reentered the CRA and showered. Thus the likelihood of contaminating the Crew Reception Area and space suit room was minimal.

Formaldehyde decontamination of the Command Module cabin and suit circuit was accomplished without reopening the hatch. Following a minimum 24-hour kill period, the hatch was opened and the cabin exhausted through the room air conditioning system. The water and waste management systems were also decontaminated with aqueous formaldehyde (formalin) for 24 hours. Spore strips were placed at random locations in the CM to verify decontamination effectiveness.

Quarantine of the Lunar Sample

The returned lunar sample was processed through a sequence of steps which resulted in the following:

1. Data upon which to base a release decision.

2. Preliminary scientific data upon which to base a sample distribution plan.

3. Portions of the lunar sample packaged for distribution to principal investigators.

4. Portions of the lunar sample sealed and protected for future experiments.

5. Time-critical experiments.

The incoming lunar material was contained in two sample return containers and one contingency bag. A portion of the sample was lunar "rock," documented as to location of collection. The bulk of the sample, however, was loose surface material, predominantly below 1 cm (.40 in.) in size. Lunar sample operations are summarized in figure 6.

On arrival at the Lunar Receiving Laboratory, sample boxes were moved through an airlock and through three decontamination chambers to sterilize the outside of the containers. They were then sent into a vacuum chamber where a technician punctured a diaphragm to draw off any gases. The sample was then passed on to a mass spectrometer to determine (1) if the interior of the boxes had been contaminated by the Earth's atmosphere, and (2) if any gases could be identified as being of lunar origin.

The boxes were opened in an environment free of terrestrial organisms. The nominal mode of operation called for opening the sample boxes in the special chamber described earlier which operated at a vacuum of 1.33×10^{-4} N/m^2 (10^{-6} mm Hg). An alternate mode employed the same chamber but with an atmosphere of sterile nitrogen at a pressure slightly below atmospheric. A contingency mode was to open the containers in a Class III biological cabinet. Each lunar rock and portion of fine material was examined, photographed from six different angles, and observed visually through glass ports and through microscopes. A representative sample was committed to quarantine testing. Small chips of each rock were examined for physical and chemical properties. Selected specimens were subjected to special tests, radioactivity determination. The balance of the material was sealed and protected for later use.

The preponderance of scientific work on the lunar sample was done by some 150 to 200 principal investigators throughout the world. Each investigator received a type and amount of lunar material suitable for his work and returned the residues to the Lunar Receiving Laboratory for further use by other researchers. A few of the principal investigators performed their experiments in the LRL during quarantine because of the time-critical nature of the data being sought.

Release of lunar samples was contingent upon meeting either one of the following:

1. Biological safety tests upon representative portions of the samples. These tests included: bacteriology, mycology, virology-mycoplasma, mammalian animals, botanical systems, invertebrate/lower vertebrate systems.

2. Sterilization of the sample by the use of dry heat during the quarantine period.

All protocols were designed to be completed within 30 days from the introduction of the sample to the laboratories. This was to be increased to 60 days in the event significant numbers of microbial contaminants were found in the sample. By 60 days, sufficient data would have been available to evaluate the requirement for second order testing.

Quarantine of Flight Equipment

All flight equipment exposed to lunar surface materials was placed under quarantine restrictions. The equipment included films, data tapes, logs, and other flight equipment.

Procedures for quarantine and release of the equipment were as follows:

Flight Film. Flight film was received in the Crew Reception Area and, after appropriate preparation, was passed out for processing. Film from the Apollo 11 mission

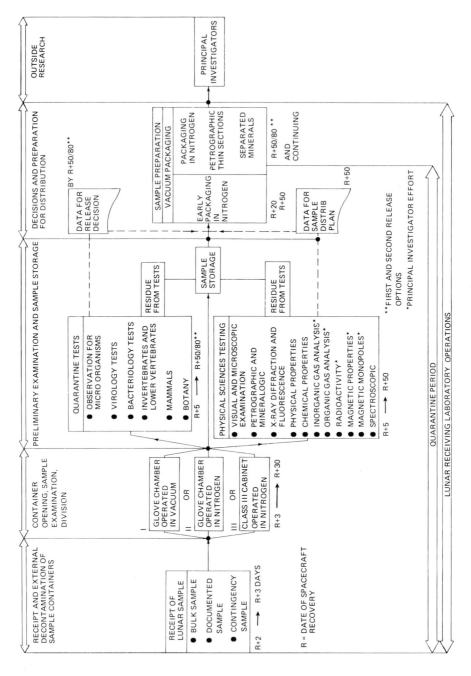

Figure 6. Lunar sample operations.

was sterilized with ethylene oxide. After the Apollo 11 mission, sterilization of flight film was not required.

Data Tapes. Data tapes were received in the CRA and, after appropriate preparation, were sterilized using ethylene oxide gas and passed through the biological barrier. The tapes were then handled using normal procedures.

Other Spacecraft Equipment. All other items were either held in approved biological containers until the release of lunar samples or were processed using the procedures outlined in figure 7. Requirements for early release were kept to a minimum.

CRA EQUIPMENT RELEASE CRITERIA

Item	Example	Treatment
Material exposed to lunar surface	Pressure suits	Hold until sample release
or		or
Equipment concentrating lunar material	LiOH canisters	Steam sterilization
or		or
LM equipment	Logs	Dry heat sterilization
		or
		Peracetic acid
		or
		Hypochlorite dunk
		or
		Formaldehyde
CM Hardware (not concentrating lunar material)	Food bags Fecal bags dse recorder	As above or Ethylene oxide and release with crew
Special Cases: Data Tape		Ethylene oxide and release with (spore strip controls included with film/tape)
Flight Film		Sterlization not required
Surveyor Equipment		See text.

Figure 7. Crew Reception Area equipment release criteria.

Summary

The crews of Apollo 11, 12, and 14 experienced no health problems as a result of their exposure to lunar material. The test species, plant and animal, which were exposed to and injected with lunar material showed no adverse alterations or ill effects from exposure. Since exhaustive studies of the astronauts and returned lunar samples from Apollo 11 and 12 indicated there was no hazard to Earth's biosphere, the Interagency Committee on Back-Contamination, in January of 1970, concurred in NASA's recommendation that stringent quarantine rules be abandoned for future Apollo missions to the moon.

To ensure that lunar material represented absolutely no danger to the Earth's environment, the quarantine program remained in effect for the Apollo 14 flight and was then abandoned. Although the formal quarantine for the crew, spacecraft, and lunar samples was over, procedures for handling lunar material and protecting it from contamination remained in effect for the Apollo 15, 16, and 17 missions. This guaranteed that scientists performing tests on the material would have uncontaminated samples.

CHAPTER 2
QUARANTINE TESTING AND BIOCHARACTERIZATION
OF LUNAR MATERIALS

by

Gerald R. Taylor, Ph.D.
Bernard J. Mieszkuc

Lyndon B. Johnson Space Center

Richard C. Simmonds, D.V.M.

U.S. Air Force

Charles H. Walkinshaw, Ph.D.

U.S. Department of Agriculture

Introduction

The objective of the quarantine testing and biocharacterization portion of the Apollo medical program was to test appropriate representative lunar samples for the possible presence of agents that might be infectious or toxic for plants, man, and other animals. The goal of the laboratory was to provide safety clearance for lunar samples within a period of approximately 30 days. Lunar materials were analyzed in an isolated environment. These analyses were performed immediately after the lunar samples were unpacked in the Lunar Receiving Laboratory (LRL) at the Johnson Space Center. Small but representative samples of lunar material were used to assess whether they contained microorganisms, and to ensure that the lunar materials were nonhazardous to the selected test species.

The quarantine testing included a wide variety of biological species. Approximately 500 gm of lunar material were required for each investigation. Analyses of data from the Apollo 11, 12, and 14 missions indicated that no microbial life forms had been recovered from the lunar material. For subsequent missions, the containment aspects of the postflight quarantine were omitted and the biocharacterization or preliminary biomedical evaluation of lunar materials was initiated. The aims were to characterize the lunar material with respect to its ability to stimulate biological activity, and to measure possible microbial contamination of lunar samples. For the Apollo 15 mission, the number of biological tests was reduced to one-third of those performed on previous missions. Further reduction in the scope of the program occurred after the Apollo 15 mission.

425

Except for the exposure of animal tissue culture cells to suspensions of lunar material, animal test systems were omitted from the Apollo 16 and 17 protocols.

All test protocols were extensively reviewed by the scientific community, the American Institute of Biological Sciences, and the Interagency Committee on Back-Contamination. The Interagency Committee was formed of representatives of various agencies of the Federal Government for the purpose of reviewing protocols to assure that the biosphere would not be contaminated with organisms from the moon. The aim was to use as many different kinds of organisms as possible. The organisms chosen were well known research tools, including mice, oysters, paramecia, and fishes.

The results of the first experiments in several completely new fields, namely lunar agriculture, lunar soil microbiology, and ecology of lunar soil on contact with terrestrial organisms, are presented in this chapter. It should be stated at the outset that the implication of the findings reported here are largely speculative because of limited experimentation. However, findings are consistent with the generally accepted hypothesis that the lunar surface is now, and has always been, sterile.

Botanical Investigations

The botanical quarantine studies at the Lunar Receiving Laboratory were designed to determine whether lunar material contained any agent capable of generating an epidemic disease in representative species of the plant kingdom. These tests were conducted under conditions which would ensure confinement of any infectious agents that might be found in the lunar materials or generated in the lunar-exposed plants (Walkinshaw et al., 1970). Class III biological glove boxes were used to achieve the required protective containment (Kemmerer et al., 1969).

A total of 35 plant species were exposed to lunar material returned during the Apollo 11 and 12 missions (table 1). Four test systems were employed. These included liquid or solid cultures of algal cells, germinating spores and seeds, actively growing seedlings, and tissue cultures on solid media.

Lunar samples used in Apollo 11, 12, and 14 studies were composites of representative rock fragments and surface fines; samples used in Apollo 15, 16, and 17 postflight studies were composites of surface fines. The samples were handled and analyzed as described by Johnson and co-workers (1972). Descriptions of the terrestrial controls may also be found in the work by Johnson and his associates.

Treatment of algal cultures with lunar material inhibited growth in dense cellular suspensions and stimulated growth in cultures grown on semisolid mineral media. Growth promotion was evident by marked increase in cell density in areas adjacent to lunar particles. Treatment of algal cells by exposure to lunar material suspended via gentle agitation resulted in cultures having higher respiration rates than untreated controls. Microscopic examination of treated cultures revealed no significant differences between lunar- and terrestrial-treated cells.

The fern, *Onoclea sensibililis L.*, which was tested with each composite sample, appeared to be the most sensitive plant for demonstrating that lunar material can act as a source of nutrients for plants. Clumps of spores germinating on lunar material placed within a well cut into mineral agar showed a severalfold increase in mass. The resulting

Table 1

Plant Species Challenged With Lunar Materials
in Apollo 11 or 12 Quarantine Studies

Species	Common Name	Challenge System*
Allium cepa L.	Onion	SG
Anacystis nidulans (Richt) Drouet	Blue-green alga	A
Brassica oleracea L.	Cabbage	SG, S
Capsicum frutescens L.	Pepper	SG, S
Chenopodium amaranticolor Coste and Reyn.	Weed	S
Chlorella pyrenoidosa Chick	Green alga	A
Citrullus vulgaris Schrad.	Watermelon	S
Citrus limonia L.	Lime	S
Cucumis melo L.	Cantaloupe	S
Cucumis sativus L.	Cucumber	S
Glycine soja (L.) Sieb and Zucc.	Soybean	TC
Haplopappus gracilis (Nutt.) Gray	Weed	TC
Helianthus annuus L.	Sunflower	TC
Lactuca sativa L.	Lettuce	SG
Lycopersicum esculentum Mill.	Tomato	S
Lycopodium cernuum L.	Clubmoss	G
Marchantia polymorpha L.	Liverwort	G
Nicotiana tabacum L. (albino)	Tobacco	TC
Nicotiana tabacum L. (habituated)	Tobacco	TC
Nicotiana tabacum L. var. Samson	Tobacco	SG
Nicotiana tabacum L. var. Xanthi NC	Tobacco	S
Onoclea sensibilis L.	Sensitive fern	SPG
Oryza sativa L.	Rice	TC
Phaeodactylum tricornutum Bohlin	Diatom	A
Phaseolus aureus L.	Mung bean	SG
Phaseolus vulgaris L.	Common bean	S
Pinus elliottii Engelm.	Slash pine	S
Pinus lambertiana Dougl.	Sugar pine	TC
Pinus palustris Mill.	Longleaf pine	TC
Prophyridium cruentum (Ag.) Naeg.	Red alga	A
Raphanus sativus L.	Radish	SG, S
Saccharum officinarum L.	Sugarcane	S
Solanum tuberosum L.	Potato	S
Sorghum vulgare Pers.	Sorghum	S
Spinacia oleracea L.	Spinach	SG
Todea barbara (L.) Moore	Fern	G
Triticum vulgare Vill.	Wheat	S
Zea mays L.	Corn	TC
Zea mays L. var. *everta*	Popcorn	S

*A = algal culture, G = gametophyte culture, S = seedling, SG = seed germination unit, SPG = spore germination unit, TC = tissue culture.

(Walkinshaw et al., 1970).

gametophytes were also greener than those treated with terrestrial basalts. Other lower plants, such as *Lycopodium cernuum L.* and *Marchantia polymorpha L.* (liverwort), exhibited similar stimulation. Measurements of chlorophyll *a* in the treated plants showed significantly higher concentrations of that pigment than of chlorophyll *b* or carotenoids.

Seeds germinated in the presence of lunar materials grew vigorously and absorbed significant quantities of aluminum, chromium, iron, titanium (Walkinshaw & Johnson, 1971), and a variety of elements including rare-earth elements. In addition, cabbage and brussels sprouts absorbed large amounts of manganese. Lettuce seedlings generally thrived in the presence of lunar material. Germ-free bean, citrus, corn, sorghum, soybean, tobacco, and tomato plants showed no deleterious effects when their leaves or roots were treated with 0.2 gm/specimen of lunar material (figure 1). Citrus, corn, and soybean plants appeared to grow consistently better if treated in the sand-water culture system originally described by Walkinshaw and co-workers (1970). Histological specimens taken from lunar-treated plants revealed no deleterious effects.

Figure 1. Corn treated with lunar material from the Apollo 17 mission.

The twelve plant tissue culture systems used in the biocharacterization program appeared to be the most useful for studying cell/lunar particle interactions (Walkinshaw et al., 1973). Lunar-treated tobacco cells accumulated approximately 30 percent more total chlorophyll *a* than did untreated ones (Weete & Walkinshaw, 1972). Relative and absolute concentrations of fatty acids and sterols were changed by lunar treatment

(Weete, Walkinshaw & Laseter, 1972). Pine cells, on the other hand, exhibited a remarkable increase in accumulation of tannin but not of fatty acids or sterols. Both stationary and suspension cultures of tobacco tissue cultures treated with lunar material exhibited an increased maturation of chloroplasts and apparent secretory activity (Baur et al., 1973).

In summary, a number of beneficial effects were observed to be associated with the use of lunar soil cultivation, and none of these effects was found to be associated with an infectious process. The absence of microorganisms or any harmful substance suggests that lunar material could be used as a support medium for the growth of many plants. The tests conducted at the Johnson Space Center indicate that ferns, liverworts, and tobacco cultures utilize lunar material as a source of nutrients (Walkinshaw et al., 1970).

Virological Investigations

Virological studies of the lunar material obtained during the Apollo missions consisted primarily of analyses for replicating agents, principally those able to reproduce. The materials tested and the systems challenged are presented in table 2. The fluid obtained from centrifuging 50 percent weight per volume (W/V) suspensions of lunar material in sterile media was used to inoculate the test systems. Mammalian and avian cultures were re-inoculated ten and twenty days later. Fish cell cultures were re-inoculated in 15 days. Cell cultures in the final passage were tested for infection. All systems were tested to make sure they would react with known viruses. African green monkey kidney (GMK) cultures were challenged with enteric cytopathogenic human orphan virus type 11; mammalian and avian cultures were challenged with pancreatic necrosis virus. Embryonated eggs were inoculated by way of the yolk sac, the chorioallantoic membrane, and the amniotic and allantoic sacs. Extracts of lunar material were inoculated into the brain and the body cavity of mice (figure 2). Materials from tissue cultures, embryonated eggs, and suckling mice were tested for hemaglutinins using chicken, guinea pig, and human type O red blood cells. Viral passage materials were processed for light- and electron-microscope examinations. Standard mycoplasma isolation procedures were used. No evidence of replicating agents was found in any of the systems used.

Additional studies were performed on the Apollo 15 lunar material to measure changes in the ability to infect the host cells. The green monkey kidney cell cultures were exposed to extracts (20 percent W/V) of lunar material and were challenged with parainfluenza and rubella viruses. The ability of the cell cultures to support virus replication was not affected. To determine the effect on growth, metabolism, and colony morphology of *Mycoplasma pneumoniae*, the organism was grown in suspensions of lunar material (ten percent W/V), in mycoplasma broth medium, and in agar containing 0.75 percent lunar material. No significant differences were observed between terrestrial basalt used to simulate lunar material and lunar material suspensions. Colonies grown on agar containing lunar material were similar to those grown on agar medium alone or on agar containing simulated lunar material.

Table 2

Systems Challenged in the Virological Analyses of Lunar
Material Obtained During the Apollo Missions

Apollo Mission	Number of Samples Tested	Tissue Cultures	Systems Challenged		
			Embryonated Eggs	Suckling Mice	Mycoplasma Media
11	3	GMK, HEK, WI-38, BEK, PEK, DEF, RTG-2, FHM, GF	X	—	X
12	2	GMK, HEK, WI-38, MDBK, PK$_{15}$, DEF, RTG-2, FHM, GF	X	—	X
14	6	GMK, HEK, WI-38, MDBK, PK$_{15}$, DEF, RTG-2, FHM, GF	X	X	X
15	1	GMK, HEK, WI-38	X	X	X
16	1	GMK, HEK, WI-38	X	X	X
17	1	GMK, HEK, WI-38	X	X	X

GMK = African green monkey kidney
HEK = Primary human embryonic kidney
WI-38 = Diploid human embryonic lung
BEK = Primary bovine embryonic kidney
PEK = Primary porcine embryonic kidney
DEF = Primary duck embryonic fibroblast

RTG-2 = Rainbow trout gonadal tissue, *Salmo gairdneri*
FHM = Fathead minnow, *Pimephales promelas*
GF   = Grunt fin, *Haemulon sciuras*
MDBK = Heteroploid bovine kidney
PK$_{15}$ = Heteroploid porcine kidney

Figure 2. Mice, inoculated with lunar sample material,
are examined by NASA technician.

Another study was performed to determine the effect of lunar materials on the stability of poliomyelitis virus. Fifty-percent suspensions of lunar material from the Apollo 11, 12, 14, and 15 missions were inoculated with poliomyelitis virus and incubated at 277°K (≈ 4°C). Virus-inoculated balanced salt solution and suspensions of simulated lunar material served as controls. Aliquots were removed for viral assay periodically. The number of virus particles in the suspensions of the lunar material was significantly lower than the number in the balanced salt solution. However, no significant differences were detected between simulated and lunar material suspensions.

Zoological Investigations

Following the Apollo 11, 12, 14, and 15 missions, 15 species of animals representing five phyla were exposed to untreated lunar material (table 3). These tests were complementary to the other protocols and were designed to detect any viable or replicating agents capable of infecting and multiplying in animals. The lunar material used for these tests came from the pooled biosamples (Long et al., 1972).

Because of the differences in maintenance techniques for the aquatic and terrestrial species, the methods of providing exposure to the lunar samples differed. The aquatic and protozoan species were exposed by adding lunar material to the medium in which the animals were living. For the Apollo 14 tests, oysters were exposed by introduction of lunar material into the shell cavity through a 0.32 cm (1/8 in.) hole drilled in the shell. Exposure of the insect species was accomplished by mixing the lunar samples with their food. The mice were exposed by inoculation into the body cavity (intraperitoneally) or the skin (subcutaneously). The guinea pigs used for evaluating pulmonary response to lunar material were exposed by inoculating this suspension into the respiratory tract (trachea). The quail were exposed by intraperitoneal inoculation.

Results of exposure of the various animal species were uniformly negative (Simmonds et al., 1972; and Benschoter et al., 1970). No viable or replicating agents, other than identifiable terrestrial microorganisms, were ever recovered or observed in the test animals. Exposure of the animals to the lunar material resulted in some minor and temporary inhibition or toxicity.

Following relaxation of the quarantine requirements after the Apollo 14 mission, lifespan studies were initiated with germ-free mice inoculated with lunar material. The response of these mice to both intraperitoneal and subcutaneous injections of aqueous suspensions of lunar material was evaluated on a long-term basis (Holland & Simmonds, 1973). Classical inflammatory reactions were noted in both intraperitoneal and subcutaneous inoculations, and the lunar material was observed to persist for the life of the animal (20 months). A low-grade inflammatory reaction and the absence of significant fibroplasia (fibrous tissue development) characterized the lesion. These observations suggest that the lunar material was relatively insoluble in tissue and that, although acting as a low-grade irritant, it has little tendency to evoke reactive fibrosis. The significance of such a chronic low-level stimulus and the various factors governing the retention, the elimination, and the turnover of lunar material in mammalian tissue have yet to be determined.

Table 3

Summary of Species Conditions and Procedures Used in
Quarantine Testing and Biocharacterization of Lunar Materials

Genus and Species (Common Name)	Lunar Material from Apollo Mission	Results
Euglena gracilis (euglena)	11	Slight reduction in locomotive ability after exposure and a return to normal activity by the fourth day. All groups had normal morphologic features.
Paramecium aurelia (paramecium)	11, 12, 14	Initial reduction in fission rates after exposure, rapidly increasing to normal after 4 to 5 days. All groups had normal morphologic features.
Dugesia dorotocephala (planaria)	11, 12, 14	No significant gross or histopathologic changes.
Crassostrea virginica (commercial oyster)	11, 12, 14	During Apollo 11 and 14 missions, large numbers of deaths were encountered in all groups but correlation could not be shown between the deaths and exposure to lunar material. During Apollo 12 mission, all oysters remained in excellent health.
Penaeus aztecus (brown shrimp)	11, 14	No abnormal behavior or significant gross or histopathologic changes.
Penaeus duorarum (pink shrimp)	12	Considerable fighting in all groups early in test. No significant gross or histopathologic changes.
Blattella germanica [German cockroach (gnotobiotic)]	11, 12, 14	No unaccountable gross or histopathologic changes.
Musca domestica (house fly)	11, 12, 14	No unaccountable gross or histopathologic changes.
Galleria mellonella (greater wax moth)	11, 12, 14	No unaccountable gross or histopathologic changes.
Lebistes reticulatus (guppy)	12, 14	No unaccountable gross or histopathologic changes.
Pimephales promelas (fathead minnow)	11	Sporadic deaths in all groups because of sodium hypochlorite spill. No unaccountable gross or histopathologic changes.
Fundulus heteroclitus (mummichog minnow)	11, 12, 14	With the exception of a few fish in each group during Apollo 12 mission (lost because of gill congestion from exposure to sodium hypochlorite), all mummichogs remained in excellent health, and no unaccountable gross or histopathologic changes were found.
Coturnix coturnix (Japanese quail)	11, 12	No unaccountable gross or histopathologic changes. Several deaths attributed to inoculation, laceration of internal organs or self-inflicted trauma.
Mus musculus [motobiotic CD-I mouse (Charles River)]	11, 12, 14, 15	No indication of any infectious-disease-producing agent or acute toxic component in lunar material. Some evidence of long-term irritative effect; however, resolution of this point must await complete analysis of data obtained from long-term test groups.
Cavia porcellus (guinea pig)	14	No unaccountable gross or histopathologic changes.

Bacteriological and Mycological Investigations

A variety of samples from all six lunar exploration missions was examined for the presence of biological forms or viable organisms (Taylor & Wooley, 1973). To evaluate lunar material for the presence of viable organisms, aliquots of each sample were inoculated into an array of culture media and incubated at several temperatures [$277°$, $297°$, $308°$, and $328°K$ ($\approx 4°$, $24°$ $35°$ and $55°C$)] in three gaseous environments (sterile nitrogen, 10 percent carbon dioxide in air, and air) (Taylor & Ferguson, 1970). No evidence of viable organisms was obtained from any of the analyses.

Following incubation of the lunar material in the culture media complexes, microbial growth dynamics studies were performed with known test species to evaluate the possible presence of toxic factors. Only extracts of culture media that had been in contact with a mixture of lunar material from both Apollo 11 core tubes proved to be toxic to all species tested (Taylor et al., 1971; and Taylor, Ellis et al., 1970). Attempts to reproduce this toxic effect with individual Apollo 11 core samples obtained at other parts of the core tube and analyzed under somewhat different conditions were unsuccessful. The mechanism causing this microbial death has not been determined. In all, 48 different lunar samples, collected to a depth of 297 cm (117 in.) from six different landing sites, were examined.

Summary

The likelihood that life existed on the moon was considered quite remote by most members of the scientific community and by NASA officials, but the extensive testing described above was conducted to ensure the safety of all life on Earth. The plants and animals which were exposed to lunar material were carefully observed for prolonged periods to determine if any mutation or changes in growing characteristics and behavior occurred. The quarantine testing was terminated after the Apollo 14 flight when it became apparent that previously returned lunar material contained no potentially harmful agents. Further biological experimentation with the lunar material was conducted to determine its chemical, physical, and nutritional qualities.

References

Anderson, D.H.: Numbering System for Moon Samples. Science, vol. 167, no. 3918, Jan. 1970, p. 781.

Baur, P.S.; Walkinshaw, C.H.; Halliwell, R.S.; and Scholes, V.E.: Morphology of *Nicotiana tabacum* Cells Grown in Contact with Lunar Material. Can. J. Botany, vol. 51, Jan. 1973, pp. 151-156.

Benschoter, C.A.; Allison, T.C.; Boyd, J.F.; Brooks, M.A.; Campbell, J.W.; Groves, R.O.; Heimpel, A.M.; Mills, H.E.; Ray, S.M.; Warren, J.W.; Wolf, K.E.; Wood, E.M.; Wrenn, R.T.; and Zein-Eldin, A.: Apollo 11: Exposure of Lower Animals to Lunar Material. Science, vol. 169, no. 3943, July 1970, pp. 470-472.

Carrier, W.D., III; Johnson, S.W.; Werner, R.A.; and Schmidt, R.: Disturbance in Samples Recovered with the Apollo Core Tubes. Proceedings of the Second Lunar Science Conference, vol. 3, 1971, pp. 1959-1972.

Carrier, W.D., III; Johnson, S.W.; Werner, R.A.; and Schmidt, R.: Core Sample Depth Relationships: Apollo 14 and 15. Proceedings of the Third Lunar Science Conference, vol. 3, 1972, pp. 3213-3221.

Holland, J.M.; and Simmonds, R.C.: The Mammalian Response to Lunar Particulates. Space Life Sciences, vol. 4, no. 1, Jan. 1973, pp. 97-109.

Johnson, P.H.; Walkinshaw, C.H.; Martin, J.R.; Nance, W.B.; and Bennett, A.D.: Elemental Analysis of Apollo 15 Surface Fines Used in Biological Studies at the Lunar Receiving Laboratory. Bioscience, vol. 22, no. 2, Feb. 1972, pp. 96-99.

Kemmerer, W.W., Jr.; Mason, J.A.; and Wooley, B.C.: Physical, Chemical, and Biological Activities at the Lunar Receiving Laboratory. Bioscience, vol. 19, no. 8, Aug. 1969, pp. 712-715.

Long, R.; Ellis, W.; and Schneider, H.: Biopreparation of Apollo 14 Lunar Material. Tex. J. Science, vol. 24, 1972, pp. 262-263.

Simmonds, R.C.; Holland, J.M.; Young, E.L.; and Boyd, J.F.: Animal Maintenance for Biomedical Evaluation of Lunar Material. J. Amer. Vet. Med. Assn., vol. 161, no. 6, Sept. 1972, pp. 720-727.

Taylor, G.R.; Ellis, W.L.; Arredondo, M.; and Mayhew, B.: Growth Response of *Pseudomonas aeroginosa* (ATCC 15442) to the Presence of Lunar Material. Bacteriol. Proceedings, 1970, p. 42.

Taylor, G.R.; Ellis, W.; Johnson, P.H.; Kropp, K.; and Groves, T.: Microbial Assay of Lunar Samples. Proceedings of the Second Lunar Conference, vol. 2, 1971, pp. 1939-1949.

Taylor, G.R.; Ferguson, J.K.; and Truby, C.P.: Methods Used to Monitor the Microbial Load of Returned Lunar Material. Appl. Microbiol., vol. 20, no. 2, Aug. 1970, pp. 271-272.

Taylor, G.R.; and Wooley, B.C.: Evaluations of Lunar Samples for the Presence of Viable Organisms. Proceedings of the Fourth Lunar Science Conference, Geochim Cosmochim Acta, vol. 2, 1973, pp. 2267-2274.

Walkinshaw, C.H.; Sweet, H.C.; Venketeswaran, S.; and Horne, W.H.: Results of Apollo 11 and 12 Quarantine Studies on Plants. Bioscience, vol. 20, no. 24, Dec. 1970, pp. 1297-1302.

Walkinshaw, C.H.; and Johnson, P.H.: Analysis of Vegetable Seedlings Grown in Contact with Apollo 14 Lunar Surface Fines. J. Hort. Science, vol. 6, 1971, pp. 532-535.

Walkinshaw, C.H.; Venketeswaran, S.; Baur, P.S.; Hall, R.H.; Croley, T.E.; Weete, J.D.; Scholes, V.E.; and Halliwell, R.H.: Effect of Lunar Materials on Plant Tissue Culture. Space Life Sciences, vol. 4, no. 1, Jan. 1973, pp. 78-89.

Walkinshaw, C.H.; Wooley, B.C.; and Bozarth, G.A.: Technology Advancements in the Growth of Germ-free Plants at the Manned Spacecraft Center. Germ-free Research: Biological Effect of Gnotobiotic Environments. Academic Press, 1973.

Weete, J.D.; and Walkinshaw, C.H.: Apollo 12 Lunar Material: Effects on Plant Pigments. Can. J. Botany, vol. 50, Jan. 1972, pp. 101-104.

Weete, J.D.; Walkinshaw, C.H.; and Laseter, J.L.: Apollo 12 Lunar Material: Effects on Lipid Levels of Tobacco Tissue Cultures. Science, vol. 175, no. 4021, Feb. 1972, pp. 623-624.

Systems

The Apollo spacecraft and space suits provided a microcosm which sustained the life of astronauts during the voyage to the moon and through periods of lunar surface exploration. This mini-world required a proper atmosphere, food and water provision, waste disposal means, and techniques for ongoing monitoring of astronaut status. The development of these spacecraft systems was a significant part of the Apollo Biomedical Program.

CHAPTER 1
APOLLO FOOD TECHNOLOGY

by

Malcolm C. Smith, D.V.M.
N.D. Heidelbaugh, V.M.D.
Paul C. Rambaut, Sc.D.
R.M. Rapp
Harry O. Wheeler, Ph.D.

Lyndon B. Johnson Space Center

C.S. Huber, Ph.D.
C.T. Bourland, Ph.D.

Technology, Inc.

Introduction

Before man ventured into space for the first time, there was concern that he might choke while attempting to swallow food in zero gravity. Foreign body pneumonia from aspiration of food particles and droplets was feared by some. The ability of man to digest and absorb food in a weightless environment was also seriously debated. These concerns for man's physiological well-being during weightlessness were augmented by fears that the unfamiliar and austere limitations imposed by the space vehicle and flight plans might place unacceptable constraints on the food system. Some food technologists doubted that edible foods could be prepared to withstand conditions of temperature, pressure, and vibration which were characteristic of unmanned space flight vehicles. Limitations on allowable weight and volume would also have direct impact on the food system.

Despite early concerns, restrictions, and technological hurdles surrounding space food development, adequate and acceptable diets were formulated and made available in sufficient time to accommodate the needs of man in space. The earliest food systems used in the Project Mercury flights and the short duration Gemini Program flights resembled military survival rations. For the first long term flight, the two-week Gemini 7 mission, nutritional criteria became important considerations and began to constrain food system designers. Adequate provisions for energy and nutrients had to be made within an exceedingly small weight and volume envelope. This food system envelope, about .77 kg per man per day (1.7 pounds) and 1802 cm^3 per man per day (110 cubic inches), also had to allow for all packaging materials needed to protect foods.

Because water produced as a by-product of fuel cell operation in the Gemini spacecraft could be made available, it became highly attractive from a food acceptance and weight savings standpoint to use dehydrated foods that could be reconstituted in flight. This was the departure point for the development of the Apollo food system, and systematic improvements were subsequently made as technology became available and the application was feasible. The results of these efforts are described in this chapter.

The Apollo Food System

The overall objective of the Apollo food system development program was to provide adequate and safe nutrition for man during the most ambitious space explorations ever attempted. This objective had to be achieved within many critical biological, operational, and engineering constraints. Considerations from which specific constraints were developed are listed in table 1. Details concerning the constraints are described in the *Apollo Experience Report – Food Systems* (NASA TN D-7720, July 1974).

Table 1

Sources of Constraints
on Apollo Food System Development

Biological	Operational	Engineering
Safety	Vehicle interface	Weight
Nutrition	Stability	Volume water for
Organoleptics	Packaging	rehydration
Personal hygiene	Storage	Pressure
Ingestion	Preparation	Temperature
Digestion	Servicing	Relative humidity
Absorption	Waste disposal	Acceleration
Gastroenterology	Schedules	Vibration
Crew idiosyncracies	Crew time	Power

Apollo food system technology evolved over a considerable period of time, with the aid of efforts from the U.S. Air Force Manned Orbiting Laboratory Program, the U.S. Army Natick Laboratories, industry, and universities. The earliest "space foods" were bite-sized foods suitable for eating with one's fingers, and pureed foods, squeezed directly into the mouth from flexible metal toothpaste-type tubes. Extensive modifications in food and food packaging were made throughout Project Mercury and the Gemini and Apollo Programs. Modifications of the food system were especially necessary during the Apollo Program for the following reasons.

1. Inflight food consumption proved inadequate to maintain nutritional balance and body weight.
2. Inflight nausea, anorexia, and undesirable physiological responses experienced by some crewmen were believed to be partly attributable to the foods.

3. Meal preparation and consumption required too much crew time and effort.

4. Water for reconstitution of dehydrated foods was unpalatable initially and contained undesirable amounts of dissolved gases.

5. Functional failures occurred in the rehydratable food packages in the early Apollo flights.

Stepwise modifications of food system technology improved system capability to deliver adequate nutrients in a form that enhanced food acceptance and convenient use. This general trend of increased acceptance was reported by each successive Apollo flight crew.

An overall impression of the evolution of the Apollo food system can be gained by comparing the flight menus for the Apollo 7, 11, and 17 missions (tables 2, 3, and 4). The similarity of the menus for each Apollo 7 astronaut should be compared with the high degree of individuality achieved for each Apollo 17 astronaut. This difference resulted from increased personal selection of food items by the astronauts as the program progressed. Table 4 also indicates the greatly increased variety of foods available for Apollo 17 crewmen.

Increased variety of foods was important, but more important was the improvement in quality of individual foods. Improved food quality is not apparent from the listing of foods. For example, fruit cocktail was reformulated because the original product became crushed by the effects of atmospheric pressure on the package and it was then difficult to rehydrate.

Details of the evolution in space food science and technology, from the first days of planning for manned space flight to the end of the Apollo Program, can be traced in reports cited in the chronological bibliography at the end of this chapter.

Each mission in the Apollo series had different objectives and requirements, and the scope of the Apollo food system was modified to fit the needs of each. The primary mission phases, from the vantage point of food provision, included times during which the crewmen occupied the Command Module (CM) and the Lunar Module (LM), and times when they were being transported in various vehicles from the recovery site to the NASA Lyndon B. Johnson Space Center in Houston, Texas. A contingency food system also was provided to be used if emergency decompression of the space vehicle occurred. For the Apollo 11 through 14 missions, a postflight quarantine period required a food system for use in the Mobile Quarantine Facility (MQF) and the Lunar Receiving Laboratory (LRL). Each of these environments presented a different set of constraints and requirements for the food system. Inflight metabolic balance studies were conducted on the Apollo 16 and 17 missions. These studies imposed unique requirements on the food system for preflight, inflight, and postflight measurements and control of dietary intake.

Before an Apollo launch, each prime and backup crewmember evaluated available flight foods and selected the food items he preferred. Then the foods were assembled into nutritionally balanced menus which were reviewed by crewmembers and nutritionists for maximum acceptability within nutritional constraints. Finally, the astronauts were briefed on spacecraft food stowage, preparation, and waste disposal.

Table 2
Typical Menu, Apollo 7-10

		A. Commander (CDR)		

Day 1	Day 2	Day 3	Day 4
		Meal A		

Day 1	Day 2	Day 3	Day 4
Peaches (R)	Applesauce (R)	Fruit cocktail (R)	Ham and apple-sauce (R)
Bacon squares (IMB)	Sausage patties (R)	Bacon squares (IMB)	Peanut cubes (DB)
Cinnamon bread cubes (DB)	Apricot cereal cubes (DB)	Cinnamon bread cubes (DB)	Strawberry cereal cubes (DB)
Breakfast drink (R)	Breakfast drink (R)	Breakfast drink (R)	Breakfast drink (R)

Meal B

Day 1	Day 2	Day 3	Day 4
Corn chowder (R)	Tuna salad (R)	Corn chowder (R)	Pea Soup (R)
Chicken sand-wiches (DB)	Cinnamon bread cubes (DB)	Beef pot roast (R)	Salmon salad (R)
Coconut cubes (DB)	Chocolate cubes (DB)	Graham cracker cubes (DB)	Cheese sand-wiches (DB)
Sugar cookie cubes (DB)	Cocoa (R)	Butterscotch pudding (R)	Cocoa (R)
Cocoa (R)		Cocoa (R)	

Meal C

Day 1	Day 2	Day 3	Day 4
Beef and gravy (R)	Spaghetti with meat sauce (R)	Potato soup (R)	Shrimp cocktail (R)
Brownies (IMB)		Chicken salad (R)	Chicken and gravy (R)
Chocolate pudding (R)	Cheese sand-wiches (DB)	Beef sandwiches (DB)	Cinnamon bread cubes (DB)
Pineapple-grapefruit drink (R)	Banana pudding (R)	Gingerbread (IMB)	Date fruit cake (IMB)
	Pineapple fruit cake (IMB)	Orange drink (R)	Orange-grapefruit drink (R)
	Grapefruit drink (R)		

B. Command Module Pilot (CMP)

Meal A

Day 1	Day 2	Day 3	Day 4
Peaches (R)	Applesauce (R)	Fruit cocktail (R)	Ham and apple-sauce (R)
Bacon squares (IMB)	Sausage patties (R)	Bacon squares (IMB)	Peanut cubes (DB)
Cinammon bread cubes (DB)	Apricot cereal cubes (DB)	Cinnamon bread cubes (DB)	Strawberry cereal cubes (DB)
Breakfast drink (R)	Breakfast drink (R)	Breakfast drink (R)	Breakfast drink (R)

R = Rehydratable
DB = Dry bite
IMB = Intermediate moisture bite

Table 2 (Continued)
Typical Menu, Apollo 7-10

B. Command Module Pilot (CMP) (Continued)			
Day 1	Day 2	Day 3	Day 4
Meal B			
Chicken sand- wiches (DB) Coconut cubes (DB) Sugar cookie cubes (DB) Cocoa (R)	Tuna salad (R) Cinnamon bread cubes (DB) Chocolate cubes (DB) Cocoa (R)	Beef pot roast (R) Graham cracker cubes (DB) Butterscotch pudding (R) Cocoa (R)	Pea soup (R) Salmon salad (R) Cheese sand- wiches (DB) Cocoa (R)
Meal C			
Beef and gravy (R) Brownies (IMB) Chocolate pudding (R) Pineapple-grapefruit drink (R)	Spaghetti with meat sauce (R) Cheese sand- wiches (DB) Banana pudding (R) Pineapple fruit cake (IMB) Grapefruit drink (R)	Potato soup (R) Chicken salad (R) Beef sandwiches (DB) Gingerbread (IMB) Orange drink (R)	Shrimp cocktail (R) Chicken and gravy (R) Cinnamon bread cubes (DB) Date fruit cake (IMB) Orange-grapefruit drink (R)
C. Lunar Module Pilot (LMP)			
Meal A			
Peaches (R) Bacon squares (IMB) Cinnamon bread cubes (DB) Breakfast drink (R)	Applesauce (R) Sausage patties (R) Breakfast drink (R) Peanut cubes (DB)	Fruit cocktail (R) Bacon squares (IMB) Cinnamon bread cubes (IMB) Breakfast drink (R)	Ham and apple- sauce (R) Strawberry cereal cubes (DB) Apricot cereal cubes (DB) Breakfast drink (R)
Meal B			
Corn chowder (R) Chicken sand- wiches (DB) Coconut cubes (DB) Sugar cookie cubes (DB) Cocoa (R)	Tuna salad (R) Cinnamon bread cubes (DB) Chocolate cubes (DB) Cocoa (R)	Corn chowder (R) Beef pot roast (R) Graham cracker cubes (DB) Butterscotch pudding (R)	Salmon salad (R) Cheese sand- wiches (DB) Peanut cubes (DB) Cocoa (R)

Table 2 (Continued)

Typical Menu, Apollo 7-10

C. Lunar Module Pilot (LMP) (Continued)			
Day 1	Day 2	Day 3	Day 4
Meal C			
Beef and gravy (R) Brownies (IMB) Chocolate pudding (R) Pineapple-grapefruit drink (R)	Spaghetti with meat sauce (R) Cheese sandwiches (DB) Banana pudding (R) Pineapple fruit cake (IMB) Grapefruit drink (R)	Potato soup (R) Chicken salad (R) Beef sandwiches (DB) Gingerbread (IMB) Orange drink (R)	Potato salad (R) Chicken and gravy (R) Cinnamon bread cubes (DB) Date fruit cake (IMB) Orange-grapefruit drink (R)

The initial Apollo inflight food system consisted of two basic food types: (1) light-weight, shelf-stable, dehydrated foods that required rehydration prior to consumption, and (2) ready-to-eat, dehydrated bite-sized foods. Dehydrated foods were selected because of shelf life and because weight was critical in the Apollo vehicle. Approximately 80 percent of the weight of fresh food is water; therefore, the removal of water resulted in a substantial reduction of food system weight. As was previously noted, water for rehydration was available as a by-product of fuel cell operation, wherein hydrogen is combined with oxygen to release electrical energy.

Freeze Dehydrated Foods

The optimal method of dehydrating food is freeze dehydration, a technique preferred because of the remarkable preservation of quality in the resulting product. Color, texture, flavor, nutrient content, and reconstitution of foods which are properly freeze-dried closely approximate the original food. However, as with any other method of preservation, the food which is preserved cannot be of higher quality than the original.

The high quality of freeze-dried food derives largely from the technique of removing the water by sublimation directly from ice to vapor with minimum exposure of the food to heat. The food is frozen rapidly in circulating air at a temperature of approximately $233°K$ ($-40°C$). The frozen food is then placed in a vacuum chamber, where the pressure is reduced to less than 270 N/m^2 (≈ 2 mm Hg). Energy in the form of heat is applied by means of heating plates maintained at temperatures of $298°$ to $303°K$ ($\approx 25°$ to $30°C$), depending on the product. Under vacuum, this heat source provides the energy required to sublime the ice while the temperature of the food is maintained below the eutectic point. The heat input is carefully controlled to provide optimum removal of water vapor, which is collected on condensers within the vacuum chamber. The core of ice in the food completely disappears when the food reaches a moisture content of approximately two percent. This residual moisture remains bound to the food, and the energy level required to free it is greater than that of sublimation.

Table 3
Typical Menu, Apollo 11-16

A. Command Module — CDR and CMP			
Day 1,* 5	Day 2	Day 3	Day 4
Meal A			

Peaches (R)
Bacon squares (8) (IMB)
Strawberry cubes (4) (DB)
Grape drink (R)
Orange drink (R)
	Fruit cocktail (R)
	Sausage patties (SBP)
	Cinnamon toasted
	  bread cubes (4) (DB)
	Cocoa (R)
	Grapefruit drink (R)
		Peaches (R)
		Bacon
		  squares (8) (IMB)
		Apricot cereal
		  cubes (4) (DB)
		Grape drink (R)
		Orange drink (R)
			Canadian bacon and
			  applesauce (R)
			Sugar coated corn
			  flakes (R)
			Peanut cubes (4) (DB)
			Cocoa (R)
			Orange-grapefruit
			  drink (R)

Meal B			

Beef and potatoes (WP)
Butterscotch pudding (R)
Brownies (4) (IMB)
Grape punch (R)
	Frankfurters (WP)
	Applesauce (R)
	Chocolate pudding (R)
	Orange-grapefruit
	  drink (R)
		Cream of chicken
		  soup (R)
		Turkey and
		  gravy (WP)
		Cheese cracker
		  cubes (6) (DB)
		Chocolate
		  cubes (4) (DB)
		Pineapple-grapefruit
		  drink (R)
			Shrimp cocktail (R)
			Ham and potatoes (WP)
			Fruit cocktail (R)
			Date fruit cake (4) (IMB)
			Grapefruit drink (R)

Meal C			

Salmon salad (R)
Chicken and
  rice (SBP)
Sugar cookie
  cubes (6) (DB)
Cocoa (R)
Pineapple-grapefruit
  drink (R)
	Spaghetti with meat
	  sauce** (SBP)
	Pork and scalloped
	  potatoes (SBP)
	Pineapple fruit
	  cake (4) (IMB)
	Grape punch (R)
		Tuna salad (R)
		Chicken stew (SBP)
		Butterscotch
		  pudding (R)
		Cocoa (R)
		Grapefruit drink (R)
			Beef stew (WP)
			Coconut cubes (4) (DB)
			Banana pudding (R)
			Grape punch (R)

 *Day 1 consisted of meals B and C only
**CMP substituted potato soup (R)
  R = Rehydratable
  I = Irradiated
 DB = Dry bite
 WP = Wet pack
IMB = Intermediate moisture bite
SBP = Spoon-bowl packet

Table 3 (Continued)
Typical Menu, Apollo 11-16

B. Command Module — LMP			
Day 1,*	Day 2	Day 3	Day 4
Meal A			

Peaches (R)
Bacon squares (8) (IMB)
Strawberry cubes (4) (DB)
Grape drink (R)
Orange drink (R)
	Fruit cocktail (R)
	Sausage patties (SBP)
	Cinnamon toasted
	  bread cubes (4) (DB)
	Cocoa (R)
	Grapefruit drink (R)
		Peaches (R)
		Bacon
		  squares (8) (IMB)
		Apricot cereal
		  cubes (4) (DB)
		Grape drink (R)
		Orange drink (R)
			Canadian bacon and
			  applesauce (R)
			Sugar coated corn
			  flakes (R)
			Peanut cubes (4) (DB)
			Cocoa (R)
			Orange-grapefruit
			  drink (R)

Meal B			

Beef and potatoes (WP)
Butterscotch
  pudding (R)
Brownies (4) (IMB)
Grape punch (R)
	Frankfurters (WP)
	Applesauce (R)
	Chocolate
	  pudding (R)
	Orange-grapefruit
	  drink (R)
		Cream of chicken
		  soup (R)
		Turkey and
		  gravy (WP)
		Cheese cracker
		  cubes (6) (DB)
		Chocolate
		  cubes (4) (DB)
		Pineapple-grapefruit
		  drink (R)
			Shrimp cocktail (R)
			Ham and potatoes (SBP)
			Fruit cocktail (R)
			Date fruit
			  cake (4) (IMB)
			Grapefruit drink (R)

Meal C			

Salmon salad (R)
Chicken and
  rice (SBP)
Sugar cookie
  cubes (6) (DB)
Cocoa (R)
Pineapple-grapefruit
  drink (R)
	Potato soup (R)
	Pork and scalloped
	  potatoes (R)
	Pineapple fruit
	  cake (4) (IMB)
	Grape punch (R)
		Tuna salad (R)
		Chicken stew (SBP)
		Butterscotch
		  pudding (R)
		Cocoa (R)
		Grapefruit drink (R)
			Beef stew (SBP)
			Coconut cubes (4) (DB)
			Banana pudding (R)
			Grape punch (R)

*Day 1 consisted of meals B and C only.

Table 3 (Continued)
Typical Menu, Apollo 11-16

C. Lunar Module

Meal A	Meal B
Bacon squares (8) (IMB)	Beef stew (R)
Peaches (R)	Cream of chicken soup (R)
Sugar cookie cubes (6) (DB)	Date fruit cake (4) (IMB)
Coffee (R)	Grape punch (R)
Pineapple-grapefruit drink (R)	Orange drink (R)

Additional Items	Units
Extra beverage (R)	8
Dried fruit (IMB)	4
Candy bar (IMB)	4
Bread (I)	2
Ham salad spread (tube food)	1
Turkey and gravy (WP)	2

D. Pantry Stowage

Accessories	Units	Breakfast	Units
Chewing gum	15	Peaches	6
Wet skin cleaning towels	30	Fruit cocktail	6
Oral hygiene kit	1	Canadian bacon	
3 toothbrushes		and applesauce	3
1 edible toothpaste		Bacon squares (8)	12
1 dental floss		Sausage patties*	3
Contingency feeding system	1	Sugar coated corn flakes	6
3 food restrainer pouches		Strawberry cubes (4)	3
3 beverage packages		Cinnamon toasted	
1 valve adapter (pontube)		bread cubes (4)	6
Spoons	3	Apricot cereal cubes (4)	3
Germicidal tablets (20)	3	Peanut cubes (4)	3
Total Units	53	Total Units	51

Rehydratable Desserts	Units
Banana pudding	6
Butterscotch pudding	6
Applesauce	6
Chocolate pudding	6
Total Units	24

*Spoon bowl package

Table 3 (Continued)
Typical Menu, Apollo 11-16

D. Pantry Stowage (Continued)			
Beverages	Units	Bites	Units
Orange drink	6	Cheese cracker cubes (6)	6
Orange-grapefruit drink	3	BBQ beef bites (4)	6
Pineapple-grapefruit drink	3	Chocolate cubes (4)	6
Grapefruit drink	3	Brownies (4)	6
Grape drink	6	Date fruit cake (4)	6
Grape punch	3	Pineapple fruit cake (4)	6
Cocoa	6	Jellied fruit candy (4)	6
Coffee (B)	15	Nutrient defined food	
Coffee (S)	15		
Coffee (C & S)	15	sticks (4)	6
Total Units	75	Total Units	48

Salads/Meats	Units	Salads/Meats	Units
Salmon salad	3	Chicken and rice[*]	6
Tuna salad	3	Chicken stew[*]	3
Cream of chicken soup	6	Beef stew[*]	3
Shrimp cocktail	6	Pork and scalloped	
Spaghetti and meat sauce[*]	6	potatoes[*]	6
Beef pot roast	3	Ham and potatoes (wet)	3
Beef and vegetables	3	Turkey and gravy (wet)	6

Total Units 57

Bread	Units	Dried Fruits	Units
Rye	4	Apricots	6
White	4	Peaches	6
Cheese	4	Pears	6
Total Units	12	Total Units	18

Sandwich Spread	Units
Ham salad (226.8 gm [8 oz])	1
Tuna salad (226.8 gm [8 oz])	1
Chicken salad (226.8 gm [8 oz])	1
Cheddar cheese (56.7 gm [2 oz])	3
Total Units	6

[*]Spoon-bowl package.

Table 3 (Continued)
Typical Menu, Apollo 11-16

E. Low Residue Diet, One Day Before Flight

Breakfast	Lunch	Dinner
Strained grapefruit 113.4 gm (1/2 c)	Beef with rice soup 113.4 gm (1/2 c)	Tomato juice cocktail 170.1 gm (3/4 c)
Cream of rice 113.4 gm (1/2 c)	Crackers (4 squares)	Roast beef au jus 170.1 gm (6 oz)
Scrambled eggs (2)	Sliced chicken sandwich 113.4 gm meat (4 oz); 2 slices of bread	Buttered noodles 113.4 gm (1/2 c)
Breakfast steak 170.1 gm (6 oz)	Cottage cheese-pear salad 1 pear half; 113.4 gm cheese (1/2 c)	Pureed beets 113.4 gm (1/2 c)
Toast (1 slice)		Hard roll (1)
Butter 9.45 gm (2 tsp)	Angle food cake with rum sauce	Butter 9.45 gm (2 tsp)
Grape jelly (or substitute)	Coffee or tea	Sherbet 113.4 gm (1/2 c)
Coffee	Sugar	Coffee or tea
Sugar		Sugar

F. Low Residue Diet, Two Days Before Flight

Breakfast	Lunch	Dinner
Tomato juice 113.4 gm (1/2 c)	Apple juice 113.4 gm (1/2 c)	Beef consomme 113.4 gm (1/2 c)
Canadian bacon (2 slices)	Broiled flounder 170.1 gm (6 oz)	Baked chicken 170.1 gm (6 oz)
Soft cooked eggs (2)	Paprika potatoes 113.4 gm (1/2 c)	Buttered rice 113.4 gm (1/2 c)
Toast (1 slice)	Pureed green beams 113.4 gm (1/2 c)	Pureed carrots 113.4 gm (1/2 c)
Butter 9.45 gm (2 tsp)	Hard roll (1)	Whipped strawberry gelatin dessert
Cream of rice 113.4 gm (1/2 c)	Butter 9.45 gm (2 tsp)	Lady fingers (2)
Sugar	Lime sherbet 113.4 gm (1/2 c)	Tea or coffee
Grape jelly	Vanilla wafers (2)	
Coffee	Coffee	

Critical relationships exist between pressure and temperature during the drying process, and criteria were developed for each food employed in the system. These criteria were developed to assure the most rapid method of processing while maintaining organoleptic quality and preventing destruction of nutrients.

Bite-Sized Foods

Bite-sized, ready-to-eat foods supplemented rehydratable foods for the first Apollo manned flight. These bite-sized foods were either dehydrated (moisture less than two percent) or prepared so that water in the product would be bound and, therefore, not available for microbial growth. The latter category is generally referred to as intermediate-moisture food to differentiate it from fresh foods at one extreme and dehydrated food at the other. The intermediate-moisture foods (moisture less than 40 percent) are highly acceptable since they closely approximate the texture of fresh foods and are ready to eat without reconstitution. Even with this combination of foods, however, the range of texture and tastes was fairly limited for early Apollo astronauts, a situation that was gradually rectified throughout the program.

Table 4
Apollo 17 Menu

A. Command Module — Commander

	Day 1,* 5, 9,** 13	Day 2, 6,*** 10, 14***	Day 3, 11	Day 4, 12
Meal A	Bacon squares (8) (IMB) Scrambled eggs (RSB) Corn flakes (RSB) Peaches (RSB) Orange beverage (R) Cocoa (R)	Spiced oat cereal (RSB) Sausage patties (R) Mixed fruit (WP) Cinnamon toast bread (4) (DB) Instant breakfast (R) Coffee (w/K) (R)	Scrambled eggs (RSB) Bacon squares (8) (IMB) Peaches (WP) Pineapple-grapefruit drink (R) Cocoa (w/K) (R)	Sausage patties (R) Apricot cereal cubes (4) (DB) Fruit cocktail (R) Pears (IMB) Cocoa (w/K) (R) Coffee (R)
Meal B	Chicken and rice soup (RSB) Meatballs and sauce (WP) Fruit cake (NC) (WP) Lemon pudding (WP) Orange-pineapple drink (R)	Corn chowder (RSB) Frankfurters (WP) White bread (2) (I) Catsup (WP) Apricots (IMB) Orange-grapefruit drink (R)	Lobster bisque (RSB) Peanut butter (WP) Jelly (WP) White bread (1) (I) Chocolate bar (IMB) Orange-grapefruit drink (w/K) (R)	Chicken soup (RSB) Ham (I) Cheddar cheese spread (WP) Rye bread (1) (I) Cereal bar (IMB) Orange beverage (R)
Meal C	Potato soup (RSB) Beef and gravy (WP) Chicken stew (RSB) Peach ambrosia (RSB) Gingerbread (4) (IMB) Citrus beverage (R)	Turkey and gravy (WP) Pork and potatoes (RSB) Brownies (4) (IMB) Orange juice (R) Lemonade (R)	Shrimp cocktail (RSB) Beef steak (WP) Butterscotch pudding (RSB) Peaches (IMB) Orange drink (w/K) (R)	Tomato soup (RSB) Hamburger (WP) Mustard (WP) Vanilla pudding (WP) Date fruit cake (4) (IMB) Orange-pineapple drink (w/K) (R)

*Meal C only
**Meals B and C only
***Meal A only

R = Rehydratable
I = Irradiated
DB = Dry bite
WP = Wet pack (thermostabilized)

NC = Nutrient complete
w/K = Fortified with 10 mEq of potassium
IMB = Intermediate moisture bite
RSB = Rehydratable spoon-bowl

Table 4 (Continued)

Apollo 17 Menu

B. Command Module — Command Module Pilot

Day 1,* 5, 13	Day 2, 6, 10, 14**	Day 3, 7, 11	Day 4, 8, 12
Meal A			
Bacon squares (8) (IMB)	Spiced oat cereal (RSB)	Scrambled eggs (RSB)	Sausage (R)
Scrambled eggs (RSB)	Sausage patties (R)	Bacon squares (8) (IMB)	Grits (RSB)
Corn flakes (RSB)	Mixed fruit (WP)	Peaches (WP)	Fruit cocktail (R)
Apricots (IMB)	Instant breakfast (R)	Cinnamon toast bread (4) (DB)	Orange beverage (R)
Orange juice (R)	Coffee (w/K) (R)	Orange juice (R)	Coffee (w/K) (R)
		Cocoa (w/K) (R)	
Meal B			
Chicken and rice soup (RSB)	Frankfurters (WP)	Lobster bisque (RSB)	Ham (I)
Meatballs with sauce (WP)	White bread (2) (I)	Peanut butter (WP)	Cheddar cheese spread (WP)
Fruit cake (NC) (WP)	Catsup (WP)	Jelly (WP)	Rye bread (1) (I)
Butterscotch pudding (WP)	Pears (IMB)	White bread (1) (I)	Peaches (RSB)
Orange-pineapple drink (R)	Chocolate pudding (RSB)	Cherry bar (1) (IMB)	Cereal bar (IMB)
	Grape drink (w/K) (R)	Citrus beverage (w/K) (R)	Orange-pineapple drink (w/K) (R)
Meal C			
Potato soup (RSB)	Corn chowder (RSB)	Shrimp cocktail (RSB)	Tomato soup (RSB)
Beef and gravy (WP)	Turkey and gravy (WP)	Beef steak (WP)	Hamburger (WP)
Chicken stew (RSB)	Chocolate bar (IMB)	Butterscotch pudding (RSB)	Mustard (WP)
Ambrosia (RSB)	Orange beverage (R)	Orange drink (w/K) (R)	Vanilla pudding (WP)
Brownies (4) (IMB)			Sugar cookies (4) (DB)
Orange-grapefruit drink (R)			Caramel candy (IMB)
			Grape drink (w/K) (R)

*Meal C only

**Meal A only

Table 4 (Continued)

Apollo 17 Menu

C. Command Module — Lunar Module Pilot

Day 1,* 5, 9,** 13	Day 2, 6,*** 10, 14***	Day 3, 11	Day 4, 12
		Meal A	
Bacon squares (8) (IMB)	Sausage patties (R)	Scrambled eggs (RSB)	Sausage patties (R)
Scrambled eggs (RSB)	Cinnamon toast bread (4) (DB)	Bacon squares (8) (IMB)	Grits (RSB)
Corn flakes (RSB)	Mixed fruit (WP)	Peaches (WP)	Peaches (RSB)
Apricots (IMB)	Instant breakfast (R)	Orange-pineapple drink (w/K) (R)	Pears (IMB)
Cocoa (w/K) (R)	Coffee (w/K) (R)	Cocoa (R)	Pineapple-grapefruit drink (R)
			Coffee (w/K) (R)
		Meal B	
Chicken and rice soup (RSB)	Corn chowder (RSB)	Potato soup (RSB)	Chicken soup (RSB)
Meatballs with sauce (WP)	Frankfurters (WP)	Peanut butter (WP)	Ham (I)
Fruit cake (NC) (WP)	White bread (1) (I)	Jelly (WP)	Cheddar cheese spread (WP)
Lemon pudding (WP)	Catsup (WP)	White bread (1) (I)	Rye bread (1) (I)
Citrus beverage (R)	Chocolate pudding (RSB)	Cherry bar (1) (IMB)	Cereal bar (IMB)
	Orange-grapefruit drink (w/K) (R)	Orange-grapefruit drink (w/K) (R)	Orange drink (w/K) (R)
		Meal C	
Lemonade (R)	Turkey and gravy (WP)	Shrimp cocktail (RSB)	Tomato soup (RSB)
Beef and gravy (WP)	Pork and potatoes (RSB)	Beef steak (WP)	Hamburger (WP)
Chicken stew (RSB)	Caramel candy (IMB)	Butterscotch pudding (RSB)	Mustard (WP)
Ambrosia (RSB)	Orange juice (R)	Peaches (RSB)	Vanilla pudding (WP)
Gingerbread (4) (IMB)		Orange drink (w/K) (R)	Chocolate bar (IMB)
Grapefruit drink (w/K) (R)			Grape drink (w/K) (R)

*Meal C only
**Meals B and C only
***Meal A only

Table 4 (Continued)
Apollo 17 Menu

D. Lunar Module — Commander

Day 6	Day 7	Day 8	Day 9
Meal B	Meal A	Meal A	Meal A
Corn chowder (RSB)	Scrambled eggs (RSB)	Sausage patties (R)	Bacon squares (8) (IMB)
Frankfurters (WP)	Bacon squares (8) (IMB)	Apricot cereal cubes (6) (DB)	Scrambled eggs (RSB)
White bread (2) (I)	Peaches (IMB)	Fruit cocktail (R)	Corn flakes (RSB)
Catsup (WP)	Peanut butter (WP)	Pears (IMB)	Beef and gravy (WP)
Apricots (IMB)	Jelly (WP)	Cereal bar (IMB)	Fruit cake (NC) (WP)
Orange-grapefruit drink (R)	White bread (1) (I)	Cheese cracker cubes (4) (DB)	Peaches (RSB)
Tea (R)	Chocolate bar (IMB)	Ham (I)	Cocoa (R)
Lemonade (R)	Pineapple-grapefruit drink (R)	Cocoa (R)	Orange beverage (R)
	Orange-grapefruit drink (w/K) (R)	Tea (R)	Tea (R)
	Cocoa (w/K) (R)	Spiced oat cereal (RSB)	
	Tea (R)	Lemonade (R)	
Meal C	**Meal B**	**Meal B**	
Spaghetti and meat sauce (RSB)	Chicken and rice (RSB)	Lobster bisque (RSB)	
Turkey and gravy (WP)	Shrimp cocktail (RSB)	Hamburger (WP)	
Pork and potatoes (RSB)	Beef steak (WP)	Mustard (WP)	
Brownies (4) (IMB)	Beef sandwiches (4) (DB)	Cheddar cheese spread (WP)	
Orange beverage (R)	Butterscotch pudding (RSB)	Rye bread (1) (I)	
Tea (R)	Graham cracker cubes (6) (DB)	Date fruit cake (4) (IMB)	
	Orange drink (w/K) (R)	Orange-pineapple drink (w/K) (R)	
	Tea (R)	Orange beverage (R)	
		Tea (R)	

Table 4 (Continued)
Apollo 17 Menu

E. Lunar Module — Lunar Module Pilot

Day 6	Day 7	Day 8	Day 9
Meal B	Meal A	Meal A	Meal A
Corn chowder (RSB)	Scrambled eggs (RSB)	Sausage patties (R)	Bacon squares (8) (IMB)
Frankfurters (WP)	Bacon squares (8) (IMB)	Spiced oat cereal (RSB)	Scrambled eggs (RSB)
White bread (2) (I)	Peaches (IMB)	Peaches (RSB)	Corn flakes (RSB)
Catsup (WP)	Peanut butter (WP)	Pears (IMB)	Apricots (IMB)
Chocolate pudding (RSB)	Jelly (WP)	Cereal bar (IMB)	Cocoa (R)
Orange-grapefruit drink (R)	White bread (1) (I)	Gingerbread (6) (IMB)	Tea (R)
Tea (R)	Orange-grapefruit drink (w/K) (R)	Ham (I)	Beef and gravy (WP)
Lemonade (R)	Cocoa (w/K) (R)	Pineapple-grapefruit drink (R)	Fruit cake (NC) (WP)
	Tea (R)	Tea (R)	
	Fruit cocktail (R)		
Meal C	**Meal B**	**Meal B**	
Turkey and gravy (WP)	Chicken and rice (RSB)	Potato soup (RSB)	
Pork and potatoes (RSB)	Shrimp cocktail (RSB)	Hamburger (WP)	
Caramel candy (IMB)	Beef steak (WP)	Mustard (WP)	
Orange beverage (R)	Beef sandwiches (4) (DB)	Cheddar cheese spread (WP)	
Tea (R)	Butterscotch pudding (RSB)	Rye bread (1) (I)	
	Graham cracker cubes (6) (DB)	Chocolate bar (IMB)	
	Orange drink (w/K) (R)	Banana pudding (RSB)	
	Orange-pineapple drink (R)	Orange drink (w/K) (R)	
	Tea (R)	Grape drink (w/K) (R)	
		Tea (R)	

Table 4 (Continued)

Apollo 17 Menu

F. Pantry Stowage Items

Beverages (R)	Qty.	Accessories	Qty.	Accessories (Continued)	Qty.
Coffee	20	Contingency beverages (R) (for contingency use only)		In-suit food bar assembly	
Tea	20			In-suit drinking device	
Grape drink	10	Instant breakfast	15	Spoon assembly (2)	
Grape punch	10	Orange drink	5	Germicidal tablets pouch (42)	1
		Pineapple-orange drink	5	Germicidal tablets pouch (20)	1
		Lemonade	5		

Snack Items	Qty.	Snack Items (Continued)	Qty.
Bacon squares (4) (IMB)	9	Sugar cookies (4) (DB)	6
Apricot cereal cubes (DB)	6	Apricots (IMB)	3
Brownies (4) (IMB)	3	Peaches (IMB)	3
Gingerbread (4) (IMB)	3	Pears (IMB)	3
Graham crackers (4)	6	Chocolate bar (IMB)	3
Jellied candy (IMB)	6	Tuna salad spread (WP) (small cans)	2
Peach ambrosia (RSB)	3		
Pecans (6) (IMB)	6	Catsup (WP)	3
Fruit cake (WP) (NC)	3	Salt packets	6

Packaging

Packaging, like food items themselves, underwent substantial modification during the Apollo Program. Flexible packaging protected each individual portion of food and made handling and consumption easier. A series of redesign cycles finally resulted in a rehydratable food package that had (1) an improved, transparent barrier-film of laminated polyethylene-fluorohalocarbon-polyester-polyethylene; (2) a water injection port consisting of a one-way, spring-loaded valve; and (3) an improved opening that permitted food consumption in weightlessness with a conventional tablespoon.

Cold [≈283°K (10°C)] and hot [≈333°K (60°C)] water were available for food preparation. Following water injection with the Apollo water dispenser, the food package was kneaded to rehydrate the food and then opened for consumption. Early packages, shown in figure 1, were fitted with plastic tubes through which rehydrated food was extruded into the mouth. This configuration was changed by the introduction of a spoon-bowl package, pictured in figure 2 and described in greater detail in the following sections.

Figure 1. Apollo rehydratable food packages

Bite-sized, ready-to-eat foods were contained in packets made from the same plastic laminate material used for packaging rehydratable foods. These packets were opened simply by cutting with scissors (figure 3). The food was eaten directly from the package or by use of the fingers.

Figure 2. Apollo rehydratable food spoon-bowl package
shown opened with spoon inserted.

Figure 3. Bite-sized, ready-to-eat, intermediate-moisture
and dry foods shown in Apollo flight packages.

Evolution in Apollo Food Technology

Improvements in the food system were aimed at maintaining astronauts in the best possible physiological condition and with a high level of morale. Modifications to improve ease of consumption, stowage weight, and nutrient intake were reviewed and implemented as dictated by changes in mission objectives, new activities, and medical, operational, and experimental requirements.

Apollo 7

The food system for the first manned Apollo mission was basically that provided in the Gemini Program but featured a wider variety of foods. However, while the availability of 96 food items for the Apollo 7 flight contributed to better acceptance and increased consumption relative to Gemini foods, the time and trouble required for meal preparation was increased.

Apollo 8

The first departure from heavy reliance on rehydratable foods occurred during the Apollo 8 flight. On Christmas day, 1968, during the first lunar orbital mission, the Apollo 8 astronauts opened packages of thermostabilized turkey and gravy and ate with spoons. This turkey entree required no water for rehydration because the normal water content (67 percent) had been retained. The thermally stabilized, ready-to-eat meal in a flexible can became known as a "wetpack," a term used to differentiate this package from the dehydrated space foods that required the addition of water before consumption. The flexible packs were made from a laminate of polyester, aluminum foil, and polyolefin.

Wet-type foods had not been used previously because of the disadvantages associated with high moisture content, particularly the requirement for sterility and the weight penalty associated with this type of food. The improved crew acceptance of the product justified the weight increase. Technology for heat sterilization in flexible packages was sufficiently advanced by the time of Apollo 8 to assure a high quality product with minimal chance for failure.

The Apollo 8 crew also used a conventional teaspoon to eat some foods, and found that this mode of food consumption in weightlessness was quite satisfactory. This finding led to food package redesign which made the use of spoons much more convenient.

Apollo 9

Beginning with the Apollo 9 mission, more wetpack items were added to the food system. The variety of foods provided for this flight made crew diets more typical of those consumed on Earth. The extensive use of wetpack containers without difficulty during this mission confirmed the potential for eating a substantial portion of food from open containers. The Apollo 9 crewmen experimented further by cutting open a rehydratable food package and eating its contents with a spoon; the experiment was successful.

During Apollo 9, the Lunar Module Pilot experienced nausea and vomiting. Menu manipulation in flight to reduce the tendency for nausea represented the first use of real-time food selection for countering undesirable physiological responses to vestibular stimuli. The Apollo 9 mission also included the first use of the Lunar Module food system.

Apollo 10

Evolution of the Apollo food system was continued with the Apollo 10 flight, during which the spoon-bowl package (see figure 2) was introduced. The spoon-bowl package permitted convenient use of a spoon for consuming rehydrated foods. This modified package had a water inlet valve at one end and a large plastic-zippered opening on the other, which provided access to the rehydrated food with a spoon. Large pieces of dehydrated meat and vegetables could now be included to provide a more familiar and acceptable texture. As a result of this modification, some Apollo crewmen expressed a preference for selected foods in rehydratable form over the wetpack equivalent.

The feasibility of eating from open containers with spoons in weightlessness was first tested in aircraft flight, and subsequently verified during the flights of Apollo 8 and Apollo 9. Using jet aircraft flying parabolic patterns, numerous foods, packages, and utensils were tested. While these flights produced only brief periods of near-weightless conditions, the results indicated that spacecraft application of the spoon-bowl concept could be made successfully without dispersal of food particles throughout the vehicle.

Apollo 10 also marked the first successful use of conventional slices of fresh bread and sandwich spreads. This bread had a shelf life at Apollo vehicle temperatures for at least four weeks when packaged in a nitrogen atmosphere (figure 4). Provision of the bread allowed crewmen to make sandwiches using meat salad spreads provided in separate containers. The sandwich spreads were preserved by thermal processing and final package closing in a hyperbaric chamber. The process enhances preservation of natural flavor and texture by reducing thermal processing time and temperature.

An additional modification for the Apollo 10 mission was the introduction of the pantry concept. Locker space was reserved for an assembly of food to provide *ad libitum* selection of meal components. This method allowed for some versatility in menu planning and for inflight dietary modification. In all subsequent Apollo flights, pantry-stocked foods augmented prepackaged meals. Even though most astronauts expressed a desire prior to flight for real-time food selection, they typically reported that this often proved to be more trouble than it was worth.

The Apollo 10 crewmen reported some discomfort from a feeling of fullness and gastric awareness immediately after eating. This was troublesome to individual astronauts throughout the Apollo Program. Many causes for this condition have been suggested. Among these are (1) aerophagia; (2) undissolved gases (oxygen and hydrogen); (3) reduced atmospheric pressure; (4) changes in gastrointestinal motility; and (5) shifts in intestinal microflora. Moreover, removal of water during the process of food dehydration is a complex phenomenon that causes many physical-chemical shifts at the cellular level. It is conceivable that, during the rehydration process, continued occurrence of microscopic phenomena could cause osmotic displacements sensed by the cells of the gastric or intestinal mucosa.

Apollo 11

New food items for the Apollo 11 flight included thermostabilized cheddar cheese spread and thermostabilized frankfurthers. Sandwich spreads were packaged in "401" aluminum cans, which featured a pull-tab for easy removal of the entire top of the can. This can proved successful and eventually became the nucleus for the development of the open-dish eating concept implemented in the Skylab Program.

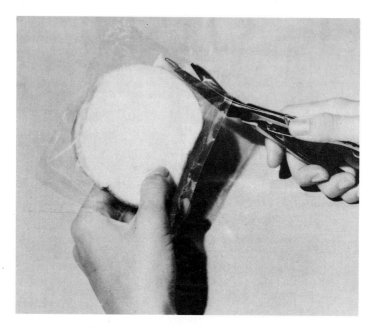

Figure 4. Irradiated bread packaged for use on Apollo missions.

Command Module food for the first five days of the Apollo 11 mission was assembled in nominal meal packages (figure 5). Forty-two man-meals (starting with day 1, meal B), an oral hygiene kit, and spoons were contained in a Command Module food locker. Command Module menus for each Apollo 11 astronaut are presented in tables 3 (A, B). Because the wetpack food items included did not require reconstitution in flight, the menu was planned for consumption of wetpack foods during the midday meal when crew activity was highest. The wetpack foods were stowed separately from nominal meal packages.

A six-day supply of food and accessory items were stowed in pantry fashion (figure 6) to permit some food selection based on real-time preference and appetite and to supplement the meal packages if more food was desired by an individual. The foods included beverages, salads, soups, meats, breakfast items, desserts, and bite-sized foods [see table 3(D) for listing]. Primary food packages were placed in nonflammable overwraps, which served to keep food groups together and to partition the spacecraft food container for ease of retrieval in flight. Germicide tablets were provided for stabilization of any food residue remaining in the primary food packages.

Four lunar surface meal periods were scheduled. The Apollo 11 Lunar Module menu is outlined in table 3(C). Foods for the four nominal meals (two each of meals A and B), spoons, wetpack food, extra beverages, and tubed ham sandwich spread were stowed in the Lunar Module food box. The remaining items (bread, candy, and dried fruit) were stowed in the utility-light compartment of the flight data file.

Figure 5. Apollo meal pack.

Another major component of the Apollo 11 food system was the system employed on the prime recovery ship in the Mobile Quarantine Facility (MQF) and, subsequently, at the Lunar Receiving Laboratory (LRL) at Johnson Space Center. A typical MQF menu is shown in table 5. The MQF foods were used from time of splashdown until the crewmen entered the LRL. The menu contained primarily precooked, frozen entrees, which were reconstituted in a microwave oven in the MQF. The LRL system used the same type of entrees with the addition of a wider variety of frozen vegetables, salads, and snacks. The LRL food system also included a "first class" restaurant service, complete with table linens, china, and silverware which was available to the flight crew, their support team, and the lunar quarantine staff of approximately 20 scientists and technicians.

Apollo 12

The food system for Apollo 12 was quite similar to that which had proven successful for Apollo 11. Freeze dehydrated scrambled eggs were introduced and were well accepted by the crew. Other changes in the menu were directed toward meeting individual crewmember nutrient requirements.

Table 5

Typical Menu for Apollo Mobile Quarantine Facility*

· Day 1	Day 2	Day 3	Day 4	Day 5
		Breakfast		
Crepes Georgia	Crepes Normandie	Crepes Diane	Crepes Georgia	Crepes Normandie
Cheese omelette	Link sausage	Cheese omelette	Plain omelette	French toast
Crisp bacon strips	Pancakes	Crisp bacon strips	Breakfast ham	Crisp bacon strips
Breakfast roll	Maple syrup	Breakfast roll	Breakfast roll	Maple syrup
Jelly		Jelly	Jelly	
		Lunch		
Roast beef sandwich	Beef stew	Spaghetti with meat sauce	Roast beef au jus	Braised beef tips
Corn relish	Dinner roll	Green beans amandine	Duchess potatoes	Tiny whole potatoes
Mixed fruit compote	Plums	Dinner roll	Glazed carrots	with green peas
Vanilla ice cream		Vanilla ice cream	Dinner roll	Dinner roll
Assorted cookies		Oatmeal-raisin cookies	Fudge brownies	Vanilla ice cream
		Dinner		
Strip steak	Chicken Kiev	Baked ham with pine-	Short ribs of beef	Lobster Newburg
Baked potatoes	White rice	apple glaze	Buttered peas with	White rice
Asparagus spears	Mixed vegetables	Potatoes au gratin	mushrooms	French style green beans
Dinner roll	Dinner roll	Buttered green peas	Whole kernel corn	Dinner roll
Apple cobbler	Fudge cake	Dinner roll	Dinner roll	Almond torte
		Cherry cobbler	Pecan pie	

*Instant coffee, tea, butter and sterilized canned whole or fresh milk available at each meal. Otherwise all foods shown were frozen.

Apollo 13

The Apollo 13 inflight explosion and loss of fuel cell systems tested the food system in an emergency situation in which fluid and electrolyte intakes were critical for life support. After the accident, crew nutrient consumption was limited by the amount of available water. Beverage bags proved to be extremely useful as an emergency means of storing water that was rapidly being depleted. The use of these packages and the availability of wetpack foods for providing fluids for the Apollo 13 crewmen has been largely credited with maintaining the health of the astronauts throughout the emergency.

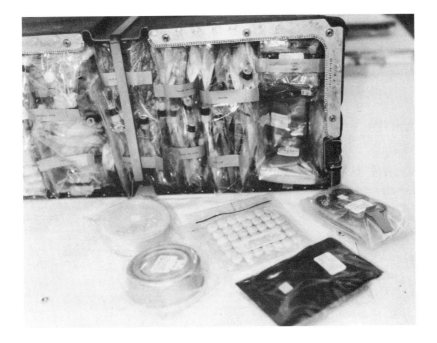

Figure 6. Apollo food and accessory items.

The beverage packages found other uses during Apollo missions and proved to be versatile, durable, and reliable. They were used in experiments on the separation of gas from liquids in weightlessness and also served as head supports on the couch during reentry of the Command Module in at least one mission.

The Apollo 13 food system included the first dehydrated natural orange juice. Orange juice had not been employed in space food systems previously because the dehydration methods available failed to prevent fusion of natural sugars with the formation of an insoluble mass. The provision of fruit juices further improved the quality and nutritional value of the food system.

Apollo 14

The Apollo 14 flight marked the first time space crewmen returned to Earth without a significant change in body weight. The Commander and the Lunar Module Pilot had consumed essentially all of their programmed food supply.

The Apollo 14 food system included an in-suit drinking device. This allowed the astronauts to better maintain fluid balance during extensive lunar surface operations.

The food safety regimen throughout the Apollo Program included the production and final packaging of all food items in a Class 100 000 filtered-air cleanroom to maintain low microbiological counts of Apollo foods. Foods were also examined for the presence of heavy metals. The only deviation from perfect performance in the food safety area was a failure in the early detection of mercury contamination in the Apollo 14 tuna fish salad. The mercury content ways in excess of maximum limits established by the U.S. Food and Drug Administration. The tuna fish was removed from the food system shortly prior to launch, and a nutritionally equivalent substitute from the pantry was used to supplement the menu.

Apollo 15

Apollo 15 crewmen consumed solid food while working on the lunar surface. High nutrient density food bars were installed inside the full pressure suit (figure 7). Figure 8 shows a view of the neck ring area of the Apollo lunar surface pressure suit with the in-suit food bar and the in-suit drink device installed. The in-suit drink device was designed to provide water or fruit flavored beverages. This crew was the first to consume all of the mission food provided. Negligible weight losses, after equilibration for fluid losses, reaffirmed that the diet provided adequately for the crew's energy requirements. The typical Apollo menu ultimately provided energy equivalent to 155±17 kJ/kg (37±4 kcal/kg) of body weight. Sliced fresh bread that had been pasteurized by exposure to 50 000 rads of cobalt-60 gamma irradiation was first used for the Apollo 15 flight.

Apollo 16

Electrocardiographic recordings for Apollo 15 crewmen indicated occasional arrhythmias believed to be possibly linked to a potassium deficit. In an effort to prevent recurrence of a similar situation in the Apollo 16 crew, a requirement was levied to provide 140±5 milliequivalents of potassium in the Apollo 16 diets daily during flight and for 72 hours both before and after flight. In addition, nutrient intake and absorption for each Apollo 16 crewman was monitored during the entire period, beginning 72 hours before flight and ending 72 hours after flight. This control of nutrient intake afforded maximum opportunity to detect physiological changes accompanying transition to and from the weightless state.

The requirement for 140±5 mEq of potassium could not be met by menu manipulations using unmodified flight-qualified Apollo foods. Therefore, potassium fortification of qualified inflight foods was investigated, and the development of modified preflight and postflight foods was undertaken. It was found that Apollo 16 beverages and soups could be modified by the addition of 10 mEq per serving of potassium in the form of potassium gluconate (2.35 gm per serving).

The physiological safety of potassium gluconate for food fortification and supplementation was verified by a search of the literature concerning its use and effects and by three studies involving human volunteers. The compatibility of this level of potassium with individual flight crewmembers was tested by providing each individual with fortified foods for consumption and evaluation.

Figure 7. High-density food bars for use in pressure suits on the lunar surface.

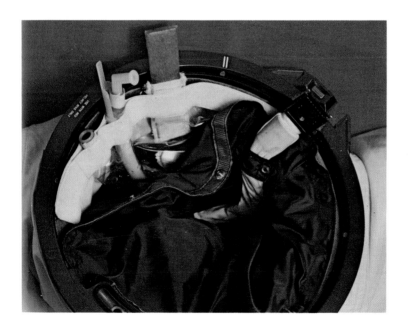

Figure 8. Neck ring of the Apollo lunar surface pressure suit showing in-suit food bar and drink device.

Apollo 16 grape drink, orange drink, pineapple-orange drink, pineapple-grapefruit drink, grapefruit with sugar, and cocoa were fortified with potassium gluconate, for an average daily inflight potassium intake of approximately 100 mEq. Real-time adjustments in nutrition were applied by menu rearrangements to counteract the gastrointestinal awareness reported by one crewmember and believed to be associated with dietary potassium intake.

Apollo 17

In addition to a liberal usage of previously described improved foods, the Apollo 17 system was modified by the inclusion of shelf-stable ham steak that had been sterilized by exposure to cobalt-60 gamma irradiation (3.7 megarads). The Apollo 17 food system also incorporated a fruit cake that provided complete nutrition in shelf-stable, intermediate-moisture, ready-to-eat form. Both proved to be highly acceptable to the crewmen. This type of intermediate-moisture food was included in the Skylab contingency food system and is being evaluated for use in the Space Shuttle food program.

Conclusions

Large improvements and advances in space food systems were achieved during the Apollo food program. Nevertheless, the majority of Apollo astronauts did not consume sufficient nutrients. Loss of body weight, fluids, and electrolytes was the rule, with few exceptions. The Apollo food program showed that man and his eating habits are not easily changed. Adequate nutrition begins with appropriate food presented to the consumer in familiar form.

A space food system must fulfill program requirements and provide proper nutrition to maintain physiological well-being during the specific environments and stresses imposed by the mission. Such a system must ultimately rely on nutritious foods that are easy to prepare, that have familiar flavor and texture, and that provide diversion, relaxation, security, and satiety.

Modifications of the Apollo food system were directed primarily toward improving delivery of adequate nutrition to the astronaut. Individual food items and flight menus were modified as nutritional countermeasures to the effects of weightlessness. Unique food items were developed, including some that provided nutritional completeness, high acceptability, and ready-to-eat, shelf-stable convenience. Specialized food packages were also developed.

The Apollo Program experience clearly showed that future space food systems will require well-directed efforts to achieve the optimum potential of food systems in support of the physiological and psychological well-being of astronauts and crews. The accomplishments of the Apollo food program provide a significant beginning.

Bibliography

1960

Finkelstein, Beatrice; and Taylor, Albert A.: Food, Nutrition and the Space Traveler. Am. J. Clin. Nutr., vol. 8, no. 6, Nov.-Dec. 1960, pp. 793-800.

Finkelstein, Beatrice: Nutrition Research for the Space Traveler. J. Am. Dietet. Assoc., vol. 36, no. 4, Apr. 1960, pp. 313-317.

Peryam, David R.; Polemis, Bernice W.; Kamen, J.M.; Eindhoven, J.; and Pilgrim, F.J.: Food Preferences of Men in the U.S. Armed Forces. Quartermaster Food and Container Institute for the Armed Forces (Chicago, Ill.), 1960.

Taylor, A.A.; Finkelstein, Beatrice; and Hayes, R.E.: Food for Space Travel. ARDC TR-60-8, 1960.

1961

Welbourn, J.L.; and LaChance, P.A.: Suitability of Tubed Foods for In-Flight Feeding. ASD TR-61-456, 1961.

1963

Chichester, C.O.: Food Technological Problems in Adverse Environments. Federation Proc., vol. 22, Nov.-Dec. 1963, pp. 1447-1450.

Heidelbaugh, Norman D.: Influence of the Package on Changes in Stored Heat-Processed Foods. M.S. Thesis, Massachusetts Institute of Technology, 1963.

LaChance, Paul A.; and Vanderveen, John E.: Problems in Space Foods and Nutrition: Foods for Extended Space Travel and Habitation. Food Technol., vol. 17, no. 5, May 1963, pp. 567-572.

Nuccio, P.P.; and Lis, S.J.: Method of Heating Foods During Aerospace Flight. AMRL TDR-63-139, 1963.

Senter, R.J.: Research on the Acceptability of Precooked Dehydrated Foods During Confinement. AMRL TDR-63-9, 1963.

1964

Harper, Alfred E.: Discussion: Proteins in Space Nutrition. Conference on Nutrition in Space and Related Waste Problems. NASA SP-70, 1964, pp. 143-145.

Hollender, Herbert A.: Development of Food Items to Meet Air Force Requirements for Space Travel. AMRL TR-64-38, 1964.

Klicka, Mary V.: Development of Space Foods. J. Am. Dietet. Assoc., vol. 44, no. 5, May 1964, pp. 358-361.

LaChance, Paul A.: Nutrition and Stresses of Short Term Space Flight. Conference on Nutrition in Space and Related Waste Problems. NASA SP-70, 1964, pp. 71-78.

Michel, Edward L.: Preparation, Handling, and Storage of Foods for Present Space Projects. Conference on Nutrition in Space and Related Waste Problems. NASA SP-70, 1964, pp. 57-63.

Sarett, Herbert P.: Use of Formula Diets. Conference on Nutrition in Space and Related Waste Problems. NASA SP-70, 1964, pp. 353-361.

Scrimshaw, Nevin S.; Johnson, Robert E.; and Davidson, Charles S.: Panel Discussion. Conference on Nutrition in Space and Related Waste Problems. NASA SP-70, 1964, pp. 367-370.

Vinograd, S.P.: Nutritional Trends in Future Manned Space Flights. Conference on Nutrition in Space and Related Waste Problems. NASA SP-70, 1964, pp. 17-21.

1965

Austin, Philip R.; and Timmerman, Stewart W.: Design and Operation of Clean Rooms. Business News Publishing Co. (Detroit, Mich.), 1965.

Hewitt, Eric J.: All-Purpose Matrix for Molded Food Bars. Report TR-FD-14, U.S. Army Natick Laboratories, 1965.

Hollender, Herbert A.; and Klicka, Mary: Development of Dehydrated and Bite-Sized Food Items. AMRL TR-65-160, 1965.

Newlin, Harry E.; and Morris, E.R.: Development of Food Bars Employing Edible Structural Agents. Report TR-FD-20, U.S. Army Natick Laboratories, 1965.

Richards, A.; Streimer, I.; and Wendrow, B.: Foods and Food Systems as Influenced by Zero-Gravity Space Flight. Vol. 5 of Physiological and Performance Determinants in Manned Space Systems, Part I, Paul Horowitz, ed., Western Periodicals Co. (North Hollywood, Calif.), 1965, pp. 31-38.

Smith, K.J.; Speckmann, E.W.; George, Marilyn E.; Homer, G.M.; and Dunco, D. Wiltsie: Biochemical and Physiological Evaluation of Human Subjects Wearing Pressure Suits Under Simulated Aerospace Conditions. AMRL TR-65-147, 1965.

Speckmann, E.W.; Smith, K.J.; Vanderveen, J.E.; Homer, G.M.; and Dunco, D. Wiltsie: Nutritional Acceptability of a Dehydrated Diet. Aerospace Med., vol. 36, no. 3, March 1965, pp. 256-260.

Winitz, Milton; Graff, Jack; Gallagher, Neil; Narkin, Anthony; and Seedman, Daniel A.: Evaluation of Chemical Diets as Nutrition for Man-in-Space. Nature, vol. 205, no. 4973, Feb. 20, 1965, pp. 741-743.

1966

Cooke, Julian P.; and Heidelbaugh, Norman D.: Rapid Decompression and Exposure of Fresh Foods to Near Vacuum Conditions. SAM TR-65-321, 1966.

Cordaro, Joseph T.; Sellers, Walter M.; Ball, Robert J.; and Schmidt, Jerome P.: Study of Man During a 56-Day Exposure to an Oxygen-Helium Atmosphere at 258 mm Hg Total Pressure: Part X — Enteric Microbial Flora. Aerospace Med., vol. 37, no. 6, June 1966, pp. 594-596.

Dymsza, H.A.; Stoewsand, G.S.; Donovan, Patricia; Barrett, F.F.; and LaChance, P.A.: Development of Nutrient-Defined Formula Diets for Space Feeding. Food Technol., vol. 20, no. 10, Oct. 1966, pp. 1349-1352.

Heidelbaugh, Norman D.: Space Flight Feeding Systems: Characteristics, Concepts for Improvement, and Public Health Implications. J. Am. Vet. Med. Assoc., vol. 149, no. 12, Dec. 15, 1966, pp. 1662-1671.

Heidelbaugh, Norman D.; Vanderveen, John E.; Klicka, Mary V.; and O'Hara, May J.: Study of Man During a 56-Day Exposure to an Oxygen-Helium Atmosphere at 258 mm Hg Total Pressure: Part VIII — Observations on Feeding Bite-Size Foods. Aerospace Med., vol,. 37, no. 6, June 1966, pp. 583-590.

Macklin, Martin: Water Handling in the Absence of Gravity. Aerospace Med., vol. 37, no. 10, Oct. 1966, pp. 1040-1045.

Smith, K.J.; Speckmann, E.W.; LaChance, Paul A.; and Dunco, Dorothea W.: Nutritional Evaluation of a Precooked Dehydrated Diet for Possible Use in Aerospace Systems. Food Technol., vol. 20, no. 10, Oct. 1966, pp. 1341-1345.

Vanderveen, John E.; Heidelbaugh, Norman D.; and O'Hara, May J.: Study of Man During a 56-Day Exposure to an Oxygen-Helium Atmosphere at 258 mm Hg Total Pressure: Part IX — Nutritional Evaluation of Feeding Bite-Size Foods. Aerospace Med., vol. 37, no. 6, June 1966, pp. 591-594.

1967

Anon.: NASA Standards for Clean Rooms and Work Stations for the Microbiologically Controlled Environment. NASA Handbook 5340.2, 1967.

Anon.: Standard Procedures for the Microbiological Examination of Space Hardware. NASA Handbook 5340.1, 1967.

Heidelbaugh, Norman D.; and Rosenbusch, Marvin A.: A Method to Manufacture Pelletized Formula Foods in Small Quantities. SAM TR-67-75, 1967.

Klicka, Mary V.; Hollender, H.A.; and LaChance, P.A.: Foods for Astronauts. J. Am. Dietet. Assoc., vol. 51, no. 2, Sept. 1967, pp. 238-245.

Nanz, Robert A.; Michel, Edward L.; and LaChance, Paul A.: Evolution of Space Feeding Concepts During the Mercury and Gemini Space Programs. Food Technol., vol. 21, no. 12, Dec. 1967, pp. 1596-1602.

O'Hara, May J.; Chapin, Roy E.; Heidelbaugh, Norman D.; and Vanderveen, John E.: Aerospace Feeding: Acceptability of Bite-Size and Dehydrated Foods. J. Am. Dietet. Assoc., vol. 51, no. 2, Sept. 1967, pp. 246-250.

1968

Heidelbaugh, Norman D.; Vanderveen, John E.; and Iger, Howard G.: Development and Evaluation of a Simplified Formula Food for Aerospace Feeding Systems. Aerospace Med., vol. 39, no. 1, Jan. 1968, pp. 38-43.

1969

Anon.: Contamination Control Handbook. NASA SP-5076, 1969.

Bychkov, V.P.: Influence of a Diet Consisting of Dehydrated Products on the Functional State of the Human Organism. Environmental Space Sciences, vol. 3, no. 4, July-Aug. 1969, pp.261-266.

Bychkov, V.P.: Metabolic Characteristics of Humans Maintained on a Diet of Dehydrated Foods for 120 Days. Environmental Space Sciences, vol. 3, no. 1, Jan.-Feb. 1969, pp. 73-76.

El-Bisi, Hamed M.; and Powers, Edmund M.: The Microbiological Wholesomeness of Space Foods. Report TR-70-41-FL, U.S. Army Natick Laboratories, 1969.

Lutwak, Leo; Whedon, G. Donald; LaChance, Paul A.; Reid, Jeanne M.; and Lipscomb, H.: Mineral, Electrolyte and Nitrogen Balance Studies of the Gemini-VII Fourteen-Day Orbital Space Flight. J. Clin. Endocr. Metab., vol. 29, no. 9, Sept. 1969, pp. 1140-1156.

Smith, Malcolm C.; and Berry, Charles A.: Dinner on the Moon. Nutrition Today, Autumn 1969, pp. 37-42.

1970

Flentge, Robert L.; and Bustead, Ronald L.: Manufacturing Requirements of Food for Aerospace Feeding. SAM TR-70-23, 1970.

Heidelbaugh, Norman D.; and Karel, M.: Changes in Pouched Heat-Processed Foods. Mod. Packaging, vol. 43, Nov. 1970, pp. 80-86.

Smith, Malcolm: The Apollo Food Program. Aerospace Food Technology. NASA SP-202, 1970, pp. 5-13.

Vanderveen, John E.; O'Hara, May J.; and Leeber, Donald A.: Consumption of Rehydratable Food in Zero-Gravity Environments Using Conventional Eating Utensils. Aerospace Med., vol. 41, no. 3, Mar. 1970, pp. 306-308.

1971

Bourland, C.T.; Huber, C.S.; and Heidelbaugh, N.D.: The Relative Effectiveness of 8-Hydroxyquinoline Sulfate and Alkyl Dimethyl Benzyl Ammonium Chloride in the Stabilization of Aerospace Food Waste. J. Milk Food Technol., vol. 34, no. 10, Oct. 1971, pp. 478-481.

Flentge, R.L.; Grim, A.C.; Doppelt, F.F.; and Vanderveen, J.E.: How Conventional Eating Methods Were Found Feasible for Spacecraft. Food Technol., vol. 25, no. 1, Jan. 1971, pp. 51-54.

Heidelbaugh, Norman D.; and Smith, Malcolm C., Jr.: Potential Applications of Space Food Processing Environment Controls for the Food Industry. Proc. of the Food Engineering Forum, American Society of Agricultural Engineers (St. Joseph, Mich.), 1971, pp. 95-105.

Heidelbaugh, Norman D.; Smith, Malcolm C., Jr.; Rambaut, Paul C.; Hartung, T.E.; and Huber, Clayton S.: Potential Public Health Applications of Space Food Safety Standards. J. Am. Vet. Med. Assoc., vol. 159, no. 11, Dec. 1, 1971, pp. 1462-1469.

Powers, Edmund M.; Ay, Carl; El-Bisi, Hamed M.; and Rowley, Durwood B.: Bacteriology of Dehydrated Space Foods. Appl. Microbiol., vol. 22, no. 3, Sept. 1971, pp. 441-445.

Smith, Malcolm C., Jr.; Huber, Clayton S.; and Heidelbaugh, Norman D.: Apollo 14 Food System. Aerospace Med., vol. 42, no. 11, Nov. 1971, pp. 1185-1192.

1972

Berry, Charles A.; and Smith, Malcolm: What We've Learnt From Space Exploration. Nutrition Today, Sept.-Oct. 1972, pp. 4-11 and 29-32.

Huber, Clayton S.; Heidelbaugh, Norman D.; Smith, Malcolm C., Jr.; and Klicka, Mary: Space Foods. Health and Food. John Wiley and Sons, 1972, pp. 130-151.

Rambaut, Paul C.; Bourland, Charles T.; Heidelbaugh, Norman D.; Huber, Clayton S.; and Smith, Malcolm C., Jr.: Some Flow Properties of Foods in Null Gravity. Food Technol., vol. 26, no. 1, Jan. 1972, pp. 58-63.

Smith, Malcolm C., Jr.; Rambaut, Paul C.; Heidelbaugh, Norman D.; Rapp, Rita M.; and Wheeler, Harry O.: Food and Nutrition Studies for Apollo 16. NASA TM X-58096, 1972.

1973

Hartung, T.E.; Bullerman, L.B.; Arnold, R.G.; and Heidelbaugh, N.D.: Application of Low Dose Irradiation to a Fresh Bread System for Space Flights. J. Food Sci., vol. 38, 1973, pp. 129-132.

Heidelbaugh, Norman D.; Rambaut, Paul C.; and Smith, Malcolm C.: Incorporation of Nutritional Therapy in Space Food Systems. Activities Report: The Research and Development Associates for Military Food and Packaging Systems, Inc., vol. 25, 1973, pp. 7-32.

Heidelbaugh, Norman D.; Smith, Malcolm C., Jr.; and Rambaut, Paul C.: Food Safety in NASA Nutrition Programs. J. Am. Vet. Med. Assoc., vol. 163, no. 9, Nov. 1973, pp. 1065-1070.

Heidelbaugh, Norman D.; Smith, Malcolm C.; Rambaut, Paul C.; and Leach, Carolyn: Space Food Processing Environment Controls and Safety Standards. AIChe Chemical Engineering Progress Symposium Series No. 132, vol. 69, 1973, pp. 87-90.

Heidelbaugh, Norman D.; Smith, Malcolm C., Jr.; Rambaut, Paul C.; Lutwak, Leo; Clinical Nutrition Applications of Space Food Technology. J. Am. Dietet. Assoc., vol. 62, no. 4, Apr. 1973, pp. 383-389.

Huber, C.S.; Heidelbaugh, N.D.; Rapp, R.M.; and Smith, M.C.: Nutrition Systems for Pressure Suits. Aerospace Med., vol. 44 no. 8. Aug. 1973, pp. 905-909.

Luckey, T.D.; Bengson, M.H.; and Smith, M.C.: Apollo Diet Evaluation: A Comparison of Biological and Analytical Methods Including Bioisolation of Mice and Gamma Radiation of Diet. Aerospace Med., vol. 44, no. 8, Aug. 1973, pp. 888-901.

Rambaut, Paul C.; Heidelbaugh, Norman D.; Reid, Jeanne M.; and Smith, Malcolm C., Jr.: Caloric Balance During Simulated and Actual Space Flight. Aerospace Med., vol. 44, no. 11, Nov. 1973, pp. 1264-1269.

Rambaut, Paul C.; Heidelbaugh, Norman D.; and Smith, Malcolm C.: Calcium and Phosphorus Mobilization in Man During Weightless Flight. Activities Report: The Research and Development Associates for Military Food and Packaging Systems, Inc., vol. 25, 1973, pp. 1-7.

1974

Bannerot, R.B.; Cox, J.E.; Chen, C.K.; and Heidelbaugh, N.D.: Thermal Preparation of Foods in Space-Vehicle Environments. Aerospace Med., vol. 45, no. 3, Mar. 1974, pp. 263-268.

CHAPTER 2
WASTE MANAGEMENT SYSTEM

by

Richard L. Sauer

Lyndon B. Johnson Space Center

George K. Jorgensen

The Boeing Company

Introduction

Defecation and urination have been bothersome aspects of space travel from the beginning of manned space flight. Ideally, waste management systems for use in space would permit elimination of body wastes and their collection to be accomplished as simply as they are on Earth. In the weightless environment, however, this is a difficult goal to achieve. Waste handling equipment must not only be designed to function in zero gravity, but must do so within the constraints of size, weight, and power imposed by spacecraft systems. These restrictions resulted in the use of the waste management systems described in this chapter.

The urine collection and transfer processes, with only minor modifications, were essentially the same for Apollo missions as they were for all prior United States space missions. Very simply described, the prime system used prior to Apollo 12 by unsuited crewmen employed the urine transfer system. This system consisted of a rubber cuff connected to a flexible collection bag. A new system, the urine receptacle assembly, was developed for Apollo and served as the prime system on Apollo 12 and all subsequent missions. This system employed a device which did not require intimate contact of the crewman during urine collection. The urine transfer system served as a backup system during the latter missions. Each of these approaches is illustrated in figure 1.

When crewmen wore space suits during launch, extravehicular activity, and emergency modes, a special device was provided for collection and intermediate storage of urine. This device, known as the urine collection and transfer assembly, is shown in figure 2 as it was worn over the liquid cooling garment. The assembly was connected by a hose to the spacecraft waste management system. Several modified devices were used when urine samples were collected for postflight analysis.

469

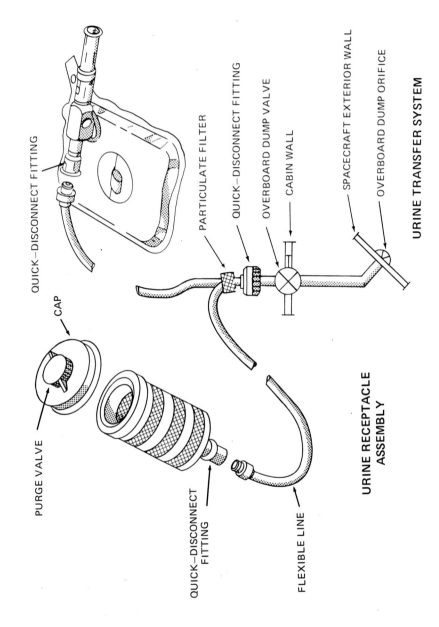

QUICK–DISCONNECT FITTING

CAP

PURGE VALVE

QUICK–DISCONNECT
FITTING

FLEXIBLE LINE

PARTICULATE FILTER

QUICK–DISCONNECT FITTING

OVERBOARD DUMP VALVE

CABIN WALL

SPACECRAFT EXTERIOR WALL

OVERBOARD DUMP ORIFICE

URINE TRANSFER SYSTEM

URINE RECEPTACLE
ASSEMBLY

Figure 1. Apollo urine collection systems — the urine receptacle assembly and urine transfer system.

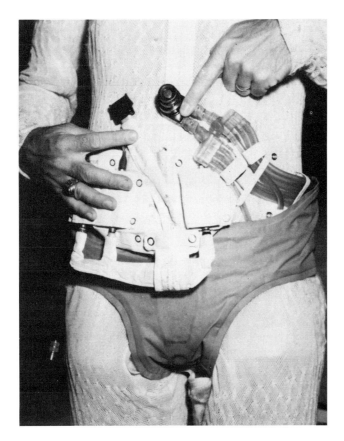

Figure 2. Urine collection and transfer assembly
worn over the liquid cooling garment.

Efforts had been made prior to the first Apollo flight to simplify the waste collection systems to allow waste collection without intimate contact devices and to permit direct overboard dumping of urine. Because of problems encountered during the development phase, the improved systems were not available in time to be used for Apollo missions.

In the absence of a system providing positive means for the removal of feces from the body, an extremely basic system had to be relied upon for inflight fecal collection. The device used was a plastic bag which was taped to the buttocks to capture feces. After defecation, the crewmember was required to seal the bag and knead it in order to mix a liquid bactericide with the contents to provide the desired degree of feces stabilization. Because this task was distasteful and required an inordinate amount of time, low residue foods and laxatives were generally used prior to launch. During flight, in addition to low residue foods, some use was also made of drugs to reduce intestinal motility.

During lunar surface activity and free space extravehicular activity, the use of the bag fecal collection system was not feasible. Should it have become impossible for a crewman to have prevented defecation during these activity periods, the fecal containment system — a pair of undershorts with layers of absorbent material — would serve to contain any excreta.

The following sections describe the Apollo waste management system in detail and briefly evaluate its performance.

Apollo Waste Management System

The function of the waste management system (WMS) was to control the disposition of solid and liquid wastes and waste stowage gases. The basic requirements of the system included collection and stowage of feces, collection and overboard dumping of urine, removal of urine from the pressure garment assembly, provision for urination while in the spacecraft couches, and venting of waste stowage gases. A urine and fecal waste stowage vent and a vacuum subsystem were part of the overall waste management system (Sauer, 1971).

The waste management system consisted of a urine subsystem and a fecal subsystem. The principal elements of the urine subsystem were the urine receptacle assembly (URA), the urine transfer system (UTS), the urine collection and transfer assembly (UCTA), and, for several missions, modified urine collection devices to provide samples to be retained for postflight analysis. The main elements of the fecal subsystem were a fecal and emesis collection device, a waste stowage compartment, a waste stowage bag, and a fecal containment garment (the "fecal containment system") for contingency and suited conditions. Figure 3 is a schematic representation of the waste management system elements within the Command Module (URA not shown).

Urine Subsystem

The urine subsystem consisted of three devices for collecting and transferring urine: the urine transfer system, the urine collection and transfer assembly, and the urine receptacle assembly. The remainder of the system consisted of a particulate filter to prevent clogging of the orifice of the urine dump nozzle (see figure 1) and a hose for transferring urine from any of the collection devices to the waste management panel for dumping.

Urine Receptacle Assembly (URA). The urine receptacle assembly (figure 4) was an open-ended, cylindrical container that could be hand-held. The receptacle was connected by a quick-disconnect fitting to a flexible urine dump line, which in turn was connected by a quick-disconnect fitting to the waste management panel. The receptacle could accommodate a maximum urine flow of 40 ml per second. Although the receptacle's volumetric capacity was only 480 ml, the effective system capacity was 700 ml with concurrent urination and dumping.

The URA contained a honeycomb cell insert that supported a 40μ hydrophilic screen. The honeycomb insert provided a large contact area that acted as a bundle of capillary tubes. The capillary action produced by each cell (0.32 cm pore size) of the honeycomb tended to hold the fluid in place in the zero-g environment until it could pass

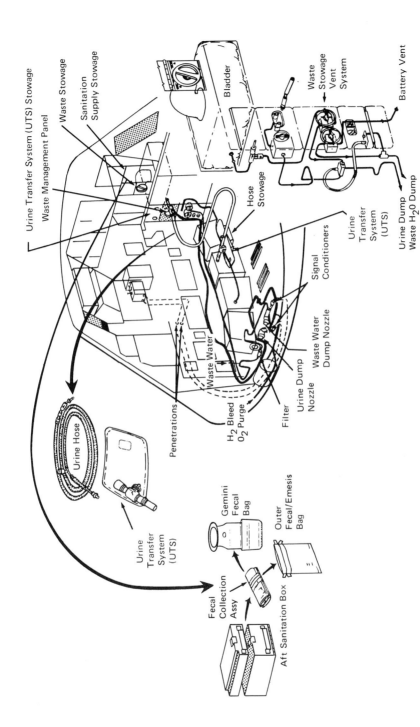

Figure 3. Waste management system (NASA, 1969).

into the urine dump line. A sealing cap installed during periods of nonuse blocked out cabin airflow and permitted the interior of the URA to be exposed to the space vacuum for venting between uses, if desired.

Figure 4. Urine receptacle assembly.

For use, the URA was taken from its stowage position, the cap removed from the receiver chamber, and the device connected to the 3.05-m long urine transfer hose, which in turn was connected to the waste management panel. The overboard dump valve on the waste management panel was rotated to the "dump" position, allowing the system to be vented to space at a pressure differential of 3.4×10^4 N/m^2 (5 psi). The man voided by directing his urine stream into the receiver chamber of the URA. When the receiver chamber had emptied, 60 seconds were allowed for clearing the hose and lines prior to closing the urine dump valve. The cap was replaced on the receiver chamber and the URA returned to its mission stowage position.

The urine transfer hose was made of flexible, convoluted fluorocarbon sufficiently strong to withstand the pressure differential and supple enough to facilitate easy handling in zero g. The hose also could be used to join the space suit urine quick-disconnect fitting to the waste management panel to facilitate emptying the urine collection and transfer assembly.

Installed between the waste management panel quick-disconnect and the hose was a 215-micrometer filter. Urine was filtered to prevent clogging the orifice of the urine dump nozzle. The dump nozzle orifice had a diameter of 0.1397 cm, which restricted gas flow to a maximum of 0.01 m^3/minute and liquid flow to 453.6 gm/minute. This prevented excessive loss of cabin oxygen during system use. Because ice formation at the dump nozzle could block flow, the nozzle was fitted with two redundant 5.77 watt heaters.

Urine Transfer System (UTS). The urine transfer system (figure 5) consisted of a roll-on cuff, a receiver, a valve with a manifold, a collection bag, and a quick-disconnect fitting. The roll-on cuff was a rubber tube that functioned as an external catheter between the penis and the receiver/valve. The cuff was designed to be used for one day (five or six urinations) and was then replaced. Ten additional color-coded cuffs per crewman were stowed. The receiver to which the cuff attached was a short tube containing a low-pressure differential check valve [262 N/m^2 (0.038 psi)] and a bypass valve.

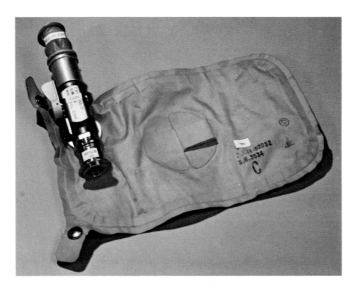

Figure 5. Apollo urine transfer system (UTS) with roll-on cuff.

The UTS could be used in two different modes: (1) dumping during time of voiding, and (2) dumping subsequent to voiding. In the first mode, the hardware was interconnected to the overboard dump system during the time of voiding, as shown in figure 1. As a consequence, the urine was immediately dumped overboard as it was voided. In the second mode, the UTS was not connected to the overboard dump system during the micturition. In this mode, urine was collected in the UTS bag. Following micturition, the UTS was connected to the overboard dump system and the urine vented overboard. The urine collection bag had a capacity of approximately 1200 ml. For reasons of sanitation, each crewman was provided a personal urine transfer system.

Urine Collection and Transfer Assembly (UCTA). The urine collection and transfer assembly (figure 6) was designed to facilitate urination when crewmen were wearing pressure suits, for example during extravehicular activities. The urine collection and transfer assembly consisted of a roll-on cuff and a collection bladder worn around the waist. The UCTA was worn over the fecal containment garment. Urine in the device could be drained either while the crewman was in the suit or after the suit was removed by connecting the urine transfer hose to the spacecraft waste management panel.

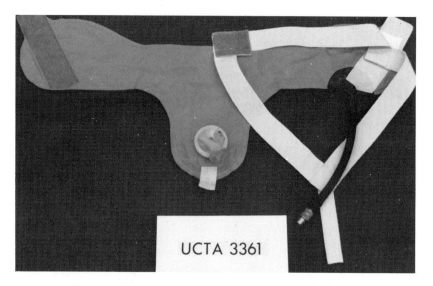

Figure 6. Apollo urine collection and transfer assembly (UCTA).

Ancillary Urine Hardware. Two ancillary urine collection devices were used. These were the return enhancement water bag (REWB) and the biomedical urine sampling system (BUSS).

The REWB, provided for the flight of Apollo 14, made available additional water storage volume onboard in the event of a partial water system failure. The REWB was also used for Apollo 15 and subsequent missions to pool urine for up to 24 hours in order to circumvent overboard dumping during certain mission periods.* After the pooling period, the REWB containing urine was dumped in a similar manner as was the urine transfer system, except that an additional urine filter was installed downstream of the REWB to prevent possible system plugging with urine precipitates formed as a result of urine storage for 24 hours.

During the Apollo 16 mission, three return enhancement water bags (one for each crewman) were provided to recover 24-hour pooled urine samples collected inflight with the urine transfer system. Boric acid preinstalled in the REWBs preserved the urine. These samples were collected to permit an investigation of fluid and electrolyte disturbances suspected to have occurred during prior missions. Figure 7 depicts schematically the urine collection system for Apollo 16.

Inflight urine samples were again collected during the Apollo 17 mission. In this case, the samples were required for a study that focused on the cations and anions critical to body fluid regulation. Twenty-four-hour urine samples were collected from each crewman on each man-day of Command Module occupancy by use of the biomedical urine

---

*It was desirable, for example, to circumvent urine dumping for the conduct of lunar optical experiments. Dumped urine tended to form a cloud of vapor around the spacecraft which fouled the optics with particulate matter and interfered with observations.

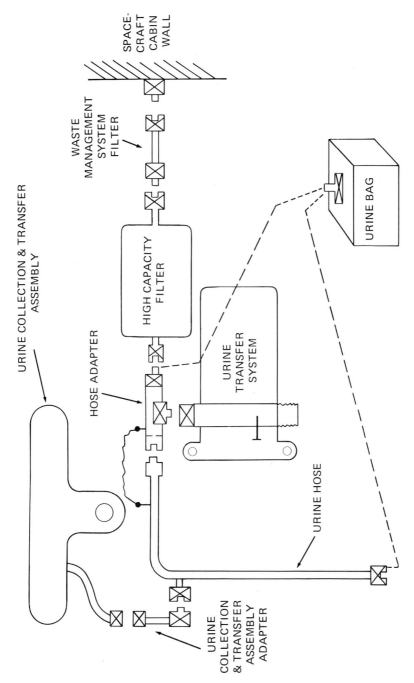

Figure 7. Apollo 16 urine collection system.

sampling systems. The BUSS consisted of two flexible plastic film containers — a 24-hour pooling container and a collection container (figure 8). One BUSS was used per man-day. This provided for transfer of a sample of pooled urine for return to Earth, with transfer of the remaining urine volume to the Command Module urine overboard dump system for disposal.

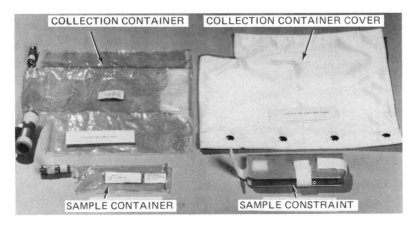

Figure 8. Biomedical urine sampling system (BUSS).

The BUSS collection container measured 30 cm^2 and incorporated a receiver/valve assembly at one corner similar to the receiver assembly used on the UTS. The collection container had a capacity of 3000 ml. The pooling bag for each BUSS contained a known amount of preinstalled lithium chloride so that postflight volume determination could be made from returned samples. (The collected sample volumes and calculated pooling volumes are listed in table 1). The pooling bag also contained boric acid for urine preservation. At the end of each 24-hour pooling period, the container was interconnected with its sample container by mating quick-disconnects, and a representative portion of the 24-hour pool was forced into the sample container. This container had a capacity of 125 ml. The sample container was then stowed for postflight recovery and the urine in the collection container was dumped overboard.

Fecal Subsystem

The fecal subsystem consisted of a fecal collection assembly, tissue dispensers, a waste stowage compartment, and a waste stowage bag. For suited conditions, the fecal containment system was provided.

The fecal collection assembly consisted of a fecal bag and an outer fecal/emesis (FE) bag bound together with a plastic wrapper. The fecal bag (figure 9) was a plastic sack with a flange at the opening and a finger cot in the center of one side. A surface of Stomaseal® tape was used for adhering the flange to the buttocks. Tissue wipes and a germicide pouch were stored in a pocket on the outside lower end of the bag. The outer transparent FE bag was used for storing the used fecal bag. Internal and external seals at the mouth of the bag made it capable of containing a 3.4×10^4–N/m^2 (5 psi) gas differential pressure.

Table 1

Apollo 17 Urine Sampling Results

Crewman	Time of Sampling, GET*		Sample Volume (ml)	Calculated Pooling Volume (ml)
	Preflight, Predicted (hr:min)	Actual (hr:min)		
CMP	18:30	18:50	110.7	1154
	35:00	34:36	85.5	811
	58:45	58:22	91.0	1875
	83:30	83:22	89.9	1034
	107:00	110:00	83.2	1500
	133:00	133:00	86.3	769
	156:10	156:10	74.8	1667
	180:45	180:40	104.9	2000
	208:00	208:30	70.4	1500
	230:25	230:28	84.0	1200
	252:50	252:45	93.7	1304
	276:50	276:30	89.8	938
	300:30	299:50	116.1	1667
LMP	18:30	18:30	84.8	750
	35:00	34:40	78.8	448
	58:45	58:20	118.0	789
	83:30	83:20	74.8	789
	107:00	110:00	78.8	1250
	230:25	230:30	71.9	714
	252:50	252:15	80.9	1111
	276:50	276:25	87.1	1304
	300:30	300:15	104.7	1579
CDR	18:30	18:46	82.0	395
	35:00	34:40	38.7	337
	58:45	58:10	94.0	750
	83:30	83:15	60.1	652
	107:00	110:00	71.1	938
	230:25	230:28	90.2	1000
	252:50	252:50	96.9	1429
	276:50	276:30	106.6	1154
	300:30	299:52	137.3	2500

*Ground elapsed time.

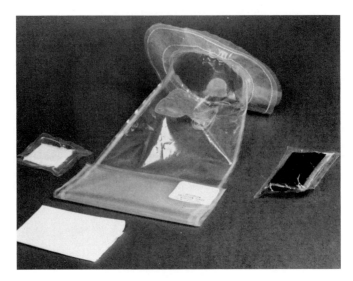

Figure 9. Fecal bag.

Briefly, the fecal collection system was used in the following way. The finger cot was employed to position the fecal bag over the anus. The finger cot was also used after defecation to separate fecal matter from the anal area and push it to the bottom of the bag. The bag was then removed from the buttocks, and the anus was cleaned with tissue wipes. These were disposed of into the fecal bag. The user then secured the germicidal liquid pouch and, after cutting the corner off the outer pouch, deposited it along with the inner pouch into the bag. The bag was then sealed. The germicidal liquid was a mixture of sodium orthophenylphenol and sodium chlorophenylphenol of amaplast blue LXT (NASA, c. 1967). The bag was kneaded to rupture the inner pouch and mix the germicide with the wastes. The inner bag was placed into the outer bag which was rolled into the smallest possible volume and then placed in the waste stowage compartment. This compartment featured a split membrane inside the door to prevent fecal bags from floating back out into the cabin once they had been placed within the compartment. For later Apollo missions, the volume provided by the waste stowage compartment was inadequate. Consequently, a waste stowage bag was provided for additional volume for the disposal of fecal bags. Both waste stowage volumes had an overboard venting capability for gases generated in the feces.

Data on returned fecal samples from Apollo crewmen are listed in table 2.

The fecal containment system (FCS) was a pair of underpants of absorbent material worn under the liquid cooling garment (LCG) during suited periods (e.g., extravehicular activity). Figure 10 shows the garment. If an uncontrolled bowel movement had occurred, the underpants would have contained the feces. During lift-off and reentry, the fecal containment systems were stowed.

Experimental Fecal/Emesis System Flown Aboard Apollo 16. Three modified fecal collection bags were flown to evaluate their performance on the Apollo 16 mission. The

Table 2

Apollo Fecal Samples

Mission Number	Label	Weight (gm)	Average Sample Weight/Mission (gm)
7	S/N* 2270	81.3	210.1
	S/N 2276	119.8	
	S/N 2277	229.8	
	S/N 2278	326.2	
	S/N 2280	340.2	
	S/N 2282	236.2	
	S/N 2299	228.1	
	S/N 2300	96.1	
	S/N 2312	233.7	
8	1	186.5	156.9
	2	85.6	
	3	198.6	
9	CMP	168.0	265.3
	CMP	190.7	
	CMP	317.5	
	LMP	385.1	
10	S/N 3513	40.0	52.4
	S/N 3527	40.9	
	S/N 3512	76.3	
11	1	208.1	122.6
	2	230.6	
	3	129.0	
	4	35.1	
	5	10.0	
12	LMP	79.7	117.6
	Unlabeled	219.1	
	LMP	143.1	
	LMP	41.6	
	CDR	133.0	
	CMP	3.3	
	CMP 79:00 GET	165.7	
	CMP 101:00 GET	109.3	
	CMP 225:00 GET	163.9	
16	LMP	134.97	185.1
		247.88	
		234.52	
		204.90	
		103.25	
	CDR	133.15	95.1
		16.17	
		135.92	
	CMP	54.69	102.6
		49.28	
		203.82	
17	CDR	48	97
		35	
		175	
		97	
		138	
		91	
	CMP	255	200
		223	
		284	
		182	
		66	
		191	
	LMP	181	167
		37	
		193	
		255	

*Serial number.

bags were of the same basic design as the Gemini-type fecal bag with the following exceptions: (1) a modified seat flange, for better fit of seat flange to buttocks; (2) a wider finger cot; and (3) an improved seal for keeping the device closed during performance of personal hygiene.

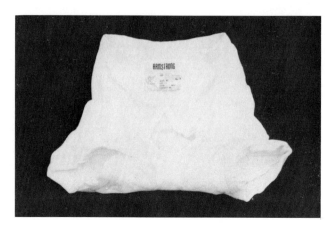

Figure 10. Fecal containment system
for use during extravehicular activity.

Lunar Module Waste Management System

The Lunar Module waste management system incorporated systems used in the Command Module. These systems were used in similar fashion in both the Lunar Module and Command Module. The principal difference was that there was no overboard dumping of wastes on the lunar surface. The urine subsystem in the Lunar Module consisted of in-suit urine containers (identical to the Command Module system), a urine transfer hose, a manually operated waste control valve, and a large (8900 cm^3) waste fluid container. To drain the in-suit device, the waste fluid container was attached to the in-suit urine container by a urine transfer hose, and the suit was then slightly overpressurized. Because of a 6.9×10^3–N/m^2 (1.0 psi) pressure differential, when the control valve opened urine flowed from the in-suit container to the waste fluid container at a rate of approximately 200 cm^3/minute. As a backup device, two 900-cm^3 waste containers were provided for direct attachment to the in-suit container. On Apollo 15 and subsequent missions, a low pressure container was installed in the descent stage of the Lunar Module. A line interconnected this tank with a urine receiver in the ascent stage. This receiver was a simple funnel-like receptacle that permitted urine collection without intimate contact.

The fecal containment subsystem in the Lunar Module was identical to the Command Module fecal subsystem.

Table 3 presents a summary of the waste management system elements used during each of the Apollo missions.

Table 3

Waste Management Systems Used on Apollo Missions

Mission Number	Waste Management Equipment
7	UCTA, UTS, FE
8	UCTA, UTS, FE
9	UCTA, UTS, FE
10	UCTA, UTS, FE
11	UCTA, UTS, FE
12	URA, UCTA, UTS, FE
13	URA, UCTA, UTS, FE
14	URA, UCTA, UTS, REWB, FE
15	URA, UCTA, UTS, REWB, FE
16	URA, UCTA, UTS, REWB, FE
17	BUSS, URA, UCTA, UTS, FE

UCTA = urine collection and transfer assembly
UTS = urine transfer system
FE   = fecal/emesis bag
URA = urine receptacle assembly
REWB = return enhancement water bag (for samples)
BUSS = biomedical urine sampling system

Overall Waste Management System Performance

In general, the Apollo waste management system worked satisfactorily from an engineering standpoint. From the point of view of crew acceptance, however, the system must be given poor marks. The principal problem with both the urine and fecal collection systems was the fact that these required more manipulation than crewmen were used to in the Earth environment and were, as a consequence, found to be objectionable. The urine receptacle assembly represented an attempt to preclude crew handling of urine specimens but, because urine spills were frequent, the objective of "sanitizing" the process was thwarted. The fecal collection system presented an even more distasteful set of problems. The collection process required a great deal of skill to preclude escape of feces from the collection bag and consequent soiling of the crew, their clothing, or cabin surfaces. The fecal collection process was, moreover, extremely time consuming because of the level of difficulty involved with use of the system. An Apollo 7 astronaut estimated the time required to correctly accomplish the process at 45 minutes.[*] Good placement of fecal bags was difficult to attain; this was further complicated by the fact that the flap at the back of the constant wear garment created an opening that was too small for easy placement of the bags.[**] As was noted earlier, kneading of the bags was required for dispersal of the germicide.

[*]Entry in the log of Apollo 7 by Astronaut Walter Cunningham.
[**]The configuration of the constant wear garments on later Apollo missions were modified to correct this problem.

Attempts to improve the fecal collection system, as exemplified by the modified fecal/emesis collection bags flown on Apollo 16, failed in the crew's estimation. During postflight debriefings, crew comments indicated that the experimental bag was not significantly better or easier to use than the baseline Gemini-type bag. Further development of the bag was, therefore, not pursued.

Summary

Although there were inherent design limitations in the waste management systems used for the manned Apollo missions, performance of the individual systems *per se* was reasonably satisfactory. However, there were some problems. In addition to being marginal from a hygienic standpoint, use of the collection devices required many steps and the expenditure of a considerable amount of time. The problem of odor was continually present because of the lack of a positive means of eliminating defecation odors.

The Apollo waste management system's design and operations pointed to the need for several improvements in future missions. These were the following:

1. Future systems should not require intimate contact.

2. The time required for system use should be significantly reduced.

3. The waste management system should provide some technique of automatically removing feces from the buttocks area.

These considerations were taken into account in the design of the improved Skylab waste management system.

References

National Aeronautics and Space Administration: Waste Management: Project Gemini, ETS-HISD-MSC1500-651208. NASA Manned Spacecraft Center Information Sheet, c. 1967.

National Aeronautics and Space Administration: Apollo Operations Handbook. Block II Spacecraft, Vol. 1. Spacecraft Description, 15 April 1969.

Sauer, R.L.; and Bustamante, R,D.: Water Supply and Waste Management in Spacecraft — Past, Present, & Future. Paper presented at the Twenty-Sixth Purdue Industrial Waste Conference (Lafayette, Indiana), May 4-6, 1971.

CHAPTER 3
BIOINSTRUMENTATION

by

Stanley M. Luczkowski
Lyndon B. Johnson Space Center

Introduction

With the inception of the United States space program, continuous monitoring of vital signs was a relatively new concept. Since that time, the technology of bio-telemetry — long distance transmission of physiological information — has come of age. Thousands of hours of data have been transmitted from space to the Earth from as far as 400 000 km (250 000 miles) away. Only when astronauts were in lunar orbit on the far side of the moon was there an interruption in the steady transmission of vital sign data to Earth-based physicians and mission controllers. All three crewmen were continuously monitored during Apollo missions 7 through 13. Beginning with Apollo 14, data were obtained on a continuous basis for at least one crewman. Both the Commander and the Lunar Module Pilot were closely monitored during the performance of lunar surface extravehicular activities, but because only one channel was available in the Lunar Module data were collected for only one crewman.

It was essential that vital signs be monitored during space flight. During early space flight operations, there was uncertainty as to the effects of space flight factors on normal physiological functioning. Transmission of physiological data provided essential information upon which a decision to abort a mission could have been reliably made from the ground, should it have become necessary. During Gemini missions, astronauts operated for the first time in the new environment of free space during the performance of extravehicular tasks. Vital sign monitoring coupled with voice communication in this instance dictated that early free space EVA be cut short because these activities proved too taxing. Later, modifications of training and procedures enabled astronauts to perform long-term extravehicular activities safely.

During Apollo missions, all three crewmen were instrumented for medical monitoring during operation in the Command Module, the Lunar Module, and during extravehicular activity in free space and on the lunar surface. Lunar surface activity imposed stresses of an unpredictable nature on the lunar surface crewmen. While attempts to simulate lunar walking and operating conditions were made during ground testing, the full nature of the effect of the lunar terrain on work efficiency and, hence metabolic rate, was not known until the first lunar surface mission. Medical monitoring during these operations permitted real-time adjustments in activity timelines formulated before flight as such alterations were needed. Such data permitted changes in the scheduling of Apollo 15 lunar surface tasks when electrocardiographic recordings and other data indicated that this crew was being subjected to excessive workloads.

The Apollo bioinstrumentation system (BIS) requirements evolved as a continuation and refinement of medical monitoring systems utilized throughout the Mercury and Gemini Programs. The BIS and related hardware provided physiological data to ground-based medical personnel for operational inflight safety monitoring; for inflight medical experiments; and for ground-based operations safety monitoring.

System Description

The Apollo BIS had two configurations. The early Apollo (Block I) Program was terminated prior to any actual space flights. All missions from Apollo 7 through Apollo 17 (Block II) utilized the BIS.

The system planned for Block I of the Apollo Program consisted of two electrocardiographs (ECG), one impedance pneumograph (ZPN), one body temperature signal conditioner, a DC to DC converter, and appropriate electrode, temperature probe, and interconnecting cables (see figure 1). The Block I configuration was designed, fabricated, and qualified for flight use, and was utilized in Block I ground tests until the spacecraft 204 accident. The design and packaging concepts were essentially the same as developed for Gemini, except for the addition of the DC to DC converter, providing a high level (0 to 5 VDC) output signals to the spacecraft telemetry system. The body temperature measuring components (figure 2) were added for ground tests only, and were not included in the flight configuration.

The Block II (figure 3) system utilized the same components as did the Block I. The only system difference was the deletion of one of the ECG measurements. The temperature measurement capability was again provided for ground testing. Block II signal conditioners differed only in their grounding configuration. Block I units had a common connection for case ground and signal-power ground, while Block II utilized separate connections for improved radio-frequency interference characteristics. Block I and II units were, otherwise, electrically and physically identical.

The Apollo signal conditioners were designed to be of uniform size, 5.84 cm x 3.81 cm x 1.04 cm (2.3 in. x 1.5 in. x 0.41 in.), with identical miniature input and output connectors. Color coding was incorporated to facilitate proper mating with their respective connectors on the bioharness and electrode harnesses.

Electrocardiogram Signal Conditioner

The ECG signal conditioner and electrodes were designed to provide inflight measurements of a crewmember's ECG activity and to develop a signal wave ranging between 0 and 5 volts peak-to-peak, which is representative of crewman ECG activity. The unit was provided with an adjustment that permitted preflight calibrations. The electrical activity sensed by the body electrode was passed into the signal conditioner which had an input impedance of greater than 40 megohms, and common mode rejection greater than 100 000 to 1. The gain of the signal conditioners was continuously variable from 600 to 4500, and the output was the amplified ECG waveform which varied ±2.5 volts about a 2.5-V bias. Harmonic distortion was less than 1.0 percent over the unit's frequency bandpass of 0.2 Hz to 100 Hz. Signal conditioner power of plus and minus 10 VDC at .5 milliamperes was required from the DC to DC converter.

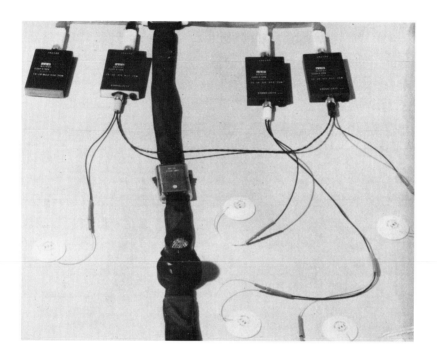

Figure 1. Apollo Block I configuration
of bioinstrumentation system.

Impedance Pneumograph Signal Conditioner

The ZPN signal conditioner and electrodes were designed for measurement of a change in the transthoracic impedance to a low level current at a frequency of approximately 50 kHz. Measurement was obtained from a pair of electrodes that developed signals (0 to 5 volts peak-to-peak) corresponding to the respiration rate over a wide dynamic range of respiratory activity. The excitation circuit accommodated electrode impedance of 100 to 1000 ohms, and the signal conditioner input impedance was greater than 1 megohm at 50 kHz and greater than 60 megohms in the 0 to 100 Hz frequency range. The output had a range of 0 to 5 VDC with the respiration signal varying about a 2.5-V bias level. Power drain from the DC to DC converter plus and minus 10-V supply was less than 7 milliamps. This unit was also provided with adjustments to accommodate the characteristics of the individual.

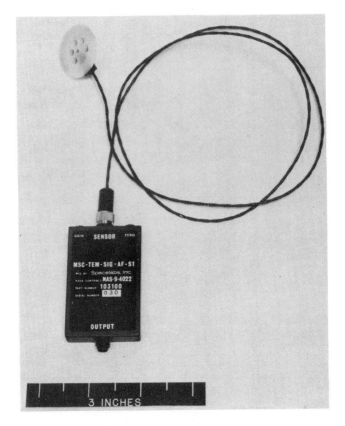

Figure 2. Body temperature measurement system.

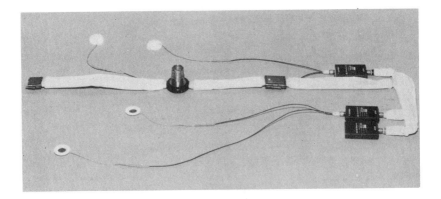

Figure 3. Apollo Block II configuration
of bioinstrumentation system.

Body Temperature System

The body temperature probe and signal conditioner produced an output voltage in the range of 0 to 5 VDC corresponding to sensed temperatures of from $303°$ to $319°K$ ($85°$ to $115°F$). The system accuracy was within $±0.17°K$ ($±0.3°F$) and had a response time to a $2.8°K$ ($5°F$) step change of five seconds. Power requirements were less than 5 milliamps from each of the DC to DC converter supply voltages.

DC to DC Converter (DCC)

The DCC as designed and delivered for Apollo provided isolated, balanced plus and minus 10-V outputs. The outputs were regulated within $±0.1$ volt over a current load range of 0 to 30 milliamperes drawn from either side and with an input voltage of between 14.8 and 20 VDC. Output impedance was approximately 3 ohms and output voltage ripple less than 1 mv peak-to-peak.

Investigation into the potential short circuit fire hazards inside the space suit revealed that, by shorting the output leads of the DC to DC converter, a spark could be produced which would ignite cotton in the presence of oxygen under conditions of 131 kN/m^2 (19 psia). This ignition source was traced to output capacitor energy storage in the DC to DC power converter and to the ability of the output capacitors to produce a high-current pulse in a short-circuit condition (even though the output current would go to 50 milliamperes in a steady-state condition). The high-current pulse and the associated ignition hazard were eliminated by installing resistors that limited the current in the positive 10- and negative 10-volt output leads of the DCC.

The incorporation of these resistors influenced performance of the DCC due to the increase in effective dynamic output impedance since the resistors could not be placed in the voltage regulation loop. Output impedance, therefore, increased by 10 ohms and the regulation increased from $±0.1$ VDC to $+0.1$ VDC, -0.4 VDC under load variations.

Electrode Harnesses

The sternal-electrode harness was a small cable used in conjunction with the ECG signal conditioner. The harness provided the electrical interface between the crewman's electrode and the ECG signal conditioner. The cable also contained the system ground electrode, which was a high-impedance ground primarily used to remove the static charge from the crewman.

The axillary-electrode harness was a small cable used in conjunction with the ZPN signal conditioner. The cable provided the electrical interface between the crewman's electrodes and the ZPN signal conditioner. Both electrode harnesses originally utilized silver/silver chloride anodized discs in an acrylic housing. The wiring to the connector which mated to the signal conditioner was Teflon insulated, and incorporated miniature pin jack connectors in-line for quick-disconnect capability.

Several changes were made to the harnesses during the Apollo Program as a result of inflight problems, testing, and operational changes. During the first manned Apollo mission, data were lost due to separation of the pin jack connections inside the space suit and also to wire breakage at the connectors. Therefore, the electrode harnesses were redesigned to eliminate the pin jack and the electrodes were wired as a permanent part of the harness (figure 4). Also, the wire was changed from Teflon insulated to polyvinyl chloride (PVC) insulated and a soft silicone rubber strain relief was added to the connector. This eliminated the problems on all subsequent Apollo missions.

Continued testing during the program revealed a sneak ground path in the input circuit of the ECG signal conditioner (which provided a current path to ground if the crewmen should contact a voltage source). The solution to this problem required increasing the input lead impedances by adding series current-limiting resistors to the sternal-electrode harness. Also, a ground electrode with a series resistor was added to reduce noise and artifact in the ECG data.

For missions through Apollo 14, the electrodes were filled with electrode paste and attached to the crewman by double-back adhesive tape. Figure 5 shows a subject wearing the biobelt with the electrodes in place. The electrodes were then covered with porous surgical tape that permitted normal skin respiration. The electrochemical activity that occurs at the electrode surface was degraded when the anodizing was damaged. This problem occurs after many use cycles. Therefore, when it was decided that, for Apollo 15 and subsequent missions, the crewmen would be permitted to remove and replace their electrodes during flight, the integrity of the anodized disc was doubtful. This problem was eliminated by replacing the disc with a pressed pellet made of powdered silver/silver chloride. This technique provided a homogeneous electrode that was not affected by small surface damage.

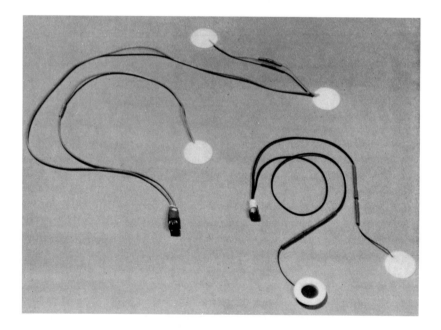

Figure 4. Apollo sternal-electrode harness
and axillary-electrode harness.

Crew Interface

The bioinstrumentation system, which was required both in the vehicle and during EVA, was designed to be worn inside the space suit. The biobelt containing the instrumentation (figure 6) provided a compact means for placement and stowage of the signal conditioners and the DC to DC converter. Snap fasteners were used to mate the biobelt to the midriff section of either the constant wear garment or the liquid cooling garment. The signal conditioners and the DC to DC converter were available for easy connection to the biomedical harness and the sensing equipment. Elastic straps were used to maintain the contents in a fixed position, and an overflap snapped over the contents of each pocket. The overflaps were fabricated of Teflon-coated Beta cloth to satisfy flammability requirements.

The electrode attachment technique was designed to maintain long-term reliable body contact for good signals, but attachment was difficult to maintain without discomfort and skin damage. Because electrodes became dislodged under such severe efforts as suit doffing and donning, a kit was provided with attachment materials to replace electrodes during unsuited periods.

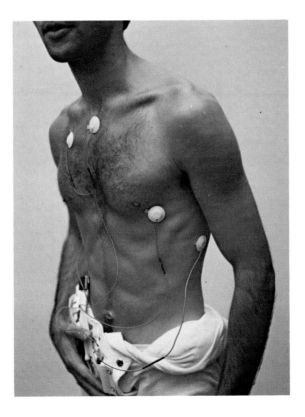

Figure 5. Biobelt being worn with electrodes in place.

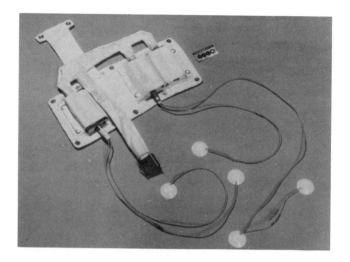

Figure 6. Bioinstrumentation system in the biobelt.

Results and Discussion

The bioinstrumentation system provided essential data in support of Apollo missions. With the incorporation of current limiting modifications, the electronic system proved to be very reliable. As expected, electrode attachment was a recurring, but minor, problem which required crewmembers to reattach the displaced electrodes.

Figure 7 represents a typical ECG signal received at the Mission Control Center during various periods of the Apollo 11 mission. Figure 8 shows electrocardiographic tracings

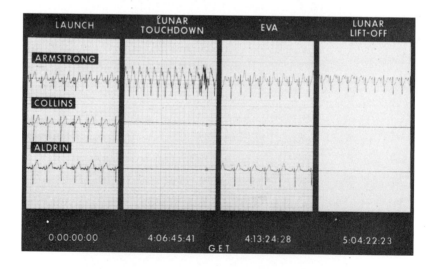

Figure 7. Typical ECG signal
received during Apollo 11 mission.

obtained during the Apollo 15 mission during periods of cardiac arrhythmia. These data led to a reassessment of workload and diet for subsequent crews, and alterations in onboard medical supplies to include antiarrhythmic drugs.

This chapter has treated bioinstrumentation from its engineering aspects. The reader is referred to Section II, Chapter 1, for clinical aspects of medical monitoring and the bioinstrumentation system.

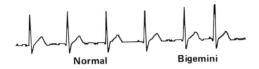

Normal   **Bigemini**

179:07:20

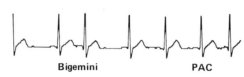

Bigeminis

179:37:25

(a)

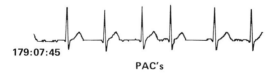

Bigemini   **PAC**

179:07:40

179:07:45

PAC's

(b)

Figure 8. Apollo 15 ECG tracings obtained during periods of cardiac arrhythmia. (a) shows the normal heart beat converting to a nodal bigemini rhythm; (b) shows the bigemini rhythm converting to premature auricular contractions.

CHAPTER 4
POTABLE WATER SUPPLY

by

Richard L. Sauer
David J. Calley
Lyndon B. Johnson Space Center

Introduction

The potable water system was an essential element in the Apollo life support system. It provided water, on demand, for drinking, personal hygiene, dehydrated food reconstitution, and for cabin cooling. Unlike earlier spacecraft which relied upon stored water as the only potable water source, the Apollo system provided for resupply of onboard stores by utilization of byproduct water from fuel cell operation.

Underlying the development of the Apollo spacecraft water system, and that used on all prior spacecraft, are unique circumstances related to operation in the space environment, in general, and in spacecraft, in particular. The absence of gravity requires that the entire water system be sealed and that positive expulsion be provided through such techniques as movable diaphragms or bellows installed in water storage containers. Spacecraft operation demands highly reliable performance and minimum weight. System reliability is insured through careful materials selection and the use of redundant or multiple components. Volume constraints within the spacecraft itself and the closed atmospheric environment severely limit the choice of materials to be used. In addition toxicological and flammability parameters require consideration.

The interdependency of spacecraft systems imposes other constraints upon the potable water system. For example, protecting the integrity of the spacecraft's cooling system demands severe limitation of the types and amounts of additives which may be used in the water system to control microbial growth, prevent corrosion, or protect the taste of the water provided.

The bacteriological quality criteria used by NASA for potable water systems required the absence of viable organisms (sterility). The criteria did not specify indicator organisms but rather included specific analyses for the absence of *E. coli*, total count, yeast and mold, and anaerobic organisms. The design characteristics of the water system, possessing several potential sources of contamination, offered little restraint in preventing microbial entry and proliferation in the water. Information concerning the interrelationship between microorganisms and man in the spacecraft environment was limited. In addition, a remote but real chance existed that fecal contamination of drinking water could occur. For these reasons, the NASA standard requires that water in all spacecraft systems be maintained free of viable organisms.

The standard for water potability formulated by NASA was based on the United States Public Health Service Drinking Water Standards, 1962. Standards for the chemical composition of spacecraft drinking water were similar to Public Health Service standards; microbiological standards were, however, more stringent. In addition, several potential contaminants unique to spacecraft water were included.

The Apollo potable water system accomplished the objectives for which it was designed, and its overall performance was good. While design and operational difficulties existed, these were all successfully resolved. This chapter traces the history and evolution of the Apollo potable water system and describes its operation and performance.

Evolution of the Apollo Potable Water System

Project Mercury Potable Water System

For the first United States manned spacecraft program, Project Mercury, potable water was supplied by a simple "fill and draw" system. All metabolic water to be used was loaded onboard before launch. The system consisted of a flexible water pouch containing approximately 2.7 kg (6 lb) of water. The water was transferred to the crewman by means of a flexible hose that terminated in a drinking tube. Water was expelled from the tube by pressure on the pouch.

Gemini Program Potable Water System

The Gemini spacecraft was the first to use fuel cells to provide electrical power. These devices combined gaseous oxygen and hydrogen through an electrode to produce an electrical current, with water as a byproduct. While considerable effort was expended during the Gemini Program to process this fuel cell-produced water by means of filtration, carbon sorption, and ion exchange resins, none of these methods proved sufficiently effective to make the water potable. Consequently, Gemini crewmembers like their predecessors relied upon a fill and draw system for drinking water.

In addition to providing water for drinking purposes, the Gemini system (figure 1) supplied water to the secondary spacecraft cooling system. In the event of a partial failure of the space radiators (the primary spacecraft cooling mechanism), or during periods of high heat rejection, secondary or supplemental spacecraft cooling was provided by the spacecraft water boiler. This device evaporated water to the space vacuum and thereby rejected heat from the spacecraft. In a contingency situation, water was supplied to the boiler in the form of humidity or suit condensate, with supplemental water provided by the potable water system. This design required that the water system and humidity condensate system be interconnected. A potential cross-contamination problem was thereby introduced – a problem which was further complicated because the humidity condensate system was interconnected with the urine management system. To obviate the potential hazard, chlorine was added to the prelaunch-loaded water to prevent microbial contamination.

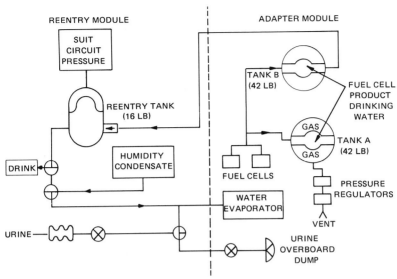

Figure 1. Gemini spacecraft water system.

Apollo Program Potable Water System

The problems encountered in the use of fuel cell-generated water during Gemini were resolved in sufficient time to make fuel cell water the principal source of potable water in Apollo Command Module spacecraft. The solution was effected by the choice of a sintered nickel electrode to replace the organic electrode used in the Gemini system. The sintered nickel electrode did not degrade as did the organic electrode, consequently, the Apollo fuel cell produced water of extremely high quality.

The water supply systems in the Command and Lunar Modules differed. In the Command Module, water was generated by fuel cell operation; in the Lunar Module, all water supplies were loaded in storage tanks before lift-off. Other differences between the two systems were dictated by the functions unique to each vehicle. In the Command Module system, provision was made for chilling and heating the water supply. No heating or cooling was be provided for Lunar Module water. The Lunar Module water supply was used as the primary means of vehicle cooling through a sublimation process. In the Command Module, the potable water system provided for supplementary cooling only via the spacecraft evaporators. (Primary sublimation cooling was accomplished through space radiators.)

Command and Service Module Potable Water System

A schematic diagram of the Command and Service Module (CSM) water management system is shown in figure 2. Water was generated by the fuel cells located in the Service Module. These fuel cells consisted of two chambers separated by porous nickel electrodes. The electrolyte was concentrated potassium hydroxide. One of the chambers was filled with oxygen (cathode), and the other with hydrogen (anode); pressure in both chambers was maintained at 4.1×10^5 N/m^2 (60 psi). Oxygen was diffused through the electrode into the hydrogen filled chamber, where the two gases reacted chemically to produce electrical power to meet the requirements of the Command/Service Module. The initial Apollo CM's were plagued with excess hydrogen in the water. As a consequence, a hydrogen separator was developed and used on Apollo 12 and subsequent missions. This device functioned as follows: hydrogen diffused from the water through the walls of palladium-silver tubes and then vented into space, and the degassed water was conveyed to the water valve (control) panel in the Command Module.

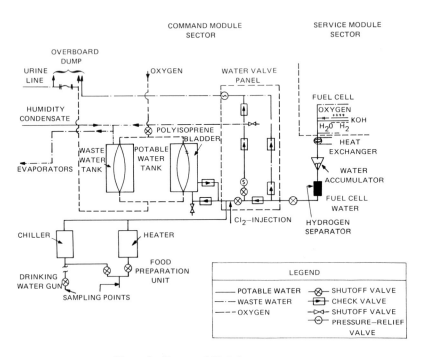

Figure 2. Command Module water system.

The fuel cells operated at a temperature of approximately 483°K (410°F) and at a pressure of 4.1×10^5 N/m^2 (60 psi), and produced water at a nominal rate of .54 kg/hr (1.2 lb/hr). The water production rate depended on the power drawn from the cells, and increased to as much as 1.0 kg/hr (2.2 lb/hr) for brief periods. Before fuel cell water was transferred to the Command Module, it was cooled to a temperature of 296°K (74°F), and then reduced to a system pressure of 1.7×10^5 N/m^2 (25 psi).

Fuel cell water was transferred to the water valve panel by means of an aluminum line. From this panel, water was routed either to the potable water tank or to the waste-water tank. From the potable water tank the water was routed to either the food preparation unit after passing through a heater, or to the drinking water gun after passing through a chiller. When the potable water tank was full, water was routed to the waste-water tank. The waste-water tank also received humidity condensate from the pressure suits and from the Command Module atmosphere. Excess water was dumped overboard.

The main controls on the water panel were two water-shutoff valves (one each for the potable water and waste-water systems), a shutoff valve that permitted access to the waste-water system, a chlorine-injection assembly, a control valve to the overboard dump, and two pressure-relief controls.

Possible microbiological contamination of the potable water resulting from the humidity-condensate input was prevented by maintaining a chlorine residual in the Command Module potable water. On Apollo flights 7 through 13, continuous minimum residual of 0.5 mg/liter was maintained by adding 22 cc of a sodium hypochorite stock solution (5000-mg/liter available chlorine) once every 24 hours. The chlorine solution was added manually at the port between the fuel cells and the potable water tank. A modified chlorine addition was used on Apollo 14 and the remaining flights. In these flights the water systems were injected with one 22 cc ampoule of sodium hypochlorite (1860 mg/l as available chlorine) and one 22 cc ampoule of mixed sodium dehydrogen phosphate (0.297 molar) and sodium nitrate (0.217 molar). The addition of sodium nitrate was found to have a conserving effect on the chloride, reducing its rate of decay in the system.

The food preparation unit consisted of a heater and two water-use ports for hot and chilled water. A pressure of 1.7×10^5 N/m^2 (25 psi) was maintained by applying oxygen to an expansion bladder in the potable water tank.

Functional Components. The following key functional components were used in the Command Module water management system.

1. *Potable Water Tank.* The potable water tank served as a water storage container in case of fuel cell failure and as an equalization tank to provide water during peak demand conditions when the water demand rate exceeded the fuel cell production rate; for example, during meal preparation times. The cylindrical vessel held a maximum of 16 kg (36 lb) of water and was fabricated from 6061 aluminum alloy. An oxygen-filled polyisoprene bladder maintained a pressure of approximately 1.7×10^5 N/m^2 (25 psi) in the tank and throughout the system. Oxygen for pressurization was obtained from a common Service Module supply that also provided oxygen for metabolic consumption and for power generation. Because free hydrogen in the water diffused through the bladder material, a low-rate gas bleed-off was provided to prevent a buildup that could result in an explosive hydrogen/oxygen mixture in the oxygen plenum.

2. *Waste-Water Tank.* The waste-water tank held a maximum of 25 kg (56 lb) of water. It was similar in design and operation to the potable water tank.

3. *Water Chiller and Water Heater.* The chiller, which had a water storage capacity of 227 gm (0.5 lb), reduced the temperature of the water from 298° to 280°K (76° to 45°F) for the drinking water gun and the food preparation unit. The heat exchanger tubes and all other components in the chiller were made of stainless steel. Chilling was provided by the spacecraft water/glycol cooling system. Heating was accomplished through electrical resistance. The water heater had a storage capacity of 1.1 kg (2.5 lb), and a maximum of two hours was required to raise the water temperature from 289°K (60°F) to the operating temperature of 341°K (154°F).

4. *Food Preparation Unit.* The food preparation unit dispensed hot or cold water in 28-gm (1-ounce) aliquots into the dehydrated food and beverages. The unit consisted of two valves and one nozzle. The configuration of the nozzle was identical to the nozzle of the water gun and permitted water to be injected into the food and beverage packages to facilitate rehydration of the contents. The valves controlled either the hot or the cold water to be used for food reconstitution. The water gun was used primarily to supply cold drinking water to the crewmen, but could also be used for the reconstitution of food and beverages requiring cold water (see figure 2).

5. *Drinking Water Gun.* A drinking water gun was connected to the water system by a 178-cm (70-in.) long flexible hose fabricated from a fluorinated hydrocarbon elastomer, Viton®. It was calibrated to dispense 14 gm (0.5 ounce) of cold water upon each activation. A counter was provided to permit inventory of the amount of water dispensed. Water was ejected from the nozzle of the gun either directly into the crewman's mouth or into a food or beverage container.

6. *Transfer Lines.* All hard lines in the system were fabricated from 0.64-cm (0.25-in.) diameter aluminum tubing.

Lunar Module Water Management System

The Lunar Module power was supplied by batteries rather than fuel cells. Therefore, no onboard fuel cell water generation was possible. Potable water, loaded prior to launch, was stored in three tanks, a 151-kg (332 lb) tank in the descent stage and two 19-kg (42 lb) tanks in the ascent stage (figure 3). The descent stage tank supplied all water during lunar orbit descent and lunar surface exploration. The ascent stage tanks supplied water during the ascent, rendezvous, and linkup phases. For the Apollo 15, 16, and 17 missions, which involved extended lunar stays, an additional 151-kg tank was installed in the descent stage.

The Lunar Module water system was pressurized by gaseous nitrogen at 3.1×10^5 N/m^2 (45 psi). This pressure was transmitted to the water by silicone rubber (Silastic)® bladders in each of the water tanks.

Lunar Module cooling was provided by a water sublimator. This device, similar in operation to the boiler in the Command Module, sublimated ice to the space vacuum through a sintered nickel plate. As in the Command Module, the feedwater was provided by the spacecraft potable water system. The requirement to minimize solids was even more stringent for the Lunar Module sublimator operation. Consequently, distilled water was loaded into the tanks to reduce to a minimum the potential blockage of the small pores of the nickel plate in the evaporator unit.

The potential hazard of cross-connection between the humidity condensate and the potable water system demanded the use of a water disinfection system in the Lunar Module as well as the Command Module. Iodine was selected instead of chlorine because it was thought that chlorine would create operating problems with the sublimation units. Iodine was added (12 mg/liter) to the water prior to launch to ensure a minimum residual of 0.5 mg/liter throughout the manning of the Lunar Module.

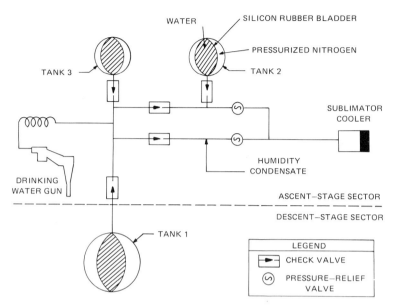

Figure 3. Lunar Module water system.

Results and Discussion

Overall, performance of the Command Module and Lunar Module water management systems was good. Problems did, however, arise. The low solids requirements constrained the use of materials for microbiological and corrosion control. Other areas of concern were taste and odor control, water potability, and materials selection. Overall system performance and resolution of problems that arose are described in the following sections.

Water System Materials Compatibility

Metallic Components. Corrosion of metallic components was found during development testing at the inlet tube to the heater, the tube in front of the drinking water gun hose connection, and the section of tubing between the chlorine injection port and the potable water tank. An investigation revealed that a pitting-type corrosion occurred throughout the system. Because of the corrosion, nickel, cadmium, and manganese were present in the water supply at levels in excess of allowable limits. Corrosion was attributable to the following factors.

1. The use of ultra-high purity water, which is corrosive by nature.

2. Incompatibility of the biocide with the system (that is, the capability of chloride ions to penetrate the passivating oxide layer formed on aluminum tubing).

3. Materials selected for system fabrication resulted in dissimilar metals being electrically interconnected. For example, the interconnection of aluminum and copper in

the water system, produced an electromotive force of approximately two volts. Internal tubing surface imperfections provided sites for active localized corrosion.

Tests indicated that the CM fuel cell water containing sodium hypochlorite (NaOCl) and sodium dihydrogen phosphate (NaH_2PO_4) at concentrations used in the spacecraft produced considerable corrosive action on aluminum. Nickel, cadmium, manganese, and, to a lesser extent, other metals were released into the Command Module water supply as a result of corrosive activity and the attendant deterioration of the nickel brazing and copper baffles in the water heater and the aluminum alloy tubing.

In addition to the problems that corrosion imposed on maintaining Command Module system integrity, corrosion also was a sink for the chlorine biocide, resulting in a rapid loss of residual biocide. To solve the incompatibility problem, sodium nitrate was added as a corrosion inhibitor.

The interaction of iodine with aluminum caused similar corrosion in the Lunar Module water system. The presence of metallic ions in samples taken from the ascent tank and the descent tank use port were evidence of this corrosion. However, because corrosion proved to be limited, inhibitors were not deemed necessary.

Synthetic Components. A problem of iodine depletion was observed in the Lunar Module. The primary cause of this depletion was the diffusion of iodine through the Silastic® membranous material used in the water tanks. This material acted as a semipermeable membrane. The rate of membrane permeation increased with increasing iodine concentration and the time of exposure of the bladder to iodinated water. To solve the permeability problem, iodinated water was not placed in the tanks during ground-based testing, and the tanks were not loaded until the latest possible time before lift-off.

Interaction between the biocide and the membranous material in the Lunar Module did not cause objectionable taste and odors as did interaction between the chlorine and the chlorine-polyisoprene bladder material in the Command Module water tank. In addition, the original neoprene hose connecting the drinking water gun to the water system in the Command Module interacted with water to produce significant taste and odors. An organic precipitate was found in the Command Module water system. The precipitate, a metal carbamate, was a curing agent was used in the polyisoprene tank bladders.

Gases. Offgassing of water at the use ports caused problems during flight because the quantity of gas in the water formed bubbles of sufficient size to inhibit direct use for drinking or food preparation. Techniques for gas/liquid separation in zero g (such as bagging and centrifugation) were not effective. Use of a hydrophobic/hydrophilic separator, which performed with reasonable success during the Apollo 11 mission, together with the palladium silver hydrogen separator that was used during the Apollo 12 and subsequent missions, relieved the problem somewhat; however, gases were still evolved.

The two major sources of gases dissolved in the Command Module water were hydrogen released from fuel cell water and oxygen diffused through the water tank bladders. Hydrogen gas was released from the fuel cell water as it passed through cascaded pressures from 4.1×10^5 N/m^2 (60 psi) to 3.4×10^4 N/m^2 (5 psi), the cabin atmosphere pressure. Oxygen, used as a pressure balance in the water tanks, diffused through the bladder membrane into the water supply. A third source of dissolved gases common to the Lunar Module and the Command Module was ground support equipment water that was not degassed before being loaded onboard the spacecraft.

Similar, but not nearly as pronounced, offgassing problems occurred at the use ports in the Lunar Module. The gases consisted either of nitrogen diffused into the water supply from the balancing plenum of the potable water tanks or air entrained in the water supply at the time of servicing (no inflight data were collected).

Chemical Quality of Water

Water used to fill ground support equipment before spacecraft loading was drawn from the resources of the city of Cocoa, Florida. The city water was filtered through particulate filters, charcoal filters, and two mixed-bed ion exchange units. This product water, which met the quality requirements shown in table 1, was then passed through 0.22μ bacterial filters and then into the ground support equipment units for the Command Module and the Lunar Module. The requirements for chemical quality for the ground support equipment water are listed in table 2.

Table 1

Water Quality Requirements for Facility Water Supply, Test Point 1*

Properties	Limits (max. allowable)
Electrical conductivity	.33 micromho/cm at 298°K (25°C)
pH	6-8 at 298°K (25°C)
Total residue	2 mg/liter
Sterility **	Reference only

*Test Point 1 is at the facility water supply/spacecraft potable water the input interface.

**Sterility samples consisted of an anaerobic and an aerobic sample. Total volume for both samples was 500 ml.

Command Module System. The Command Module water system was subjected to a 24-hour disinfection soak with chlorinated water (10 to 20 mg/liter). The ground support equipment water was prepared with the chlorine solution plus sodium dihydrogen phosphate (100 to 200 mg/liter) for pH buffering, and sodium nitrate (52 to 62 mg/liter) as a corrosion inhibitor. This solution was loaded into the Command Module system. At the end of the 24-hour period, the Command Module system was emptied, flushed, and refilled with unchlorinated, high purity water from the ground support equipment. The quality requirements for this water are cited in table 3. The water remained in storage in the Command Module potable water tank for five to seven days. Between two to nine hours before lift-off, chlorine and buffer/inhibitor solutions were added to the storage

Table 2

Water Quality Requirements for
Ground Support Equipment Water Supply, Test Point 2[a]

Properties	Limits (max. allowable)
Electrical conductivity	1.0 μmho/cm at 298°K (25°C)
pH	6-8 at 298°K (25°C)
Total residue	2 mg/l
Fixed residue	0.5 mg/l
Taste and odor	Threshold No. 3
Turbidity	11 units
Color, true	5 units
Particulate[b]	
Particle size range	No. of particles/500 ml fluid CSM/LM
0-10 μ	Unlimited[c]
10-25 μ	875
25-50 μ	100
50-100 μ	50
(over)100	2
Ionic species	
Cadmium	0.01 mg/l
Chromium (hexavalent)	0.05 mg/l
Copper	1.0 mg/l
Iron	0.3 mg/l
Lead	0.05 mg/l
Manganese	0.05 mg/l
Mercury	0.005 mg/l
Nickel	0.05 mg/l
Selenium	0.01 mg/l
Silver	0.05 mg/l
Zinc	5.0 mg/l
Chloride	—
Magnesium	—
Iodide	—
Aluminum	—
Calcium	—
Potassium	—
Silica	—
Total nitrogen	10.0 mg/l (CSM only)
Bactericide	0.5 mg/l
Sterility[d]	—

aTest Point 2 is defined to be at the last possible, but practical, point prior to the potable water load line/spacecraft load point interface; this test point allowed water sampling without breaking or remaking of water servicing system connections. Water was required to meet the Test Point 2 maximum property limits at the beginning of water servicing prior to bactericide/additive addition if used, or prior to servicing the spacecraft if bactericide was not used.

bThe particulate sample was taken immediately following final servicing of the spacecraft.

cUnlimited means that particles in this size range were not counted; however, any obscuring of the filter grid lines was cause for rejection.

dSterility samples consisted of an anaerobic and an aerobic sample: total volume for both samples was 500 ml.

Table 3

Water Quality Requirements for
Spacecraft Water Supply, Test Point 3[a]

Properties	Limits (max. allowable)	
Electrical conductivity	Reference only	
pH	6-8 at 298°K (25°C) for CSM	
	4-8 at 298°K (25°C) for LM	
Total residue	14 mg/liter CM/LM	
Taste and odor	Reference only	
Turbidity	11 units	
Color, true	Reference only	
Particulate[b]		

Particulate Size Range	No. of Particles per 500 ml Fluid CSM	No. of Particles per 500 ml Fluid LM
0- 10 microns	Reference only	Unlimited[c]
10- 25 microns	Reference only	875
25- 50 microns	Reference only	200
50-100 microns	Reference only	100
100-250 microns	Reference only	10

Ionic species		
Cadmium	0.01 mg/l	
Chromium (hexavalent)	0.05 mg/l	
Copper	1.0 mg/l	
Iron	0.3 mg/l	
Lead	0.05 mg/l	
Manganese	0.05 mg/l	
Mercury	0.005 mg/l	
Nickel[d]	0.05 mg/l	
Selenium	0.01 mg/l	
Silver	0.05 mg/l	
Zinc	5.0 mg/l	
Chloride	—	
Magnesium	—	
Iodide	—	
Aluminum	—	
Potassium	—	
Silica	—	
Total nitrogen	10.0 mg/l (CSM only)	
Bactericide	0.5 mg/l	
Sterility[e]	Free of viable organisms	

[a]Test Point 3 is defined to be the onboard test/use ports in the LM and CSM.

[b]The particulate sample was taken immediately following final servicing of the spacecraft.

[c]Unlimited means that particles in this size range were not counted; however, any obscuring of the filter grid lines was cause for rejection.

[d]For the CSM and for missions when water was used from the CSM for no more than 14 days duration, the maximum allowable limit of the effective nickel concentration was 1.0 mg/liter.

[e]Sterility samples consisted of an anaerobic and an aerobic sample: total volume for both samples was 500 ml.

tank by means of injection ampoules (22 cc). Water was cycled from the use ports to distribute the injected solutions from the injection port (figure 2) into the storage tank. During flight, injections were repeated at approximately 24-hour intervals. The corrosion inhibitor described above was used only on the flights after Apollo 13.

Separate ampoules containing sodium hypochlorite (5000 mg/liter as chlorine) and sodium dihydrogen phosphate buffer (0.7 molar) were used for inflight injection of the Apollo 7 through 13 Command Module water systems. After the Apollo 13 mission, sodium nitrate was added to the buffer ampoules to provide water system corrosion inhibition. The water systems were injected with one ampoule of sodium hypochlorite (1860 mg/liter as chlorine) and one ampoule of mixed sodium dihydrogen phosphate (0.297 molar) and sodium nitrate (0.217 molar).

Three hours before lift-off, and at 24-hour intervals inflight, water was withdrawn through the drinking water gun or the food preparation unit to permit a flow of fuel cell water past the biocide injection point and into the potable water tank, after which the contents of the ampoules were injected. The injected solutions were flushed into the potable water storage tank by flowing fuel cell water past the chlorine injection port and into the tank (figure 2). Most of the biocide and buffer passed the service line branching point and was carried into the storage tank, but a small fraction remained in the injection tee or was diffused into the service line. After a ten-minute contact time, an ampoule of water was withdrawn through the injection point. As a result of withdrawal, any chlorine solution in the service line was pulled back into the main line, where the chlorine was transferred into the storage tank by the fuel cell water. Before the water was used, an additional 20-minute period was required to allow biocide, buffer, and inhibitor to disperse in the potable water tank. The treated water was withdrawn for consumption through the drinking water gun and the food preparation service outlets.

On several occasions during the early Apollo flights, the crewmembers reported that the water had a strong chlorine taste. In most instances, the difficulty was traced to a procedural error that occurred during the injection of the chlorine and buffer. When clear and concise procedures were developed and used, the crewmembers had no objection to the taste of the water.

The chemical characteristics of the ground support equipment load water (test point 2) and the spacecraft water (test point 3) are shown in table 4. As the table indicates, the only potential contaminant consistently found was ionic nickel. The Apollo 12 ground support equipment load water sample was the only sample in which nickel appeared at a level above the specification limit. But, an excess of nickel was contained in five samples taken from the drinking water gun. The excess amounts were not considered medically significant for the short duration Apollo flights. Preflight samples from the hot water port were examined, and they, too, were contaminated with nickel. Based on these findings, a study was conducted to determine the inflight nickel content in the hot water port on the Apollo 14 flight. A good correlation existed between nickel concentrations found in flight and those found immediately after recovery (table 5). Postflight concentrations (6.0 mg/liter) exceeded preflight load water specifications in nine out of ten samples taken within 40 hours of recovery. All evidence suggested that the hot water heater was the source of the contaminant and that the concentration

Table 4

Preflight Chemical Analysis of Command Module Potable Water, Apollo 7 through 17

Parameter	Ground Support Equipment Test Point 2 Range	Spacecraft System Test Point 3 Hot Water Port Range	Spacecraft System Test Point 3 Drink Gun Range
pH (units)	4.76 – 7.65	5.50 – 7.79	4.82 – 7.60
Electrical conductivity (umho/cm)	0.31 – 2.30	0.28 – 7.90	.25 – 3.90
Total residue (mg/l)	0.72 – 2.70	0.62 – 17.50	.60 – 4.70
Taste and odor (threshold)	All <3	All <3	All <3
Turbidity (nephlos)	0.5 – <1	0.2 – 7.0	0.2 – 11.00
Color (true)	<1. – 1	<1 – 5.0	<1 – 5.0
Ionic species (mg/l)			
Aluminum	<0.1 – 0.28	<1 – 3.2	<0.01 – 1.8
Cadmium	All <0.01	<0.01 – 0.02	<0.01 – 0.13
Calcium	<0.01 – 0.34	<0.01 – 1.2	<0.01 – 1.08
Chromium (+6)	<0.01 – 0.05	<0.01 – 0.06	<0.01 – 0.06
Copper	<0.01 – 0.07	<0.01 – 0.06	<0.01 – 0.11
Iron	<0.01 – 0.05	<0.02 – 0.03	<0.01 – 0.06
Lead	<0.01 – <0.05	<0.01 – <0.05	<0.01 – <0.05
Magnesium	<0.01 – 0.5	<0.01 – 0.14	<0.01 – <0.5
Manganese	<0.01 – 0.05	<0.01 – 0.07	<0.01 – 0.07
Mercury	All <0.005	<0.005 – 0.006	<0.005 – 0.006
Nickel	<0.05 – 0.26	<0.01 – 1.30	<0.01 – 0.18
Potassium	<0.01 – 0.50	<0.01 – <0.50	<0.01 – <0.50
Selenium	<0.01 – 0.20	<0.01 – <0.20	<0.01 – <0.20
Silicon	All <0.5	All <0.5	All <0.5
Silver	<0.01 – <0.02	<0.01 – <0.02	<0.01 – <0.02
Sodium	<0.02 – 0.41	0.01 – 0.60	0.01 – 0.83
Zinc	<0.01 – 0.07	<0.01 – 0.10	<0.01 – 0.72
Total nitrogen	All <10	All <10	All <10

Table 5

Postflight Chemical Analysis of Command Module Potable Water, Apollo 7 Through 17

Parameter	Drink Gun Test Point 3 Range		Hot Water Port Test Point 3 Range	
pH (units)	6.0 —	7.4	6.5 —	7.7
Electrical conductivity (umho/cm)	2.13 —	260.0	1.87 —	210.0
Total residue (mg/l)	11.56 —	214.4	7.72 —	178.8
Taste and odor (threshold)	<3 —	5	All	< 3
Turbidity (nephlos)	0.3 —	2.0	0.4 —	18.0
Color (true)	<1 —	5	<1 —	5
Ionic species (mg/l)				
Aluminum	0.07 —	1.5	0.59 —	0.08
Cadmium	< .01 —	< .05	<0.01 —	<0.05
Calcium	.02 —	0.57	0.02 —	2.70
Chromium (+6)	<0.01 —	<0.05	<0.01 —	<0.07
Copper	<0.01 —	0.05	<0.01 —	0.08
Iron	<0.02 —	0.09	0.01 —	0.04
Lead	<0.01 —	<0.05	<0.01 —	<0.05
Magnesium	0.04 —	0.82	0.03 —	0.50
Manganese	<0.01 —	0.06	<0.01 —	0.07
Mercury	All	<0.005	All	<0.005
Nickel	0.02 —	1.12	0.34 —	6.0
Palladium	<0.01 —	<0.05	<0.01 —	<0.05
Potassium	<0.01 —	0.36	<0.01 —	<0.5
Selenium	<0.01 —	<0.08	<0.01 —	<0.08
Silicon	All	<0.5	<0.5 —	0.8
Silver	<0.01 —	<0.02	<0.01 —	<0.02
Sodium	10.2 —	59.9	6.4 —	50.0
Zinc	0.03 —	0.17	<0.01 —	0.08
Total nitrogen	<10 —	10	All	<10

of nickel increased after the heater was activated inflight. A substantial quantity of nickel brazing material was used in the construction of the heater. In addition, small amounts of nickel appeared to be leaching because of corrosion from other components of the potable water system. A review of the medical literature indicated that ingestion of nickel in the amounts found for the relatively short duration Apollo missions would not create an acute or chronic toxicological problem, but that reconsideration would be required for missions of longer duration.

Command Module Fuel Cell Water Quality. Chemically, the fuel cell byproduct water was of equal quality to distilled water, but the water was saturated with hydrogen gas. The total dissolved solids in this water averaged 0.73 mg/liter, with an average pH of 5.6. Analyses for total solids, turbidity, and particulates during chamber testing indicated that the water met specifications except for the presence of a metal carbamate, Bis-(pentamethylenedithiocarbamate) Ni (II). As noted previously, this precipitate appeared only after fuel cell water had collected in the water storage tank.

Lunar Module Water Quality. The Lunar Module water tanks were filled with ground support equipment load water containing 20 to 30 mg/liter iodine solution for disinfection. After three to four hours contact time, approximately one-fourth of the loaded water was drained out and uniodinated water added. This process resulted in a final load iodine concentration of 11 to 13 mg/liter. No provision was made for the inflight addition of iodine to the water storage tanks. In most cases, the degradation rate of iodine in the system was such that the initial load concentrations were adequate for biocidal action during the entire Lunar Module mission. The iodine concentrations were checked three times before lift-off, and depletion curves were plotted from the data. The depletion rate, projected for the duration of the flight, had to be low enough that an iodine concentration of at least 0.5 mg/liter was maintained during the period of Lunar Module manning When preflight data indicated a depletion rate that was too rapid to maintain an adequate iodine residual during the mission, a bacterial filter was installed in the line just ahead of the water use port.

The preflight chemical quality of the Lunar Module ground support equipment load water (test point 2) and of water from the spacecraft system (test point 3) is shown in table 6. As with the Command Module, comparison of these data with specification requirements listed in tables 2 and 3 shows that the upper range of certain parameters, slightly exceeded specification limits. These were turbidity test point 2 and nickel in test point 3 samples. These excursions were not considered to be medically significant. No data were collected to determine inflight Lunar Module potable water quality.

Microbiological Quality of Water

The NASA specifications for potable water require that water be "sterile"[*] throughout the course of a mission. The use of a biocide in the water system was necessary to meet this requirement. Command Module and Lunar Module data indicated adequate control of microbial growth existed when a proper biocide concentration was maintained. Preflight data gathered on the Command Module water demonstrated that system sterility could not be maintained without an adequate biocide residual.

During the preflight water storage period, several microorganisms were found in routine sampling of the water system. Because the growth phenomenon was consistent throughout the Apollo Program, chlorination of each CM water system (normally three hours before lift-off) was accomplished. Verification of the effectiveness of this procedure was obtained from Apollo 17 prelaunch water samples. For this mission, the water system was chlorinated nine hours before lift-off and microbiological samples were taken two hours before lift-off. These samples were negative for all forms of microbial growth.

---

[*]Sterile is defined as the absence of viable organisms when employing specific analysis procedures, as in the filtration of three 150-ml samples through 0.45-micrometer filters, and then applying selective media for *E. coli,* total count or yeast mold to each of the filters. In addition, a qualitative anaerobic analysis was performed.

Table 6

Preflight Chemical Analysis of Lunar Module Potable Water, Apollo 9 through 17

Parameter	Ground Support Equipment Test Point 2 Range		Spacecraft System Test Point 3* Range	
pH (units)	5.10	— 7.7	4.3	— 7.4
Electrical conductivity (umho/cm)	0.35	— 4.2	0.37	— 10.5
Total residue (mg/l)	0.2	— 2.7	0.49	— 8.3
Taste and odor (threshold)	All <3		All< 3	
Turbidity (nephlos)	0.2	— <5	0.2	— 22.0
Color (true)	0.2	— 1.0	1.0	— >100
Ionic species (mg/l)				
Aluminum	0.04	— <0.5	0.4	— < 0.5
Cadmium	All <0.01		<0.01	— 0.039
Calcium	<0.01	— 0.03	<0.01	— 2.0
Chromium (+6)	<0.01	— <0.05	<0.01	— 0.08
Copper	<0.01	— <1.0	0.01	— 0.12
Iodide	<0.05	— <0.1	0.1	— 7.6
Iron	0.01	— <0.30	<0.01	— 0.04
Lead	<0.01	— <0.05	<0.01	— < 0.05
Magnesium	<0.01	— <0.5	<0.01	— < 0.5
Manganese	<0.01	— <0.05	<0.01	— < 0.06
Mercury	<0.005	— <0.013	All	< 0.005
Nickel	<0.02	— 0.35	<0.01	— 0.25
Palladium	<0.01	— <0.02	<0.01	— < 0.05
Potassium	<0.04	— <0.10	<0.01	— 0.30
Selenium	<0.01	— <0.2	<0.01	— < 0.2
Silicon	All <0.5		All< 0.5	
Silver	<0.01	— <0.05	<0.01	— < 0.02
Sodium	<0.01	— 0.21	<0.1	— 0.76
Zinc	<0.01	— 5.0	<0.01	— 0.12
Total nitrogen	All < 10		All<10	

*Test Point 3 was the use port inside LM cabin, with water drawn from the descent
storage tank.

The types and numbers of microorganisms isolated from preflight and postflight
samples are listed in tables 7 and 8. The most commonly found microorganisms were
Flavobacteria. Seven species of this group were identified in preflight samples. At least one
Flavobacterium species was found before each Apollo mission. Approximately 90 percent
of the preflight samples taken during the storage period prior to chlorination contained
viable microorganisms.

The single common-use water dispenser provided for the three Apollo crewmembers
inflight offered no protection against microbial transfer from crewman to crewman. The
Command Module water dispenser was attached to a 178-cm (70-in) flexible hose. The
water in the hose had little or no residual biocide after remaining unused for extended
periods: consequently, bacterial growth could occur during these periods.

Table 7

Microorganisms Isolated from Preflight and Postflight Apollo
Command Module Potable Water Samples

Microorganism	Number of Microbes in Preflight Unchlorinated Water	Number of Microbes in Postflight Water
Aeromonas hydrophila	17	
Cephalosporium acremonium		15
Corynebacterium sp.	7	
Flavobacterium harrisonii	17	
Flavobacterium sp.	7, 15,16,17	14, 15
Flavobacterium sp II	11, 12, 17	12
Flavobacterium sp. III a	1, 8, 9, 10, 12, 14	11
Flavobacterium sp. III b	9, 10, 12, 14	10, 12
Flavobacterium sp. III c	7	
Flavobacterium sp. IV c	7, 12	
Flavobacterium sp. IV e		14
Gram negative rod	16, 17	
Herellea sp.	7	
Micrococcus sp.	7, 17	
NCDC Group III b	17	
NCDC Group IV c	16	16
NCDC Group IV d	16	16
NCDC Group IV e	16	16
Pseudomonas aeruginosa	16	
Pseudomonas maltophila	14	
Pseudomonas stutzerii	17	
Rhizopus sp.	7	
Sarcina sp.	7	
Staphylococcus, betahemolytic (Not Group A)	7	
Staphylococcus epidermidis	9, 12	
Streptococcus equinus	14	
Unidentified	11, 12	7,13
Yeast/mold growth	7, 13	

It had been noted that maintenance of system sterility could not be achieved in the absence of residual biocide. Connections, valves, metering dispensers, and O-rings in water systems could harbor bacteria, rapidly recontaminating the water. Back-contamination at use ports also occurred. Bacterial growth in the water storage tanks was unexpectedly rapid. During Command Module chamber tests when no biocide was used, bacterial levels of 6×10^6 organisms/100 ml of water were found during the time when the water was stored in the spacecraft. The source of the nutrients to support this growth is unknown; however, the nutrients may be received from the tank bladder material, the fluorocarbon hose, or other carbonaceous compounds.

Postflight potable water samples were taken from all missions except Apollo 13. The genus *Flavobacterium* was again the most commonly occurring microorganism (tables 7

Table 8

Microbial Concentrations Found in Preflight
Command Module Unchlorinated Potable Water Samples

Apollo Mission	Range of Concentrations*	Ratio of Samples with Positive Growth to Total Number of Water Samples
7	Negative to TNTC**	7:11
8	$3 \times 10^2 - 1.1 \times 10^6$	5:6
9	Negative to 5.25×10^4	7:8
10	$86 - 1.2 \times 10^5$	6:6
11	$10 - 2.1 \times 10^5$	5:5
12	$1.1 \times 10^3 - 1.05 \times 10^5$	4:4
13	$6.0 \times 10^2 - 9 \times 10^6$	6:6
14	$4.5 \times 10^3 - 1.215 \times 10^6$	4:4
15	Negative $- 1.13 \times 10^7$	3:4
16	$4.2 \times 10^5 - 1.9 \times 10^7$	4:4
17	$3 - 9.0 \times 10^5$	4:4

*Concentration = Total microbes /150 ml of water
**TNTC = Too Numerous to Count

and 9). It was found in samples from five of the eleven Apollo missions. In addition, the National Communicable Disease Center group IVc, IVd, and IVe microorganisms isolated from Apollo 16 samples are very closely related to the *Flavobacteria* and some classifications include them with *Flavobacteria*.

The potable water samples from three missions (Apollo 8, 9, and 17) contained no microorganisms. All other mission samples contained concentrations ranging from three organisms per 150 ml of water to those too numerous to count (table 9). Based on preflight experience and public health data, microorganisms will not propagate in the presence of chlorine or iodine biocide in concentrations of approximately 0.1 mg/liter or higher. It must be assumed that residual chlorine was very low or absent in postflight water samples containing viable organisms. The inflight schedule called for chlorine addition to the water at approximately 24-hour intervals. The final inflight chlorinations were accomplished between 13 and 21 hours before splashdown. Samples for microbiological analysis were taken between 7.5 and 40 hours after splashdown. This schedule allowed the passage of approximately 25 to 55 hours, during which any residual chlorine could become depleted from the system before samples could be taken. It is known from qualification testing data that, in most cases, chlorine concentrations within the water system are greatly reduced or disappear within 24 hours.

As soon as possible after the recovery operation, the residual chlorine concentration in the hot water port and drinking water gun distribution systems was determined. These values are cited in table 10. As shown, chlorine residuals were present in the water in

Table 9

Microbial Quality of Postflight Command Module Potable
Water Samples Collected 14 to 40 Hours After Splashdown

Apollo Mission	Microorganism	Ratio of Samples With Positive Growth to Total Number of Samples Taken	Concentration of Microbial Numbers Found (Irrespective of Species)
7	Unidentified	1:2	TNTC**
8	Negative	0:2	
9	Negative	0:2	
10	*Flavobacterium* sp. III b	1:2	20
11	*Flavobacterium* sp. III a	1:2	3
12	*Flavobacterium* sp. II b	2:2	TNTC
	Flavobacterium sp. III b		
13	No determinations		
14	*Flavobacterium* sp.	2:2	1.5×10^5
	Flavobacterium sp. IVe		
15	*Cephalosporium acremonium*	2:2	No determination
16	NCDC* Group IVc	2:2	1.1×10^6
	NCDC Group IVd		
	NCDC Group IVe		
17	Negative	0:2	

 * NCDC = National Communicable Disease Center

**TNTC = Too Numerous to Count

seven of nine missions. No determinations were made after the Apollo 13 and 14 missions. Chlorine concentrations ranged from zero in the Apollo 15 and 16 missions to as high as 6.0 mg/liter in the Apollo 10 drinking water gun sample. The postflight samples for microbiological analysis were taken simultaneously with those for chlorine residual determination. As can be seen, there were occasions when there was both a biocide residual and an indication of viable microbiological contamination. It is noted that the biocide depletion rate in the system is proportional to the area-to-volume ratio. Therefore it is probable that while postflight analysis indicated the presence of biocide (in effect the presence of biocide in the water tank because of sample volume), the biocide level was nil in the water use ports and interconnecting tubing where there is a high area-to-volume ratio. This could account for microbial growth in these portions of the system and the positive analyses. Because of the requirement for a biocide contact time and the immediate reduction of the biocide upon sample collection (sodium thiosulfate) it is possible to have an indication of a biocide concentration and still have viable organisms present.

Table 10

Postflight Chlorine Residuals in
Command Module Potable Water System

Apollo Mission	Postflight Chlorine Residual, mg/l		Time Lapse Since Last Inflight Chlorination, hr
	Drink Gun	Hot Water Port	
7	0.13	Not determined	25
8	2.0	0.1	17
9	2.0	1.0	40
10	6.0	0.5	27
11	0.8	0.05	29:30
12	Not determined	0.125	35:30
13	Not determined	Not determined	
14	Not determined	Not determined	
15	0.0	0.0	25
16	0.0	0.0	30
17	0.01	0.01	32

Summary and Conclusions

The Apollo potable water system satisfied the dual purpose of providing metabolic water for the crewmen and water for spacecraft cooling. The overall performance was good. Although design and operational difficulties existed, these were not insurmountable despite the complexities of the unconventional type of water system required for space travel.

The problems documented in this chapter were successfully resolved in the Apollo Program. These efforts led to numerous technological advances including those in the following general areas.

1. Selection and evaluation of new types of water system materials.

Metallics: Evaluation of corrosion resistance of certain metal alloys, their physical characteristics as water system components, and their compatibility with biocides.

Nonmetallics: Endurance and permeability characteristics of polymeric membrane materials; material compatibility with water, gases, and biocides; and taste and odor problems related to material use.

2. Selection and evaluation of water biocides.

3. Selection and evaluation of physical and chemical corrosion inhibitors.

4. Importance of sanitary engineering concepts in the design, development, and testing phases of potable or multiuse water systems.

The information, equipment, and instrumentation developed in the Apollo Program will contribute toward the needs of future space flight missions. In addition, this technology may have useful application in municipal, industrial, and private water conservation programs.

References

Anon: Apollo Block II ECS Components, No SS-1959-R. Garrett Airesearch Manufacturing Division, March 1968.

Anon: Apollo Operations Handbook, Vol. 1. NASA SM 2A-03, Block II (1). North American Rockwell, 15 April 1969.

Anon: Public Health Service Drinking Water Standards, 1962. U.S. Department of Health, Education, and Welfare, Public Health Service. Public Health Service Publication No. 9516. United States Government Printing Office.

NASA: Command Service Module/Lunar Module/Orbital Workshop Potable Water Specification and Test Procedures. National Aeronautics and Space Administration, Manned Spacecraft Center, July 1971.

Sauer, Richard L.: Spacecraft Metabolic Water Supply. Paper presented at Spacecraft Potable Water Symposium, American Chemical Society, Division of Water and Waste Management (Houston, Texas), Feb. 28, 1970.

Sauer, Richard L.; and Calley, David J.: Apollo Experience Report: Potable Water System. NASA TN D-7291. June 1973.

CHAPTER 5

APOLLO COMMAND AND SERVICE MODULE AND LUNAR MODULE
ENVIRONMENTAL CONTROL SYSTEMS

by

James C. Brady
Donald F. Hughes
Frank H. Samonski, Jr.

Lyndon B. Johnson Space Center

Roger W. Young
David M. Browne

The Boeing Aerospace Company

Introduction

The Apollo Command and Service Module (CSM) and Lunar Module (LM) proved to be highly successful space vehicles. Instrumental in the success of these spacecraft was the satisfactory and reliable operation of their environmental control systems. This chapter describes the systems and system requirements and discusses the performance of both Command Module and Lunar Module environmental control systems during the Apollo Program. The bulk of the material contained in this Chapter was orginally published in Brady and co-workers (1973), and Hughes and co-workers (1973).

The concept of the Apollo mission itself and the spacecraft that would be needed to complete it can be traced back to 1955. In March of that year, the feasibility of a one million pound thrust liquid-fueled rocket engine to launch the vehicle on its path to the moon was established. By late 1962, the broad conceptual design of the Apollo spacecraft and the lunar landing mission was complete. During 1963, formal contract negotiations for the spacecraft were completed, and by June of 1963 most of the subsystem designs for the Command Module (CM) were finalized. At the same time, critical decisions were being made concerning the Lunar Module (LM). The key items affecting its design included the decision to rotate the CSM and manually maneuver it into a docked position with the LM; that the crew would operate the LM from a standing position; and, most important for the environmental control and life support systems, that the Lunar Module would be capable of supporting the operations of two men on the lunar surface for up to 24 hours plus 24 hours in flight. Before the end of 1963, the Lunar Module mockup was completed and, in early 1964, the Block II CSM configuration was completed. The

517

requirement for a second configuration was necessitated by a decision to execute a lunar landing and to do so by lunar orbit rendezvous, a decision which had a substantial impact on system design. The vehicles resulting from these development efforts were described and pictured in Section I, Chapter 2, *Apollo Missions*.

Command and Service Module Environmental Control System

System Requirements and Description

Briefly enumerated, the system requirements for the Apollo Command Module environmental control system (ECS) were as follows:

1. Oxygen atmosphere in the pressurized cabin of 34.5 kN/m^2 (5 psia).

2. Normal shirtsleeve mode except for critical mission phases.

3. Cabin pressure maintained at 24.1 kN/m^2 (3.5 psia) under certain defined emergency conditions.

4. Carbon dioxide (CO_2) removal by lithium hydroxide (LiOH) absorption and limited to a partial pressure of 1013 N/m^2 (7.6 mm Hg).

5. Cabin temperature maintained at $297^\circ \pm 3^\circ \text{K}$ ($75^\circ \pm 5^\circ \text{F}$) with relative humidity limited to the range of 40 to 70 percent.

6. Thermal control provided for the electrical and electronic equipment.

To accomplish these design objectives, the ECS interfaced with the electrical power system for electricity, fuel cell system for water, and cryogenic storage system for oxygen.

A schematic diagram of the ECS is shown in figure 1. For convenience of description, the system may be divided into six major subsystems: oxygen, pressure suit circuit, water, coolant, waste management, and postlanding ventilation. These subsystems interacted to meet the total ECS requirements.

The oxygen subsystem was supplied from the Service Module cryogenic storage tanks and controlled the distribution of oxygen within the Command Module. It stored a reserve supply of oxygen, regulated several levels of supplied oxygen pressure, controlled cabin pressure in normal and emergency modes, and provided for purging of the pressure suit circuit.

The pressure suit circuit subsystem provided the crew with a continuously conditioned atmosphere. It automatically controlled suit gas circulation, pressure, and temperature, and removed debris, excess moisture, odors, and carbon dioxide from both suit and cabin gases.

The water subsystem received the potable water produced as a byproduct of fuel cell operation, stored the water, and chilled or heated the water for drinking and food reconstitution. The waste water section collected and stored water extracted from the suit heat exchanger and provided it to the evaporator for evaporative cooling. Potable

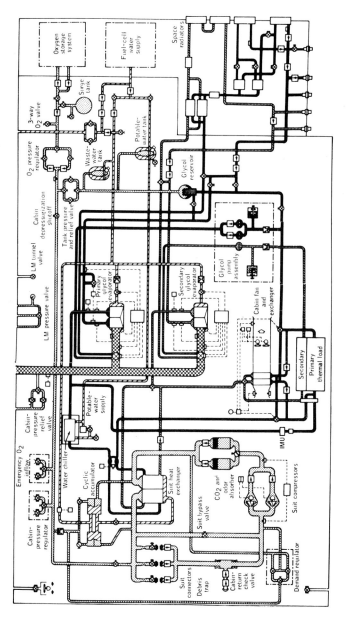

Figure 1. Apollo CSM environmental control system schematic.

water not needed for crew consumption was added to waste water storage. Water in excess of system requirements was dumped overboard through a heated water dump nozzle.

The coolant (water/ethylene glycol) subsystem supplied cooling for the pressure suit circuit, potable water chiller, and electrical and electronic equipment mounted on coldplates in the Command and Service Modules. It also supplied heating or cooling for the cabin atmosphere. Independent primary and secondary (backup) coolant loops were provided, with each loop utilizing space radiators as the basic heat rejection mechanism and water boiling from the glycol evaporator for supplementary heat rejection.

The waste management subsystem provided for dumping overboard of urine through a heated nozzle and for storage and venting of solid wastes. An interconnect capability with the waste water dump system was available as a backup for all fluid dumping.

The postlanding ventilation subsystem provided means for circulating ambient air through the cabin after landing.

Mission Performance

Oxygen Subsystem. The oxygen subsystem of the ECS, exclusive of the cryogenic oxygen system, performed satisfactorily throughout the Apollo missions. Separate regulation levels were maintained at nominal values of 690, 140, and 35 kN/m^2 (approximately 100, 20, and 5 psi), and the flow restrictors/heat exchangers demonstrated satisfactory operation for flows approaching maximum capability. No emergency cabin pressure regulation was required, and all planned depressurizations and repressurizations were without incident. Oxygen allocated to the ECS was originally 78.29 kg (172.6 lb) for a 14-day mission. Principal items were .82 kg (1.8 lb) per man-day for crew consumption and 2.18 kg (4.8 lb) per day for cabin leakage. Additional allowances were made for the extravehicular activity in the later missions. Actual consumption, as shown in table 1, proved to be less than allocations, primarily because of lower cabin leakage and crew requirements. A comparison of a typical mission with the specification requirements is shown in table 2.

Pressure Suit Circuit Subsystem. The pressure suit circuit subsystem satisfactorily accomplished all its design requirements. With the confidence gained during the program, fully suited operation was eventually limited to launch and Lunar Module jettison. No difficulty was ever encountered with the integrity of the Command Module pressure shell. Therefore, the suit loop was not used as an emergency environment for the crew. During the Command Module extravehicular activities on the Apollo 15, 16, and 17 missions, use of the suit loop was required to support two crewmen, but no problems resulted and pressure regulation was within the required 24.1 to 27.6 kN/m^2 (3.5 to 4.0 psia) range.

The original concept of using 100 percent oxygen as the cabin gas during the prelaunch and launch periods was abandoned following the Apollo 204 accident in favor of a 60 percent oxygen/40 percent nitrogen mixture with the suit circuit remaining at 100 percent oxygen. This required the inclusion of a pressure sensor to indicate suit-to-cabin differential pressure, and the direct oxygen valve was used to provide a constant 0.23 to 0.32 kg/hr (0.5 to 0.7 lb/hr) flow into the suit loop. This flow compensated for metabolic usage and suit circuit leakage with some excess flow to keep the loop at a positive pressure and provide a purge through the suit circuit relief valve. Although brief periods of negative pressure resulted from crew movement in the suits, the system was judged to perform acceptably.

Table 1

Actual Environmental Control
System Oxygen Consumption

Apollo Mission Number	Duration Days:Hours	Oxygen Consumed kg (lb)	
7	10:20	46.26	(102)
8	6:03	23.13	(51)
9	10:01	44.91	(99)
10	8:00	32.21	(71)
11	8:03	37.19	(82)
12	10:05	44.91	(99)
13	5:23	13.61	(30)
14	9:00	42.64	(94*)
15	12:07	49.44	(109**)
16	11:02	48.08	(106**)
17	12:14	49.90	(110**)

*Includes 4.5 kg (10 lb) for high flow demonstration test of cryogenic system.

**Includes 11 to 13 kg (24 to 29 lb) for EVA flow and cabin repressurization.

Specification requirements called for the lithium hydroxide absorber elements to be capable of removing carbon dioxide at a maximum average removal rate of 0.064 kg/hr (0.142 lb/hr) for 24 hours [1.54 kg (3.4 lb) total for 93 percent utilization]. With two elements in parallel, the partial pressure of carbon dioxide was to be maintained at less than 1013 N/m^2 (7.6 mm Hg). Flight measurements indicated that this level was never exceeded and that carbon dioxide partial pressure seldom rose above 400 N/m^2 (3 mm Hg). For three-man operations, the elements were changed every 24 hours, but the replacement times were staggered every 12 hours to reduce the variation in carbon dioxide partial pressure levels. For single-man operations, the changeout times were lengthened proportionately.

In an effort to verify performance of the elements, chemical analyses of all of the returned elements were performed and a correlation was attempted with their length of time in service (equivalent to three-man usage). The results, indicated in figure 2, showed considerable scatter when plotted against this time variable. The figure shows how much lithium hydroxide has been turned into lithium carbonate, indicating carbon dioxide production and, thus, metabolic rate. The scatter shows that metabolic rates were different from flight to flight, but that there was a predictability within a certain band. Additional refinements were attempted to account for estimated crew metabolic rates, activity levels, and spacecraft environments. None of these was particularly successful in consolidating the data. Considering the lack of sufficient instrumentation and knowledge of actual metabolic levels, tolerances of the chemical analyses, and possibility of out-of-order use by the crew, the results appear to be representative of the element usage.

Table 2

Environmental Control System
Oxygen Consumption Breakdown

Item	Specification Requirement (14 Days)		Apollo 15 Mission (12.3 Days)	
	kg	(lb)	kg	(lb)
Crew consumption	34.29	(75.6)	22.09	(48.7)
Cabin leakage	30.48	(67.2)	2.68	(5.9)
Cabin repressurizations	5.31	(11.7)	4.08	(9.0)
One CM puncture	1.63	(3.6)	—	—
LM support	6.58	(14.5)	5.94	(13.1)
Tank bleeds			4.45	(9.8)
Cabin & WMS purges			3.49	(7.7)
EVA flow			6.67	(14.7)
TOTALS	78.29	(172.6)	49.40	(108.9)

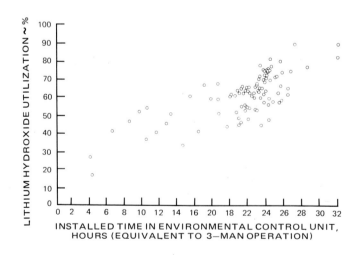

Figure 2. Apollo missions 8 to 16 returned LiOH canisters.

Water Subsystem. The water subsystem typically managed from 180 to 225 kg (400 to 500 lb) of water with normal fuel cell production rates of 0.68 to 0.91 kg/hr (1.5 to 2.0 lb/hr). Because these rates far exceeded the requirements of the crew and evaporator operation, most of the water was dumped overboard. Routine flight operation consisted of maintaining a full potable water tank and alternately filling and dumping the waste tank between limits of 10 percent and 85 percent full. On occasion, dumping was inadvertently continued until the waste tank was completely empty, and some of the potable water was dumped without adverse system effect. During later missions, the waste water tank was kept almost full at Command Module/Service Module separation to improve the spacecraft's lift/drag characteristics during reentry. A water balance for a typical mission is presented in table 3. Quantities were determined from telemetered tank quantities, calculated evaporative usage, and standard values for the lithium hydroxide reaction and metabolic oxidation. (See Section VI, Chapter 4, *Potable Water Supply,* for additional information.)

Table 3

Typical Environmental Control System
Water Balance Summary (Apollo 15)

Initial Onboard Water	Quantity kg (lb)	
Potable tank	13.15	(29)
Waste tank	12.25	(27)
Subtotals	25.40	(56)
Water gained		
Fuel cell production	235.87	(520)
LiOH reaction	12.25	(27)
Metabolic oxidation	11.79	(26)
Subtotals	259.91	(573)
TOTALS	285.31 kg (629 lb)	
Final onboard water		
Potable tank	14.06	(31)
Waste tank	23.13	(51)
Subtotals	37.19	(82)
Water lost		
Body waste water	43.09	(95)
Evaporator operation	3.63	(8)
Overboard dumping		
Waste tank	191.42	(422)
Potable tank	7.26	(16)
URA flushing and samples	2.72	(6)
Subtotals	248.12	(547)
TOTALS	285.31 kg (629 lb)	

Initial onboard water + water gained = final onboard water + water lost.

The hot water provided for food and drink reconstitution was greatly appreciated by the flight crews and improved the diet over the cold diet supplied on earlier space flight missions. However, while mechanical failures in the water system were infrequent, the system itself was the source of frequent negative comments by the crew. These concerned two aspects of system performance, gas in the water and problems with the sterilization injection system.

Gas in the potable water originated from two sources. Water produced as a byproduct of fuel cell operation was saturated with hydrogen gas at a pressure of 415 kN/m² (60 psia). When this water was supplied to the environmental control system through a 140 kN/m² (20 psig) regulator, approximately one liter of hydrogen per day was released. This gas was removed from the water system on Apollo 12 and subsequent missions by passing the water through a hydrogen gas separator. The separator removed about 99 percent of the hydrogen, reducing the partial pressure in the water to 4.1 N/m² (0.6 psia).

The other source of gas in the drinking water was oxygen from the bladder in the drinking water storage tank. This tank contained an oxygen bladder pressurized to 140 kN/m² (20 psig) to expel the water. Oxygen permeated the bladder material until the partial pressure was about equalized across the bladder. When the water was used by the crew in the 35 kN/m² (5 psia) cabin, oxygen was released. This was particularly troublesome when preparing food because large bubbles often formed in the food bags and prevented proper reconstitution. A gas separator cartridge assembly was developed for attachment to the water delivery port starting with the Apollo 11 mission. The assembly separated the free gas from the water but was only partially successful due to size and configuration limitations.

Subsequent to final design of the water system, a requirement for water sterility was placed on the system. A method was devised by which 30 cm³ (1 ounce) of chlorine solution and 30 cm³ (1 ounce) of buffer solution could be injected into the water system every 24 hours through a fitting containing septa. The solutions were contained in hard-case, Teflon ampoules with flexible inner bags. During development, problems were encountered with corrosion of the aluminum tubing and with chemical mixing. During the first several missions, the crews complained of a strong chlorine taste after injections. These problems were solved by (1) having the crew perform the injections just prior to the sleep period, and (2) developing the use of sodium nitrate as a corrosion inhibitor for addition to the buffer ampoules. The inhibitor was effective in preventing the chlorine from reacting with the aluminum and allowed a decrease in the concentration of the chlorine injected from 5000 mg/liter (5000 ppm) to 1860 mg/liter (1860 ppm). Use of the modified chlorine and buffer ampoule solutions began with the Apollo 14 flight. The injection procedure itself posed certain problems primarily from ampoule bag leakage. Additional preflight inspections improved this situation.

Coolant Subsystem. The coolant subsystem provided adequate thermal control throughout the missions in spite of operational limitations imposed by procedural requirements or by occasional hardware malfunctions. Early flights demonstrated that a passive thermal control (PTC) mode, accomplished by a slow, controlled CSM roll, allowed satisfactory heat rejection by the space radiators during most periods. During the translunar and transearth phases, the radiator outlet temperature seldom exceeded 283°K (50°F) and often was below 280°K (45°F). When the temperature was below 280°K the Service Module bypass valve was required to operate and control the Command Module coolant temperature to 280°K (45°F). Evaporator operation was required only during portions of launch, Earth orbit, lunar orbit, and entry, and during certain fixed attitudes which prevented effective radiator operation. Starting with Apollo 11, when steam discharge interfered with visual sightings and caused perturbations in orbital tracking and attitudes, evaporator operation was inhibited except for launch, Earth orbit, and entry. The resulting system temperature measured at the evaporator outlet exceeded the normal 278° to 283°K (40° to 50°F) range and cyclically increased during lunar orbits to 297°K (75°F) or more. Typical lunar orbit system performance with and without evaporator operation is illustrated in figures 3a and 3b. Principal impact of this excessive temperature cycling was to increase the condensation on the colder cabin surfaces after the higher temperature portions of the orbits.

The coldest coolant flowed through the suit heat exchanger for gas cooling and condensate removal and then to the cabin heat exchanger for cabin gas cooling before going to the electronic heat load. However, because the noise of the fans and the gas flow passing through the cabin heat exchanger was amplified by the cabin structure, the crews did not operate the cabin fans except during short specified periods and relied upon the suit heat exchanger for the total thermal control of the cabin gas. This mode of operation was normally adequate during translunar and transearth phases when the crews were comfortable or slightly chilly. The higher coolant temperatures during lunar orbit presented some discomfort, but the problem was not significant.

Early flight configurations of the evaporator showed a tendency to dry out under low heat loads and required inflight reservicing. Later modifications, which included relocated wetness sensors and trimming of the water distribution sponges, provided satisfactory units. During the Apollo 16 mission, the mixing valve was operated in a manual mode for almost the entire flight due to failure of the mixing valve controller. Less than a half dozen adjustments were required by the crew, and overall system temperature increased less than 3°K (5°F) which constituted adequate system performance.

Radiator heat load and rejection was determined by use of the total flow and radiator inlet and outlet and evaporator outlet temperature measurements. Typical heat load and rejection under favorable conditions during translunar or transearth PTC ranged between 1170 and 1470 watts (4000 and 5000 Btu/hr). Knowing the approximate electrical and metabolic heat load, the heat loss through the structure was determined. Experience from Apollo 7 and 9, both Earth orbit missions, showed that heat loss through the cabin structure varied from 380 to 675 watts (1300 to 2300 Btu/hr), depending on the extent of CM electrical load. This loss was largely due to heat shorts near the coldplates and was greater than originally estimated.

Waste Management Subsystem. The environmental control system portion of the waste management system provided for the disposal of crew waste liquids and solids. The performance of this system is discussed in Section VI, Chapter 2, *Waste Management.*

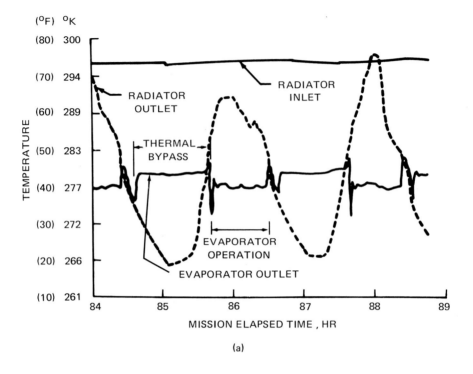

(a)

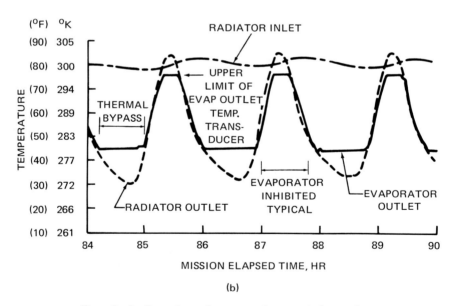

(b)

Figure 3. Apollo coolant subsystem performance in lunar orbit
with and without evaporator operation.

Apollo 13 Emergency. The Apollo 13 mission started in a routine manner with environmental control system operation proceeding normally. However, with the loss of the Service Module cryogenic oxygen tanks, the ECS was without its main source of supply for oxygen, water, and electrical power. To preserve the remaining onboard quantities, the surge tank and repressurization package tanks were isolated, water tanks were depressurized, and the Command Module was completely powered down. The Lunar Module was activated as a "life-boat" to sustain the crew, and it operated in this capacity for approximately 83-1/2 hours until jettison prior to reentry. With certain operational restrictions imposed, the Lunar Module consumables proved adequate for all purposes except for providing drinking water and removing carbon dioxide. Drinking water was obtained from the Command Module on several occasions by briefly pressurizing the oxygen system and withdrawing water. To supplement the Lunar Module lithium hydroxide cartridges, a method was devised for CM lithium hydroxide elements to be utilized with the LM atmosphere revitalization section.

During the powered down period of operation, the temperature inside the Command Module slowly decreased and the crew noted considerable condensation within the cabin. The CM was powered up briefly for data transmittal twice during the dormant period. A summary of the temperature changes is included in table 4.

A reported inability by the crew to obtain additional drinking water and a subsequent thermal model analysis indicate that the water tanks, or more probably the water lines in the aft compartment, froze late in the powered down period. Command Module ECS operation after reactivation and during entry was satisfactory.

Dust Control

A problem encountered with the start of the lunar landing missions was effective control of lunar dust. After lunar EVA, the crewmen and the samples they had collected were covered with this fine lunar material. Despite attempts at cleanup and packaging in the Lunar Module, transfer of crew and materials back to the Command Module resulted in contamination of the CM atmosphere. This was an undesirable situation in view of the objectives of the quarantine program which sought to minimize contamination of the CM, and thereby minimize the potential hazard of contaminating the biosphere after reentry of the spacecraft. Earlier contamination testing and analysis had shown that continuous cycling of cabin gas through the lithium hydroxide elements (and filters) effectively removed particles 5 microns or even less in diameter, even though 50 percent of the flow was bypassed. Disadvantages to this automatic method were the relatively slow removal rate and introduction of additional particles whenever a dusty item was moved or disturbed. To speed up the capture of suspended material, a filter was developed for use with the cabin fans. The filter, in a shape of a pleated bag, was made from the same Armalon felt filter material used in the elements and was attached to the outlet of the fans. When used for several hours during and after crew and sample transfer, the filter was effective. An additional benefit was obtained by installing the filter shortly after launch, thereby preventing floating objects from entering the inactive fan enclosure.

To assist in removing dust from suits and sample containers, a hand-held vacuum cleaner (figure 4) was developed that used the qualified suit circuit compressor as a

Table 4

System Parameters During Apollo 13
Powered Down Period

Parameter	Units	Ground Elapsed Time (GET) ~ Hours				
		57:54 (1)	58:35 (2)	102:00 (3)	123:06 (4)	141:15 (5)
Cabin temperature	°K (°F)	288 (58)	292 (66)	284 (52)	281 (46)	279 (43)
Evaporator temperature	°K (°F)	279 (43)	293 (67)	285 (54)	281 (46)	278 (41)
Suit inlet temperature	°K (°F)	286 (56)	288 (59)	285 (53)	280 (45)	278 (41)
Pri-radiator outlet temperature	°K (°F)	274 (34)	294 (69)	288 (58)	283 (49)	278 (40)
Helium tank (near water tanks)	°K (°F)					274 (33)
Surge tank pressure	kN/m² (psia)	5929 (860)	5929 (860)	5254 (762)	5150 (747)	5081 (737)

(1) Glycol pump deactivated (2 hours after accident)
(2) Instrumentation deactivated
(3) Instrumentation activated momentarily
(4) Instrumentation activated momentarily
(5) Glycol pump activated

blower. Replaceable bags were fabricated from the Armalon felt, and a brush was added to the compressor inlet. A 4.27-m (14-ft) power cable for attachment to the Command Module utility outlet enabled use in both the CM and LM. The device was effective for removing dust before transfer of the items from the LM, and reduced the contamination entering the CM. Heavy usage, however, tended to clog the inlet screen and impeller and required frequent cleaning.

Figure 4. Hand-held vacuum cleaner.

EVA Provisions

The addition of the Service Module Experiment Bay on Apollo 15, 16, and 17 added an ECS requirement to provide extravehicular activity (EVA) capability for the support of one crewman while retrieving the experiment film containers. The system was designed to provide suit pressure control and latent metabolic heat removal.

Oxygen flow from the cryogenic system originally was limited to two restrictor/heat exchangers. In order to achieve the flow capability required for EVA, a third restrictor/heat exchanger was added in parallel, increasing flow capacity to 4.54 kg/hr (10 lb/hr) minimum. Downstream of the restrictor manifold, and upstream of the remaining ECS, a new EVA panel and life support system were added as shown in figure 5.

Safety features, consistent with simplicity, were added to enhance problem detection and backup provisions.

1. The EVA panel pressure gage was monitored for high pressure oxygen [1030 kN/m² (>150 psia)] by one of the two crewmen in the cabin.

2. The suit control unit (SCU) orifice controlled the flow rate to 5.0 ± 0.5 kg/hr (11.0 ±1.0 lb/hr) at 280°K (45°F) with 690 ± 35 kN/m² (100 ±5 psia) at the umbilical inlet. In the event of a severed umbilical, reverse oxygen flow from the suit was limited by the

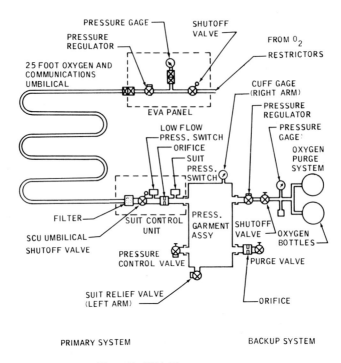

Figure 5. EVA life support system.

orifice. This allowed time [6.9 kN/m^2 (1 psi) drop in 80 seconds] for the EVA crewman to close the SCU shutoff valve.

3. The pressure switch upstream of the orifice in the SCU activated a warning tone in the EVA crewman headset should the umbilical pressure drop below 415 kN/m^2 (60 psig), indicating a low flow condition [2.7 kg/hr (6 lb/hr)]. Use of the pressure switch as a means of low flow detection was possible since flow rate through the orifice was sonic, and therefore, a function of upstream pressure.

4. The pressure switch downstream of the orifice in the SCU also activated the warning tone in the EVA crewman headset and gave warning of low suit pressure [less than 23.4 kN/m^2 (3.4 psig)].

5. The pressure control valve (PCV) controlled the suit pressure to 26 ± 1 kN/m^2 (3.80 ± 0.15 psig). The PCV was designed so that suit pressure would not fall below 20 kN/m^2 (3.0 psia) in the event the PCV failed in the open position.

6. A backup oxygen purge system (OPS) provided up to 3.6 kg/hr (8 lb/hr) oxygen flow for 30 minutes. A purge valve controlled the flow for this system, utilizing either a high flow or low flow setting.

Although no telemetry was added for the EVA hardware, existing telemetry and crew data readouts indicated the system performance as given in table 5 was normal. No flight problems were encountered with the EVA system, and the EVA crewmen commented that thermal conditions were adequate for the time and metabolic rates involved.

Table 5

EVA System Performance

Parameter	Units		Apollo Mission Number		
			15	16	17
Suit circuit pressure	kN/m²	(psia)	26.9 (3.9)	25.9 (3.8)	25.5 (3.7)
EVA suit pressure	kN/m²	(psia)	27.6 (4.0)	26.5 (3.8)	25.9 (3.8)
EVA panel pressure gage	kN/m²	(psia)	2068 (300)	2068 (300)	2413 (350)
Calculated EVA flow at vacuum [using restrictor delta P at 294 °K (70°F)]	kg/hr	(lb/hr)	5.0 (11.0)	4.6 (10.2)	4.7 (10.4)
EVA duration		minutes	31	73	58

Program Considerations and Recommendations

Redundancy Utilization. The requirements for reliability dictated that practically all components with moving parts have redundancy or backup provisions. In the oxygen system, which was especially critical for life support, all regulators and relief valves had parallel redundancy and both were used together. In addition, regulators contained relief features set slightly above regulation setting to allow for a failed open regulator. Each regulator had a separate isolation capability. Redundancy for electrical switches, electrical circuits, and manual shutoff valves was not normally provided. Therefore, backup provisions were made for items essential to crew safety or mission success.

Very few hardware failures resulted in required use of redundant components, but backup provisions were used to extend the capability of the ECS. For example, the secondary glycol loop proved useful for warming the crew during prelaunch when childown of the primary glycol loop by ground support equipment was necessary for equipment cooling. The manual backup provision on the glycol temperature valve was used when the controller failed during the Apollo 16 flight. The suit loop, usually considered as a backup for cabin cooling and ventilation, bacame the prime system because the crew preferred to keep the cabin fans off. The secondary glycol loop was never required as a backup for the primary loop. However, it proved useful during flight as a means of cold soak prior to reentry. In this mode of operation, the coldest fluid of the secondary loop was sent to the suit heat exchanger. Again, accomplishing this without hardware changes was made possible by backup provisions such as bypass and isolation valves.

Material Age Life Investigation. The specification design age life for the Command and Service Module environmental control system was three years. It became apparent that much of the hardware manufactured for the program would exceed this specification life, particularly since several spacecraft were nearing or had already completed installation and checkout and were scheduled for storage because of program changes. Such was the case of CSM 111, designated for the Apollo Soyuz Test Project (ASTP).

An age life analysis investigation was initiated. Each material, its application, failure criticality, and rationale for age life extension, was listed and reviewed by material and subsystem personnel. As a result of the review, the static age life of most materials was extended to ten years. Also as a result of the study, specific valve positions were identified to reduce material "set" during any storage periods.

Problem Summary and Recommendations

During the Apollo flights, several environmental control system problems were experienced. None of the problems can be classified as a major anomaly and none affected crew safety or mission success. Minor problems, however, encompassed almost all aspects of ECS operation and can be used as a valuable source for identifying system weaknesses and recommending future improvements. The listing in table 6 includes all of the more significant problems encountered in the flight program, corrective action applied, and recommendations for future design.

Lunar Module Environmental Control System

System Description

The Lunar Module environmental control system was comprised of four main sections: atmosphere revitalization, oxygen supply and cabin pressure control, water management, and heat transport.

The atmosphere revitalization section (ARS) consisted of a suit circuit assembly and suit liquid cooling assembly. The ARS is illustrated in figure 6. The suit circuit assembly was a closed-loop recirculation system that cooled and ventilated the two pressure garment assemblies (PGA) through flexible umbilicals. The suit liquid cooling assembly circulated water through, and controlled the temperature in the liquid cooling garment, circulated cabin gas via a cabin fan when required, and removed lunar dust from the cabin after ascent from the lunar surface.

The oxygen supply and cabin pressure control section (OSCPCS) stored gaseous oxygen, supplied oxygen to and maintained pressure control of the suit circuit and cabin, and provided refill oxygen to the portable life support system (PLSS). A schematic of the OSCPCS is shown in figure 7.

The water management section (WMS) supplied water for drinking, food preparation, cooling by heat transport section sublimators, and refilling the PLSS water tank. Figure 8 is a diagram of the WMS.

The heat transport section (figure 9) contained the hardware that heated or cooled the gas flow to the PGAs and cabin, cooled the electronic equipment and batteries, and rejected heat to space. It consisted of a primary coolant loop for normal operation and a secondary loop which cooled critical equipment in the event the primary system failed. A water/ethylene glycol solution circulated through each loop.

Table 6

Mission Problem Summary

Problem Description	Apollo Mission	Cause	Mission Impact	Corrective Action	Recommendation for Future Systems Design
Oxygen Subsystem					
High oxygen flow (procedural error)	Most	Manual overboard dump valve remained open	Increased O_2 usage	None	Include time-to-close feature in manual purge valves
Slow oxygen tank repressurization	9	Valve indicator misaligned—valve partially closed	None	Preflight inspection	Include greater detent identification or integral position indicators
Cabin fans (a) Noisy	All	Lack of noise suppression	Discontinued most fan use	None	Add acoustical design requirements
(b) Failed to operate	9	Foreign objects in fan area	Inspection	Protect fan inlet and outlet with screens
Toggle pin failure—main regulator shutoff valve (postflight)	15	Tolerance buildup allowed pin movement	Unknown	Inspection of all valves	Increase review of detail design of vendor parts
Discrepant CM/LM $\triangle P$ gage readings	15	Valve position arrow chipped off	Confusion during integrity check	Metalcal arrow substituted	Design indicators into manual devices
Pressure Suit Circuit Subsystem					
Return filter screen partially plugged	All	Cabin debris from manned operations	Required daily crew cleaning	Incorporated in crew procedures	Design filters for accessible cleaning or replacement
Free water in suit hoses	7; 15	Prelaunch degradation of suit heat exchanger condensate flow	None (droplets minor)	Improved servicing techniques	Minimize use of sintered plates or design for in-place restoration to original flow
LiOH elements sticking in ECU canister	16	Adverse operating conditions—temp control failure and flow valves mispositioned	None	Preflight fit check requirements tightened; crew procedures revised	Design for contingency conditions; use automatic valves to minimize crew operation

Table 6 (Continued)

Mission Problem Summary

Problem Description	Apollo Mission	Cause	Mission Impact	Corrective Action	Recommendation for Future Systems Design
Coolant Subsystem					
Evaporator dryout	7, 8, 9	Wick sensor location not representative of wick wetness	Manual reservicing required	Relocated sensors; removed sponges locally near sensors	Adequately develop test liquid systems in 6 axes to verify operation in zero gravity
Evaporator dryout	10	Microswitch misadjustment	Manual reservicing required	Added preflight inspection	Limit switches should be individually verified after installation. Functional tests inadequate
Evaporator outlet temperature high	10	Backpressure valve boot lost elasticity	None (recovered satisfactorily)	None	Adequately attach nonmetallic flow devices to the driving mechanism
Radiator proportioning valve system switched over to backup	7, 17	Electrical bus transient	None	None	Design electronics to be unaffected by short bus transients
Condensation on cold coolant lines	All	Lines not fully insulated	None	Increased line insulation	Provide adequate insulation for lines operating below dew point. Locate coldest lines away from electronics if possible
Primary accumulator quantity decayed	11	Valve not fully closed due to excessive knob play	None	None	Provide greater detents, eliminate all play between knob and valve
Glycol temperature exceeded control tolerance	11	Bearing failure in control valve drive mechanism	None (recovered satisfactorily)	None	Use limit switches on control valves to prevent continuous drive signals when valves are on end stops
Same	17	Gear lashup in drive mechanism due to pitch diameters not tangent	None (recovered satisfactorily)	None	Same

Table 6 (Continued)
Mission Problem Summary

Problem Description	Apollo Mission	Cause	Mission Impact	Corrective Action	Recommendation for Future Systems Design
Coolant Subsystem (Continued)					
Higher than expected radiator outlet temperatures	15	Lunar attitude holds and possible radiator coating degradation during launch	Increased cabin condensation and excessive temperature excursions	None (Launch procedures unique to Apollo 15)	Protect thermal coatings from mission contamination if possible, configure for minimum attitude hold impact
Glycol temperature controller failed in automatic mode	16	Silicon controlled rectifiers (SCR) turned on without a gate drive signal	Manual control required with increased condensation and LiOH element swelling	Controllers screened to determine condition of SCR's	Include proper part derating and parts application in electronics design phase
Water Subsystem					
Leakage during crew installation of quick-disconnect	7	Threads crossed	Water leaked while dumping	Threads inspected	Use automatic and built-in systems to minimize crew operations
Gas in potable water	All	Fuel cell carrier gas and bladder permeability	Crew discomfort	Added hydrogen separator and gas separator cartridge assemblies	Eliminate bladder and gas blanket type tanks, provide adequate gas separators
Hot water valve leakage	12, 14	Tolerance buildup with heated water	None	Added hot water expulsion tests	Provide system checkout in all operational modes
Potable water tank failed to fill	15	Contamination on check valve seat	None	None	Verify system cleanliness and filter all fluids entering the spacecraft
Leakage at chlorine injection port	15	Threaded septum retaining nut worked loose	Water (1 quart) leaked into cabin	Revised assembly requirements	Include locking features on threaded components

Table 6 (Continued)

Mission Problem Summary

Problem Description	Apollo Mission	Cause	Mission Impact	Corrective Action	Recommendation for Future Systems Design
Water Subsystem (Continued) Chlorine and buffer ampules leaked when injected	15, 16, 17	Inner bag breakage due to bonding problems and pinching between wall and end plate	Required additional crew time and cleanup	Added inspection requirements and revised crew procedures	Provide automatic or semi-automatic systems to reduce crew operation
Waste Management Subsystem Urine filters partially clogged	12	Urine breakdown due to overnight storage	Required replacement with spares	Revised crew procedures; added larger filter for mission requiring storage	Anticipate contingency requirements during initial design
Urine dump line partially frozen	14	Undetermined	Urine backup — temporary blockage	Revised crew procedures to minimize flush and require gas purge	Minimize lengths of dump lines; provide adequate heater and orifice sizes
Miscellaneous Vacuum cleaner failed to operate	16	Dust accumulation between turbine wheel and housing	Cleanup time lengthened	Revised crew procedures	Adequately protect all fans with filters
Instrumentation calibration shifts, erratic operation and failures	Many	Contamination, internally and externally generated; corrosion, electronic failures	Backup instrumentation utilized, flight procedures modified	Internal epoxy coating added; inlet filters provided; corrosion displaced by cycling; modified design	Protect pressure sensors with filters including static sense lines, since contamination migration may occur in zero gravity

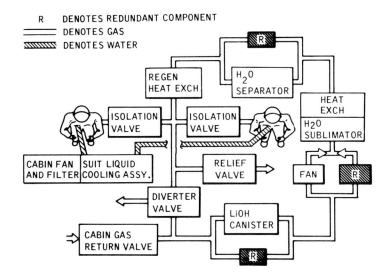

Figure 6. Atmosphere revitalization section.

Mission Performance

Cabin Leakage. The Lunar Module was pressurized after transposition and docking. During the translunar coast of the vehicles, the pressure decay of the LM was monitored. The rate of pressure loss was used to evaluate the leakage of the cabin in space. The range of leakages obtained for Apollo 11 through 17 was between 14 and 23 gm/hr at 35 kN/m^2 (0.03 and 0.05 lb/hr at 5 psia). The maximum allowable specification leakage of oxygen from the LM cabin to space was 90 gm/hr (0.2 lb/hr) at a total pressure of 35 kN/m^2 (5 psia). Thus actual leakage rates that existed were generally between one-seventh and one-fourth of the allowable specification rates.

Consumables. Careful predictions were made in advance of lunar surface missions of the quantities of water that would be required, based on planned Lunar Module usage and planned lunar surface activities. The predictions compared well with actual usage data.

Water consumption for a typical mission during which a total of 181.4 kg (399 lb) of water was used was subdivided as follows: approximately 1 kg (2.3 lb) for the sublimator fill, 22 kg (48 lb) for PLSS water refills, 4.5 kg (10 lb) for drink bag fills, and 3.7 kg (8.2 lb) for metabolic nonreclaimables.

The oxygen consumption was the total of the oxygen consumed due to crew metabolic consumption, leakage, cabin pressurization, and PLSS refills. The oxygen consumption rate was equal to the sum of the metabolic rates of each man [Joules/hr (Btu/hr)] multiplied by 0.07052 kg/J (1.64 x 10^{-4} lb/Btu). This was based on a respiratory quotient (RQ) of 0.82. The oxygen consumption due to leakage was a function of the vehicle configuration.

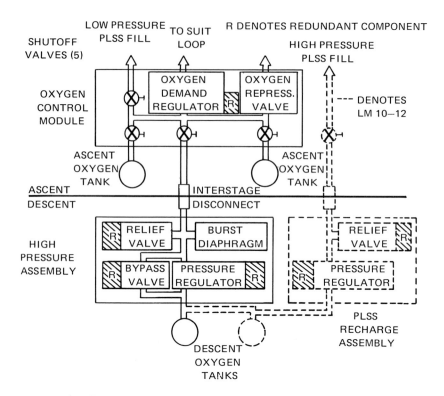

Figure 7. Oxygen supply and cabin pressure control section.

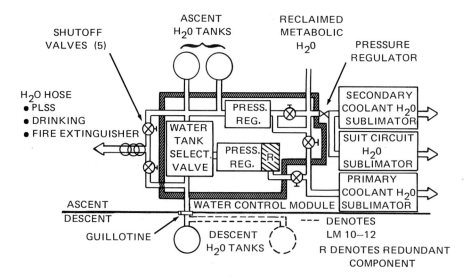

Figure 8. Water management section.

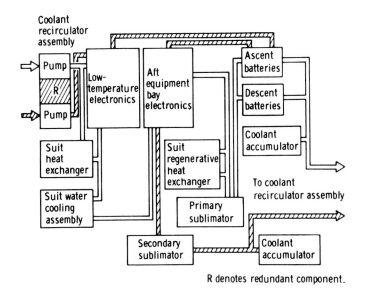

R denotes redundant component.

Figure 9. Heat transport section.

The total descent oxygen consumed for the Apollo 17 mission was 21.2 kg (46.6 lb). This compared very well with the preflight prediction of 20.7 kg (45.5 lb). Comparable values for the Apollo 11 flight were 8.6 kg (19 lb) consumed versus 10 kg (22 lb) predicted. The higher predicted value for Apollo 11 can be attributed to conservative estimates of expected crew metabolic levels during earlier flights.

Apollo 13 Emergency. The Apollo 13 mission was aborted approximately 56 hours after launch. The Apollo 13 mission started in a routine manner, however, the Service Module cryogenic oxygen supply was lost and the environmental control system in the Command Module was without its main source of supply for oxygen, water, and electrical power. To preserve the remaining onboard quantities, the surge tank and repressurization package tanks were isolated, water tanks were depressurized, and the Command Module was completely powered down. The Lunar Module was activated to sustain the crew. This support was required for about 83½ hours, which was nearly twice the duration of the planned Lunar Module utilization.

Early assessment of the problem indicated that with no cabin repressurizations, oxygen was not a critical consumable. However, since only 154 kg (338 lb) of water was available in the Lunar Module, it was decided to utilize Command Module water for drinking and food preparation and to limit the heat loads by activating a minimum of electronic equipment. Power levels were maintained between 350 and 400 watts for most of the Apollo 13 flight by limiting the operation of the electrical equipment. The greatly reduced thermal loading resulted in cabin temperatures between 286° and 289°K (54° and 60°F). The low power level resulted in an average water consumption rate of 1.6 kg/hr (3.5 lb/hr) and approximately 132 kg (290 lb) of water was consumed during the mission.

Sufficient lithium hydroxide cartridges, the carbon dioxide control system of the spacecraft, were not available in the Lunar Module to sustain the crew. The primary and secondary cartridges supplied in the Lunar Module were used until the carbon dioxide level reached approximately 2000 N/m^2 (15 mm Hg). Since additional lithium hydroxide was needed, a means was developed for adapting the Command Module elements for use in the Lunar Module system. Figure 10 shows the system ultimately devised.

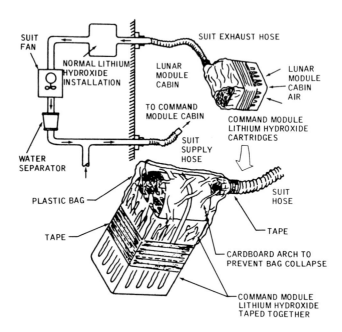

Figure 10. Supplemental carbon dioxide removal system.

Space suit return hoses were taped to plenum chambers, constructed by the crew from onboard documents and tape, and attached to the Command Module environmental control system elements. Cabin gas drawn through the elements by the atmosphere revitalization system was successfully scrubbed of carbon dioxide. After about 20 hours of operation, an additional unit was stacked on each original cartridge to improve the removal of carbon dioxide. With this configuration, the indicated carbon dioxide level was maintained between 13 and 240 N/m^2 (0.1 and 1.8 mm Hg). This special procedure was used for 47 hours until the Command Module was activated and the Lunar Module jettisoned.

Flight Problems

The problems encountered during flight were not serious in terms of crew safety or mission success. Two of the more interesting problems involved the water separators and oxygen demand regulators.

Water Separator. During the Apollo 11 and 12 flights, the crews reported free water in their suits during lunar operations. Prior to the Apollo 12 flight, a thermal and system analysis indicated that the most probable cause of the problem was bypass flow through the separator selector valve, a part of the water separator. The problem could not be reproduced during ground tests. However, during Apollo 12, free water was again reported in the pressure suits.

Following the Apollo 12 flight, a detailed bench test was again performed to identify the problem. It was found that the suit loop gas flow drove the separator too fast, resulting in water carryover. To correct the difficulty, an orifice was incorporated in the primary lithium hydroxide cartridges to limit the suit loop flow in future vehicles.

The Apollo 13 and 14 crewmen reported no free water. However, the indicated separator speeds read "High" during some flight periods. In fact, in certain suited configurations (for example, helmets and gloves removed), pressure resistance in the suit was lowered and gas flow became unacceptably high. Therefore, the operating procedures were modified to maintain adequate flow resistance during all modes of operation.

Oxygen Demand Regulator. Suit circuit and cabin pressures were controlled by two oxygen demand regulators which sensed suit circuit pressure and supplied oxygen. The regulators normally operated concurrently. Two pressure ranges could be selected: cabin mode and egress mode.

While the cabin was being depressurized prior to the third lunar excursion during the Apollo 17 mission, the suit circuit gas pressure increased above a normal regulator lockup. The situation was cleared by manual shutoff of one of the two parallel oxygen demand regulators. The mission was completed with exclusive use of the second regulator. Postflight data review indicated that the pressure rise could have been caused by inadvertently bumping the regulator out of its "Egress" position or by contamination between the regulator poppet and seat.

Experience

The experience gained in the development and operation of the LM environmental control system may prove to be useful in the design of future systems. The following sections relate the more important derivatives of the program.

Instrumentation Adequacy. The initial system design incorporated instrumentation to allow assessment of system performance and mode of operation during mission phases. However, since the crews were expected to follow the specified procedure and flight timelines, certain instrumentation was deleted. As a result, there were periods of uncertainty. For example, the exact position of a valve might have been unknown to ground controllers. Moreover, ground-to-crew communications to verify performance were limited by mission and scientific activities.

Additional instrumentation would have been useful to provide engineering determination of flight discrepancies. This lack of data was aggravated as the vehicle was nonrecoverable and postflight verification was not possible.

Component Redundancy. The Lunar Module ECS was designed with sufficient redundancy in critical life support areas to provide a "fail operational, fail safe" design. The hardware performed successfully throughout the Apollo flights. Only during the last flight, previously discussed under flight problems, was a redundant component required.

Redundancy considerations were simplified by the multiple function component design. Hardware complexity and costs were high compared to single function components. For system design where weight, volume, and manual operation are premium design requirements, the use of multiple function components should be considered in lieu of multiple single function components.

Modular Construction. Modular packaging concepts were used in several places in the ECS where groupings of equipment appeared desirable. The major package in the Lunar Module ECS was the suit circuit assembly which contained the necessary atmosphere processing equipment. The suit circuit assembly was densely packaged to accommodate the required hardware in the allotted space. Use of the modular concept was necessary because of the weight and volume constraints, but this led to a number of problems.

It had been planned to replace the entire package in the field if any component required change. Changing an entire package was a relatively long process. A large number of tests were required to verify that all the components within the replacement package were functioning after installation. For this reason and wherever possible, the practice of changing individual components with the package installed was adopted. This practice, which was successfully performed on a number of occasions, saved time in the vehicle cabin and generally avoided schedule delays.

Subatmospheric Design. The Lunar Module environmental control system was designed for optimum performance when operated at subatmospheric pressure and zero to one-sixth Earth gravity. As this equipment could not be operated at sea level pressure, considerable ground checkout problems and lengthy test flows resulted. For example, the suit and cabin pressure control system, designed for absolute pressure maintenance, would not function unless the suit circuit or cabin pressure was reduced to, or below, the system control pressures. This design prevented normal system operation unless the vehicle was placed in a vacuum chamber and its ambient pressure reduced to effectively zero. Inadvertent operation of the suit and cabin fans at pressures greater than 70 kN/m^2 (10 psia) required considerable analysis and tests to certify that the affected hardware was acceptable for flight. Nevertheless, some fans were replaced.

In order to simplify ground checkout and limit test errors which result in hardware replacement or reverification, future design efforts for spacecraft environmental control systems should include requirements for normal operation at sea level environments.

Summary

The performance of both the Command Module and Lunar Module environmental control systems during the Apollo Program was highly satisfactory. Only minor problems were experienced. These systems provided the astronauts with the necessary life sustaining functions, with as much added comfort as possible. The knowledge gained in the system design and performance should be beneficial to the development of future trouble-free systems.

References

The bulk of the information in this chapter appeared in the following two articles:

Hughes, D.F.; Owens, W.L.; and Young, R.W.: Apollo Command and Service Module Environmental Control System — Mission Performance and Experience. ASME Paper No. 73-ENA-29, American Society of Mechanical Engineers (New York), 1973.

Brady, J.C.; Browne, D.M.; Schneider, H.J.; and Sheehan, J.F.: Apollo Lunar Module Environmental Control System — Mission Performance and Experience. ASME Paper No. 73-ENA-28, American Society of Mechanical Engineers (New York), 1973.

CHAPTER 6
EXTRAVEHICULAR MOBILITY UNIT

by

Maurice A. Carson
Michael N. Rouen
Charles C. Lutz
James W. McBarron, II
Lyndon B. Johnson Space Center

Introduction

The Apollo extravehicular mobility unit was designed to meet a unique set of needs. To assure the maximum return of scientific information from the moon, a method was required for collecting samples, deploying/retrieving instruments, and performing experiments on the lunar surface and in free space. Man had to be able to operate safely in free space to provide an emergency mode of translation from the Lunar Module to the Command Module in the event a complete linkup could not be accomplished after lunar lift-off. Since the weight required to provide redundant pressure vessels for each spacecraft would have been prohibitive, a space suit was required.

The extravehicular mobility unit (EMU) design reflected these needs. Figure 1 is a cutaway representation of the EMU. The unit consisted of a highly mobile, anthropomorphic pressure vessel and a portable life support system (PLSS). The pressure vessel, known as the pressure garment assembly (PGA), when operated in conjunction with the Command Module and Lunar Module life support systems, provided pressurization backup during critical mission phases, including launch and return. It provided primary pressurization for the extravehicular activity conducted from the Command Module during the missions of Apollo 15, 16, and 17. Traverses of four to seven hours' duration were made with the PLSS on the lunar surface to perform the lunar science tasks.

A description of the EMU used for the first lunar landing is given here. A short description is included of the changes made in the EMU design during the program to incorporate the results of experience and to provide new capabilities.

The EMU was supplied by three different concerns. The pressure garment assembly was supplied by ILC Industries, Incorporated, and the portable life support system by the Hamilton Standard Division of United Aircraft Corporation. Both were under the monitorship of the Crew Systems Division of the Engineering and Development Directorate of the Johnson Space Center. The communications equipment was supplied by RCA under the monitorship of the Tracking and Communications Development Division, also of the Engineering and Development Directorate.

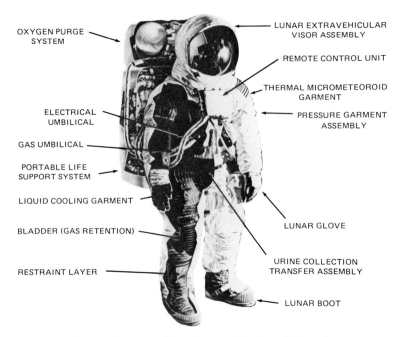

OXYGEN PURGE SYSTEM

LUNAR EXTRAVEHICULAR VISOR ASSEMBLY

REMOTE CONTROL UNIT

THERMAL MICROMETEOROID GARMENT

ELECTRICAL UMBILICAL

PRESSURE GARMENT ASSEMBLY

GAS UMBILICAL

PORTABLE LIFE SUPPORT SYSTEM

LIQUID COOLING GARMENT

LUNAR GLOVE

BLADDER (GAS RETENTION)

URINE COLLECTION TRANSFER ASSEMBLY

RESTRAINT LAYER

LUNAR BOOT

Figure 1. Cutaway of Apollo extravehicular mobility unit.

Apollo 11 Pressure Garment Assembly Configuration

Two configurations of the PGA were worn on the Apollo 11 mission. The intravehicular configuration was worn by the Command Module Pilot (figure 2). The extravehicular configuration, shown in figure 3, was worn by the Commander and Lunar Module Pilot. The two configurations were similar in most respects. However, the intravehicular version was equipped with a lighter weight and less bulky coverlayer and did not include hardware and controls necessary for extravehicular use.

Both versions of the PGA consisted of a torso-limb suit assembly (TLSA) with an integrated protective coverlayer, a pressure helmet, pressure gloves, controls, instrumentation, and communication equipment. In addition, extravehicular equipment consisting of a lunar extravehicular visor assembly, lunar boots, a liquid cooling garment, and fecal and urinary containment systems were provided to complete the EVA PGA configuration. These components of the EMU are pictured in figure 4.

Apollo space suits were individually tailored for each mission. Fifteen suits were required to fully equip the mission. Each prime crewmember had three suits — a training suit and two flight suits, and each backup crewmember had two suits — a training suit and a flight suit.

The following sections describe the components of the extravehicular PGA configuration. Table 1 lists the characteristics of the suit assembly.

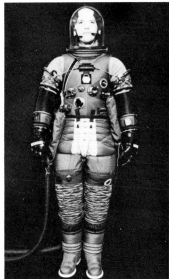

Figure 2. Extravehicular configuration of the EMU.

Figure 3. Intravehicular configuration of the EMU.

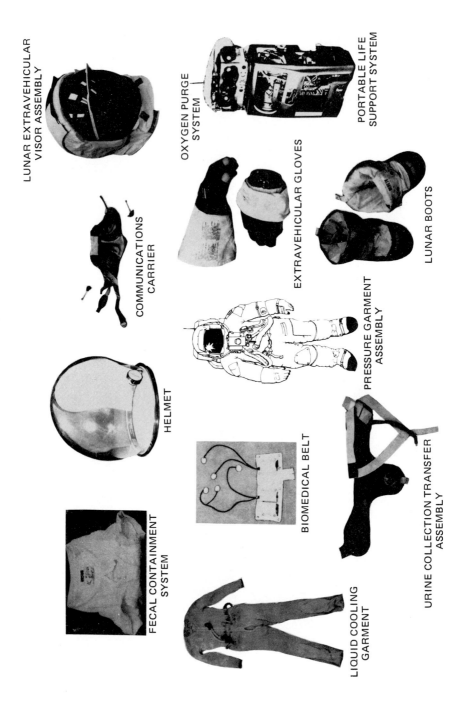

LUNAR EXTRAVEHICULAR VISOR ASSEMBLY

OXYGEN PURGE SYSTEM

PORTABLE LIFE SUPPORT SYSTEM

COMMUNICATIONS CARRIER

EXTRAVEHICULAR GLOVES

LUNAR BOOTS

HELMET

PRESSURE GARMENT ASSEMBLY

BIOMEDICAL BELT

URINE COLLECTION TRANSFER ASSEMBLY

FECAL CONTAINMENT SYSTEM

LIQUID COOLING GARMENT

Figure 4. Extravehicular configuration of torso limb suit assembly (TLSA).

Table 1

Pressure Garment Assembly Characteristics

Characteristics	Pressure Garment Assembly with Thermal Micrometeoroid Garment	
Weight	19.69 kg	(43.42 lb)
Operational temperature limitations	$\pm 394^\circ$K	$(\pm 250^\circ$ F)
Leak rate at 25 511 N/m^2 (3.7 psig) (maximum)	180 scc/min	(.0315 lb/hr)
Operating pressure	25 855 $\pm$ 1724 N/m^2	(3.75 $\pm$ 0.25 psig)
Structural pressure	41 369 N/m^2	(6.00 psig)
Proof pressure	55 158 N/m^2	(8.00 psig)
Burst pressure	68 948 N/m^2	(10.00 psig)
Pressure drop, water		
.34 m^3/min (12 cfm), 24 132 N/m^2 (3.5 psia), $\approx$283°K (50° F), and inlet diverter valve open (IV position)	11.9 cm	(4.70 in.)
.17 m^3/min (6 cfm), 26 890 N/m^2 (3.9 psia), $\approx$298°K (77°F), and inlet diverter valve closed (EV position)	4.6 cm	(1.80 in.)
Pressure gage range	17 237 to 41 369 N/m^2	(2.5 to 6.0 psig)

Torso-Limb Suit Assembly (TLSA)

The torso-limb suit assembly consisted of that portion of the PGA which encompassed the entire body with the exception of the head and hands. The extravehicular configuration is shown diagrammatically in figure 5. The torso portion was custom-sized and the limb portions were graduated in size and were adjustable to accommodate individual crewman limb lengths.

A pressure sealing and restraint slide fastener permitted the crewman to enter the suit. A lock assembly prevented inadvertent opening. The pressure-containing bladder of the TLSA was a neoprene-coated nylon fabric. Directly over the bladder outer surface was a nylon restraint layer that controlled the conformal shape and provided structural support to the bladder. Dipped rubber convoluted joints were located at the shoulders, elbows, wrists, hips, knees, and ankles, to permit movement with a minimum expenditure of energy. Restraint cables or cords sustained axial limb loads during pressurized operation and prevented ballooning of the convoluted joints. A biomedical injection patch was built into the right thigh portion of the torso-limb suit to permit a crewman to self-administer a hypodermic injection without jeopardizing the gas retention quality of the PGA.

The arm assembly had a bearing to enhance rotational movements above the elbow. The PGA boot, which was connected to the torso-limb suit, was sized to the individual crewman's foot and had an ankle convolute which permitted ankle extension and flexion movements.

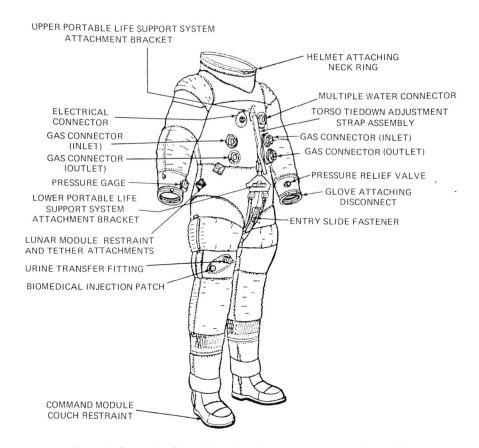

Figure 5. Extravehicular configuration of torso limb suit assembly (TLSA).

The innermost layer of the torso-limb suit was a nylon liner (figure 6) for comfort and improved donning. A series of noncollapsible ducts attached on the inner surface of the pressure bladder served as part of the ventilation system.

The ventilation system directed all inlet gas flow to the helmet for respiration and helmet defogging during lunar surface operations. The gas flow then traveled over the body to the extremities where return ducting routed the flow to the suit outlet. A ventilation flow director valve was located on the inlet gas connectors. The PGA suit pressure was displayed on a gage mounted on the lower arm.

Pressure Helmet Assembly

The pressure helmet was a detachable, transparent closure with provisions for feeding, drinking, and attachment of the lunar extravehicular visor assembly (LEVA). The helmet was made by a special heat forming process from high optical quality polycarbonate plastic. The helmet and neckring which attached it to the torso-limb suit are shown in figure 7. It contained a feedport which allowed insertion of a probe for administering water and contingency food to a crewman while wearing the complete PGA in either the pressurized or unpressurized condition. A synthetic elastomer foam vent pad was bonded to the back of the helmet shell to provide a headrest, and to act as a ventilation flow manifold for directing the flow of gas to the oral-nasal area. This flow caused an efficient exhaust of carbon dioxide from the nasal area through the torso neck opening.

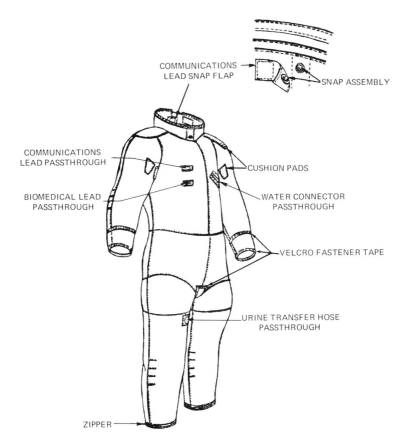

COMMUNICATIONS LEAD SNAP FLAP

SNAP ASSEMBLY

COMMUNICATIONS LEAD PASSTHROUGH

CUSHION PADS

BIOMEDICAL LEAD PASSTHROUGH

WATER CONNECTOR PASSTHROUGH

VELCRO FASTENER TAPE

URINE TRANSFER HOSE PASSTHROUGH

ZIPPER

Figure 6. Pressure garment assembly (PGA) liner.

The lunar extravehicular visor assembly, shown in figure 8, furnished visual, thermal, and mechanical protection to the crewman's helmet and head. It was composed of a plastic shell, three eyeshades, and two visors. The outer, or sun visor was made of high-temperature polysulfone plastic. The inner, or protective visor was made of ultraviolet-stabilized polycarbonate plastic. The outer visor filtered visible light and rejected a significant amount of ultraviolet and infrared rays. The inner visor filtered ultraviolet rays, rejected infrared and, in combination with the sun visor and pressure helmet, formed an effective thermal barrier. The two visors in combination with the helmet protected the crewmember from micrometeoroid damage and from damage in the event

of falling on the lunar surface. A hard shell protected the sun visor during non-use
periods. The eyeshades were adjusted by the crewman to prevent glare from hampering
vision during EVA. The central eyeshade was added at the suggestion of the Apollo 11
lunar surface crew who reported the need for greater glare protection.

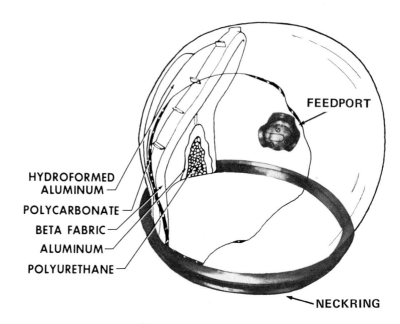

Figure 7. Pressure helmet.

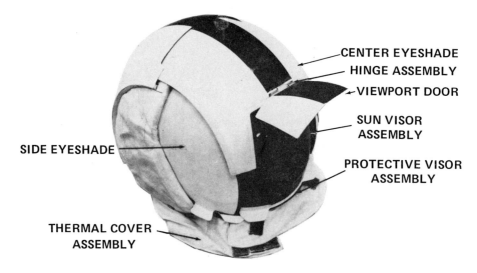

Figure 8. Lunar extravehicular visor assembly (LEVA).

Pressure Gloves

The pressure glove was a flexible, gas-retaining device which was attached and locked to the torso-limb suit by means of a quick-disconnect coupling. The glove (figure 9) was a protective hand covering which was attached to the torso-limb suit prior to egress for extravehicular operations.

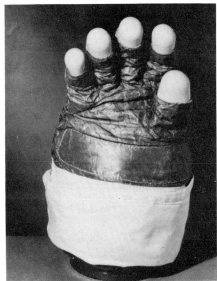

Figure 9. Extravehicular pressure gloves.

The glove consisted of a modified intravehicular pressure glove covered by a glove shell. The shell covered the entire hand and had an integral cuff or gauntlet which extended above the wrist disconnect on the arm as far as the PGA pressure gage or the pressure relief valve. The gauntlet provided a convenient surface on which to put a checklist for lunar extravehicular activities (figure 10).

The extravehicular glove shell was a multilayered assembly which provided scuff, abrasion, and thermal protection to the pressure glove. A woven metal fabric (Chromel-R) was incorporated over the palm and fingers to provide abrasion protection. The thumb and fingertip shells were made of high-strength silicone rubber-coated nylon tricot for improved tactility and strength. A silicone dispersion coating was applied to the palm, around the thumb, and to the inner side of each finger to improve the grip. The outer cover conformed so that it did not appreciably restrict dexterity. A palm restraint strap could be tightened to minimize the ballooning effect of pressurization. The shell assembly was secured to the pressure glove at the back and palm areas of the hand by hook-and-pile fastener tape and near the tip of each finger by two anchor straps and neoprene adhesive.

Figure 10. Extravehicular pressure gloves showing gauntlet checklist.

Cotton wristlets were used to prevent arm chafing caused by the pressure garment assembly wrist disconnects when the gloves were removed and the torso-limb suit was worn. Comfort gloves constructed of nylon tricot were worn under both intravehicular and extravehicular gloves. The comfort glove made donning the pressure glove easier and acted as a sweat absorption layer between the hand and the pressure glove bladder.

Electrical Harness and Bioharness

The PGA electrical harness shown in figure 11 provided electrical connections for the biosensor harness and for communications equipment. A central 61-pin connector was designed to receive the engagement mechanism of the communications and bioinstrumentation umbilical of the spacecraft or the portable life support system.

Integrated Thermal Micrometeoroid Garment

The integrated thermal micrometeoroid garment (ITMG) (figure 12) was a lightweight multilaminate assembly which covered the torso-limb suit assembly to afford protection against the thermal and micrometeoroid hazards encountered during free space and lunar excursions. Figure 13 illustrates the makeup of the suit, layer by layer. For protection against abrasion, an additional external layer of Teflon fabric was attached to the knee, waist, elbow, and shoulder areas, and a layer of Chromel-R was added on the back under the PLSS. Pockets and flaps accommodated items needed by the crewman and permitted the use of the urine transfer connector.

Lunar surface boots covered the PGA boots exclusive of the sole and heel. Boots were made of the same material as the garment itself. Tape and lacing cords secured the ITMG boots to the PGA boots at the boot top and around the sole and heel area. A zipper at the top of each boot attached the boot to the leg of the ITMG. A Teflon patch encircling the ankle of the boot prevented abrasion caused by the lunar boot.

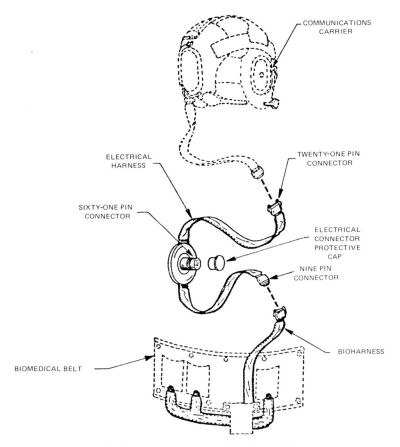

Figure 11. Pressure garment assembly electrical harness.

Liquid Cooling Garment

A liquid cooling garment (LCG) was worn next to the skin under the pressure garment assembly during lunar and free space extravehicular activity. The LCG (figure 14), made of nylon-spandex knit, provided for comfort, perspiration absorption, and thermal transfer. The garment supplied a continuous flow of temperature-controlled water through a network of polyvinylchloride (PVC) tubing stitched to the inside surface of the open-mesh fabric garment (figure 15). A lightweight nylon comfort liner separated the body from the tubing network. The network had a parallel flow path for maximum surface coverage and optimum cooling. The LCG could be supplied with coolant water from the Lunar Module support system and, during EVA, from the portable life support system.

The coolant water was warmed by heat transfer from the crewman's body and was returned to the PLSS through the outlet channel of the multiple water connector. The LCG could remove heat at a maximum rate of 62 112 J/hr ($\approx$2000 Btu/hr). Characteristics of the LCG are listed in table 2.

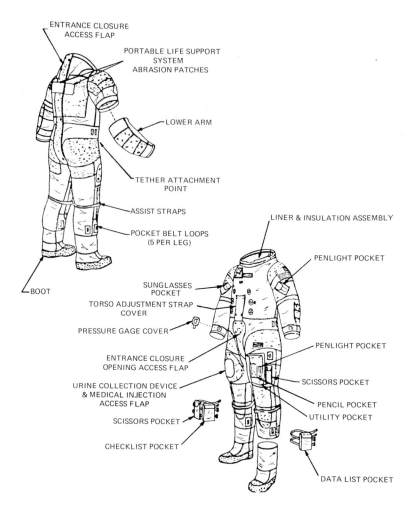

ENTRANCE CLOSURE
ACCESS FLAP

PORTABLE LIFE SUPPORT
SYSTEM
ABRASION PATCHES

LOWER ARM

TETHER ATTACHMENT
POINT

ASSIST STRAPS

POCKET BELT LOOPS
(5 PER LEG)

BOOT

LINER & INSULATION ASSEMBLY

PENLIGHT POCKET

SUNGLASSES
POCKET

TORSO ADJUSTMENT STRAP
COVER

PRESSURE GAGE COVER

PENLIGHT POCKET

ENTRANCE CLOSURE
OPENING ACCESS FLAP

SCISSORS POCKET

URINE COLLECTION DEVICE
& MEDICAL INJECTION
ACCESS FLAP

PENCIL POCKET
UTILITY POCKET

SCISSORS POCKET

CHECKLIST POCKET

DATA LIST POCKET

Figure 12. Lunar integrated thermal micrometeoroid garment configuration.

Lunar Boots

The lunar boots, donned prior to lunar surface activity, provided thermal and abrasion protection for the pressure garment assembly boots during lunar surface operations. The outer layer of a lunar boot, except for the sole, was fabricated from Chromel-R and the tongue area was made of Teflon-coated Beta cloth. Ribs projected from the bottom of the silicone rubber sole to increase thermal insulation qualities, to provide lateral rigidity, and to provide traction on the lunar surface. The inner layers consisted of two layers of Kapton followed by five layers of aluminized, perforated Mylar. The Mylar layers were separated by four layers of nonwoven Dacron followed by an inner liner of Teflon-coated Beta cloth. Two layers of Nomex felt in the sole provided additional thermal insulation from the lunar surface. Figure 16 shows the lunar boot.

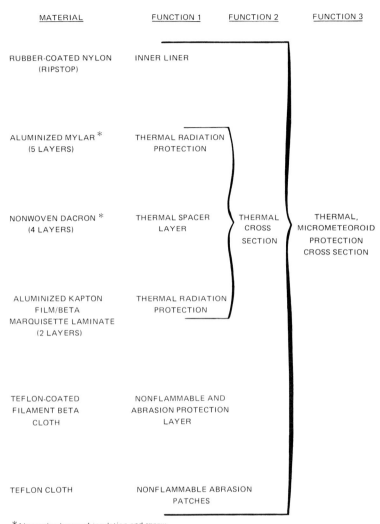

*Alternating layers of insulation and spacer.

Figure 13. Material cross-section of Apollo 10-14
lunar integrated thermal micrometeoroid garment.

Constant Wear Garment

The constant wear garment (CWG) (figure 17) was a cotton fabric undergarment worn next to the skin during intravehicular Command Module operations. It provided for comfort and perspiration absorption, and for attachment of a biobelt which contained the bioinstrumentation system. In the Command Module, the CWG was worn under the pressure garment assembly. A fly opening and a rear buttock port allowed for urination and defecation.

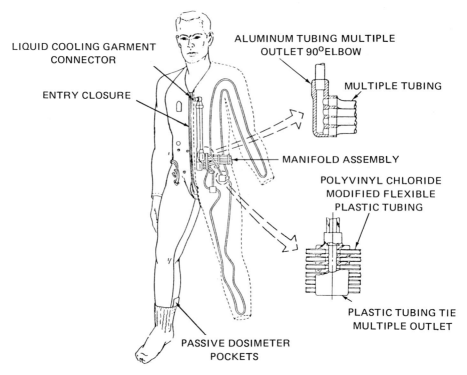

Figure 14. Liquid cooling garment and coolant system.

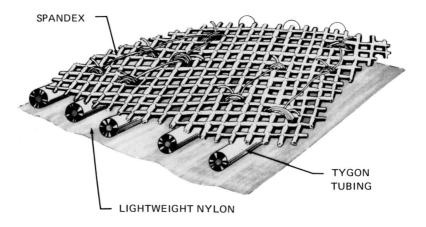

Figure 15. Liquid cooling garment construction.

Table 2

Liquid Cooling Garment Characteristics

Characteristic	Value	
Weight (charged)	2.09 kg	(4.60 lb)
Operating pressure	28 958 to 158 579 N/m^2	(4.20 to 23.0 psig)
Structural pressure	217 185 ± 3447 N/m^2	(31.50 ± 0.50 psig)
Proof pressure	217 185 ± 3447 N/m^2	(31.50 ± 0.50 psig)
Burst pressure	327 501 N/m^2	(47.50 psig)
Pressure drop, 1.81 kg/min (4 lb/min) at ≈ 294° ± 5.5°K (70° ± 10°F) inlet	22 063 N/m^2 (including both halves of connector)	(3.2 psi)
Leak rate, 131 000 N/m^2 (19 psig) at ≈ 280°K (45°F)	0.58 cm^3/hr	

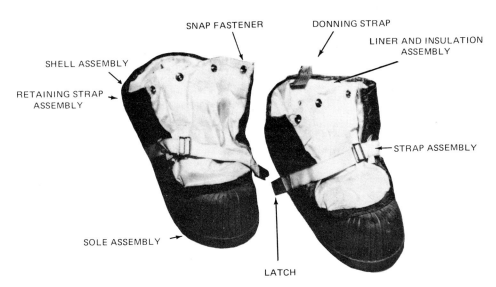

Figure 16. Lunar boots.

Communications Carrier

The communications carrier (figure 18) provided redundant microphones and earphones in a soft-suspension skull cap. Proper fitting insured acoustic isolation between the earphone and microphone. The connection could be made directly to the spacecraft communications system or through the PGA internal communication harness. Bioinstrumentation associated with the PGA is described in Section VI, Chapter 3. The communications carrier permitted suited crewmen to talk to each other, and to the Mission Control Center, through the Lunar Module systems. Telemetry data from both crewmen were also communicated to the ground through the Lunar Module.

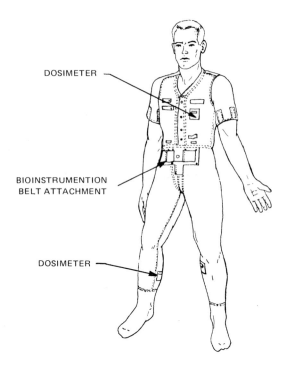

DOSIMETER

BIOINSTRUMENTION
BELT ATTACHMENT

DOSIMETER

Figure 17. Constant wear garment.

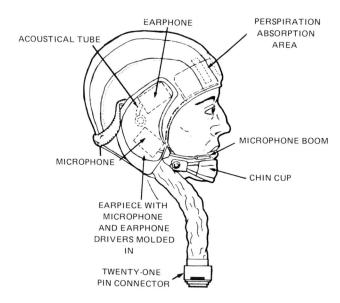

EARPHONE

PERSPIRATION
ABSORPTION
AREA

ACOUSTICAL TUBE

MICROPHONE BOOM

MICROPHONE

CHIN CUP

EARPIECE WITH
MICROPHONE
AND EARPHONE
DRIVERS MOLDED
IN

TWENTY-ONE
PIN CONNECTOR

Figure 18. Communications carrier.

Portable Life Support System

To provide a suitable protective environment during both lunar surface and free space excursions, the astronaut carried on his back a compact assembly of various environmental control devices, which formed the portable life support system (PLSS), pictured in figure 19. Figure 20 shows two views of the system packaged as it would be for a mission. The PLSS supplied breathing oxygen; controlled suit pressure; recycled oxygen by removing carbon dioxide, odors, moisture, and some trace contaminant gases; controlled temperature; provided warnings of system malfunctions; and provided voice communications and telemetry data. Table 3 lists the specifications for the PLSS. A separate emergency system provided oxygen for breathing, suit pressure, and cooling in case of PLSS failure. This system was called the oxygen purge system (OPS) and was manually activated.

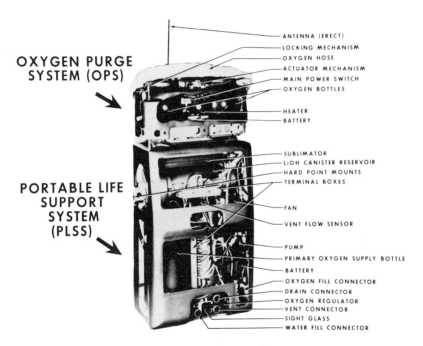

OXYGEN PURGE SYSTEM (OPS)

PORTABLE LIFE SUPPORT SYSTEM (PLSS)

- ANTENNA (ERECT)
- LOCKING MECHANISM
- OXYGEN HOSE
- ACTUATOR MECHANISM
- MAIN POWER SWITCH
- OXYGEN BOTTLES
- HEATER
- BATTERY
- SUBLIMATOR
- LiOH CANISTER RESERVOIR
- HARD POINT MOUNTS
- TERMINAL BOXES
- FAN
- VENT FLOW SENSOR
- PUMP
- PRIMARY OXYGEN SUPPLY BOTTLE
- BATTERY
- OXYGEN FILL CONNECTOR
- DRAIN CONNECTOR
- OXYGEN REGULATOR
- VENT CONNECTOR
- SIGHT GLASS
- WATER FILL CONNECTOR

Figure 19. Portable life support system and oxygen purge system.

The portable life support system supplied oxygen to the pressure garment assembly and cooling water to the liquid cooling garment. The PLSS subsystems were an oxygen ventilating circuit, a primary oxygen subsystem, a liquid transport loop, a feedwater loop, and an electrical power subsystem.

Oxygen Ventilating Circuit

The oxygen ventilating circuit (figure 21) provided temperature, humidity, and contaminant control of breathing oxygen. Recycled gas and fresh oxygen entered the suit, absorbing heat, moisture, and body contaminants. The contaminated gas was then returned to the PLSS contaminant control assembly where contaminants were removed. The decontaminated gas then entered the sublimator (heat exchanger) where heat was given up, and the excess moisture in the stream was condensed. Next, water was removed by a water separator and transferred to a storage reservoir. A fan forced the air through a back flow check valve, finishing the recycling process.

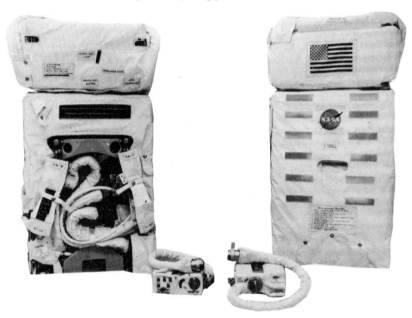

Figure 20. Operational packaging of portable life support system.

Table 3

Specifications for the Portable Life Support System

Design Requirements	Specifications	
	Apollo 11 — 14	Apollo 15 — 17
Average metabolic load	6694 J/hr (1600 Btu/hr)	6694 J/hr (1600 Btu/hr)
Peak metabolic load	8368 J/hr (2000 Btu/hr)	8368 J/hr (2000 Btu/hr)
Maximum heat leak in	1046 J/hr (250 Btu/hr)	1255 J/hr (300 Btu/hr)
Maximum heat leak out	1046 J/hr (250 Btu/hr)	1464 J/hr (350 Btu/hr)
Maximum CO_2 partial pressure	2000 N/m^2 (15 mm Hg)	2000 N/m^2 (15 mm Hg)
Pressure garment assembly pressure	26 545 N/m^2 (3.85 psia)	26 545 N/m^2 (3.85 psia)
Ventilation flow	.1557 m^3/min (5.5 cfm)	.1557 m^3/min (5.5 cfm)
Duration	4 hr	7 hr
Oxygen charge pressure at $\approx$ 294°K (70°F)	7 032 652 N/m^2 (1020 psia)	9 721 607 N/m^2 (1410 psia)
Battery capacity	279 W-hr	431 W-hr
Emergency oxygen		
Duration (minimum)	30 min	30 min
Maximum flow	3.63 kg/hr (8 lb/hr)	3.63 kg/hr (8 lb/hr)
Pressure garment assembly pressure	25 510 N/m^2 (3.7 psia)	25 510 N/m^2 (3.7 psia)

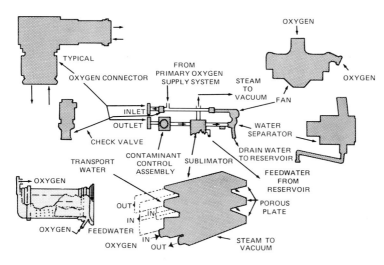

Figure 21. Oxygen ventilating circuit schematic

Primary Oxygen Subsystem

The gaseous oxygen in the portable life support system primary oxygen subsystem (figure 22) provided oxygen for suit pressurization and astronaut breathing. Oxygen, stored in the primary bottle, was regulated to the correct pressure before entering the rest of the system. A quick-fill connector allowed for oxygen recharging.

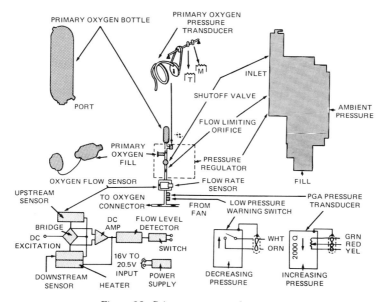

Figure 22. Primary oxygen subsystem.

Liquid Transport Loop

The liquid transport loop (figure 23) was the primary means of crewman temperature control. Water from the liquid cooling garment entered the loop through the multiple water connector. The water was then pumped through the sublimator where heat was given up. The cooled water was used for fan motor cooling before return to the LCG through the multiple water connector.

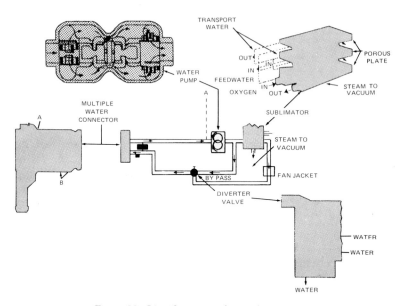

Figure 23. Liquid transport loop schematic.

Feedwater Loop

The feedwater loop (figure 24) supplied expendable water to the sublimator for cooling, and stored condensation removed by the water separator in the oxygen ventilation circuit. As the water passed through the sublimator, it absorbed system heat. The hot water was then discharged to the outside.

Electrical Power Subsystem

The electrical power subsystem provided electrical power to the fan and pump motor assemblies, the communications system, and the instrumentation. The extravehicular communications system (EVCS) provided voice communications and telemetry transmission of system operation. The capabilities included voice communication between the spacecraft and the astronaut, voice communication between astronauts, and voice communication between Earth and astronaut. The EVCS consisted of two extravehicular communicators that were integrated with the PLSS. The first extravehicular communicator (EVC-1) consisted of two amplitude-modulated (AM) transmitters, two AM receivers, one frequency-modulated (FM) receiver, signal-conditioning circuits, a telemetry system, a warning system, and other components required for operation. The EVC-2 was similar to the EVC-1 except that the EVC-2 had an FM transmitter instead of an FM receiver.

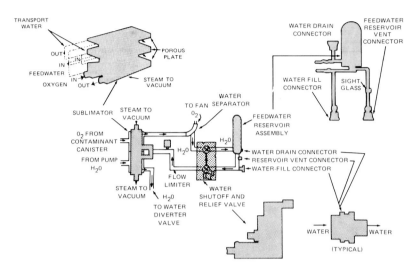

Figure 24. Portable life support system feedwater loop schematic.

Much of the instrumentation was located in the remote control unit. This chest-mounted unit, shown in figure 25, housed electrical controls for the PLSS, a primary oxygen quantity indicator, and warning devices. The warning devices would signal the astronaut if system components failed to work properly. Malfunctions checked were low feedwater pressure, low ventilation flow, low PGA pressure, and high oxygen flow. In an emergency, the mission would be aborted or the emergency oxygen purge system activated.

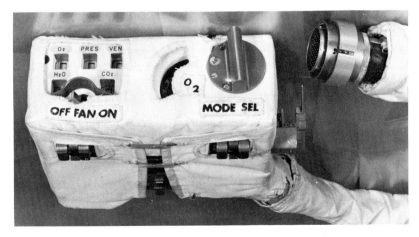

Figure 25. Portable life support system remote control unit.

Oxygen Purge System

The oxygen purge system (OPS) (figure 26) provided an oxygen supply and pressure control for certain failure modes. In the normal EVA configuration, the OPS was mounted on top of the PLSS and used only for emergencies. The OPS was self-contained, independently powered, and nonrechargeable. The OPS provided a minimum of 30 minutes of operation. The system consisted of two interconnected bottles of high pressure oxygen, an automatic temperature control module, a pressure regulator, a battery, an oxygen indicator, and the necessary checkout instrumentation. The OPS had no communications capability, but provided the mount for the PLSS very-high-frequency (VHF) antenna.

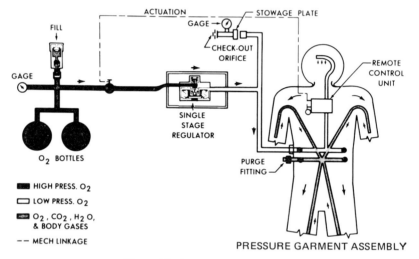

Figure 26. Oxygen purge system.

EMU Performance

The life support system underwent changes during the program to meet new requirements and incorporate improvements based on experience. The PLSS was redesigned for Apollo,15, 16, and 17 to allow longer lunar missions by increasing oxygen storage pressure, adding more contaminant control material, increasing the size of the power supply, and adding an auxiliary feedwater tank. A longer duration emergency system was required for Apollo 14, 15, 16, and 17 because of the greater distances of traverse from the Lunar Module. This requirement was accomplished by the addition of the buddy secondary life support system (BLSS) shown schematically in figure 27. It could provide backup cooling in the event of a failure of the PLSS cooling loop.

The extravehicular mobility unit was one of the outstanding engineering successes of the Apollo Space Program. While there were some minor problems experienced with the suit, for example, the lunar visor tended to scratch easily and finger dexterity was not optimum, never was a major or even minor failure experienced with the suit or backpack system.

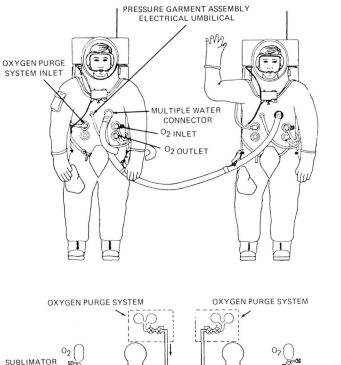

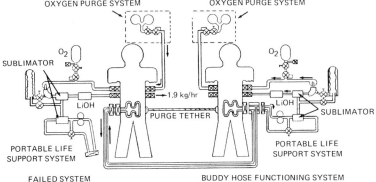

Figure 27. Buddy secondary life support system.

Rigorous preflight testing was accomplished during suit development, and each individual flight suit was tested prior to every mission. The Apollo suits were impact tested against various objects, including extremely sharp devices, for resistance to penetration and rips. Quality control was meticulous. Pins used in the manufacture of the garment were accounted for and each suit was X-rayed to preclude the possibility of an oversight. Training suits were used in most preflight tests rather than flight suits to ensure there would be no compromise of the integrity of the flight suit. However, each flight suit was tested in a limited number of altitude chamber tests, after which the suits were thoroughly inspected for any possible damage.

The helmet used during EVA had an extremely high resistance to impact. The helmet material, Lexan, will not break even upon impact with a hammer. Lexan was substituted for the Project Gemini visor material. The latter lacked the impact resistance necessary for lunar operations. During one Gemini reentry, the visor cracked when the astronaut lurched forward, hitting the instrument panel.

The extravehicular mobility unit and its associated components, the pressure garment assembly, the portable life support system, and the oxygen purge system, were used in various configurations in the Apollo 7 through 17 missions. Components were operationally tested before integration into the EMU. In all cases, the components performed effectively.

No outside spacecraft activities were performed during the missions of Apollo 7 and 8. The only EMU system aboard the spacecraft, therefore, was the pressure garment assembly for use as a backup to the pressure and environmental control system and for protection against noise and vibration during launch and reentry. The pressure garment assembly performed satisfactorily during these missions, and crews reported that ventilation in the PGA was adequate during the orbital phase. Further, donning and doffing were found to be much easier at zero g than at one g.

The first use of the complete EMU under flight conditions was accomplished during the Apollo 9 mission. The Lunar Module Pilot, wearing the complete EMU, opened the side hatch of the LM and stepped out to simulate contingency transfer to the Command Module. At the same time, the Command Module Pilot operating with an interface with the environmental control system, opened the Command Module side hatch and stood up in the hatch area several times to retrieve thermal samples and take photographs. Both crewmen reported that they were comfortable and experienced no visual problems with the extravehicular visor assembly.

After completion of the EVA, the Lunar Module Pilot doffed the PLSS, the OPS, and the LEVA with no problems. At this point, the PLSS was successfully recharged in the Lunar Module cabin for possible contingency reuse and for demonstration of this operation under actual flight conditions. Each Apollo 9 crewman wore his PGA for approximately 52 hours, for most of this time with the helmet and gloves off.

The Apollo 10 mission was similar to the Apollo 7 and 8 missions in that the EMU was not used for extravehicular activities and the PGA was used only as backup to the Command Module environmental control system. Again, the performance of the PGA was satisfactory.

The Apollo 11 mission was the first mission during which the EMU was exposed to the lunar environment for which it had been designed. All aspects of EMU operation demonstrated during testing and on previous flights were proved on the lunar surface. No significant problems were noted at Lunar Module egress. The crew stated that they were comfortable wearing the PLSS/OPS and that the mass of the unit was not objectionable. In fact, the lunar surface crewmen reported that they were so comfortable in the suits that, after a brief period of time on the lunar surface, they virtually forgot they were wearing them. Mobility and balance were sufficiently adequate to allow stable movement while performing lunar surface tasks. The Lunar Module Pilot demonstrated the capability to walk, run, change directions while running, and stop without difficulty.

The liquid cooling garment worn by the crew was controllable by each astronaut to maintain a temperature suitable for his needs. During the Apollo 11 mission, the

Commander kept his LCG temperature much higher than did the Lunar Command Pilot, at his own option.

The Apollo 12 mission was the first mission involving two periods of extravehicular activity. Both crewmen spent approximately four hours on the lunar surface during each of the EVAs, with the EMU performing satisfactorily. Because of the additional EVA, a recharge of each PLSS was performed for the first time. No problems were noted.

The full EMU was not used during the Apollo 13 mission, as the mission was aborted and a lunar landing was not made. The pressure garment assemblies were worn, however, as backup to the spacecraft environmental control system.

The Apollo 14 mission included two EVA periods, and was the first mission during which the buddy secondary life support system was carried as the crewmen traversed approximately 1.5 kilometers from the Lunar Module. Again, performance of the EMU was satisfactory.

The lunar roving vehicle was used for the first time during the mission of Apollo 15. The vehicle allowed the astronauts to travel farther from the Lunar Module than on earlier missions. For the mission, the portable life support system carried additional expendables (water, power, lithium hydroxide for absorption of carbon dioxide, and oxygen) which allowed for much longer extravehicular activities than had been possible before. In addition, the number of EVA periods was increased from two to three to permit more extensive lunar exploration.

The Apollo 15 mission included an EVA from the Command Module in addition to the lunar surface EVAs. During the return to Earth from the moon, the Command Module Pilot performed the EVA to retrieve a film package from the Service Module portion of the spacecraft. Oxygen was supplied for this EVA by an umbilical from the Command Module life support system, and the astronaut wore the oxygen purge system as a backup.

The Apollo 16 and 17 missions, like the Apollo 15 mission, involved three lunar surface extravehicular activity periods and one Command Module EVA on each mission. The longest EVA of the Apollo Program was the second lunar surface EVA on Apollo 17, which lasted seven hours and thirty-seven minutes.

Summary

On July 20, 1969, man took his first step onto the surface of another planet and collected scientific data while his life was sustained by the extravehicular mobility unit. Throughout the course of the Apollo Program, the EMU was used to provide a habitable environment for astronauts on seven different missions. During its entire span of performance, no significant problems were experienced with any part of the system. The emergency oxygen system provided never had to be used.

A Summing Up

CHAPTER 1
SUMMARY AND CONCLUSIONS

by

Lawrence F. Dietlein, M.D.

Lyndon B. Johnson Space Center

This book closes yet another chapter in the continuing effort of biomedical scientists to characterize the responses of man to perhaps his last frontier — space. The results of Project Mercury (1961-1963) have been well documented (NASA, 1965) and need not be reiterated here. Chapter 2 in the continuing manned space flight epic was the Gemini Program (1965-1966). The principal objectives of the ten Gemini Missions were to perfect the techniques of rendezvous, station keeping, docking, and extravehicular activity — all critical to the Apollo lunar landing goal. Three flights of the Gemini series were of biomedical interest: Gemini 4, 5, and 7, lasting four, eight, and fourteen days, respectively. Several inflight measurements or experiments were accomplished on these missions, as well as preflight and postflight studies.

The significant results of the Gemini investigations are listed in table 1. In general, the presence of postflight orthostatic intolerance observed following Mercury flights was confirmed. Other biomedical findings included: moderately decreased postflight exercise capacity and red cell mass; minimal loss of bone mineral and muscle nitrogen; and the relatively high metabolic cost of extravehicular activity. These findings have been reported in detail elsewhere (NASA, 1967; 1968).

The Apollo (1968-1973) results presented in this volume constitute the third chapter of the biomedical manned space flight story. Eleven manned missions were completed in the five-year span of the Apollo Program, from prelunar flights (missions 7 through 10); the first lunar landing (mission 11), and five subsequent lunar exploratory flights (missions 12 through 17). Apollo 13 did not complete its intended lunar landing mission because of the pressure vessel explosion in the Service Module. Instead, it returned to Earth following a partial lunar orbit.

As stated elsewhere in this report, biomedical studies in Apollo were limited essentially to the preflight and postflight mission phases, along with inflight crew monitoring and observation. Inflight biomedical experiments were originally planned for Apollo. These, however, were subsequently cancelled by senior program management on the basis of the operational complexity of the Apollo flights. Despite this setback, considerable biomedical information was gathered and served as a basis of the ambitious Skylab Program, then in its formative stages.

Table 1

Significant Biomedical Findings in Gemini

- Moderate postflight orthostatic intolerance
- Moderate postflight loss of exercise capacity
- Moderate loss of red cell mass
- Minimal loss of bone calcium and muscle nitrogen
- Minimal loss of bone density
- High metabolic cost of extravehicular activity

The purpose of this section is to summarize the significant Apollo biomedical findings and the tentative conclusions that may be drawn.

Crew Health Monitoring

Preflight Phase

Apollo crew health problems in the preflight period were generally minor in nature and, for the most part, involved the skin. Viral upper respiratory and gastroenteric illnesses were next in frequency. The Apollo 9 launch had to be postponed for three days because the three crewmen developed viral upper respiratory symptoms. The only other instance in which preflight mission plans had to be altered for medical reasons was the Apollo 13 mission. The exposure of one of the crew to rubella (German measles) and his lack of demonstrable immunity to this viral disease resulted in a management decision to substitute a backup crewman on this mission. Beginning with the Apollo 14 mission, a Flight Crew Health Stabilization Program was instituted for the purpose of limiting, insofar as was practicable, the exposure of the prime and backup crews to communicable, infectious diseases. This program was described in Section II. Although it is difficult to assess the effectiveness of such a program, it doubtless served to focus attention on the problem, and in all probability reduced the number of direct crew contacts with persons who could possibly transmit infectious agents, particularly upper respiratory viruses, to the members of the crew.

Inflight Phase

Apart from cases of minor superficial dermatitis and skin or mucous membrane irritation secondary to trauma, abrasion or exposure to spacecraft environment, several more potentially serious inflight medical events deserve mention. The Apollo 7 crew developed viral upper respiratory infections during their mission which were uncomfortable nuisances and responded fairly well to decongestants. No secondary bacterial infections developed, and antibiotic therapy was not required. Apollo 7 was NASA's first experience with inflight illness.

In the ill-fated Apollo 13 mission, prostatic congestion, dehydration secondary to emergency water intake restriction, and prolonged wearing of a urine collection device together induced a urinary tract infection in one crewman. The infectious agent in this case was *Pseudomonas aeruginosa.* The astronaut responded well to postflight antibiotic routine supportive therapy.

One of the Apollo 15 crewmen experienced a single run of bigeminal cardiac rhythm (22 coupled beats) as he lay in his couch observing Lunar Module tunnel leak rates. This was the first significant arrhythmia observed during any American space flight. Another Apollo 15 crewman exhibited a few supraventricular premature contractions resulting in coupled beats but not a sustained bigeminal rhythm. It was at first conjectured that a dietary deficiency of potassium might have been a contributory factor. Subsequent careful analysis of the dietary intake and mission simulation studies with potassium restriction failed to substantiate this hypothesis. The etiology remains obscure. Fatigue following strenuous lunar surface activity most certainly was a factor. Other contributory factors are speculative and are likely to remain so. It should be noted that the crewman with the sustained bigeminal episode subsequently sustained a myocardial infarction in April 1973, some 21 months after his flight of July 1971. Thus, coronary atherosclerosis was very likely a factor in this case.

Perhaps the most significant inflight illness from an operational viewpoint, and from its probable impact on future missions, was "space motion sickness." Thus, Apollo witnessed the addition of vestibular disturbances to the list of significant biomedical findings incident to space flight.

Vestibular disturbances with nausea were noted by Soviet Cosmonaut Titov during his one-day, Vostok 2 flight on August 6, 1961, and by the crews of other later Soviet flights. No astronauts had been subject to any motion sickness symptoms until the early Apollo experience. In retrospect, however, the anorexia and reduced caloric intake observed on certain Gemini and later Apollo flights, may have been, in fact, early symptoms of vestibular disturbance.

Apollo 8 and 9 especially were plagued with vestibular problems: five of the six crewmen developed stomach awareness, three of the six, nausea, and two of these six proceeded on to frank vomiting. In Apollo 15 and 17, three of six of the crewmen also experienced stomach awareness. The flight plans of Apollo 8 and 9 required that certain crewmen leave their couches soon after orbital insertion. All three Apollo 8 crewmen noted some motion sickness symptoms (stomach uneasiness or awareness, nausea, or vomiting), confined generally to the first day of flight. There is some confusion concerning the etiology of the Apollo 8 crew's symtomatology, since the Commander felt that a viral gastroenteritis accounted for (or aggravated) his symptoms. In Apollo 9, the vestibular disturbance lasted for a considerably longer time and, in the case of the most severely affected crewman, necessitated a postponement of the flight plan. Thus, an additional problem area was introduced into the American space experience. This disturbance, which had long plagued the Soviets, and which had been predicted in the early 1960's as a probable effect of weightless flight, had made its belated American debut. Its late appearance was probably related to the relative immobility of the crews in their spacecraft during the Mercury and Gemini flights and the absence of any rotation of the vehicles themselves.

Postflight Phase

The principal astronaut illnesses during the postflight period were upper respiratory infections (four instances) and influenza (types B and A_2) contracted during numerous debriefing sessions and public relations appearances. The only other unusual finding of this period was probably related to vestibular dysfunction. A single astronaut reported a mild sensation of being tilted slightly "head down," particularly when recumbent. This sensation lasted for about seven days after the flight. It is an interesting observation of presently obscure etiology.

Significant Findings

Vestibular

The late appearance of the space motion sickness syndrome in the American manned space flight experience and its sudden elevation to prominence as a problem of compelling concern in future manned space flight activities are sufficient reasons to warrant a few additional comments on the subject. Increased mobility of head and body permitted by the larger volume of the Apollo spacecraft, as compared with earlier vehicles, apparently results in motion sickness symptoms during the early adaptive period following orbital insertion. Individual susceptibility varies widely and neither previous history of motion sickness at one g nor responses to current vestibular tests at one g have any predictive value for susceptibility aloft.

It should be stressed that most Apollo crewmen experienced only mild motion sickness symptoms, and only three vomited. Most symptoms subsided completely after two to five days in space. Further, symptoms could be controlled or lessened by reducing head movement during the first few days of flight, although some head and body movement is required for the process of adaptation to proceed. Extravehicular activity at one-sixth g on the lunar surface resulted in no disorientation or vestibular disturbance, nor was there any apparent change in the sensitivity of the vestibular system on suddenly returning to one g. Indeed, there was only one episode of postflight vestibular disturbance.

Clearly, then, we are confronted with a complex problem. An aggressive attack on the problem from several approaches is indicated: to devise reliable predictive tests; to improve medications for symptom control; to investigate training methods and procedures which will increase the threshold to space motion sickness or to mitigate its symptoms during flight. A formidable task awaits us.

Cardiovascular

Postflight orthostatic intolerance was consistently demonstrated in Apollo. The familiar signs of increased pulse rate, decreased systolic and reduced pulse pressures were universally demonstrated during appropriate stress testing, lower body negative pressure, or passive standing. This intolerance was short-lived and, except in the case of the Apollo 15 crew, was not apparent beyond the second or third postflight day. Other postflight corroborative data such as decreased body weight, diminished resting calf girth, reduced supine leg volume, decreased cardiothoracic ratio, and decreased red cell mass all argue in favor of reduced effective circulating blood volume as an important principal factor in the orthostatic intolerance phenomenon. The Apollo findings do not indicate whether the intolerance is present during flight, and if so, its onset and time course.

The answers to these questions must await inflight testing. If intolerance does develop during flight, it apparently is of little consequence, since it had no discernible effect on Apollo crew performance. The positive pressure garment tested in Apollo appeared to offer some protective benefit by reducing the pooling of extravascular fluid in the lower extremities.

Exercise Tolerance

Reduced work capacity and oxygen consumption of significant degree was noted in 67 percent (18 of 27) of the Apollo crewmen tested on recovery. This decrement was transient, and 85 percent of those tested (23 of 27) returned to preflight baseline values within 24 to 36 hours. A significant decrease in cardiac stroke volume was associated with diminished exercise tolerance. As we noted in the case of the cardiovascular "deconditioning" phenomenon, the Apollo findings do not indicate whether the exercise decrement has its onset during flight. If it does, Apollo could shed no light on its inflight time course. Judging from the astronauts' performance on the lunar surface, we have no reason to believe that any serious exercise tolerance decrement occurs during flight, except that related to lack of regular exercise and muscle disuse atrophy.

There can be no doubt of the decrement in exercise tolerance in the immediate postflight period. It would seem that multiple factors are probably responsible for the observed decrement. Lack of exercise and muscle disuse atrophy have already been mentioned. Catabolic tissue processes may be accentuated by increased cortisol secretion as a consequence of mission stress and individual astronaut reaction to such stress. Additional factors associated with the return to Earth's gravity may also be implicated. Thus, the observed diminished stroke volume (cardiac output) is certainly contributory and, in turn, is doubtless a reflection of dimished venous return and contracted effective circulating blood volume induced by space flight factors. Other probable contributory factors are unstable fluid and electrolyte flux states and fatigue, both of which defy accurate objective assessment.

Nutrition and Mineral Balance

Apollo crewmen were provided with adequate dietary nutrients and exhibited clinically normal gastrointestinal function, although their appetites were generally somewhat diminished. Since no strict metabolic balance study was performed during Apollo, only relatively crude estimates of the various balance parameters can be made.

The diminished appetites aloft may have been due primarily to early space motion sickness symptoms such as stomach awareness or mild nausea. There is no evidence that any inflight metabolic anomaly, including hypokalemia, was secondary to marginal or deficient nutrient or mineral intakes.

All Apollo crewmen lost weight ranging from one to twelve pounds with a mean loss of approximately six pounds on a balanced diet providing 2500 calories (10,475 Joules) per man per day. Again, not all the food provided was consumed. Most of the weight loss (roughly 60 percent) was attributable to water and electrolyte loss; the remainder of the loss was attributed to lipid (30 percent) and muscle (10 percent) catabolism.

The partially controlled metabolic study conducted in conjunction with the Apollo 17 mission provided our only insight into inflight mineral balance during the Apollo Program. These data must be regarded as only grossly indicative of actual balance trends. The results argue in favor of a mild to moderate negative balance of sodium, potassium, nitrogen, phosphorus and calcium. Exchangeable potassium values were decreased in Apollo 15 and 17 but not in 16. The increased inflight cortisol secretion would argue in favor of increased tissue catabolism and potassium loss. The negative calcium balance observed in Apollo 17 and the slight losses in bone density in about half of the Apollo astronauts are consistent with the losses observed in subjects at bed rest for a comparable time period.

Postflight decreases in total body water and intracellular fluid volume are consistent with body weight loss and contracted effective circulating blood volume. Decreased potassium 40 and exchangeable potassium with increased urinary nitrogen argue in favor of muscle catabolism and potassium loss.

Postflight increases in renin, aldosterone, and antidiuretic hormone are consistent with the body's attempt to expand various body compartment volumes, conserve water and electrolytes, and restore venous return, cardiac output, and orthostatic tolerance to preflight levels. The finding of increased inflight aldosterone secretion is somewhat unexpected.

Blood Volume

Investigations in Gemini revealed that effective circulating blood volume was reduced following flight. This reduction was effected by a decrease in red cell mass, averaging about 17 percent and by a decrease in plasma volume in most instances. The mean red cell mass loss in Apollo 7 and 8 was two percent with a ten percent loss registered for Apollo 14 through 17. Plasma volume was also consistently decreased following these Apollo flights.

The loss of red cell mass in Gemini was thought to be due to hemolytic destruction of the cells secondary to oxidative changes in the corpuscular membrane. The Apollo data, however, revealed no change in red cell survival times, indicating that the red cell mass decrement is relative to inhibition of erythropoiesis rather than to intravascular hemolysis.

Thus, red cell mass loss was demonstrated in Apollo, but to a lesser extent than in Gemini. Determination of the precise stimulus responsible for red cell loss (marrow depression), the time course of the red cell mass reduction and its subsequent recovery must await further study. It is generally held, however, that this phenomenon is another in a series of adaptive changes to the space environment, that it is self-limiting in character and that it poses no threat to extended manned space missions.

General Summation

Table 2 lists the significant biomedical findings of the Apollo experience. In substance, the findings indicate that man generally adapts well to and functions effectively in the space environment (and on the lunar surface) for time periods up to two weeks in duration. Inflight medical problems such as space motion sickness and the cardiac arrhythmias episode were observed for the first time in the American manned space flight experience. Although these problems are potentially serious, they are not insurmountable. Once their etiology is understood, they can be dealt with effectively.

Table 2

Summary of Significant Biomedical Observations in Apollo

- Vestibular disturbances
- Inflight cardiac arrhythmia
- Reduced postflight orthostatic tolerance
- Reduced postflight exercise tolerance
- Postflight dehydration and weight loss
- Flight diet adequate; food consumption suboptimal
- Decreased red cell mass, plasma volume
- Negative inflight blance trend for nitrogen, calcium, other electrolytes
- Increased inflight adrenal hormone secretion
- No inflight diuresis

A number of decremental biomedical changes have been observed following the Apollo missions — which are thought to be accommodative changes of the various body systems to the new space environment — and to weightlessness in particular. It is felt that many of these accommodative changes are self-limiting in nature such as decreased red cell mass, orthostatic intolerance and vestibular disturbances; others, such as reduced exercise tolerance, muscle mass loss, and bone demineralization may require preventive or remedial measures, particularly on long-duration space flights.

Understanding the mechanisms of action responsible for the Apollo biomedical findings and devising suitable countermeasures where appropriate will challenge the ingenuity of biomedical scientists for years to come. We feel that we can meet that challenge.

References

NASA: Gemini Midprogram Conference, Including Experimental Results. NASA SP-121, Manned Spacecraft Center (Houston, Texas), February 23 - 25, 1968.

NASA: Gemini Summary Conference. NASA SP-138, Manned Spacecraft Center (Houston, Texas), February 1 - 2, 1967.

NASA: Space Medicine in Project Mercury. NASA SP-4003, Scientific and Technical Information Division, 1965.

CHAPTER 2
PERSPECTIVES ON APOLLO

by

Charles A. Berry, M.D.[*]

**President, The University of Texas Health
Science Center at Houston**

Introduction

From its inception, the United States space program has been dedicated to the concept of manned space flight. We have always viewed man as a vital element in the system. Man's adaptive intelligence proved to be indispensable during many critical operations. In 1961, when we became committed to a national objective to place an American on the moon within nine years, virtually nothing was known about man in space, beyond the fact that he could survive. Yet, NASA was charged with the responsibility to send men on a mission that would take them beyond the Earth's gravitational field, into orbit around the moon, and safely back to Earth after a stay on the lunar surface. Such a mission could not be accomplished in less than eight days of exposure to stresses whose effects were still a mystery.

People who were concerned with the future of man in space quickly became aligned with one of two points of view. On the one side, there were the more cautious and conservative members of the medical and scientific community who genuinely believed man could never survive the rigors of the experience proposed for him. The spirit in the other camp ranged from sanguine to certain. Some physicians, particularly those with experience in aeronautical systems, were optimistic. But by far the most enthusiastic proponents were the very individuals who would themselves make the historic journey to the moon. The population from which the astronaut corps was formed had considerable test pilot experience. Pilots, and the engineers who develop the aircraft they fly, characteristically view man as an element of the operational system that is every bit as strong and reliable as any other component of that system. It became the task of the medical team to work toward bringing these divergent views toward a safe middle ground

---

[*]Formerly NASA Director for Life Sciences.

where unfounded fears did not impede the forward progress of the space program, and unbounded optimism did not cause us to proceed at a pace that might compromise the health or safety of the individuals who ventured into space.

At the start of the space program in this country, many scientists had qualms about man's ability to survive in space. Since there were so many unknowns about the environment and it was presumed to be hostile, some focused on the known limitations of the delicately balanced human physiological system. In order to survive, the human body requires food, mental stimulation, waste disposal, a relatively narrow temperature range, and oxygen at a particular pressure for absorption into the blood stream. Those who were discouraged or pessimistic about the fate of astronauts envisioned dire consequences; for they felt the space flight environment would not allow these requirements to be met. Before Cosmonaut Gagarin flew, some scientists predicted that an astronaut would never survive launch because launch acceleration would cause heart rate to soar, creating severe pathologic disorders or terminal fibrillation. Some believed the phenomenon of weightlessness would result in a plethora of difficulties for an erect animal like man. Man had evolved through millions of years with organs that had been genetically designed to pump blood against the pull of gravity and to maintain an internal fluid balance based on a gravity system. Some thought man would not be able to urinate, swallow, or perform any physiological function that seemed to be gravity-dependent. Others felt his vision might be impaired, and predicted empty field myopia would result from staring endlessly into the void of space. Among other physiological disruptions feared were cardiac arrhythmias, muscular atrophy, hallucinations, disorientation, and nausea.

Because of the rapid progress of the program and the fact that so few astronauts were actually flown, decisions concerning appropriate mission lengths had to be made conservatively. Far less medical information was available for decision making than would ideally have been the case. At the conclusion of the Mercury Program, the longest U.S. manned space flight was 34 hours. Mercury 9 was scheduled to be the last flight in the Mercury series, to be followed by the first Gemini mission, slated for seven days. However, the last two Mercury astronauts had shown significantly reduced cardiovascular tolerance upon reentering Earth's gravity, engendering reluctance to commit man to a week-long flight without additional medical data. One solution would have been to fly another Mercury mission to bridge the gap. From a medical standpoint, the question of man's safety in space was, at that point, still a serious one. Only electrocardiographic and blood pressure monitoring were available.

Budgetary and other considerations precluded a Mercury 10 mission. Moreover, an additional Mercury flight might have diluted the effort directed toward Gemini and interrupted its momentum. The solution was to schedule the first Gemini mission for four days rather than seven. If a four-day mission went well, a second mission of eight days could be safely recommended, which in turn, would provide a sound basis for proceeding with a fourteen-day mission. A fourteen-day mission was deemed necessary because it was projected that no Apollo mission would exceed two weeks. With two weeks worth of medical data, man could be committed safely, from a physiological standpoint, to a lunar landing mission.

Conduct of medical investigations during the two-week Gemini mission was critical to planning for lunar landings. Because there was a paucity of information concerning man in the environment of space flight, every opportunity had to be exploited to collect data in a systematic way. However, some compromises had to be made for operational reasons. One of the astronauts selected for the fourteen-day Gemini mission exhibited a liver enzyme abnormality. Ideally, from a purely medical experimentation point of view, such an individual would not have been chosen because his condition could be expected to influence hematological findings. From an operational standpoint, however, he was the man for the job.

The medical experience of Gemini was extremely valuable, and plans had been made to continue medical experimentation in the early Apollo flights. When the Apollo 204 fire tragically supervened, a planned series of inflight medical experiments was deleted and all energies were directed toward engineering and other operational problems.

Amassing medical information was difficult for numerous technological reasons, and was further compounded by certain attitudinal issues. Some astronauts were reluctant to admit physiological difficulties for various reasons, some purely pragmatic. In military aviation, the field from which the vast majority of astronauts were selected, the flight surgeon is required to keep close watch over pilots and to disqualify them when they are unfit for flight. The psychological set of the astronauts may have caused them to fear exclusion from the program for medical reasons.

With the enormous investment of time and training in the astronaut corps, the medical approach in the space program was quite different. Every effort was made to keep these highly select, highly trained individuals qualified for flight. One astronaut who had been scheduled for a mission was not permitted to participate because a bony bridge developed on a cervical vertebra and had to be removed surgically. After surgery, he was requalified and flew on a critical space mission. Another astronaut who suffered from Ménière's syndrome was also qualified after surgery corrected the situation with an endolymphatic shunt.

A final aspect of the philosophy which governed the manned space flight program in general and the Apollo Program in particular is worthy of note. Space flight created a unique problem for personnel charged with medical management. Many aspects of the entire space flight experience, during all phases — before flight, during flight, and after flight — have a potential for straining the privileged communication between doctor and patient. The entire issue of medical privacy is, and always has been, a very difficult one for physicians involved with persons of any notoriety. Astronauts, as such a group, lost many of their rights of privacy by virtue of their position. An individual who has volunteered as an astronaut in our nation's space program must pay a certain price and owes a certain debt for the privilege of his participation. As part of this debt, he must give up a certain amount of privacy and be willing to sacrifice an "image" where such a sacrifice bears on the success of his mission or future missions. A physician monitoring a space mission has to receive reports on such intimate issues as the number of bowel movements, the types of pains suffered, the amount of sleep obtained, and so forth. Reporting this information was particularly irksome to many astronauts, especially since this information had to be transmitted over open loop telemetry links and became public knowledge. The small number of astronauts involved in any mission made it impossible to maintain anonymity for the individual. For example, if a crewman had vomited in the spacecraft during a mission, the press, as a whole, was unable or unwilling to accept a statement to the effect that a crewman had vomited. They demanded to know which crewman. The astronauts became, in a sense, public property. They belonged to the entire nation, and the press felt they had an obligation to report their status to the people.

Every effort was made, however, to safeguard the privacy of astronauts as individuals wherever possible. A distinction was drawn between information of medical importance related to the safety of a mission or to the safety of future missions, and medical information which was not of such import and could properly be maintained as privileged doctor-patient information. This point can clearly be illustrated in the case of information sought by Congressional committees concerning the crewmen who perished in the Apollo 204 incident. Congressional committees in both the House and Senate spent a substantial amount of time interviewing NASA staff members concerning the fire to attempt to determine any factors that could prevent such an incident in the future. This was their proper concern. At one point during the investigation, however, a fire occurred in an altitude chamber at the Brooks Air Force Base and an airman was killed. The House Armed Services Committee then became involved in a situation which was not totally dissimilar from that faced by the Senate and House Committees concerned with aeronautics and astronautics. The Armed Services Committee asked to have the medical records of the deceased Apollo crewmen made available to them. The medical records per se were privileged information and could not be surrendered. Instead, all pertinent facts related to the accident and causes of death that were relevant to the Committee's concern were presented.

Every hour crewmen spent in space and all their responses to that peculiar environment were important, not just to ensure their safety but to provide for the safety of crews who would fly for longer periods of time. Every data point assumed much greater importance because data points were few.

A Medical Chronology

Many of the early biomedical preconceptions concerning man in space were answered during Mercury and Gemini flights. Project Mercury's indispensable legacy was that man could survive in space and, moreover, that he could do useful tasks. The legacy of Gemini was in many respects an even richer one. The fourteen-day Gemini mission demonstrated that weightlessness does indeed cause changes in man. Cardiovascular and bone density changes were just two findings that signaled that the world of zero gravity profoundly affected the human. Gemini missions also provided a fund of knowledge concerning the measurement of physiological functioning at a distance. But, at the end of the 2000 man-hours of Gemini, we were confronted with difficult issues. Because the number of individuals involved was small, we could not tell whether genuine space-related phenomena were being observed or whether the changes reflected individual variations. If the changes seen were authentic responses to the space environment, we could not at that point say whether they represented the beginning of downward trends, whether they would level off in time, or whether, perhaps, they would be cyclic. The contribution of confinement to physiological effects observed during and after space flight had also to be assessed, along with numerous less-well-defined factors. This was Gemini's legacy to Apollo, and it became the task of the Apollo Program to search for answers.

The Apollo Program provided an opportunity to gain biomedical information in a more orderly manner than was possible during the Gemini missions. More definitive data now could be obtained concerning man's performance during what was truly a space voyage. Biomedical information returned from the later Apollo missions has allowed us to progress significantly toward a detailed description of man's behavior in space and the physiological changes which occur.

Apollo 7 marked our first experience with inflight illness. It also represented our first experience in diagnosing and treating illness via telemetry across the void of space. This situation illustrated the difficulty of dealing with medical issues privately. Space flight procedures called for all consultations to be effected through the Capsule Communicator and not directly between the physician and patient, eliminating the possibility for privileged communication. The Apollo 7 crew suffered colds and upper respiratory symptoms. Colds on Earth are bothersome enough, but weightlessness exacerbates symptoms still further. In zero gravity, mucous clogs the nasal passages and does not drain. Even decongestants seem less effective; shrinking of the membranes gives no relief because there is no drainage from the sinuses. There was some concern on the part of the crew about the possibility of rupturing their eardrums if they wore helmets during reentry and were unable to perform a modified Valsalva maneuver to equalize pressure on either side of the tympanic membrane. The crew made the decision to reenter with helmets off despite opposition from the ground. As it turned out, the crewmen were able to ventilate the ears during reentry.

In Apollo 8, the first incident of vestibular illness was encountered during an American space flight. When the astronauts left their couches after the spacecraft had entered orbit, all three developed vertigo. One crewman had a vestibular problem for about two and one-half days and suffered nausea; another vomited and had diarrhea. For the first time, astronauts were moving around rapidly in a spacecraft with a relatively large volume, and some of them were quite susceptible to motion sickness. The effects of Seconal, a sleeping medication, and viral gastroenteritis have been implicated, but vestibular disturbance may well have been a significant factor in the difficulties suffered by the crew.

Even more severe vestibular disturbances were experienced during the Apollo 9 mission, and a portion of the scheduled extravehicular activity had to be cancelled as a result. There was grave concern over this incident because, for the first time, vestibular disturbances interfered with performance of mission-related tasks. This was a distressing discovery because it suggested, ominously, that missions could indeed be compromised by vestibular problems. In the extreme case, mission success and even crew lives could be threatened.

The mission of Apollo 9 underscored the problems that could be created by any illness in flight, and alerted us to the hazards of clinical illness. At that time, there was no preflight isolation program, and crews engaged in a rigorous preflight schedule of activities. After the flight, there were press conferences and tours to be taken, and the astronauts were not allowed sufficient time to readjust before they engaged in these activities. In fact, the launch of Apollo 9 had to be delayed for three days because all three crewmembers developed upper respiratory symptoms. The problem of the lack of a preflight isolation program to prevent clinical illness was brought into sharp focus. This topic has been dealt with in detail in several chapters of this book, and will be discussed further later in this chapter from the point of view of medical program management.

Apollo 10 was the first Apollo mission during which no inflight illness occurred. While there was still no highly structured preflight preventive medicine program, illness was kept in check.

Apollo 11, the first lunar landing mission, gave man the first opportunity to visit an extraterrestrial body and to experience an environment where the gravity was one-sixth what it is on Earth. There had been concern in many quarters about man's capability to operate effectively in this environment. Some felt man would be disoriented in lunar gravity, and, when he attempted to walk on the moon, would become motion sick and vertiginous and be unable to move in a given direction. This fear was resoundingly demonstrated to be baseless by Apollo 11.

Apollo 12 gave us further confidence about man's capabilities in a 1/6-g field. Projections concerning metabolic cost of work in this environment proved to be reasonably accurate. Metabolic cost of routine locomotion and nominal tasks was not excessive, nor was it detrimental to adequate lunar surface performance.

Apollo 13 was the most difficult, danger-ridden mission in the U.S. space program. Even before the flight, the mission had been threatened by medical difficulties. The incident in point began just before the 21-day examination period. Astronaut Charles Duke, a backup crewmember, and his family spent a weekend with friends. Two of the children in the household had rubella (German measles), and Astronaut Duke contracted it. Detailed blood studies were conducted, and other viral illnesses were considered because rubella is easily misdiagnosed. When the illness was confirmed as rubella, an epidemiological investigation was initiated. A flight surgeon visited the family from whom the disease had been contracted, and blood samples and epidemiologically significant data were collected. Next, complete immunologic evaluations were made of the Duke family and of all prime and backup crewmen.

On the day before Astronaut Duke exhibited the rubella rash, a prime crewman had worked with him in the Command Module Trainer. The crewman, Thomas K. Mattingly, was the only individual in the prime crew who showed no protective antibodies against the disease. With the launch fast approaching and the crew already at Cape Kennedy making preparations, a complex epidemiological and medical situation was created. Daily flights were made between Houston and the Cape to study blood samples collected from the prime crew. Specialists from the National Institute of Allergy and Infectious Diseases were consulted on the problem, and assisted in evaluating the risks. By this time, the crewman's measles exposure was public knowledge. Agency officials were queried from many quarters, some requesting daily briefings concerning the status of the flight.

There was no question of the risk involved, and a decision had to be made to substitute a backup crewman. The decision to make the crew substitution was based on medical advice given by many respected individuals. In fact, Mattingly did not develop rubella, although he just as easily might have. He was subsequently immunized to the disease and participated in a later mission.

The events surrounding the harrowing inflight experience of Apollo 13 are well known. The only medically significant occurrence during that mission was a urinary tract infection in one crewmember resulting from reduced water intake and the cold environment of the Lunar Module "life boat." The afflicted individual had chills and fever associated with the illness, but he did not identify these as symptoms of clinical illness because all crewmembers were chilled by the cold.

Apollo 14 was unremarkable from a medical standpoint. This was the first mission for which a full-fledged Flight Crew Health Stabilization Program was in effect. This program, and the effectiveness with which it was executed, must be credited for its contribution to the reduction of inflight clinical problems on this flight and subsequent missions.

Apollo 15 will remain an anomaly in the Apollo Program. Preflight and inflight activities went well. The lunar surface operations were characterized by heavy work schedules and some sleep difficulties. The crewmen worked to a point of near exhaustion on some occasions, and the Commander pulled a shoulder muscle while operating the lunar surface drill. The pain from the muscle injury interfered with his sleep on the lunar surface and during the return flight to Earth, and persisted for several weeks. At the conclusion of Apollo 15's lunar surface activities, a very tired crew departed the moon to rendezvous with the Command Module.

The schedule of the labors after the link-up was also heavy, and the Command Module Pilot had to rely on his already fatigued companions to transfer equipment from the Lunar Module to the Command Module, a task he himself had been slated to perform. Once transfer operations were complete, difficulty was experienced in sealing the hatch between the two vehicles. This problem necessitated two additional lunar orbits and additional labors before the tunnel connecting the vehicles was successfully sealed and the LM could be jettisoned.

After Lunar Module jettison, the crew was engaged in a space suit integrity check when a bigeminal rhythm appeared on the console monitoring Astronaut Irwin's electrocardiogram. Paper copies of the trace were called for to establish that the irregularity was not artifactual. The bigeminal arrhythmia lasted for 10 to 20 beats, and was followed by a series of premature ventricular and atrial beats, interspersed with normal ones. One other crewman had exhibited some arrhythmias, but they were far less serious than those with which Astronaut Irwin was afflicted. The crew had transmitted no messages indicating a problem. In fact, Astronaut Irwin reported later that he had experienced a feeling of a brief loss of contact as though he had momemtarily gone to sleep. In retrospect, this episode could have been a momentary loss of consciousness at the precise time the arrhythmia was noted. After the arrhythmias were noted, continuous electrocardiographic recordings were obtained for all three crewmen while they slept.

It took the Apollo 15 crew three to four weeks after the flight to return to preflight normal levels of exercise and cardiovascular orthostatic tolerance. This was the longest recovery period seen in our space program and was uncomfortably reminiscent of the findings of the eighteen-day Soviet Soyuz 9 mission. This Soviet mission had been marked by a prolonged recovery wherein cardiovascular, vestibular, and musculoskeletal difficulties were experienced by the crewmen. While it would have been, ideally, preferable to shield the two astronauts from public attention, it was judged in the best interest of the space program to provide information about their conditions.

There is a reasonable basis for suspecting that the Apollo 15 crew was launched with a potassium deficit. They had engaged in very rigorous training for lunar surface tasks prior to this space mission in intense summer heat. The crew drank considerable amounts of an electrolyte solution during this training, which tended to leach potassium from the system. These factors, coupled with inflight diets that were not particularly high in potassium, are believed to have contributed to negative potassium balances.

Apollo 16 and 17 crewmen were free of any cardiac difficulties during their missions. This may have been in part due to the institution of a program involving dietary potassium supplements and revised work/rest schedules to preclude a negative potassium balance. Such a negative balance can contribute to cardiac irritability and can predispose to arrhythmias. The crews of both missions were also free of any clinical illness during flight. Again, the meticulously conducted Flight Crew Health Stabilization Program seemed to be effective. All crewmen took sleeping medications to ensure sufficient rest to complete busy lunar surface schedules. Both the Apollo 16 and 17 missions were unqualified successes from an operational and a medical standpoint.

Flight Crew Health Stabilization

The clinical illnesses which were encountered in the early Apollo missions clearly indicated the need for a health stabilization program during the preflight period. Uncertainty about the nature of potential lunar soil contaminants dictated in the minds of some individuals in the scientific community the necessity for a postflight quarantine program after the first several lunar surface missions. Details of these programs can be found in Section II, Chapters 1 and 6, and in Section V of this book. Some of the nuances surrounding the establishment and the conduct of the isolation and quarantine programs are presented here.

As mentioned earlier, the launch of Apollo 9 had to be delayed for three days because of the development of upper respiratory infections in the crew. That was the first instance of medical problems impacting the operational aspects of a space flight. Understandably, there were some objections to the sort of control medical management proposed to exercise during the preflight period. But the facts were immutable. Crewmen were becoming ill during flight, and an illness of any severity could seriously jeopardize the safety of a mission and crew. Some form of preflight isolation was mandatory.

A postflight quarantine period was to be required for the first lunar landing and for the missions of Apollo 12, 13 (not conducted because the lunar landing was aborted), and Apollo 14. The Interagency Committee agreed to remove this requirement when exhaustive studies conducted by NASA indicated beyond a doubt that no life of any kind existed on the moon.

Every precaution was taken which feasibly could have been taken to safeguard the objectives of the quarantine program. When Lunar Receiving Laboratory technicians and other persons were accidentally exposed to lunar materials through breaks in the gloves which allowed manipulation of these materials, off they went into "exile" with the crew and quarantine support personnel until the official quarantine period had ended.

Had there been an organism on the moon, the quarantine program would, in this writer's opinion, have had about a 90 percent chance of containing it. Preflight isolation simplified the matter of identifying the etiology of any illness that might have arisen postflight. Catalogs of crew microorganisms allowed for postflight identification of organisms as terrestrial versus lunar.

The problems associated with conducting the isolation periods preceding and following space flight were myriad. Emotions ran high when families had to be separated, and there were occasional tense moments.

Apollo 11 demonstrated that man could indeed fly the Lunar Module after having flown only a training device, which was, of course, not an exact duplicate. In fact, not only could he fly the vehicle near the lunar surface and effect a landing, but he could change the coordinates of that landing based upon terrain characteristics making such a change necessary. This was the case with the Apollo 11 lunar landing. Astronaut Armstrong did a masterful job conducting the landing and demonstrated man's capability to execute such control operations under adverse circumstances.

There had been much conjecture concerning man's response to the one-sixth gravity environment. Serious concern also existed about his ability to work effectively in 1/6 g in a pressure suit. Therefore, his capability to do so was measured by conducting lunar surface-type activities in simulated 1/6-g conditions on the ground. Man's responses were also evaluated in underwater, neutral buoyancy simulations in order to determine the metabolic loads associated with various activities. The first true data obtained from the Apollo 11 crew's lunar experience indicated that the real metabolic cost of 1/6-g activities was an acceptable one.

At first, it was speculated that time spent in 1/6 g might have a salutary effect after zero-g exposure, and perhaps reduce the postflight "deconditioning" effect. However, it was not possible to show any salutary effect on deconditioning from the brief periods spent at 1/6 g, perhaps because these effects were obliterated by the additional two and one-half to five days spent in weightlessness on the return flight to Earth. However, in the case of one astronaut, 1/6 g did appear to counteract vestibular disturbances – stomach awareness and vertigo – experienced in zero g.

Psychological Issues

One of the questions most frequently asked about space flight is what psychological effect does it have on astronauts? Do they experience fear? What is their reaction during launch when seven and one-half million pounds of thrust catapults them from the surface of the Earth? How do they feel when they are approaching the moon? Are they compatible in the cramped quarters of a spacecraft?

It is perhaps remarkable that there was virtually no difficulty from a psychological and psychodynamic viewpoint among highly competitive, driving, and forceful individuals. Some of the success in the psychological sphere must be attributed to the original astronaut selection process. All Apollo astronauts were carefully screened psychologically and psychiatrically prior to entry into the program; and attempts were made to assess their ability to deal with stressful situations. The fact that most astronauts were veteran military pilots aided in the selective process since this served to indicate they could keep emotional reactions under control and were capable of professional behavior during conditions of danger. This was buttressed by numerous observations made during medical and other types of training and monitoring activities in the preflight period.

Certainly there were times when tempers flared and differences of opinion led to arguments. But at no time were any psychological responses observed before, during, or after flight which could be considered in any way abnormal.

Careful psychological screening and selection excluded individuals with any psychopathology from the astronaut corps. The astronauts were intrinsically stable individuals. But several other important factors accounted for the high degree of psychic stability exhibited in some exceedingly stressful inflight situations. The first, and perhaps most important, was the level of motivation among these individuals. Astronauts are an exceedingly motivated group. Their training program is an extremely rigorous one. It involves countless hours of difficult training, some of which is unpleasant and some frankly dangerous. All astronauts must go through this training, even before they are designated to fly on a particular flight. Many never will participate in a space mission, and they know it. By the end of the Apollo Program, only 52 percent of the astronaut corps ever actually flew an operational mission. All of these factors are testimony to the inherent motivation of these people. This spirit allowed them to overcome many difficulties which would have been extremely bothersome to other individuals less determined to succeed.

Space flight operations clearly have aspects that would frighten any ordinary person. Nothing on Earth could have prepared these men for the stillness of the void of space or the experience of being weightless. And, a whole complex of emotions must have been produced by knowing one was totally alone and literally out of this world. Workload played an important part in helping the astronauts manage the anxiety-provoking parts of the space flight experience. Time lines were constantly active. This allowed little time for deep contemplation. In the author's opinion, had there been long periods of unprogrammed time, it is possible that some difficulty might have developed in the psychological sphere.

A voyage to the moon is unquestionably one of the most profound experiences encountered by man. It would have been shortsighted of us to have believed that such an experience would not impact our astronauts at some later time. It is perhaps surprising that more individuals did *not* react in some marked way to this experience.

Several astronauts had some rather well publicized difficulties in the psychological sphere after flight. Astronaut Aldrin was clinically depressed after his mission. By his own account, the largest factor contributing to this depression was difficulty in handling public exposure after Apollo 11. Further, he had expected that the landing of men on the moon would have a tremendous impact on the world. He was extremely distressed to find that the world did not change appreciably, and certainly not immediately, as a result of the achievement of Apollo 11.

Two other individuals radically changed their way of life after space flight. Astronaut Irwin became actively involved in evangelical religion, and Astronaut Mitchell in parapsychology. Neither of these developments was especially surprising in view of the interests each individual had prior to space flight in these respective areas. In this writer's opinion, neither one of these astronauts exhibited any behavior which could be described as psychologically aberrant. Having gained new perspectives, they simply chose different life styles.

Space flight must be recognized as an experience which taxes the individual every bit as much psychologically as it does physiologically. This aspect of the experience must not be overlooked.

Conclusions

Before the Apollo program began, there were many questions regarding the physiological phenomena space flight produced. The Apollo missions answered many questions left unresolved by the Gemini Program, and, as is so often the case where phenomenological issues are involved, it raised as many new questions as it answered. The biomedical results of Apollo assured us that our planning and preparation had been of great value. Almost every observation in the physiological realm had been identified, at least in kind if not in degree, by the Gemini experience. Physiological changes did indeed occur, but these were all reversible shortly after flight. The single exception to this rule was the Apollo 15 crew. Apollo 15 stands out as an anomaly. It took this crew nearly a month to recover from the effects of space flight. The anomalous findings of Apollo 15 will perhaps never be totally understood, but they were probably due largely to a lack of adequate potassium intake. Cardiac arrhythmias suffered by two members of this crew had not been seen in other missions and were not seen following increased potassium intake in the two subsequent crews. It is, of course, difficult to be certain that potassium deficits were the cause or, for that matter, that potassium supplements were the cure.

We learned from Apollo that man can perform very nicely in a one-sixth gravity environment. One-sixth of the gravity to which he is accustomed proved to be sufficient to give man a feeling of near normalcy for performing functions with at least the same ease as he does on Earth and, in some cases, with greater ease. The astronauts adapted quickly to movement in the lunar gravity environment and traversed the surface of the moon rapidly using many gaits, some of them fanciful but all of them efficient. Apollo lunar surface activity also demonstrated that the metabolic costs of working in that environment were completely acceptable. On the basis of this experience, a lunar surface laboratory in the future is not only feasible but may be highly desirable. Perhaps an international laboratory will ultimately be established there for the study of our solar system and the universe.

The Apollo experience also emphasized the importance of preflight isolation of crewmen to guarantee, insofar as is medically possible, that no infectious illness will intervene in the inflight or the immediate preflight period. We learned the importance of closely following the immunologic status of crewmen and of immunizing them adequately against childhood diseases. Postflight quarantine was an interesting and valuable exercise which provided experience for future quarantine programs. We learned in the course of a carefully conducted program, however, that there are no organisms, live or dead, on the lunar surface.

Satisfying the medical objectives of the Apollo Program had a number of unanticipated benefits. Much of what we have come to call spinoff was produced by the program. Technology developed in support of Apollo missions has found useful and widespread application in the public sector. A few of the many examples which can be cited have been selected for comment. A one-sixth gravity simulator originally designed to allow the astronaut to adapt to lunar surface gravity in advance of his mission has been used in rehabilitating the physically handicapped. The Apollo liquid cooling undergarment has found medical application in the symptomatic treatment of sustained, high febrile states and in persons working in high thermal environments, such as oil well fire fighting. A portable, noninvasive, continuous blood pressure monitoring and recording system has made possible biomedical monitoring of hypertensive patients during uninterrupted, normal daily activities. Laminar airflow clean room techniques, used in the Lunar Receiving Laboratory and the crew quarters at Cape Kennedy to reduce the spread of infectious agents, are used with enormous success in hospitals and surgical suites for identical reasons.

Probably the most impressive aspect of the Apollo medical program and its most important accomplishment was that man could be supported in the hostile operating environments of space and the lunar surface. This was done with minimal data and in the face of difficulty in obtaining some of the data. We monitored man's vital signs across the void of space and could offer him assurance of his safety during dangerous and difficult operations. The Apollo medical program supported man on his journey to the moon and back and provided a fund of information that will form the medical data core for allowing him to venture still further into the solar system and, perhaps, live and work in lunar laboratories of the future.

The Apollo Program triumphantly closed man's first decade in space. To reach for the moon in 1961 when man's total orbital flight time was less than two hours, and to declare that we would attain it before the decade was out, was an extremely ambitious goal. The vehicle for this achievement was the Apollo spacecraft, and it served its purpose well. The Apollo Program placed twelve men on the moon, leaving them there for a total of over four man-weeks, and returned them safely to Earth. It was an engineering and medical feat with few parallels in the history of mankind. The universe is man's destiny, and the Apollo Program was the first definitive step toward that destiny. The term space flight always connotes *manned* space flight in my view. No machine can observe space and celestial bodies with the resourcefulness and intuition that man can bring to the task.

☆ U.S. GOVERNMENT PRINTING OFFICE : 1975—O-589-437